The Ori...

Related Pergamon Titles of Interest

Books

CHAPMAN
Solar and Middle Atmosphere Variability

GOMBOSI *et al.*
Cometary Environments

HORWITZ
Geospace Plasmas

JONES
The Solar System

NEIDIG & HUDSON
Solar Physics in the 1990s

REASENBERG & VESSOT
Relativistic Gravitation

Journals

Advances in Space Research

The Astronomy Quarterly

Journal of Atmospheric & Terrestrial Physics

Planetary & Space Science

Vistas in Astronomy

Details of all Pergamon publications/free specimen copy of any Pergamon journal available on request from your nearest Pergamon office.

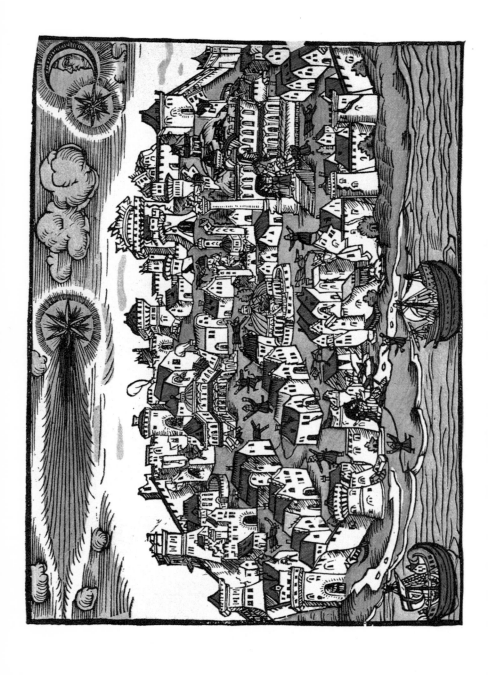

The Origin of Comets

by

M. E. Bailey
Department of Astronomy, University of Manchester, England

S. V. M. Clube
Department of Astrophysics, University of Oxford, England

and

W. M. Napier
Royal Observatory, Edinburgh, Scotland

PERGAMON PRESS

Member of Maxwell Macmillan Pergamon Publishing Corporation

OXFORD · NEW YORK · BEIJING · FRANKFURT
SÃO PAULO · SYDNEY · TOKYO · TORONTO

U.K.	Pergamon Press plc, Headington Hill Hall, Oxford OX3 0BW, England
U.S.A.	Pergamon Press, Inc., Maxwell House, Fairview Park, Elmsford, New York 10523, U.S.A.
PEOPLE'S REPUBLIC OF CHINA	Pergamon Press, Room 4037, Qianmen Hotel, Beijing, People's Republic of China
FEDERAL REPUBLIC OF GERMANY	Pergamon Press GmbH, Hammerweg 6, D-6242 Kronberg, Federal Republic of Germany
BRAZIL	Pergamon Editora Ltda, Rua Eça de Queiros, 346, CEP 04011, Paraiso, São Paulo, Brazil
AUSTRALIA	Pergamon Press Australia Pty Ltd., P.O. Box 544, Potts Point, N.S.W. 2011, Australia
JAPAN	Pergamon Press, 5th Floor, Matsuoka Central Building, 1-7-1 Nishishinjuku, Shinjuku-ku, Tokyo 160, Japan
CANADA	Pergamon Press Canada Ltd., Suite No. 271, 253 College Street, Toronto, Ontario, Canada M5T 1R5

First edition 1990

Library of Congress Cataloging in Publication Data
Bailey, M. E.
The origin of comets/by M. E. Bailey, S. V. M. Clube and W. M. Napier.
p. cm.
Includes bibliographical references.
1. Comets. 2. Astronomy—History.
I. Clube, S. V. M. II. Napier, W. M. III. Title.
QB721.B35 1989 523.6—dc20 89–48010

British Library Cataloguing in Publication Data
Bailey, M. E.
The origin of comets.
1. Comets
I. Title II. Clube, S. V. M. (Stace Victor Murray), *1934–* III. Napier, W. M.
523.6
ISBN 0–08–034859–9 (Hardcover)
ISBN 0–08–034858–0 (Flexicover)

Printed in Great Britain by BPCC Wheatons Ltd, Exeter

Contents

Illustrations

Tables

Preface

"It is indeed a feeble light that reaches us from the starry sky. But what would human thought have achieved if we could not see the stars?"

Jean Perrin.

Astronomers find themselves with a very special responsibility. Whilst our understanding of the Universe and the wider world in which we live has advanced in recent years almost beyond measure, the questions raised, and the detailed issues now debated in scientific circles and elsewhere, frequently appear to be esoteric and far-removed from everyday experience. There is a sense in which astronomy can be said to have grown 'too big', that we have already 'learned enough', and that possibly the best course for all concerned is to call a halt (or at least put on the brake), before being engulfed by the tidal wave of knowledge that threatens to overwhelm us.

Not without reason, then, are astronomers increasingly called upon to explain their work, by friends, members of the public and funding agencies alike. Indeed, because their discoveries have become increasingly hard to comprehend, the need for explanation has never been greater. However, although theories have become steadily more complex, it is essential also to provide *simple* explanations and descriptions of these advances, not least so that those who pay for them may also benefit from the knowledge. 'Simple' in this context does not, of course, mean elementary; but the beauty of astronomy is that, whilst addressing some of the most profound questions in Nature, many of its most basic concepts can be presented in terms which anyone can understand. Throughout this book, therefore, we have attempted to describe the various ideas on cometary origin in language which does not depend on prior astronomical or physical knowledge on the part of the reader. True there is the odd equation scattered here and there, but we assume the disinterested reader will see the words between and not lose the thread. Above all, we hope to identify the essential concepts relating to cometary

origin, covering ideas ranging from those of the earliest Babylonian astronomers up to the most modern viewpoints, and in a
manner that makes them accessible to the widest possible read-
ership. Nevertheless, we are not professional communicators,
and only the reader can judge whether we have been successful.

We should emphasize, however, that we have deliberately
tried not to *oversimplify* our explanations. Many populariza-
tions of science, on which most citizens perforce depend for their
detailed information, seem to fail on this point. The descriptions
they give are frequently quite elementary, almost to the point
of patronizing the educated reader, and they often make bland
assertions of 'fact' while at the same time being seriously 'eco-
nomical' with the truth. These errors and omissions are usually
justified, of course, in the interests of saving space; but the net
effect is that they present a seriously distorted picture.

In truth, the subject of cometary origin is enormously complex, with links encompassing the origin of stars, nebulae, and
planetary systems; the structure and evolution of galaxies; the
history and evolution of the earth; and, more recently, aspects of
the evolution of Man's scientific knowledge from the time of the
Babylonians and Ancient Greeks up to the present day. Even
now, there is no general agreement as to 'the' origin of comets.
The plain fact is no-one knows for sure, and to pretend otherwise
merely stores up disappointment for the future.

Our book is intended to be self-contained, comprehensive
and up-to-date (though most readers will find some aspects that
would merit further development). The general reader should
need only this one book (at least so far as the *origin* of comets
is concerned). We have deliberately excluded a detailed discussion of the *physics* of comets: the structure of their nuclei, the
chemistry of the coma and the dynamics of their tails, except
where an understanding of such aspects of comets bears directly
on the question of their origin. The reader interested in pur-
suing these branches of the subject, or indeed any other facet
of the burgeoning debate about 'origins', will find more than a
thousand literature references to guide him, whilst we hope that
the associated sprinkling of the text with references to specialist

papers and books does not prove too much of a distraction.

By approaching the subject in chronological order, so far as possible, we hope that the important rôle played by the history of cometary astronomy in the development of astronomical thought will be brought to the fore. In turn, we hope that this helps to tie down many of the otherwise loose ends in the argument for cometary origin, particularly those dealing with the geological record of earth and the development of early cosmological concepts. In science, the underlying *picture* is often more important than the detail; and we hope that our explanation of the origin of comets does, in the end, finally provide a complete picture, blemishes and all.

In reviewing the origin of comets, therefore, we introduce the reader to an exciting and vital area of science: to an understanding of the forces which drove the original development of astronomy and of the reasons for its continued importance in modern society, especially the cometary connexion. Comets are an enigma: they arrive unpredictably, yet — unlike quasars and radio galaxies — the brightest of them become visible to all. Their decay products: asteroids, boulders and dust, have had, over historical and geological timescales, an almost immeasurable influence on the earth. This influence is active today, and will continue more so in the future. The fact that the source of this influence remains uncertain, even at the present time, is a crucial challenge to astronomers. To quote Toulmin (1985): 'Human beings are the beneficiaries of history ... our fate within this historical scheme depends ... on the adaptiveness of our behaviour, and ... on the use that we make of our intelligence in dealing with our place in Nature.' The quest is scarcely begun. Indeed, as we show in this book, a successful outcome is hardly possible without a full understanding of the origin and behaviour of those bodies in whose presence Man formerly quailed.

M.E. Bailey   Manchester
S.V.M. Clube   Oxford
W.M. Napier   Edinburgh
                                               June 1989.

Acknowledgements

The book owes its inception to Peter Beer and Archie Roy, of the editorial board of *Vistas in Astronomy*, for having encouraged us to join forces and write a review article on the origin of comets. The article was eventually expanded into the present volume. We thank Peter Henn and colleagues at Pergamon Press for displaying such tolerance and patience in awaiting the arrival of a book which seemed at one time to be in a state of almost permanent near-completion; while their technical advice during the production stages of this camera-ready copy was particularly helpful in developing the present satisfactory appearance of the book. We also thank John Rowcroft and Marjorie Fretwell for the care and attention they gave to the drawing of many of the Figures in the text, whilst much of the photographic material was kindly provided by Ian Callaghan of Manchester University and Brian Hadley and staff of the Royal Observatory Edinburgh. Our particular thanks, of course, go to those who commented on our review article and the present manuscript at various stages of its preparation, and to those who gave us permission to use material from published work or generously provided original photographic material. The rapid production of this book in its present form would have been impossible without use of the LATEX word-processing facility provided at the University of Manchester STARLINK node, and we thank the local users for their forbearance during the book's production and the STARLINK manager, Peter Allan, for his help during the early stages of the book's development.

Finally, our greatest thanks must go to our families, especially our respective wives: Rowena, Moira and Nancy. No book is written in a day; and they too have been stretched to the limits of tolerance and patience. We dedicate this book to them.

1

Introduction

"Time and pains will discover what is now unknown and posterity wonder that we did not know such plain things."

Seneca.

The problem of the origin of comets is one of the oldest unsolved mysteries in astronomy, with roots pre-dating the ancient Greeks, reaching almost to the dawn of civilization. Comets are also amongst the most primitive astronomical bodies, and the question of their origin is inextricably linked with problems of cosmogony, the formation of stars and the birth of the solar system.

The story of Man's understanding of comets, therefore, is not only associated with the oldest known speculations in natural science and cosmology but also extends to include some of the most recent advances in astrophysics. It makes an excellent backdrop against which to view the development of modern astronomical ideas and concepts, though at times the many interweaving threads of argument may seem rather tangled. In this monograph we attempt to lead the reader through the resulting maze of theory and hypothesis, explaining ideas on comets and their origin from the earliest times right up to the present day.

Advancement of the subject has been closely allied to progress in other fields of astronomy, giving a survey of cometary origins considerable historical interest. Even regarded as a mere instance in the zigzag progression of scientific ideas, the origin of comets soon shows a depth and complexity rarely approached by other individual subjects.

In order to highlight these links with other fields, and to illustrate the apparently perverse back-tracking and retracing of paths that are so often the rule in the progress of science, we have presented the story wherever possible in chronological order. Following this course we hope that the reader may better appreciate the strengths and weaknesses of the arguments

1

about comets which were promoted and believed by leading astronomers and philosophers of the past. The fact that these past arguments have frequently been proved false, or at best only half-true, suggests that the currently accepted picture may even now be largely incomplete.

Although the question of the nature and origin of comets has played an important rôle in the development of astronomical ideas, the rapid advances made during the present century in new areas of astrophysics — stellar, galactic and extragalactic — have combined almost to overwhelm the traditional disciplines which previously dominated the field. This has been especially true of solar system and cometary astronomy, and it is only in the last decade or so, with the advent of space technology and the launching of vehicles to other planets, that interest in comets and their origin has once again come to the fore.

Indeed, the relative decline of cometary astronomy during this century has been so great that many astronomers nowadays have grown up believing not only that comets are amongst the smallest bodies in the universe but also that they are among the least significant. Popular accounts often seem to mention them only to introduce some disparaging remark about the fear and concern that comets used to arouse among our ancestors, while more serious commentators frequently place them at the end of a book or chapter, seeing them, all too clearly, as merely of secondary interest. Indeed, the problem of the origin of comets is sometimes scarcely mentioned! Given that cosmology and astrophysics are now virtually inseparable, this feeling about the status of comets has inevitably become part of the modern world-view, with an associated tendency to self-perpetuation.

However, the mass of material in comets, setting aside hydrogen and helium, is now believed to be similar to that in stars; but because it is not readily apparent it is not generally reckoned with. Likewise, because the more massive representatives of the cometary flux are not often seen, we tend to ignore both their existence and possible effects on terrestrial evolution. In this way, we may obtain a very distorted image of the importance of

Figure 1.1: Composite photograph of the coma and tail of Halley's comet on 10th March 1986, taken with the U.K. Schmidt Telescope. Courtesy of Royal Observatory, Edinburgh.

comets, including, for example, their potential significance for theories of geological and biological evolution, and for a proper understanding of recorded history. These are weighty issues, and one is bound to ask whether astronomical science has yet produced a balanced view of the origin of comets and their association with the earth.

Indeed, these possible blind spots in modern cometary science have interesting parallels in modern galactic astronomy, where progress is now continually hampered by a lack of knowledge concerning the nature and origin of the unseen 'dark matter'. This too, excusing the pun, is a weighty issue, and it is an interesting speculation whether a solution to all these pressing problems in modern astrophysics will turn out to have major aspects in common. If so, there would be no doubt as to the fundamental importance of cometary studies for cosmology and astrophysics.

For these and many other reasons, not least the arrival of the space age, recent years have seen a resurgence of activity in cometary astronomy. This culminated in 1986, with a rendezvous of Soviet, Japanese and European space probes with Halley's comet. From these we learned, for example, that the activity on the surface of a cometary nucleus is confined to a number of small areas where gas and dust emerge in narrow jets before spreading into the coma and tail (see Figures 1.1 and 1.2). In fact, it seems from the evidence of the jets that comets may be rather porous, low-density bodies, and therefore fragile, whilst their surfaces are more or less asteroidal in appearance. Such findings now provide a firmer foundation on which to base our understanding of how cometary tails are produced and how they evolve under the influence of the solar wind and radiation pressure. But despite these achievements telling us about the appearance and behaviour of observed comets, the question of their origin — whence they come and how they are formed — has proved much harder to resolve.

Nevertheless, this branch of the subject is now also undergoing rapid progress, and important new arguments have recently

HMC COMPOSITE IMAGE

IMAGES 3416,3457,3475,3480,3491,3496,3500

Figure 1.2: Composite image of the nucleus of Halley's comet taken by the Halley Multicolour Camera on board Giotto. Courtesy of Dr. H.U. Keller.

been advanced which are leading to a complete reappraisal of the previously accepted picture of the nineteen-sixties and seventies. Some of these arguments even hint at a general malaise with the whole concept of a 'primordial' comet cloud, however familiar it may be, suggesting perhaps that the competing idea of an interstellar origin for comets might now have to be taken seriously. An account of these developments is therefore timely, especially considering the part played by Halley's comet in the history of the subject, while this most famous comet is yet fresh in our minds, still influencing the cometary debate worldwide.

2

Babylonian beginning

"Twinkle twinkle little star, how I wonder what you are!"

Jane Taylor.

2.1 First steps

2.1.1 BIRTH OF ASTRONOMY

The ancient land of Shinar, including much of what is now modern Iraq, comprised the vast alluvial plains between the rivers Tigris and Euphrates. Systematic astronomy seems first to have originated here during the third millennium BC (*cf.* Neugebauer 1945), while the same region, around 2000 BC, is also associated with the conception and drawing of the first constellation maps of the sky (Roy 1984). These maps continued in use unchanged for the subsequent one or two thousand years, possibly becoming more widely known through the activities of the early Minoan and Phoenician seafarers (*cf.* Ovenden 1961, 1966).

In fact, archaeological excavation of the former cities of this region provides extensive cuneiform evidence, recorded on thousands of clay tablets, of a more of less continuous tradition of Chaldean astronomy dating back nearly three thousand years before the dawn of the Christian era. The most important of these finds are concentrated in and around the ancient city of Babylon, which was a leading centre of commerce and culture for the region, and which became the capital of a flourishing empire about the start of the second millennium BC. It is here that astronomy is first recognized as becoming a science.

Cuneiform literature contains a wealth of detailed information on a variety of astronomical topics, including the observation of comets, meteors and meteorites (*e.g.* Thompson 1900, Virolleaud 1905, Kugler 1907). Remarkably little of this knowledge, however, seems to have gained the attention of anyone except a handful of Assyriologists, and it is notably through the work of Pannekoek (1961), Neugebauer (1967) and van der Waerden (1974) that something of the spirit of this knowledge has reached a wider audience in recent times.

Indeed, almost from the development of writing itself, it is clear that the peoples of the ancient Near East knew of and frequently described phenomena which may be interpreted in terms of comets, shooting stars, fireballs and meteor showers (e.g. Bjorkman 1973). Moreover, there is no reason to suppose that these events were of purely incidental interest: observations of such phenomena were plainly inspired by a concern for their repetition, and were frequently used as a basis for the prediction of future events. Even the study of astronomy itself seems to owe as much to concerns of this kind as it does to the gentler pressures of time-keeping and orientation. In addition to highlighting the importance attached by these peoples to cometary and meteoric phenomena, the early cuneiform literature demonstrates a clear understanding of their extraterrestrial provenance, including that of meteorites, and shows that the cultures of the ancient Near East must have been well aware of the essentially astronomical nature of the events in question.

Thus, although our modern word 'comet' ultimately derives from a Greek word κομήτης meaning 'long-haired one', Man's interest in the subject can be traced back far further than the time of the Greeks. Indeed, the available records indicate that comets and comet-related phenomena seem to have played an important part in the beliefs and social habits of most known civilizations from the very earliest times. Excellent accounts of this fragmentary early evidence relating to the cometary and meteoric record have been given, for example, by Newton (1897), Nininger (1952) and Krinov (1960). The latter even cites evidence that a necklace of iron-meteorite beads was placed in an Egyptian pyramid dating from around 3000 BC, while in every case still available for study it has been claimed that the early word for 'iron' translates directly or very closely to the phrase 'metal from heaven' (Zimmer 1916, Rickard 1941, Paneth 1956; cf. Bjorkman loc. cit.).

Figure 2.1: Photograph of a meteor or shooting star: the final fate of cometary dust as
it enters the earth's atmosphere.   Taken from
Babadžanov & Kramer (1968).

This suggests that knowledge of the falls of iron meteorites,
and presumably the associated prospect of long comet-like trains
of fiery débris stretching across a large part of the sky, was
already well established by the time the Chaldean astronomer-
priests of Babylon first began to scan the skies from their watchtowers or ziggurats, making careful astronomical observations.
Although we cannot thus directly infer the origin and purpose

of Babylonian astronomy, this and other evidence (*e.g.* Neuge-bauer 1967) suggest that a particularly portentous or miraculous view of meteoric phenomena was not generally prevalent in early times. Rather it suggests a more matter-of-fact view of the cosmos, with the none too discouraging prospect that we should eventually be able to piece together an understanding of learned opinion about comets and its development for at least the past five thousand years!

2.1.2   CHALDEAN IDEAS

In the absence of explicit accounts of the views taken by these early civilizations concerning comets, we may perhaps approach the truth by noting a much later reference to their ideas by the Roman writer and politician Seneca (4 BC – 65 AD). He devoted a whole volume of his treatise on natural science *Quaestiones Naturales* to a description of comets and cometary phenomena (see Clarke & Geikie 1910), and reported the views of two authors in particular: Epigines, a Greek astronomer of Byzantium (*c.*330 BC or 200 BC; *cf.* Hellman 1944, van der Waerden 1974), and Apollonius Myndus (either *c.*330 BC or 220 BC; *cf.* Clarke & Geikie 1910, van der Waerden 1974).

These astronomers both claimed to have studied amongst the Chaldeans, but gave what are usually considered to be conflicting accounts of their beliefs. The former asserted that the Chaldeans understood nothing about comets, believing them simply to be a kind of atmospheric fire caused by an unusually violent kind of whirlwind; while Apollonius Myndus reported that they classified comets with the wandering stars (*i.e.* planets), and had in some cases even determined their orbits.

Although we cannot be certain of the accuracy of these edited accounts, especially in relation to the views of the earliest Babylonian astronomers, such reports are nevertheless of great interest in that they evidently hint at a much deeper understanding of comets in the past than is usually believed. Thus, while it is of the nature of comets generally to disintegrate under the influence of solar heating into bodies of ever smaller size, several of them in fact also circulate about the sun in fairly permanent elliptical orbits with similar short periods to those of planets. In these cases, their chief disintegration products, tiny fragments of dust, gradually spread around the orbit to form dense currents of circulating dust particles, called meteor streams. These become the source of the visible meteor trails, or shooting stars, that are seen in the earth's upper atmosphere when the streams are encountered by our planet.

The Chaldean view about cometary orbits as expressed by Apollonius Myndus thus comes surprisingly close to the modern picture; while the second idea, linking comets with a fiery atmospheric phenomenon induced by some kind of circulation, suggests knowledge of a rather direct connexion between comets and meteors. Seneca's brief references to Babylonian views are therefore consistent with the existence of a fairly accurate understanding of the behaviour of comets in the early civilizations of Mesopotamia, suggesting that the earliest known ideas about comets may have been remarkably close to the truth.

To infer confusion on the part of the Chaldeans from the reports of Epigenes and Apollonius may therefore simply be to impose upon these early peoples an ignorance of the true nature of comets which the ancients did not possess. In the remainder of this chapter we discard such an assumption, and place the Chaldean ideas in a more complete historical perspective. In particular, we examine the rise and fall of ancient Babylonian astronomy and discuss the main factors — especially the cometary connexion — motivating its original development.

2.2   Signs from heaven

2.2.1   Astronomania

In spite of developing what therefore appears to have been an essentially correct understanding of the celestial nature of comets and meteors, there are other aspects of the Babylonian world-view which are certainly more unexpected. In particular, the Babylonians combined their astronomy with the idea that history repeats itself, and with a very strong belief that celestial events exercised control over terrestrial ones. Why the latter assumption should have arisen amongst the ancient cultures of Mesopotamia has always been something of a mystery to historians (e.g. Frankfort et al. 1946, Butterfield 1981), conditioned, as one now is, to the idea of the rotating celestial sphere serving merely as a passive backdrop against which to register celestial events.

Indeed, it is clear that astronomy in the ancient Near East assumed an urgency in public affairs quite unlike the remote and detached business it has now become. The importance attached by these early civilizations to astronomical observations is reflected, for example, in the fact that watchtowers or ziggurats were provided for the use of astronomer-priests in almost every city of the land, rather like the churches and municipal buildings of modern times. Indeed, the amount of time and energy apparently devoted to such activities seems to have been quite out of proportion to anything which might reasonably be justified or explained on the grounds of idle curiosity, suggesting that the primary motivation for making the observations was once perhaps as compelling and as powerful as the defence of the realm.

Moreover, it does not seem as if the ultimate cause of this excessive interest in astronomical events can ever have been a purely local (or even national) phenomenon. For example, studies of other civilizations at about this time also hint at a strong degree of astronomical involvement in everyday activities, suggesting that these cultures too were similarly obsessed by celestial affairs. Indeed, even the scattered communities of Western Europe developed strong cultural ties with the heavens, constructing stone circles and astronomically aligned megaliths at almost every conceivable opportunity (e.g. Thom 1967, 1971; cf. Heggie 1981).

Here, although the precise astronomical purpose of the stand-

Figure 2.2: Illustration of megalithic markings which may have had a cometary inspiration. The rock carving comes from a sacred prehistoric site at Traprain Law, Midlothian, Scotland, dated approximately 2000 BC. Photograph courtesy of the National Museum of Antiquities of Scotland.

ing stones is still unknown, the artistic contemporaries of their architects in Britain were evidently able to produce designs which are surprisingly accurate renditions of modern descriptions of fireballs or even comets (compare, for example, Figures 2.2, 2.4 and 4.1). It thus appears that observations of astronomical phenomena, and of cometary and meteoric phenomena in particular (Clube & Napier 1982c, p.262), also played an important rôle in the developing cultures of ancient Britain. If this interest extended to include observations of meteor streams, or even corresponding streams of fireballs (cf. Halliday 1987, Terentjeva 1989), it is tempting to speculate that certain extremely precise megalithic alignments (e.g. Bailey et al. 1975), which surprisingly have no obvious lunar, solar or even stellar connexion, might now be interpreted as indicating the radiants of previously recognized intense meteor showers, such as the Taurids (*cf.* Section 2.2.3, p.18; Section 17.1.4, p.397).

These arguments suggest (*e.g.* MacKie 1977) that astronomy in Western Europe at this time may have had an importance similar to that in the Near East, where it is clear from the cuneiform records that observations made from the watchtowers played a significant part in the life of the community. In Mesopotamia, for example, the astronomical observations (or their implications) were disseminated throughout the land by a complex network of beacons and messengers, and the results then examined and assessed by high officials in a centralized organization. This body seems to have been charged with a primary responsibility for the well-being of the state and of its leader (*e.g.* Oates 1979, Butterfield 1981).

It is still customary to suppose that astronomy would inevitably have originated in an agricultural community of the kind known to have been present in Mesopotamia through its calendrical and (to a lesser extent) navigational requirements, never to have become an *urgent* occupation of the state. Nevertheless, it appears that there must have been other forces at work. The dilemma facing modern scholars who confront this situation is well expressed by Neugebauer (1946, p.38), who admits: 'Mesopotamian "astrology" can be much better compared with weather prediction from phenomena observed in the skies than with astrology in the modern sense of the word.'

Indeed, the use of the meteorological analogy is particularly apt, since the Chaldeans not only expected periodic astronomical phenomena to affect the earth but the same weather to recur in cycles of twelve solar years, along with good crops, famines and pestilences (Sayce 1874). The ancient Mesopotamian attitude to astronomy is thus generally recognized as being very strange, the more so since it appears also to have involved a considerable element of fear and trepidation: the overriding impression to emerge from the cuneiform literature as a whole (Jacobsen 1946) is of an astronomical phenomenon with a potential vastly more oppressive than the weather!

2.2.2   PROPHETIC LINK

Accordingly, since they believed that celestial and terrestrial events were physically connected and that history might repeat itself, the Chaldeans had a strong inclination to record astronomical phenomena and correlate changes in the sky with events on earth. The lists of such interrelations are known as 'omens', and always take the form: 'If [astronomical observation] then [terrestrial effect].' For example, using a reference cited by Bjorkman (1973): 'If a shooting star flashes as bright as a light or as a torch from east to west and disappears on the horizon, the army of the enemy will be slain in its onslaught.' This may be reliably interpreted to mean that a bright meteor *did* once appear on the occasion of the enemy being slain in battle; and the nature of the Babylonian belief was that they presumed the same terrestrial result would occur upon other instances of the identical celestial occurrence.

Eventually, following a lengthy period of strife punctuated by great floods and the not infrequent collapse of cities, serious attempts were made to systematize the celestial observations made before about 2000 BC and organize their supposed association with terrestrial events. One substantial compendium from this so-called omen literature, known as *Enūma Anu Enlil* (i.e. 'In the time of Anu and Enlil'), coming to us from the Kassite period (c.1700–1100 BC) but drawing upon earlier sources, comprised a list of about seven thousand omens based on past events. This collection of prophecies is now regarded as representing a very high degree of scholarly achievement (Oppenheim 1964).

Anu and Enlil were two of a triad of principal sky-gods in the Sumerian pantheon, which also included Ea, and were generally regarded as exercising the dominant influence on the fate of mankind. Indeed, it is possible that the fear of what either Anu or Enlil might do was the principal motivating force

of Babylonian astronomy. However, although the general behaviour of Anu and Enlil seems to have been reasonably well
understood, it appears that they might also exercise their power
in an unpredictable way. In modern parlance, the astronomer-
priests were performing their duties in the presence of a natural
phenomenon whose regular, time-averaged characteristics were
broadly known, but which in practice had an exceedingly capri-
cious incidence.

Cuneiform experts tend to assume that Anu and Enlil must
always have been invisible, in keeping with current views about
the nature of ancient gods, but the fact that they were frequently portrayed alongside visible planets and constellations
(e.g. Figure 2.3) is more consistent with a perception of them
as physically real entities. It is also difficult to see how such a
reaction to the astronomical environment could have arisen in
the Mesopotamian world, unless the two principal sky-gods of
the Sumerian pantheon had made their presence felt in some
fairly direct and extreme way during the third millennium BC,
and had then acted in a manner subsequently from time to time
that had revived memories of this earlier extreme behaviour.
The *prima facie* evidence is thus of two well-recognized celestial
bodies which wreaked havoc on earth and continued to evolve
in a manner suggesting that such events were likely to recur.

If this view is correct, however, it has also to be accepted
that the power of Anu and Enlil did eventually wane and become more diffuse; a thousand years later, for example, the two
sky-gods seem to be more closely connected with extended regions of the zodiacal band, and there is of course no sign of
them now! Thus, Anu appears later to have been linked with
the plane of the ecliptic, while Enlil was associated with the
higher latitudes to the north (see Figure 2.3, *cf.* van der Waerden 1974). Such a transformation is not as strange as it might at
first appear, however, since it is possible that the dust and débris
generated by two exceptionally conspicuous cometary gods in
regular short-period orbits could have given rise to temporarily
visible zodiacal bands. Even later, one would expect such dust

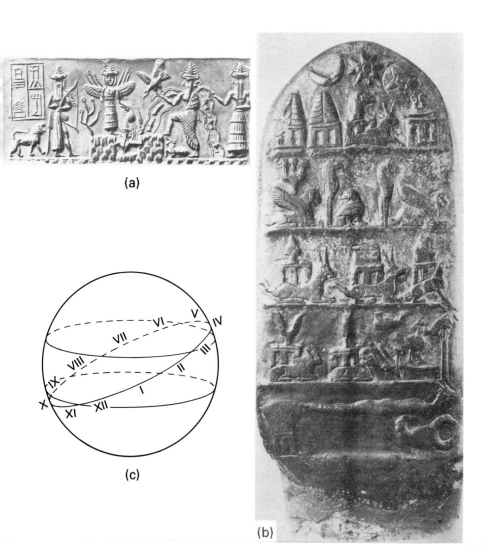

Figure 2.3: Evolution of Babylonian representations of the deities Anu, Enlil and Ea: (a) as horned sky-gods (on cylinder seals) e.g. Ea, second from right; (b) as pre-planetary zodiacal symbols (on *kudurrus* of the second millennium BC) e.g. first three of four on second register; and (c) as ecliptic zones (first millennium BC; *cf.* van der Waerden 1974) e.g. Enlil and Ea, the upper and lower zones respectively.

to spread all around the sky, producing two pairs of rings symmetrically above and below the ecliptic, and it may be significant that such rings, previously unsuspected in modern times, have recently been discovered by the infrared astronomical satellite IRAS (*cf.* Section 3.1.3, p.46). There is therefore nothing particularly implausible about the view that the Babylonians had an essentially correct understanding of comets and meteors in the past, although one might then have to accept that in the first instance some of these bodies were also identified as celestial deities.

2.2.3   WHY FEAR COMETS?

The acknowledged purpose of the omens was to provide a record down the centuries of the connexion between celestial events and particular occurrences on earth, especially those that had grievous consequences such as the death of a king or the laying waste of the land. However, as a basis for prediction the list was beset with difficulty, since not all omens were unfavourable. For example, a luminous bolide might simply be a message in fire which conveyed greetings to the king from Enlil!

Nevertheless, despite such occasional light relief, the omens show that the sudden appearance of a bright meteor or a lingering comet was usually viewed by the Babylonians with a good deal of fear and superstition. This attitude to comets was evidently coupled with the generally baleful character of the Mesopotamian universe, a vestige of which has extended down the ages almost to the present day. However, although there is now a case for linking Anu and Enlil with the appearance of two bright and conspicuous short-period comets in the ancient sky, the reason for so deep-seated a *fear* of comets has never been properly addressed by modern scholars.

Thus, despite this popular fear persisting right into the twentieth century, its cause until now has remained a tantalizing enigma. After all, the most recent appearance of Halley's comet gave no immediate cause for alarm, and presumably most comets, even if rather brighter, must have as little direct influence on terrestrial affairs. A way around this apparent difficulty is to recognize that events which have been witnessed only during the relatively short period of recorded scientific history, covering little more than two or three hundred years, are probably not a fair representation of Man's experiences, or Nature's activities, on a longer timescale.

Indeed, recent researches in modern cometary astronomy now independently suggest that the civilizations of antiquity may have experienced happenings in the sky which have not since been repeated on the same scale (Clube & Napier 1986a, 1989b; cf. Chapter 17). For example, many astronomers now recognize a possible connexion between Encke's comet and the body that gave rise to the huge Tunguska explosion in Siberia on the 30th of June 1908 (e.g. Kresák 1978a; cf. Sekanina 1983). This particular comet must have been a far larger and more luminous body in proto-historic times, suggesting that the first glimmerings of early civilization could well have coincided with a rather more active celestial environment than we are now used to. Moreover, Encke's comet is also associated with the broadest known meteor stream, namely the Taurids (Whipple 1940, Whipple & Hamid 1952). This independently suggests a recent very large progenitor; and although encounters like the Tunguska explosion are still commonly treated as random occurrences and correspondingly rare (the appropriately sized lunar craters indicate an average terrestrial rate of one per approximately 500–1000 years; Shoemaker 1983), the connexion with a recent large progenitor is indicative of a much higher overall frequency of impacts during the last few thousand years (Clube & Napier 1986a, 1989a,b; Clube 1987b).

This result obviously has important implications for present interpretations of ancient cosmologies and astronomical traditions, particularly since most investigations of the omen literature have been conducted by historians and scientists working in relative ignorance of modern astronomical developments and of the ways in which evolving comets might affect the earth.

These specialists have generally adopted a somewhat dismissive attitude to the physical associations between the sky and the earth implied by Babylonian fears and beliefs; but the connexion between Encke's comet and the Tunguska event is just one way in which astronomers now recognize that such fears can be realized (see Chapter 17).

It is possible, then, that a once extra-luminous comet in an earth-crossing orbit underwent violent fragmentation, producing at least two conspicuous bodies which, with their associated bolides and zodiacal dust, were originally connected in Babylonian minds with a variety of celestial divinities, particularly Anu and Enlil. This is clearly a very speculative interpretation, given the nature of the evidence; but the implication that the ancient sky was once the scene of much greater activity than now would also explain (for instance) the common knowledge and acceptance of the falls of iron meteorites in antiquity, especially in relation to the rarity of such events nowadays (*cf.* Zimmer *loc. cit.*, Paneth *loc. cit.*). Moreover, this view might similarly furnish the basis for an understanding of the strange fear and superstition which is so often associated with the cometary phenomenon. In this way, it is possible that one should now regard the later emergence of Graeco-Christian cosmology in a new light: that is, as a deviation from a former quite realistic view of the universe, first held by the Sumero-Babylonians and subsequently amplified and broadly confirmed by the results of modern post-Newtonian investigators.

2.3   Astrological advance

These recent developments, linking Sumero-Babylonian astrology and modern scientific astronomy, call for a reassessment of the status of 'astrology'. For example, whilst there is a general tendency nowadays to regard 'astronomy' as rational and its predecessor 'astrology' as irrational, thereby reinforcing a rather self-serving belief that ancient astronomy is not particularly relevant to modern science, the assumption that ancient astronomy is mostly irrational is certainly not supported by historians. Indeed, historians tend to argue that the only really defensible course is to regard the astronomy as understood and practised down the ages as an expression of the most rational thinking of the time. In drawing an evolutionary distinction between astrology and astronomy, therefore, it is not rationalism that is at stake, but the way in which the underlying principles associated with celestial studies developed.

In particular, the distinction often drawn between ancient and modern astronomy is the level of commitment down the ages to some kind of *physical* association between celestial and terrestrial events. As we have seen, the devotion to this principle was virtually absolute in Babylonian astronomy from its inception, whereas by the time medieval astronomy was giving way to scientific astronomy in the post-Newtonian era any such principle was more or less completely abandoned. The current belief that ancient astronomy is largely irrelevant is based on a surviving assumption that there is no serious connexion between celestial and terrestrial events.

During the Newtonian era, this assumption was essentially based on the stand taken by counter-reforming Christian theologians during the sixteenth and seventeenth centuries against the assumed operation of 'first causes' in terrestrial affairs (*e.g.* Thomas 1971). It was apparently necessary, therefore, in order to counter the zealotry of much Christian theology of this period, to exorcise the magical and the miraculous from natural philosophy; and for this purpose, any *direct* celestial interference in terrestrial affairs was firmly denied. Nevertheless, there is no *modern* justification of this assumption, and it follows that there is now a basis for regarding both ancient astronomy and astrology as essentially rational, and treating each on its merits.

In the remainder of this section, the gradual development of ancient Babylonian astronomical and astrological ideas is described, showing how the original link with observations slowly came to be broken. This development culminated in the appearance of a completely erroneous 'horoscopic' theory of celestial influences on the earth, and led to the establishment of an equally erroneous view of comets and their decay products, in which comets eventually came to be seen as mere atmospheric visions or celestial signs.

2.3.1   JUDICIAL ASTROLOGY

Broadly speaking, historians now recognize the existence of four phases in the evolution of astronomy: judicial astrology, zodiacal astrology, horoscopic astrology and scientific astronomy. The first of these phases, judicial astrology, implied a very strong connexion between purposeful celestial bodies and harmful events on earth. Subsequently, however, any adverse effects (or otherwise) came to be seen more as 'influences', attributable in turn first to fixed locations in the zodiacal band (zodiacal astrology), and then to the wandering planets (horoscopic astrology), before eventually giving way to the modern picture in which even the existence of such influences is finally denied.

According to the beliefs underlying judicial astrology, the idea that celestial events might significantly affect the welfare of the community was such a plain truth that, as we have seen, much of the energy of the state was devoted to observing the sky and developing a process of prognostication based upon this belief. There was also a sense in which an omnipotent deity was believed to impose and maintain strict order on both the celestial and the terrestrial scenes. This understanding of the underlying character of the universe is still reflected much later in the Greek word 'cosmos'. Indeed, to the extent that 'religion' in its Latin derivation means 'scrupulous observance' or a 'way of binding oneself with respect to the gods' (*e.g.* Nielsen *et al.* 1983, Vallée 1989), this understanding persists to the present day.

Celestial order was presumed to extend to human affairs as well, and there was a clear implication that the deity might exercise his might (usually with the aid of thunder-bolts!) to preserve good conduct here below. In practice, new kings and their subsequent dynasties were often in the habit of assuming their right to rule as a consequence of the apparent dictates of this deity, who frequently co-operated by promptly laying waste any opposition (*cf.* Frankfort 1948, Clube 1989b,c). This idea — the divine right to rule — has proved to be an extremely potent force throughout most of recorded history, and was not finally abandoned until well into the present millennium. Even Napoleon, for example, is believed to have seriously desired the arrival of a comet to justify his assumption of power! On this basis, therefore, there can be little doubt as to the intensity of feeling with which the precepts of judicial astrology were held by the Babylonians and their Sumerian predecessors.

2.3.2 ZODIACAL ASTROLOGY

However, although the Babylonians were initially fearful of their celestial environment, judicial astrology gradually underwent a slow transformation. By the early part of the first millennium before Christ it is clear that a new form of astrology was being practiced, now called 'zodiacal astrology' (van der Waerden 1974). According to this picture, the region of sky once considered to be the domain of Anu and Enlil — the zodiacal belt — was divided into sections, each of which was perceived as wielding some kind of influence on terrestrial affairs below.

Nevertheless, although the principal occupants of the zodiacal belt are nowadays the sun, moon and planets, there are no very strong reasons for believing that any of these bodies yet played a significant rôle in the supposed influence of the zodiac on the earth. Rather, these objects, which vary their stations along the ecliptic, seem to have been used more as calendrical or chronological markers, a great event in the sky being appropriated by the king (or his minions) and dated by the position of the sun and the moon and the disposition of the planets amongst the constellations. This view is supported, for example, by recent studies of the astronomical iconography of *stelae* and of *kudurrus* (Tuman 1986) which indicate that planets, in the first instance at least, were observed for purely calendrical purposes.

A possible explanation of these developments can now be advanced in terms of the evolution of short-period comets in earth-crossing orbits close to the plane of the ecliptic. Such bodies would have been recognized by their associated meteor streams, which, especially in their initial stages, might have exerted a strong influence on our planet. If the number of such comets was in a state of decline during the third and second millennia before Christ, many of them becoming asteroidal in appearance or dark, it is reasonable to infer that what eventually became a less frequently realized source of fear or physical damage would have become increasingly associated with 'hidden influences'. This viewpoint is also consistent with Aristotle's otherwise inexplicable remark (*Meteorologica,* 345a, 6–11), speaking of an earlier time, that much dust had been deposited in the tropical zone (the region of the zodiacal cloud: see Section 3.3, p.64) because of a decline in the number of comets!

Indeed, unless we reject Aristotle's comment as meaningless, we seem here to have a direct report of a possible association between comets and the zodiacal belt. Inasmuch as a belief in the latter's hidden influences was also developing during the first millennium BC, we should also note the expressed rôle played by comets and meteors in human affairs: these bodies were believed to carry the respective souls of both mighty and ordinary folk from earth to heaven and *vice versa* (Eisler 1946, p.65).

Moreover, it is remarkable that the ancient gods whose names are now attached to the planets: Mars, Jupiter and so on, often have strong cometary associations in astrology. In a Greek omen text of about 150 BC falsely attributed to the Egyptian priest Pelósiris, for example, different types of comet are associated with Venus the *horseman;* with Mercury the *swordsman* and the *torch-holder;* with Jupiter the *long-haired;* with Saturn the *disc-thrower;* and with Mars the *typhoon* (Whipple 1985). This belief in fact persisted for centuries, and even survived to be recorded during the renaissance of Islamic science. According to Kitab

Latin name (c.100 BC)	Late Antiquity (c.200 BC)	Scientific name (c.400 BC)	Divine name Hellenistic/ Babylonian	Main associations
Mercurius	Hermes	Stilbon Gu-utu, Gud-ud	Star of Hermes/ Nabu	Herald, (1,2,4) Proclaimer, Messenger, Torch-holder
Venus	Aphrodite	Phōphōrus Dili-pat, Muldilbat, Nabat kakkabē	Star of Hera, Star of Aphrodite/ Ishtar	Shining One, Light-bringer, (1–4) Lucifer, Horseman
Mars	Arēs	Pyroeis Sal-bat-a-ni, Zal-bad-anu, Mushtaburu mutanu	Star of Arēs/ Nergal	Fire, war, (1,2,4) fever, blood, death, pestilence, Typhoon
Jupiter	Zeus	Phaeton Mulu-babbar, Sag-me-gar, Mul-babbar	Star of Zeus/ Marduk	White Star,(1–4) Chief Oracle-giver Beaming Star, Long-haired One
Saturn	Kronos	Phainon Kaimânu, Lu-bad Sag-ush, Kaiawanu	Star of Kronos, Star of the Sun/ Ninib	Steady One, Constantly (1–4) Plodding, Circle of the Shining Star, Disc-thrower

Table 2.1: The evolution of planetary names during the classical period. The source code is (1) van der Waerden (1974); (2) Eisler (1946); (3) Aristotle (*Meteorologica*, 392a5–30); (4) Whipple (1985). Whilst the scientific names appear to emerge about 400 BC, the divine names (Column 4) are very ancient. It might even be questioned whether the early and late designations relate to the same celestial objects at all.

al-Mughni, for example, a ninth-century astrologer from Baghdad, the planetary names still followed the Greek classification but the illustrations and descriptions were remarkably cometary (Whipple *loc. cit.*, Figure 1). The same planetary names, as recorded on Babylonian astrolabes, are also frequently associated with *fixed* zodiacal longitudes, whereas true planets (as van der Waerden has pointed out) are bound to vary their position along the zodiac. This discovery suggests that some planetary names, perhaps originally associated with observed comets, later became identified with certain times of the year when the earth intersected their corresponding fixed meteor streams in the zodiacal band.

If this admittedly speculative picture is correct, the attachment of divine names to the real planets must have been a relatively late occurrence, possibly prompted by the disappearance from the sky of the bright cometary bodies to which the names were originally applied (Clube & Napier 1982c). In fact, there are indications that the planetary names underwent considerable evolution during the classical period (see Table 2.1), though most scholars still regard these changes as being of relatively little significance, consistent with the prevailing view that early astronomy developed exclusively out of agricultural, navigational and calendrical needs. Nevertheless, there are now reasonable grounds for believing that Babylonian astronomy (as manifested by judicial and zodiacal astrology) was founded on a possibly fearful attempt to understand and predict the flux of fireballs and meteors.

2.3.3 HOROSCOPIC ASTROLOGY

It is important to realize that this interpretation of the evolution of Babylonian astronomy is not at odds with its development also for purposes of timekeeping nor with the fact that Chaldean astronomers created a highly sophisticated lunar calendar (*e.g.* van der Waerden 1974). Indeed, the Babylonians developed a rudimentary perturbation theory for the purposes of calculating lunar ephemerides, and it was largely the arithmetical and algebraic techniques associated with this theory that the Greeks later took over when formulating their geometrical model of the cosmos, with its elaborate system of epicycles and deferents to explain planetary motions (Neugebauer 1948, 1967).

However, it also appears that the Greeks were so entranced by the assumed validity of their geometrical modelling that they eventually adopted a physical scheme in which the planetary motions, including those of the sun and moon, were considered to be supported by a complex set of interlocking crystalline spheres. The presumed existence of these spheres was clearly an obstacle to the passage of celestial missiles such as comets, which thus posed something of a difficulty for the model, since the latter implicitly ruled out any possibility of celestial bodies affecting the earth. The influence of such effects was still widely accepted at this time, and it is clear that the burgeoning Greek world-view required a complete reappraisal of the precepts of Babylonian astrology.

The appeal to geometry by the Greeks, then, is associated with the emergence during the fourth century before Christ of a totally new form of physical astronomy now known as 'horoscopic astrology'. This revolutionary development was based, in fact, on the completely false premise that *planets* exerted a distant influence on terrestrial affairs. However, unlike either judicial or zodiacal astrology, which as we have seen might have had a proper physical basis involving a direct contact between astronomical objects and the earth, horoscopic astrology, being specifically related to an *imagined,* remote influence of the planets (*i.e.* 'action at a distance'), is entirely spurious.

A direct consequence of this new theory was that otherwise unimportant planetary conjunctions or alignments were now perceived as having great significance. Here again we are dealing with a contrived, yet false transformation of ideas, for in the original judicial astrology there is some evidence that a catastrophe was widely associated with the aftermath of a conference or gathering of the gods (Butterfield 1981). Times of acute crisis might originally have been associated quite plausibly with conjunctions of cometary bodies or extended swarms of fireballs, but the later association attributing significance to the conjunction of planets is patently absurd.

Nevertheless, despite these somewhat contrived aspects of Greek astronomy, the theory of horoscopic astrology, with its geometrical modelling, was intensely attractive mathematically and ultimately became extremely influential. Much of this influence may presumably be attributed to the far-reaching near-Eastern hegemony established at this time by the Greeks, which eventually led to horoscopic astrology completely displacing zodiacal astrology during the centuries around the time of Christ.

This change was inevitably accompanied by the replacement of an originally oppressive view of the cosmos by a more optimistic outlook on the world, a form of 'enlightenment' that went with the growing belief in fundamentally benevolent gods which is now associated with the advance of Hellenism (James 1962). At the same time, the implied magical influence of the planets on terrestrial affairs rapidly led to the growth of numerous 'astral' religions throughout the Near East (van der Waerden 1974), each with its own claims to a special understanding of divine intentions and cosmic functions. The basic ideas, however, remained an exclusively Greek invention, and eventually came to maturity in Alexandria with the seminal works of Ptolemy during the second century AD. Thereafter, subsumed into Christian doctrine and promulgated by the Roman Church, the theory was to become a persistently recurrent theme in western science for nearly fifteen hundred years.

The advent of horoscopic astrology is now seen to have been an almost unmitigated disaster. It was a serious hindrance to the proper development of science during the Middle Ages, and its eventual overthrow, during the Renaissance and the Age of Enlightenment, was only possible after the further crucial change of paradigm that preceded the development of modern science. The two-thousand year period of horoscopic astrology's dominance, from about 300 BC to 1700 AD, bounded by major shifts of paradigm, is also commensurate with the period in which comets were viewed as atmospheric visions or celestial signs. It seems therefore that these false ideas about comets, which ultimately emanated from ancient Greece, may have had their origin in the decline of a perfectly rational Babylonian science, and owed their persistence to the contemporaneous growth of Christian doctrine, itself the probable child of an astral religion (e.g. James 1962, van der Waerden 1974).

2.4   Interweaving paradigms

This understanding of how astronomy evolved, through phases of judicial, zodiacal and horoscopic astrology, suggests that an original, fundamentally correct understanding of comets was subsequently lost at some stage prior to the start of the Christian era (cf. Section 2.1.2, p.10). Clues to the reason for this reversal may be found in the quite different approaches displayed by the Chaldean and Greek astronomers to their science. Whereas the former showed a distinct preference for the use of algebraic methods of calculation, the latter were much more inclined to work with geometrical techniques. Moreover, it has long been recognized that the guiding principles of mainstream Greek science, especially after the third century BC, differed quite markedly from those of Chaldean science, despite the latter's essentially rational character (e.g. Farrington 1944, Lloyd 1979, Neugebauer 1945). Thus, whilst it is clear that the Babylonians shaped and influenced Greek astronomy to a considerable degree, the differences in approach suggest that large-scale revisionism in science occurred during the immediate post-Socratic period, indicating a significant shift in paradigm of the kind explored by Kuhn (1962).

2.4.1   ATHENIAN BLUEPRINT

Indeed, looking at the classical period more broadly, one cannot help but notice that it is generally characterized by the presence of two main views about the natural world, one ancient and the other relatively new. On the first, there was a tendency to regard the environment as a purposefully-driven, overpowering system containing a variety of larger-than-life forces which might impress themselves rather adversely upon mankind. This view of the cosmos is largely outside our present range of experience, but if the existence of such forces was not in doubt, it is hardly likely that Man would have questioned the sanctions that could ultimately be brought to bear on human behaviour: thus, questions of morality would not have been regarded as matters for persistent debate. However, there was plainly also a desire at this time to associate the common view of nature with more benign influences, and it was Plato's comprehensive analysis of history, science and human behaviour which became the springboard for increasingly moral outlooks on Nature's plan. In this way, larger-than-life forces could be contemplated with either the optimism of an Epicurean or the pessimism of a Stoic.

On the other hand, Plato's analysis also implied more an outlook based on calculated resolve: there emerged, therefore, a growing tendency to view the facts with a certain degree of clinical detachment, even to deprive the world of some of its substance in the attempt to achieve a new synthesis. Cosmic forces, even if not altogether passive, can under these circumstances appear to be less than real, and there is then a tendency for the calculated resolve of a Platonist to give way to the detached equanimity of an Aristotelian. On the former view, comets may still retain the characteristics of being destructive, potentially devastating bodies; whilst on the latter, they become intrinsically harmless, amounting to little more than atmospheric visions or celestial signs.

However, the new thinking did not emerge along any single clear path. While the first indications of a paradigm shift arose in Athens during the fifth century BC, to be tested almost immediately in the wider Greek arena, it took at least another century before the new spirit of Hellenism advanced like a wave over Alexander's vast near-Asian empire, first gaining footholds in Assyro-Babylon and Egypt, then only to be engulfed by a second, mentally less dextrous wave from Rome.

The emergence of the new Greek thinking, essentially in the period between 300 BC and 150 AD, coincided with a period of great turmoil and social upheaval in the Near East. During this period, the older order of warring city states, conditioned to the former theological view of the world in which larger-than-life forces held ultimate sway, finally gave way to a new mightier form of empire in which more secularly minded men assumed for themselves the reins of power. Thus, whilst theology at this time was acquiring for itself a secular core, the conditions in which most levels of society were obliged to exist remained so oppressive as to be hardly conducive to an immediate general acceptance of developing learned opinion about the heavens.

Nevertheless, the founders of the Hellenic empire were able to establish the famous Alexandrian school in Egypt, which eventually became a secure, remote haven in which Greek natural philosophy was able to develop, taking on in its maturity much the form it was to assume during the eighth century and later once the Islamic empire was established. Elsewhere, we find only a relatively small community of Roman philosophers and writers, such as Seneca, who belatedly tried to bridge the gap between Athens in its heyday and what eventually turned out to be the start of the Christian era in Rome. Almost inevitably, it seems, these intellectuals of a steadily maturing Roman empire found themselves drawn into much the same divisions of opinion which had previously been experienced by their Greek mentors.

2.4.2 ROMAN COPY

Locally it was more the older Etruscan tradition that was gradually replaced in Rome (*e.g.* Cristofani 1979), just as the ancient Babylonian views, transmitted by the pre-Socratic sages from Ionia, had been overtaken in post-Socratic Athens. Thus, in formulating his palpably scientific cosmology, Seneca (see Cristofani *loc. cit.*, p.95) remarks: 'There is this difference between us Romans and Etruscans. We believe that lightning is caused by clouds colliding, whereas they believe that clouds collide in order to create lightning. Since they attribute everything to the gods, they are led to believe not that events have a meaning because they have happened, but that they happen in order to express a meaning.'

However, in our haste to approve the teleological doubts expressed by this commentary, we must be careful not to overlook the facts. The lightning referred to by Seneca was called *manubia* by the Etruscans and was believed to be sent by the gods from their heavenly dwellings in the zodiac. Such lightning appears to have been a meteoric phenomenon and its significance lay in its capacity to warn of impending terrestrial events. Depending on the circumstances, it could be sent as a warning (*fulmen praesagum*) or as a sign of judgement, generally intended to punish but sometimes also bringing favourable consequences (*fulmen ostentorium*), or possibly being the source of effects which were always harmful (*fulmen peremptorium*), *i.e.* 'it devastates whatever it strikes and changes the state of public and private affairs.'

These categories are identical to those found in the ancient Babylonian literature; indeed, the possibility in the past of Etruscan links with the Near East cannot be overlooked (Cristofani, *loc. cit.*). The implication seems to be that the Romans, like the Athenians, also experienced an 'enlightenment', seeing the universe as it was eventually presumed to be, *i.e.* orderly rather than apocalyptic. But if the early tradition was rational, as now seems to be the case, the fact of *manubia* and its immediate currency in Etruscan circles are in no way gainsaid by Seneca's expression of teleological doubt.

It is interesting to speculate, therefore, whether or not there was a connexion between the revival of 'enlightenment' in Rome and the gradual perfection of the Aristotelian cosmos in Alexandria, culminating with the work of Ptolemy. By the second century AD, apocalyptic and messianic claims were undergoing a significant retreat, and the period of widespread upheaval in the

Near East (300 BC – 100 AD) had come to an end. The question may be raised, therefore, whether the world was emerging from a renewed bout of meteoric activity at this time.

It will be noted later (Section 4.1.2 p.72) that periods of social upheaval followed by enlightenment, which are correlated with increased and reduced meteoric activity, appear to be more the rule than otherwise. Further, it has never been at all clear why Seneca's successors were unable to capitalize upon his eminently sensible view of cometary and meteoric phenomena (Section 3.2.4, p.63); but if potential interest in the subject died out simply because meteoric activity entered a period of relative decline, the turn of events does become a little more comprehensible. Moreover, since the straightforward apocalyptic view of the world inherited by many early Christians came to be abandoned during this period (100–300 AD) in favour of what seemed at first to be a more mysterious (Pauline) view of events, involving a temporary divine presence on earth, it is perhaps understandable why the subsequent debate over cometary and meteoric phenomena should then also have become scientifically sterile (Cronin 1981). In this way, it appears that because academic opinion now placed its weight behind a world-view which was orderly rather than apocalyptic, considerable encouragement was given once again to the belief that comets were merely atmospheric phenomena or celestial signs.

The final picture that emerges, therefore, is one in which during a very early period, prior to the second millennium BC, Man's knowledge of the prevailing celestial environment gave him a relatively accurate understanding of comets and their potentialities. In due course, as the supposed activity in the sky declined (Clube & Napier 1986a, 1989b), the opportunities to associate this essentially correct view with direct observational experience gradually became less frequent, until finally, during the period of Roman stability (100–300 AD) at the close of the classical period, such opportunities became so rare as to cause the understanding itself to be called into question. As a consequence, Greek science, Christian cosmology and Roman theology became firmly rooted in the idea that the cosmos was both divine (a very old notion) and largely unchanging (a very new notion!). The parallel concepts of heavenly permanence and perfection clearly had *some* basis in reality (and were to prove very fruitful), but as a foundation for true science, as is now well known, they were basically flawed and carried the seeds of their own destruction.

2.5   Meteoric record

Although much detailed historical research remains to be done before we can be certain whether this pattern in the advance of astronomy is correct, it provides a useful backdrop against which to view the early development of ideas about comets. In particular, it focuses attention on the varying fireball and meteor flux, and it is interesting to ask whether resurgent meteoric activity during and after the fourth century AD could produce any long-term changes in cosmological speculation which resemble the shifts in opinion that occurred during the fourth century BC (Athens-Alexandria) and the first century AD (Etruria-Rome). In fact, it is known from Chinese and scattered European sources (Biot 1848, dall'Olmo 1978) that the incidence of meteor showers has risen and fallen fairly often during the past two millennia, with significant renewed activity centred on the fifth, eleventh, fourteenth, sixteenth and nineteenth centuries, the first of these periods probably lasting several hundred years. In Europe at least, each of these high points in the meteor flux seems to have been marked by renewed millennial fears and intellectual doubts, if not social upheaval as well, from which there duly emerged a new level of understanding more or less rejecting the apocalyptic world-view (Clube & Napier 1989b).

2.5.1   ASTRONOMICAL TABLETS

If meteoric activity goes hand in hand with the temporary emergence of apocalyptic views, as we now suppose, the late cuneiform records from Babylon and Uruk should be examined from this perspective. It has been through studies of the more readily understood lunar and planetary ephemerides recorded on the tablets of the late Seleucid period (300–0 BC) that the significant mathematical differences between contemporary Babylonian and Greek astronomy came to be recognized (Neugebauer 1945). Most of the available tablets do not correspond to ephemerides, however, but appear to be actual observations or the calculations associated with their reduction; these are the so-called 'diaries' of events, many of which still await translation and interpretation (Sachs 1974). It is an interesting question, therefore, whether these diaries also indicate any of the changes in meteoric flux that are thought to have taken place.

To gain some insight into the rôle of these observations, we may perhaps use as a guide the output of the only other centrally organized school of astronomers which maintained astrological traditions, namely the Chinese. By the time we are now considering, professional astronomy was already a vital component of the Chinese bureaucratic state, and among official observations, those of comets, meteors and fireballs were undoubtedly of substantial importance. Not only was a sophisticated classification scheme for comets in existence by the middle of the second century BC (Figure 2.4; cf. Figure 4.1, p.69), but for the next eighteen centuries China was to maintain a professional interest, albeit of varying intensity, in recording the incidence of fireballs, meteor showers and comets. These data now provide us with invaluable knowledge not only of past comets and the variable occurrence of meteoric phenomena but also, it seems, of the variable attention astronomers pay towards such happenings! In particular, they provide us with a useful guide to understanding the activities of Babylonian astronomers.

The Babylonian astronomical data for the years between 771 BC and 84 AD are strongly concentrated into the last three hundred years of the period before the birth of Christ, and show a distinct maximum around 150 BC (see Figure 2.5). Although this pattern may simply reflect a fortuitous distribution of clay

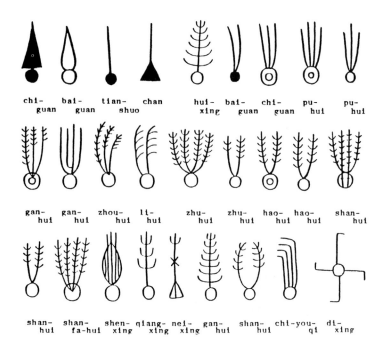

Figure 2.4: Chinese classification scheme for comets, taken from a book copied on to silk found in tomb No. 3 at Mawang-dui, near Changsha. The tomb comes from the Han dynasty and is dated 168 BC. See Xi Ze-zong (1984)

tablets uncovered by archæologists, it has been suggested also that it may reflect a real increase in astronomical activity (Oates 1979, p.179), such as may arise in response to enhanced activity in the sky — meteoric processes being the obvious candidate.

2.5.2   SHEEP OR STARS?

In fact, although the diaries of the late Seleucid period are mostly devoted to day-to-day records of astronomical and meteorological phenomena, several groups of statements appear at the end of each month which can be understood as summarizing average conditions during the month, such as the height of the

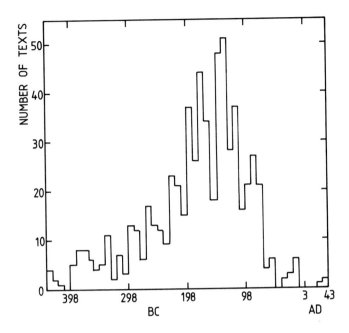

Figure 2.5: The number of astronomical cuneiform texts from Babylon, arranged per decade (after Neugebauer 1967). It is possible that this may reflect the varying degree of meteoric activity in the sky.

river and various economic data, including the prices of barley, dates, cassia, sesame and wool (Sachs 1974). Such items seem to be quite irrelevant in an astronomical context, but they nevertheless figure prominently in the very first cuneiform lists drawn up by Sumerian astronomer-priests (Butterfield 1981), and often have specific meteoric associations in the subsequent Kassite literature (c.1500 BC; cf. Bjorkman 1973).

Why these particular meteoric associations should exist is admittedly very obscure, but presumably depends in some way on the prevailing astrological beliefs and the varied appearances of shooting stars and fireballs. Moreover, while the derivation of wool from sheep is virtually assured, it can hardly be ignored that in ancient Sumerian the respective words for 'wild sheep' and 'sheep pen' are identical to those for 'moving star' and 'circular enclosure in the sky'. A celestial shepherd and his flock shedding strands of wool whilst scuttling around the sky is reasonable imagery to associate with a large disintegrating comet and the fireballs it deposits on the earth. Indeed, the same association even extends to the word 'astronomy' (Herschel 1858, p.11), which comes from the Greek words $A\sigma\tau\acute{\eta}\rho$ ('star') and $\nu\acute{o}\mu o\varsigma$ ('law') or $\nu\acute{\epsilon}\mu\epsilon\iota\nu$ (meaning 'to tend', as a shepherd tends his flock). The significance of these ancient connexions during the late Babylonian period is not known, but the suggestion that various aspects of the data recorded in the 'diaries' relate to meteoric activity cannot obviously be excluded.

2.5.3 BABYLONIAN END

The data appear to indicate, therefore, a heightened degree of meteoric activity in the sky during the period in question. This conclusion is strengthened by the fact that Chinese astronomers recorded some remarkable meteor storms at this time (Tian-shan 1977), while the presence of a classification scheme for comets from the Han dynasty of this period (see Figure 2.4) indicates that some degree of professional interest in the behaviour of related bodies was certainly being shown elsewhere in the world. Nearer at hand, one also finds an increased awareness of meteoric phenomena amongst contemporary Romans; and, as Cornford (1971) has emphasized, even the poet Lucretius (Latham 1951) was inordinately concerned with frightening, unpredictable events in the sky. Moreover, the last three centuries of the pre-Christian era are notable for the generally raised expectations amongst the populace at large of impending world-end and doom (Butterfield 1981).

In this way, the evidence suggests that a greatly increased flux of fireballs may have been observed by the still fearful Babylonian astronomers during the last three hundred years BC. However, as we have seen, by surviving such a 'bombardment' the more passive view of the cosmos originally articulated by the Greeks was gradually reinforced, leaving the much earlier Babylonian picture of the world to go into terminal decline. Indeed, it is not without interest that the survival of a nation seems also to be linked at this time with its perception of the cosmos. Thus, whereas the late rise and fall of the Seleucid empire and the Babylonian world-view correlates with an apparent resurgence and decline of meteoric activity, the corresponding fall and subsequent rise of the Greek world-view may be associated with the fortunes of the Roman empire during the two or three centuries either side of the time of Christ. In this way, it seems that essentially correct ideas and beliefs about comets and meteors which had been in the ascendant for at least the previous three thousand years were gradually dissolved.

Inasmuch as astronomy and cometary science are part and parcel of history itself, it is likely that a variety of influential new ideas about the fundamental nature of the world played an important rôle at this time in underwriting some of the new, but erroneous ideas about comets. In particular, by overturning an established view of the heavens, with which a good deal of modern research is perfectly compatible, the ideas associated with the formative period of the Christian era had the profound effect of deflecting academic enquiry along a completely false trail for almost two thousand years. It is amusing to note that this enormous detour seems to have established itself far more strongly amongst intellectuals with a mathematical bent than in the population at large, suggesting either an extreme propensity for wishful thinking amongst the learned, or too symbiotic an association with masters who are similarly deluded as to the extent of their power. Indeed, the same style of thinking may even have pervaded cometary science right up to the present day, and conceivably still impedes the proper development of modern cosmological investigations!

3

Classical diversion

"Probable impossibilities are to be preferred to improbable possibilities."

Aristotle.

3.1 Greek theories up to Aristotle

3.1.1 THALES OF MILETOS

Setting aside the tantalizing hints about comets which can be unearthed amongst the very first descriptions of astronomical bodies, the earliest theories of comets about which we can be reasonably sure date from the beginning of early Greek science. This is usually associated with the Ionian or Milesian school, whose foundation in Miletos is generally attributed to Thales (c.624–548 BC). This Greek city-state, originally populated from Crete around 1100 BC, had grown by the sixth century BC to become the foremost trading community on the western fringe of Asia Minor (see Figure 3.1), and was reputedly the mother of more than ninety colonies. Miletos had extreme wealth and influence, and its leading citizens must presumably have lived lives of considerable luxury and leisure.

Thales, traditionally one of the seven wise men of antiquity, appears to have been a politician and statesman of great practical sense and achievement. For example, he was frequently credited with predicting the eclipse of the sun in May 585 BC which ended a five-years' war between the Lydians and the Medes, and certainly had many interests in mathematics, engineering and astronomy. Although the suggestion that he accurately foretold the solar eclipse is widely discounted nowadays, it is nevertheless generally accepted that Thales was the first Greek cosmologist.

He began the continuing quest for a primary substance and cause of all things, and taught that the earth was simply a flat disc or short cylinder floating upon a vast underlying ocean of

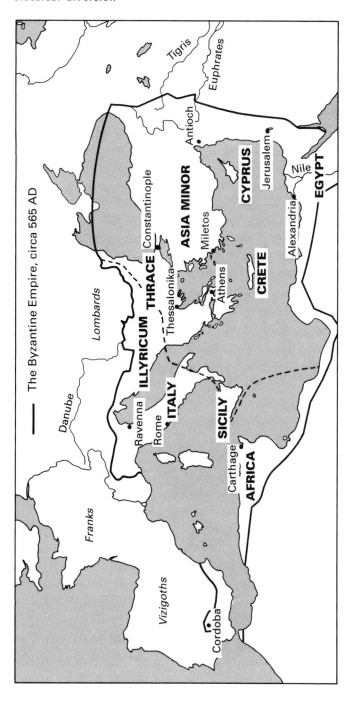

Figure 3.1: The cradle of civilization: the western approach.

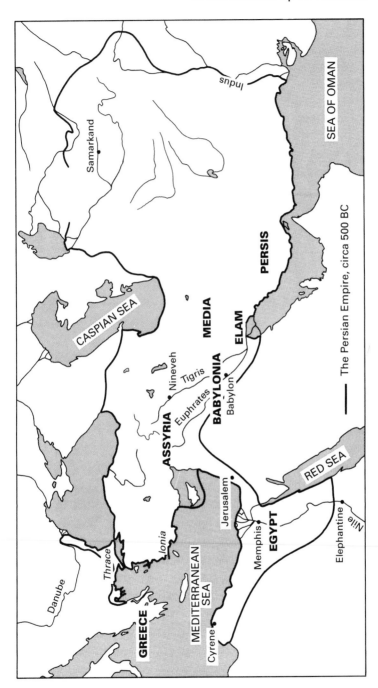

Figure 3.2: The cradle of civilization: the eastern approach.

primordial stuff, which he identified with water. However, whatever the merit of these ideas and their influence on later thinkers, he is now mostly remembered as the unfortunate subject of an apocryphal tale reported by Plato (see Heath 1913). According to this story, while star-gazing and looking upward he once had the mischance to fall into a well, upon which he was rallied by a clever and pretty maid-servant from Thrace, for being so keen to know what was in the heavens when he could not see what was in front of him, still more beneath his feet!

Thales was followed by Anaximander (c.610–545 BC), an important and influential thinker who is believed both to have introduced the gnomon to the Greeks from the Babylonians, and to have drawn the first map of the inhabited world. Anaximander is also known to have developed a more detailed and complex world-view, abandoning water as the ultimate material of the universe whilst elaborating his belief that there was a 'something', an Infinite or Boundless, from which everything else derived.

In his attempt to explain the origin of the astronomical bodies, Anaximander supposed that all things were obtained from an original undifferentiated living mass or medium, in a manner that could be likened to organic growth from a kind of primeval cosmic egg. In this process, which led to the systematic separation of material into different arrangements, four elements emerged: first a fiery substance, then air or mist, then water, and finally earth (e.g. Farrington 1947, p.9).

The suggested order of events bears some similarity to certain aspects of the origin of the universe as described in the book of Genesis or those incorporated into modern cosmological theories. As a result, there is a growing tendency these days to be impressed by how much our present ideas, for example about the Big Bang, often seem to take their lead from concepts originally introduced by the earliest Greek writers. Anaximander is even credited with having vaguely anticipated certain parts of the theory of evolution! However, there is no question of any special insight on the part of these early Greek philosophers into aspects of the universe which were then completely unknown, and a potentially more informative line of enquiry nowadays is to associate their cosmological speculations with aspects of the solar system environment with which they were more obviously in contact. Indeed, if our understanding of the development of Babylonian astronomy is correct, some acquaintance with the behaviour of bright comets at an earlier time would not be an unreasonable assumption.

3.1.2 JETS OF FIRE

Anaximander argued that in emerging from the primeval substance, the air or denser vapours would somehow have burst out of their fiery surrounding membranes to enfold and confine the remaining flames, producing wheels or enclosed hoops of opaque misty material. These constrained fires in turn completely encircled the earth (Williams 1969).

On this picture, planets and stars were regarded as circular wheels of fire which only became visible due to the presence of holes or apertures in their enclosing hoops, which allowed the fiery substance to leak out. Anaximander's concept of the heavenly bodies therefore had something of the character of a lighted jet of gas spurting out of a punctured pipe. Such imagery is plainly well suited to comet tails, but the model was nothing if not adaptable. Thus, although the stellar apertures were believed to be fixed in the revolving hoops about the earth, he was also prepared to drop this assumption, as necessary, in order to accommodate the relative motions of the sun and moon against the stellar background and the changing shape of the moon.

There is no direct record of Anaximander's thinking about comets, but from this account it appears that he would have tried to explain them along similar lines: as changing, temporary holes in the primordial hoops of celestial fire. Another possibility is that the hoops were a visualization of cometary orbits, and that the fiery jets were actually a description of shooting stars, or meteors, observed when the whirling hoops intersected the earth.

As for the earth, Anaximander believed that it was a short, squat cylinder three times as broad as long, surrounded by air and floating freely at the centre of the observable universe in infinite space. Apart from its flattened, pill-box shape, it was thought to be entirely composed of the four elements which had separated from the primeval stuff: earth, water, air and fire. This model of the *earth* was persistent in ancient Greece, but it is nevertheless very strange, and it has never been explained why it should have been credited with such explicit dimensions, nor why it should have been associated with fire. If the 'earth' in question were *celestial,* however (*cf.* de Santillana & von Dechend 1970, Clube & Napier 1989b), and identified with a formerly more conspicuous zodiacal cloud around the sun, these difficulties would not be so formidable. Such an identification would be manifestly in accordance with the 'central fire' proposed somewhat later by the Pythagorean, Philolaus (Section 3.1.7, p.53).

Anaximander also taught that the inhabited world was transitory, liable eventually to disperse back into the boundless space from whence it had come, and that there were many other worlds. These he identified with gods, which like the earth were also believed to be transient and subject to infinite renewal, each cycle associated with a definite beginning and end. There are suggestions that some of these ideas derived originally from an earlier Iranian cosmology, and that the infinite or boundless space which was envisaged extended all the way to the 'Beginningless Lights', presumably the celestial sphere (*e.g.* West 1971).

3.1.3   Distance of the stars

An important, but curiously unremarked, feature of Anaximander's system was his insistence that the hoops representing the stars lay *below* the sun and moon. The fantastic imagery, involving wheels of fire and the relative position of the stars with

Figure 3.3: Nineteenth century view of the zodiacal light, taken from Guillemin (1865).

respect to the sun and moon, has often seemed rather mysterious to modern commentators (*e.g.* Dicks 1970), but it might be viewed, not unreasonably, as an account of the sky dominated by a bright short-period comet. The rapid motion of an elongated cometary object across the sky, or a collection of bright comet trails of the kind recently detected at infrared wavelengths by the infrared satellite IRAS (Davies *et al.* 1984, Sykes *et al.* 1986, Sykes 1988), could have contributed to the image of a wheel of fire, and the associated intense meteor shower or storm might easily have given the impression that stars lay below the sun and moon.

Indeed, 'stars' were variously described at this time: as nails in the firmament, as floating leaves, and even as 'fiery plates of gold, resembling pictures' (Goodwin 1871, p.139). This raises questions as to whether the Greek word for 'star', like the Baby-

Ionian, was ever used to describe a single class of body, a doubt which is reinforced by the fact that 'stars' were sometimes even recorded as disappearing from view towards the north, due to their increasing distance from us (West 1971).

This suggests that some of the 'stars' of the early philosophers should really be identified with comets or cometary débris (*e.g.* meteors and the like), although such a connexion does not seem explicitly to have been made before (*cf.* Bailey *et al.* 1986). If this is correct, the early accounts of a primordial cosmic body producing a temporary flattened world might be viewed (*cf.* Clube & Napier 1984b, Section 6) as bearing a considerable resemblance to modern ideas in which decaying short-period comets become the source of dust particles and meteor streams which evolve to produce a flattened zodiacal dust cloud. The zodiacal light (see Figure 3.3) is generally brighter, even now, than the more familiar Milky Way, and one can readily imagine that a more luminous structure might have existed several thousand years ago (*cf.* Section 3.3, p.64).

3.1.4   EARTHY BODIES

The last of the Milesian school was Anaximenes (*c.*500 BC). The views of this author differed in several respects from those of Anaximander. First, he returned to Thales's doctrine in giving a concrete identity to the primeval substance, this time treating it as 'air' (or more accurately a form of fire); secondly, he believed that the earth had a flat plate-like structure which allowed it to float on the air; and thirdly, he attempted to unify the known forms of matter, by proposing that the four basic elements were derived from the original fiery substance by a physical process of increasing density analogous to one of compression or condensation. Finally, he considered that heavenly bodies were ultimately derived from the earth. This last feature is of particular interest, since it suggests a firm connexion had then been made between terrestrial bodies and the stars, the latter still believed to be largely fiery in nature.

Figure 3.4: Fall of the Sikhote-Alin meteorite on the 12th February 1947, from the painting by P.I. Medvedev in the USSR Academy of Sciences. Illustration courtesy of Professor Yu. A. Shukolyukov.

It is possible, also, that this line of argument developed from the conception of the earth as an extension of the zodiacal dust cloud, and that the latter, through its association with occasional newly discovered comets, might have been regarded as a source of heavenly bodies. On the other hand, such a development might simply have been introduced in order to explain meteorites, which although earthy in nature are observed to fall directly from the sky and are frequently enveloped in thick smoke and fire. (A modern example of such a fall, on the western fringes of the Sikhote-Alin mountain range, is shown in Figure 3.4; this involved a meteorite originally weighing about a tonne, see Krinov 1963.) Both these explanations, however, suggest a possible cometary link in the development of early Greek cosmologies, and, although we cannot be absolutely sure, it is reasonable to suppose that Anaximenes would have ascribed an 'earthy' nature to comets too. Indeed, since he taught that many earthy bodies lie in regions occupied by the stars (Heath 1913), such a conjecture seems almost certainly correct.

Within a hundred years, therefore, Thales and his followers may have acquired a surprisingly realistic picture of their universe. In particular, there is good reason to suppose that they had arrived at a celestial understanding of comets, seeing them as temporary, transient holes in the hoops of constrained fire surrounding the earth, or as earthy bodies made fiery by their position above the earth and their rapid motion through space.

3.1.5   Burning clouds

At around the same time as these developments were taking place, Xenophanes of Colophon (c.570–470 BC), one of the founders of the Eleatic school, was adopting a rather less sophisticated cosmological picture with Babylonian overtones. He perceived the earth not as a floating disc, but instead as a flat region perched on top of a solid column or permanent body 'rooted in the infinite' (e.g. Koestler 1968, p.24). The heavenly bodies were thought to be transient structures, the results of cloudy exhalations from the permanent earth at the top of the column. This suggests a link with the picture developed by Anaximenes, in which stars were ultimately derived from the earth; but according to Xenophanes the vapours simply caught fire as they rose.

This model could readily accommodate sudden and unexpected changes in the heavens, but was much less successful at explaining the more regular movements and constant patterns in the sky. In fact, Xenophanes suggested that even the fixed stars, sun and moon were burnt out each day, and rekindled the following day or night from new exhalations continuously produced by the earth! Not surprisingly, he placed comets in the same general category, believing them simply to be groups of moving, burning clouds (Fairbanks 1898, p.85).

In this way Xenophanes became the first to be associated with a purely atmospheric theory of comets, arguing that they were fiery cloud-like structures produced by invisible dry exhalations from the earth, in a manner similar to the formation of clouds from the sea.

3.1.6   STAR-CHAINS AND CONJUNCTIONS

The line of rationalist Ionian natural philosophers was completed by Anaxagoras of Clazomenae (c.500–428 BC), the first philosopher to take up abode in Athens. He extended the work of Anaximenes to the limit in which both the sun and the moon were regarded as essentially 'earthy' bodies, and argued that the moon was generally similar to the earth, shining simply by the light it received from the sun. The sun itself was perceived to be a huge red-hot stone, the source of the great meteorite which had fallen in 467 BC (Williams 1969). Unfortunately, the time was not ripe for such a radical idea, and for holding such an impious belief about a god Anaxagoras was banished from Athens, finishing his days at Lampsacus.

Anaxagoras, together with the atomist Democritus of Abdera (c.450 BC), developed yet another theory of comets, namely planetary conjunctions (Fairbanks 1898, p.255). According to this picture, described and criticized in detail by Seneca (Clarke & Geikie 1910, p.283), the close approach, or conjunction, of two or more planets could cause their lights to merge, producing the appearance of a single elongated star resembling a comet. However, by Seneca's time planetary conjunctions were regarded as significant events for horoscopic astrological reasons (*cf.* Section 2.3.3, p.27, and modern explanations of the biblical Star of Bethlehem, *e.g.* Hughes 1979, De Young & Hilton 1987), and it is quite possible that the kind of conjunction which Anaxagoras had in mind had very little to do with planets. For example, a rather similar idea for comets was also advocated by Diogenes of Apollonia (*c.*430 BC), who taught that stars were rocky bodies akin to pumice stone and that comets were chains of such stars (Guthrie 1965, p.370). This account again suggests that the connexion between comets and *planetary* conjunctions may be a later distortion, possibly based upon a misunderstanding as to the kind of conjunction which was observed.

It is conceivable, in fact, that a comet may have been identified as a swarm of 'stars', suggesting in this context that the word 'star' should be understood to mean 'meteor' or 'fireball'. In this case the proposed model might be viewed as a surprisingly realistic picture of a meteor stream, such as might be produced by a decaying comet. Indeed, now that a system of this kind has been recently observed circulating in the Taurid meteor stream (Dorman *et al.* 1978, Clube 1987b), Diogenes's account may be more securely based than one might have thought.

Although Seneca's summary of the planetary conjunction theory shows how easily it could be made to look foolish if interpreted literally, the original idea continued to attract attention. For example, the Stoic philosopher Zeno of Citium (*c.*300 BC) believed that stars could sometimes combine their rays to create an image or illusion of an elongated cometary star, while Artemidorus of Parium also elaborated upon the same general idea (see Clarke & Geikie 1910, p.286). This author extended the theory by speculating that it might also apply to innumerable undiscovered planets which only became visible if they happened to come close enough to the earth, or to each other, to combine their light suitably to produce a comet.

The notion that there might be many invisible planets in the heavens had been previously used by Anaximenes and Diogenes in order to explain meteorites, and by Anaxagoras to explain eclipses (Guthrie 1962, p.134; Fairbanks 1898, p.255). Again, now that we are aware that some Earth-crossing asteroids are probably of recent cometary origin (*e.g.* Fox *et al.* 1984, Hahn & Rickman 1985, Rickman 1985; *cf.* Sections 6.4.1 and 17.1.3, pp.124, 394), these surprisingly accurate early Greek ideas may take on a new significance. Unfortunately, Artemidorus of Parium cannot be dated reliably, although judging from Seneca's description of his cosmology it seems likely that he followed either Parmenides of Elea (*c.*515–450 BC) or Philolaus (*c.*450 BC). In any case, it is probable that this line of thinking is very old, since Proclus (410–485 AD), who later headed the Platonic Academy in Athens, provides us with an authoritative non-Ptolemaic interpretation of Plato's *Timaeus*, in which invisible stars are said to be circulating in large numbers in elongated orbits.

3.1.7   PLANETARY THEORY

It is an interesting fact that the Ionian school had very little, if anything, to say about the planets, so much so that one might even suppose the planets were not considered important by the pre-Socratic Greeks. Indeed, although the earliest indication that the planets were noticed is commonly attributed to Pythagoras (*c.*572–497 BC) and the celebrated school he founded in Italy, even here the familiar planetary names seem not to have been mentioned until about the fourth century BC (*cf.* Table 2.1, p.25); while it was Eudoxus (*c.*408–355 BC), on the Greek mainland, who first provided the geometrical basis for understanding their motions across the sky. Although the idea may of course be very old, an important innovation attributed to the Pythagoreans is the abandonment of the geocentric view. Philolaus, for example, treats the earth as a planet like the other planets, revolving with the sun and moon around a central fire which he calls the hearth of the universe, the house of Zeus and the mother of gods. Within this central fire, invisible to us, is the force which directs the activity of the universe. The nature of such imagery has always been somewhat obscure to later commentators, but associations with the Ionian flat disc and the modern zodiacal cloud are not at all implausible. It is therefore conceivable that later interpreters may simply have misunderstood the general import of the earliest Greek ideas, possibly through ignorance of evolutionary aspects of a phenomenon, namely comets, which we now know might have been much more prominent during proto-historic times.

The mention of Pythagoras brings us to two further ideas about comets dating from the early pre-Socratic period. In the first, Aristotle, writing in the *Meteorologica* (see Ross 1968, 342b30), mentions that some of the Italian Pythagoreans considered 'the comet' to be a rare apparition of one of the planets, echoing the theory attributed to the Chaldeans by Apollonius Myndus (Section 2.1.2, p.10).

A similar view, according to Aristotle, was also held by the mathematician Hippocrates of Chios (c.430 BC) and his pupil Aeschylus. [Hippocrates of Chios should not be confused with his more famous contemporary Hippocrates of Cos (c.460–377 BC), the father of medicine.] Hippocrates and Aeschylus subsequently extended the 'planetary' idea to explain the transient nature of the cometary tail, and proposed in particular that this was simply an optical illusion produced by sunlight reflected from the vapours attracted to the comet.

The second suggestion is also related to the Pythagoreans. Aëtius (c.150 AD), writing in *De Placitis Philosophorum* (usually found in editions of Plutarch's *Moralia*; see Pearson & Sandbach 1965), records that some among their number believed that comets were mere optical illusions, produced by reflected sunlight giving an appearance of comets 'much after the same manner as images are reflected in mirrors' (Goodwin 1871, p.149).

In this way, in the space of just two hundred years, that is by the beginning of the fourth century BC, at least seven distinct theories of comets had emerged during the reflections of Greek natural philosophers. Two of these, namely atmospheric fires caused by violent kinds of whirlwind and earthy bodies basically similar to planets, may have arisen during the early development of Babylonian astronomy; but the others: jets of flame from the enclosed fiery hoops surrounding the world, burning clouds of invisible vapours exhaled from the earth, optical illusions, and planetary conjunctions or chains of wandering stars, visible or invisible, seem all to be genuinely new ideas, and evidently signal a serious concern amongst the Greeks for an issue that was far from resolved. Although these early ideas were each strongly motivated and constrained by the underlying philosophical beliefs of their various proponents, there are already signs that purely materialistic explanations of comets were soon to be abandoned, and hints of the later division into either 'atmospheric' or 'celestial' theories. At the risk of some oversimplification, therefore, the early debate about cometary origins may be conveniently thought of in these terms.

3.2   Aristotle and beyond

The next significant advance in Greek thinking is associated with the ideas generated by what are usually regarded as the three most important Greek philosophers of this period: namely, Socrates (c.469–399 BC), Plato (c.428–358 BC) and Aristotle (384–322 BC). These authors represent the pinnacle of Athenian philosophical and scientific achievement, and their combined efforts laid the foundations for almost the whole of Near Eastern and European philosophy for the next two thousand years.

As has already been described in relation to the early Babylonian beliefs (Section 2.3.3, p.26), the period leading up to about 300 BC saw a major shift of emphasis in philosophical thought. In the Greek sphere, an era of active and largely unconstrained speculation about cosmology and physics now gave way to considerations of equally intractable problems of human life and conduct. As previously indicated, this switch of interest was apparently triggered by a growing conviction that the celestial gods were fundamentally benevolent, or at least neutral. This inevitably gave rise to a view that our troubles here on earth were largely man-made, and that the really important issues to be addressed were not so much the nature of the physical world but questions of social and moral behaviour.

Such an attitude tends to place politics, in the broadest sense, above the level of astronomy, with the corresponding risk that fundamental concepts arrived at in the political arena, for example, may influence and distort the development of cosmological views. A somewhat similar switch of interest occurred much later during the eighteenth and early nineteenth centuries (cf. Section 5.2.2, see p.103), leading to a scientific conviction that comets similarly were fundamentally benevolent, or at least neutral, and that meteoric phenomena were probably harmless or had no effect on the earth. To the extent that this view of meteoric phenomena has been adhered to rather strongly throughout the twentieth century, these developments in advanced Greek society can be readily understood. For example, most twentieth century statesmen have seen present-day problems in exclusively social terms, while most twentieth century astronomers have little or no interest in solar system bodies and pay no attention to meteoric phenomena.

Thus, almost imperceptibly, whilst still recognizing the 'true' nature of the physical world, it seems that academe slowly downgraded the astronomical scene and began to treat the terrestrial system in all its aspects, including evolution, as a self-propelling machine not directly affected by the outside world. That such attitudes to the world can become very deeply ingrained is illustrated even nowadays by the almost irrational response which sometimes emerges when it is suggested (e.g. Hoyle & Wickramasinghe 1985), contrary to the prevailing view, that evolution may be fundamentally driven by extraterrestrial influences.

The emergence of these attitudes in ancient Greece, together with the increasing trend among contemporary opinion to regard philosophers as a 'useless sort of people' (Guthrie 1962) and the turbulent political pressures of the time, meant that many possible lines of enquiry were soon terminated. Alternative cosmological views were advanced for a while by a few, such as the development of a heliocentric cosmology, begun by Philolaus, explored by Plato and continued by Heracleides of Pontus (c.375–310 BC) and Aristarchos of Samos (c.300 BC), the latter proposing the first truly sun-centred system (e.g. Jeans 1947, Koestler 1968, p.50). However, these important ideas (though correct) advanced no further and were soon overtaken by the increasing power and influence of the Aristotelian school.

3.2.1   ATMOSPHERIC THEORY

Aristotle's contribution to science was enormous, and reading his works one cannot fail to be impressed by the depth and breadth of his knowledge about the natural world. However, his conclusions about astronomy and cosmology left much to be desired, a result which we now recognize as being especially unfortunate since his work proved to have such an extraordinary and enduring influence on the studies of many leading philosophers and commentators in later years.

According to Aristotle, an immobile earth at the centre of things was surrounded by nine concentric spheres, containing the respective heavenly bodies: Moon, Mercury, Venus, Sun, Mars, Jupiter, Saturn, and the fixed stars (see Figure 3.5). The possibility of the revolution of the earth around the sun was rejected by Aristotle on the ground that such a revolution would cause an apparent displacement of the stars, and considering that in his day the immense distances of the stars were not known, this objection seemed a valid one. His views about planetary motion clearly followed the course set by Eudoxus, in that the planetary motions were made up by combining a number of intrinsically circular motions, while the planets themselves were said to be

Figure 3.5: The arrangement of the heavenly spheres according to Aristotle. Illustration taken from Apian (1531), courtesy of the John Rylands University Library, University of Manchester.

maintained in motion about the earth by an outer ninth sphere, the 'Prime Mover' of Aristotelian dynamics. Any bodies whose movements were not of this orderly character (and comets definitely fell into this class) were consigned to the sublunary region, lying between the earth and the moon.

Aristotle proposed that the upper reaches of the atmosphere contained dry 'windy exhalations' from the earth, which were distributed about the upper region like a kind of fuel, whose essential properties were such that it burst into flame when set in motion by the regions beyond (Ross 1968, 341a37 *et seq.*). Using the analogy of terrestrial fires, such as the burning of stubble in a field (*loc. cit.*, 341b25), Aristotle argued that depending on the disposition and quantity of the material, one could obtain various kinds of fiery phenomena. In this way, he suggested that comets, shooting stars, and even the regions of the Milky Way (see Section 3.3, p.64) were basically fiery atmospheric phenomena produced by violent winds at the top of the atmosphere.

Now, if it were possible to concede that 'the earth' in this context was the zodiacal cloud; that 'the earth' was looked upon as some kind of extension of our planet in the general direction of the sun, corresponding to the central fire proposed by Philolaus; and that the 'windy exhalations' in this instance were recognized meteor streams projecting from the zodiacal cloud in the plane of the ecliptic rather like so many spokes projecting from the hub of a bicycle or cartwheel, then it is conceivable that one might begin to make sense both of Anaximander's imagery and Aristotle's arguments for transferring an astronomical phenomenon to a pseudo-terrestrial location within the present earth, namely an 'atmospheric' region lying some distance above *terra firma*. As it is, however, one can only suppose that Aristotle meant what he has usually been interpreted ever since as saying.

It should be kept in mind, of course, that Aristotle was not a professional astronomer. For his information he relied largely upon the works of Eudoxus and Calippus, and in his treatise 'On the heavens', where he is mainly concerned with abstract astronomy, his primary contention is that the physical universe is spatially finite and temporally infinite, a vast bounded sphere which has existed without beginning and will continue without end. However, it was the events of the sublunary zone that clearly occupied the attention of most early Greek scientists, and it was in his 'Meteorology' that Aristotle was most evidently concerned to supply his own explanations of the observed phenomena. The work has a strong empirical base with evidence of the author's capacity to assess a prodigious quantity of detailed information before placing it in order. Nevertheless, it is also firmly governed by theory, and the unity it possesses undoubtedly derives largely from the dominance of a single notion: that of 'exhalations'.

Aristotle held that 'exhalations' or evaporations are continuously being given off by 'the earth'. They divide into two kinds, wet or steamy, and dry or smoky; and their action explains, in a unified way, most of the events recurring in the atmosphere. In this way, four qualities — coldness, wetness, dryness, hotness — are invoked as paired attributes of the four basic constituents of the sublunary world — earth, water, air, fire — and it is clear that Aristotle envisaged a general intermingling of these elements in which fire, left to itself, will move upwards and find its place at the outermost edge of the universe. Nevertheless, it is also stated with some approval that 'our remote ancestors have handed down remnants to their posterity in mythical form to the effect that these [heavenly bodies] are gods and that *the divine encompasses the whole universe.*'

It seems to remain Aristotle's view, therefore, that the primary substances are divine, and that they should be sought in the heavens; so it is curious — to say the least — that the fiery exhalations are regarded by commentators as exclusively associated with the earth as it is now understood. Indeed, Aristotle also invoked a fifth element or 'quintessence'; for 'there is some other body, separate from those about us here, whose nature is more honourable, in that it is further removed from the world below.' However, he also argues on the basis of an earthly attribute, namely 'it is the function of what is most divine to think and use its intellect', that heavenly bodies are alive and intelligent! (For a more detailed assessment of Aristotle's world-view, see for example Barnes 1982.)

The point to be made, then, is that despite the general belief arising from Aristotle's works that he clearly separated earth from heaven, there are definite indications that he also saw them very much as an interactive whole, with the heavenly attributes merely at one extreme end of a continuum. It is therefore possible to see in Aristotle's cosmological views more in common with those of his predecessors than is usually supposed, and it is conceivable that much of our present understanding of these views has been strongly coloured by later interpreters misinformed as to the probable nature of the celestial environment.

3.2.2 LUMINOUS CLOUDS

After Aristotle, cosmological speculation entered a period of relative decline in Greece, and new ideas about the nature and origin of comets occurred much less frequently. In fact, we know of only three new theories of comets dating from the immediate post-Socratic period, and it is now fairly clear that the Aristotelian view quickly gained acceptance in the Alexandrian school if not immediately elsewhere, and thereafter reigned virtually unchallenged in learned circles for almost two thousand years.

Two of these new theories may be regarded as little more than modifications of Aristotle's atmospheric hypothesis. The first, proposed by Heracleides, was simply that comets were very high clouds illuminated by the Pythagorean 'upper fire' (Heath 1913, p.254), while the second, due to Metrodorus of Chios (c.330 BC), suggested that the luminous cometary phenomenon could be explained by a kind of forcible influx of the sun into certain clouds, which caused them to sparkle like fire (Hellman 1944, p.24). A rather similar view was expressed at nearly the same time by Strato of Lampsacus (fl.288 BC), who believed that comets could be attributed to the light of a star which happened to lie within a thick cloud (Hellman 1944, p.23).

The latter picture in fact gives a very good description of the usual appearance of a typical run-of-the-mill comet: as a fuzzy, luminous blob surrounding a bright stellar nucleus. Indeed, the view of Halley's comet itself was recently described (Bode 1985) as 'like a headlight in dense fog', and those who saw the comet during its last apparition will attest to the accuracy of this, and Strato's, account.

3.2.3   CELESTIAL THEORY

The third new theory was described by Seneca and attributed to Apollonius Myndus, who is variously assumed to have flourished around either 330 BC or 220 BC (cf. Clarke & Geikie 1910, van der Waerden 1974). This author had a remarkably percipient view of comets, believing that they were distinct heavenly bodies, like the sun or moon, to be regarded as essentially akin to planets, neither optical illusions nor trails of fire produced by conjunctions.

He argued against the Italian Pythagorean idea that 'the comet' was simply a rare sighting of an ordinary planet, analogous to the infrequent occasions on which a planet like Mercury can be easily seen, and said that there is no reason to expect the same comet to reappear. Moreover, he believed that comets were as varied in their sizes and other characteristics as they were numerous. The changing brightness of comets was put down to the same cause as that for planets, namely an apparent waxing and waning due to the varying distance of the object from the earth (Clarke & Geikie 1910, p.290).

Despite such ideas having more than a grain of truth, Seneca strongly criticized them and followed Aristotle in pointing out that true planets would have to move within the zodiacal limits, which comets do not, adding also that because stars and planets are occasionally seen through or behind a comet, this implied that comets could not be true 'stars' at all, but instead must be merely irregular, insubstantial fires.

3.2.4   Seneca and the Stoics

This brings our discussion finally to the dawn of the Christian era and to Seneca's own views about comets. Seneca, who was originally tutor to the young Nero, lived in a particularly unfortunate period (Clarke & Geikie 1910), under Caligula the madman (37–41 AD), Claudius the imbecile (41–54 AD) and Nero the monster (54–68 AD). The scientific work for which he is famous, *Quaestiones Naturales*, was written shortly before his death in 65 AD, when he was forced to commit suicide by his former pupil, Nero. He was (had to be!) a Stoic, and although we have already mentioned Zeno's stellar or planetary-conjunction belief about comets, according to Seneca this was not the view held by most of the School.

Instead, Stoic philosophers, such as Posidonius (*c*.135–51 BC), were inclined to follow Aristotle's lead (*loc. cit.*, p.293), believing that comets were fiery atmospheric phenomena, moving across the sky in erratic, unpredictable paths depending on the available supply of fuel. Boëthus (*c*.100 BC), for example, supposed that a comet was 'an elevation of spirit or wind mixed with an earthy substance and set on fire' (Holland 1603). Other Stoics, however, such as Panaetius of Rhodes (*c*.130 BC), considered that comets were mere optical illusions or false images of stars (Clarke & Geikie 1910, p.304), thus taking a view of comets that is not unlike the Epicurean view of gods as described by Lucretius in his *De Rerum Natura* (Latham 1951).

Nevertheless, Seneca wholeheartedly subscribed to none of these beliefs (*loc. cit.*, p.295), and instead argued that one should draw a clear distinction between genuine atmospheric phenomena, which usually last at most for a few hours at a time, and 'comets', which persist for much longer periods and are observed to follow systematic, curved paths on the sky. This, and their generally extended, luminous appearances, led him to argue that comets must be permanent celestial bodies, but with a fiery nature quite unlike that of either stars or planets.

His earlier criticism of the planetary viewpoint of Apollonius Myndus (see p.62) could in principle be applied to his own theory too, while there was the additional difficulty of explaining how it was possible occasionally to see stars and planets lying apparently behind or through visible comets. Here, now attributing the argument to 'Apollonius' (possibly of Tyana, a near contemporary of Seneca), Seneca pointed out that when one's line of sight does seem to pass through a comet, it usually passes through the gaps in the fire (*loc. cit.*, p.300), and this, it was thought, was sufficient to resolve the apparent difficulty with the concept of 'fires'.

Seneca's views on comets were thus a kind of compromise between the atmospheric and celestial viewpoints. Although one might imagine later investigators using his discussion as a kind of springboard from which to launch the subject, in fact, as we have already noted (Section 2.3.3, p.26), this did not happen, and Seneca's writings now stand in splendid isolation, more perhaps as a monument to what might have been than to progress itself.

3.3 The problem of the Milky Way

An important part of Aristotle's thesis which has gone largely unremarked (*e.g.* Jaki 1972; *cf.* Clube & Napier 1984b) is that he also believed the Milky Way to lie in the sublunary zone, even going so far as to claim (*loc. cit.*, 345a10) that it was a hot accumulation of the disintegration products of many comets. This may be taken to imply that the Milky Way was once much nearer to the ecliptic plane than now, though there is no known mechanism which could alter the earth's orbit to such an extent yet leave the earth unscathed!

It is perhaps for this reason that such assertions by ancient philosophers have not been given the attention by scholars that they deserve. But there is no doubt that a large number of the pre-Socratic sages and their followers held similar, though to us perverse, views about both the Milky Way and the relative positions of the heavenly bodies.

Thus (*cf.* Section 3.1.3, p.46), Anaximander, Parmenides, Leucippus (the founder of the Atomists), Metrodorus, and Crates all shared the view that the stars lay closest to the earth, below both the sun and moon (Guthrie 1962, p.93–94; Fairbanks 1898, p.110). Indeed, this opinion was also held by the earliest Babylonian and Persian astronomers (Eisler 1946, p.171), though it is difficult to believe, for example, that any of these individuals were unaware of the phenomenon of lunar occultations, in which the moon passes in front of a star.

Similarly, Metrodorus and the mathematician and astronomer Oenopides of Chios (*c*.450 BC) both taught that the Milky Way was the former path of the sun (Guthrie 1965, p.360; Arago 1855, p.353), while Anaxagoras and Democritus claimed that the Milky Way lay in the earth's shadow, as if shielded from the sun's rays (Guthrie 1965, pp.309, 422). Moreover, some of the Pythagoreans taught that the Milky Way and comets were both produced by the same mechanism: as a kind of optical illusion caused by the reflection of our sight upon the sun (*e.g.* Goodwin 1871, pp.148–149).

From these descriptions, it is reasonable to conclude that the earliest philosophers of this period knew from direct experience, or at least from that of their forebears, of an essentially correct association between cometary disintegration products and the formation of a luminous dust cloud in the plane of the ecliptic (*i.e.* a zodiacal cloud, see Figure 3.3, p.47), albeit one which was supposed to come between us and the moon. Under these circumstances, any meteor-stream intermediary would certainly have been very conspicuous, and one might have expected an associated awareness of 'stars' coming between us and the moon. For example, one may compare both ancient and modern descriptions of meteor storms (*e.g.* Olmsted 1834a,b; Hawkins 1964, Hughes 1982a), which as well as bearing striking similarities to one another frequently refer to 'falling' or 'flying' stars.

These arguments suggest that the rise of ancient Greek civilization coincided with or followed a period of intense activity in the sky. As we have already noted, this could give an important clue to the origin of Anaximander's somewhat surrealistic picture of heavenly bodies resembling vast wheels of fire, and might also explain several other hitherto puzzling facts about the period in question.

For example, the major concern of Aristotle's *Meteorologica* and of classical philosophers generally (*e.g.* Cornford 1971), was not with 'meteorological' phenomena as its name implies, but with 'meteoric' phenomena. Moreover, the fact that the Greeks took the trouble to classify observed comets into three broad types: 'bearded', 'cypress-tree' and 'torches', of which the several kinds of the latter (see Clarke & Geikie 1910, pp.37–40 *et seq.*) are clearly descriptions of bolides or even falls of meteorites, indicates that such phenomena were probably not at all infrequent in those days. These points, together with the arguments marshalled by Zimmer (1916) and Paneth (1949, 1956), strongly suggest that our present sense of long-term uniformity in celestial affairs may be less secure than is commonly thought (*cf.* Section 17.1.5, p.401).

Thus, although the amount of attention given to meteoric phenomena in classical times nowadays strikes a somewhat discordant note, an enhanced meteoroidal flux during the classical period is well within the bounds of possibility. Aristotle and his Greek and Babylonian contemporaries may well have finally settled on the mistaken idea that comets, and even the Milky Way, ultimately derived from a kind of fiery terrestrial whirlwind, but the Greek cosmologists were certainly not lacking in logic, and we cannot be sure that the imagined action of whirlwinds was not simply an explanation based on visible meteor streams that extended well into the sublunary zone.

4

Medieval commotion

"When beggars die, there are no comets seen:
The heavens themselves blaze forth the death of princes."
                    Calphurnia, in *Julius Caesar*.

4.1 First millennium

4.1.1 DECLINE AND FALL

Taken as a whole, the first thousand years following the birth of Christ were ones of immense social change and political turmoil, including periods of mass migration and intellectual dark age. However, the millennium began with a period of stability, under the spreading influence and authority of the Roman empire, which bound the individual nations of Europe and around the Mediterranean into a vigorous economic and cultural union. This resulted in an era of comparative peace and prosperity which lasted some two or three hundred years, until around the end of the third century AD (*e.g.* Boardman *et al.* 1986). During this time the civilized peoples of the empire came to enjoy a previously unknown measure of security and protection, which ensured an air of general contentment and a steady rise in the standard of living.

One might have thought that such circumstances would have been auspicious to progress, both in the overall level of education and in philosophical inquiry generally. But although Rome made substantial advances in fields such as construction, commerce and administration, its achievements in more abstract areas of endeavour, including art, philosophy, mathematics, natural sciences, and the whole of astronomy, seem to have been almost non-existent.

Apart from mere imitation, then, the Romans tended to ignore their astronomical and philosophical heritage. This is remarkable, because they were certainly well informed, as shown by the detailed accounts of Greek ideas by authors such as Seneca and Plutarch; but for some reason they seemed to lack either the vision or motivation to add anything significant to the teachings of ancient Greece. More charitably perhaps, we might suppose that through their own independent studies the Romans had it forcibly impressed upon them that the Greek view of the universe, rather than the Babylonian, provided an essentially correct interpretation of natural phenomena.

Thus, with the passage of time Roman views on comets and astronomy in general came to mirror, in an increasingly rigid and distorted manner, the ideas which had first been formulated by Aristotle and his contemporaries more than five hundred years before. The only notable advance so far as comets were concerned was the extension of the Greek classification scheme for comets by the elder Pliny (*Natural History, c.*77 AD) to cover twelve types or forms. A number of these are shown in Figure 4.1, taken from Guillemin (1877), and also in Figure 4.2.

The remarkably slow development of cometary astronomy during this time may be further illustrated by the fact that views very similar to those of Posidonius (see p.63) were still being expounded by Arrian during the second century AD, while at about the same time Ptolemy (*c.*130 AD, see Hellman 1944; Brandt & Chapman 1982) scarcely bothered to mention comets at all! This period therefore saw the Aristotelian notion of comets as atmospheric fires becoming firmly established, though they continued to inspire fear in the beholder, and remained associated in the public mind as heralding great news, either victory or defeat in battle, or the death of a great ruler.

As it turned out, however, the edifice of the Roman empire was built on faulty foundations. Despite great wealth and power, its underlying social structure was rotten at the core, tainted by greed and corruption and an economy founded on slavery and the spoils of conquest. This spiritual imbalance, so the story goes, meant that when tested the empire lacked the intellectual resources necessary to adapt to changing circumstances, changes which nowadays are generally supposed to

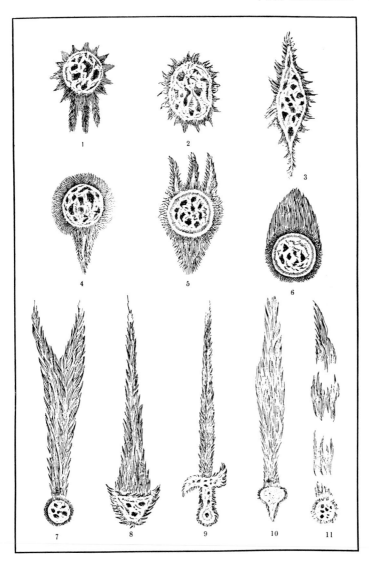

FORMS OF COMETS ACCORDING TO PLINY,

Taken from the *Cometographie* of Hévélius.

Cometæ : 1. Discei, disciformis. — 2. Pithei, doliiformis erectus. — 3. Hippei, equinus barbatus. — 4–5. Lampadiæ, lampadiformis. — 6. Barbatus.—7. Cornutus bicuspidatus.—8. Acontiæ, faculiformis lunatus.—9. Xiphiæ, ensiformis.—10. Longites, hastiformis.—11. Monstriferus.

Figure 4.1: The variation of cometary forms according to Pliny, as illustrated in the *Cometographia* of Hevelius (1668). Taken from Guillemin (1877).

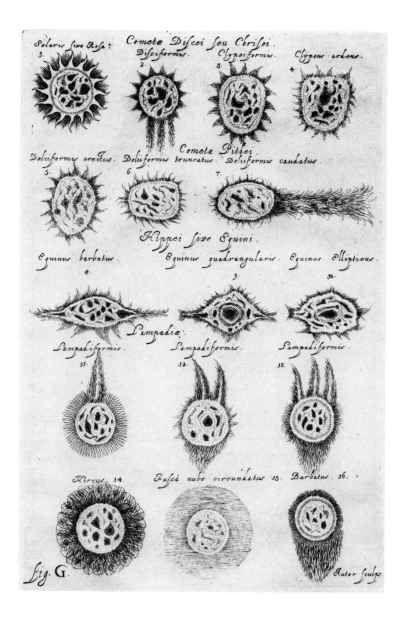

Figure 4.2: Depiction of sixteenth and seventeenth century comets according to Hevelius (1668), following the Greek and Pliny classification scheme.

have been forced upon it by the increasing economic and social pressures within. Following the empire's initial foundation and subsequent consolidation, Rome is then seen as having lost its way, to such an extent that there becomes a certain inevitability about its subsequent decline and fall.

Whether or not this explanation of Rome's fortunes based on purely social forces at play is entirely true, the middle of the third century AD certainly saw a gradual recession in the power of the empire and of its governing institutions, which then continued unabated for nearly two hundred years. Ultimately, the armies of the empire were unable to maintain a sufficient defence against the onslaught of foreign hordes entering through the northern approaches, and in Western Europe at least, the final collapse was relatively sudden. But in more general terms, there was simply a steady intensification of conflict and disorder until, by the middle of the fifth century, effective control from Rome ceased. This is not to say that various forms of official contact were not maintained thereafter, or that some kinds of intellectual activity were not still pursued, but the former cohesion of the empire had been destroyed and any sign of intellectual light reaching Northern Europe from the Mediterranean was in the end largely extinguished. The integrity of the eastern end of the empire, ruled from Byzantium, was effectively preserved, however, for somewhat longer.

The period that followed, known as the Dark Age, eventually lasted almost four centuries. Astronomy, as a science, virtually ceased. However, to the extent that cosmological and theological ideas frequently go hand in hand, the various convolutions of Christian doctrine before and during the Dark Age together with the attention given to celestial matters, such as the dating of Easter (e.g. Newton 1972), might suggest that such an assessment of astronomy is rather superficial. The revival of paganism in the late Roman period, along with the specification of various Christian heresies at this time (resulting subsequently in far-flung missions to enforce Christian orthodoxy), seems to have been part of a general process in which more apocalyptic visions of the universe were successfully sustained against the standard Pauline view (Fox 1986). Given such a struggle, the fate of an empire appears once again to have been linked with its associated world-view. However, in this case the destruction and chaos accompanying the fate of the Roman empire was all but total, the almost complete breakdown of the old order leading to a loss of the accumulated knowledge and wisdom of antiquity which was far from temporary.

4.1.2   DARK AGE

A study of Chinese astronomy probably provides us with the most complete understanding of what might have been going on in the sky during this period. Unlike contemporary European society, Chinese civilization managed to remain under some degree of central control, however unstable at times (Needham 1959), and there is an almost continuous sequence of astronomical records which cover the period from around 200 BC to 1600 AD. This is illustrated in the accompanying Figures 4.3, 4.4 and 4.5. The first of these shows the number of comets observed per century by Chinese astronomers, as described by Ho (1962), while the latter, derived from Biot (1848) and Tianshan (1977) respectively, shows the fireball flux and incidence of meteor showers during the same years. Whereas fireball records generally arise as a result of isolated observations by astronomers in the course of their professional duties or through reports by members of the public (probably only communicated to astronomers outside times of civil strife), meteor showers would seem to be more stressful events and tend to be known through reports of other kinds (diaries *etc.*), independent of the activities of astronomers.

These are particularly interesting data, since while Figure 4.3 demonstrates an almost constant rate of discovery of comets during the whole of the first millennium (the mean discovery rate only increases by a factor of two from 200 BC to 1600 AD; *cf.* Figure 7.1, p.133), Figure 4.4 indicates a massive growth in the

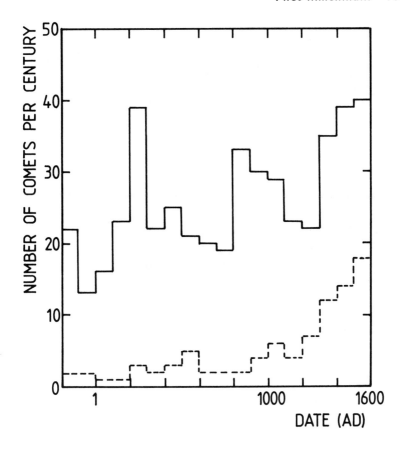

Figure 4.3: The number of comets observed per century up to
1600 AD derived from Chinese records (Ho 1962). For comparison we also show (dashed line) the corresponding number of
entries in Marsden's 1982 *Catalogue of Cometary Orbits*.

flux of fireballs from about the eighth century. The latter apparently reached a sharp maximum during the latter part of the
eleventh century AD before eventually subsiding in an equally
rapid decline.

It is important, of course, not to overinterpret such data.
Many of the comet observations are by their nature unconfirmed,
and the observed fluctuations over the centuries are not certain

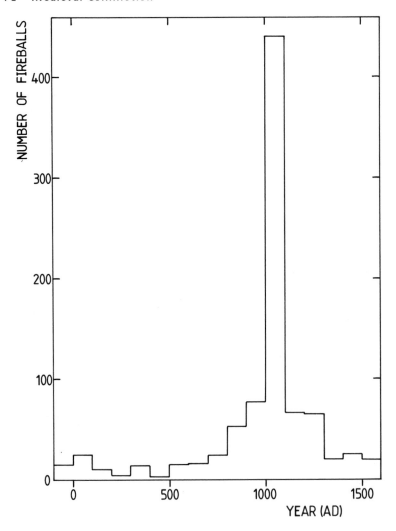

Figure 4.4: The fireball flux between the first century BC and the sixteenth century AD based on Chinese records (Biot 1848). The extreme flux during the eleventh and surrounding centuries has been roughly corrected to allow for the increased activity of professional astronomers resulting in the detection of many weaker fireballs at all times of the year. The remarkable eleventh century excess is believed to have arisen from a fragmentation in the Taurid meteor stream.

(but see Link 1958). Moreover, the secular increase probably simply reflects the gradual extension of Chinese astronomical practices to Korea and Japan. Nevertheless, the steep rise and decline of the fireball flux compared to the more constant cometary flux is clear, while there is additional circumstantial evidence that the maximum may be associated with an enhancement of the fireball flux from the Taurid meteor stream at about this time (Astapovič & Terenteva 1968).

It is possible, therefore, that a contemporary awareness of increased meteoric activity in the sky may have generated a somewhat greater attention to celestial events, although without a more thorough study of the Chinese sources we cannot be altogether sure of the relative comet-to-fireball frequency with the passage of time. Contemporary interest in astronomical phenomena, particularly at the royal court, did in fact reach a very high pitch during the period in question (Schafer 1977), and it seems probable that the least biased measure of relative meteor activity during the Dark Age is now provided by the recorded incidence of meteor *showers* (see Figure 4.5). If so, we cannot exclude the possibility that meteor activity generally was at a significantly higher level throughout the Dark Age than is usually supposed or commonly experienced at present.

Nevertheless, the eleventh century pattern is rather similar to that inferred from the accumulated observations of the Late Seleucid period (Section 2.5, p.34), and it is possible that in this instance too, at the end of the first millennium AD, the period of heightened celestial activity was caused by the gradual break-up, over a period of several centuries, of a large body in the Taurid meteor stream. Such an event, assuming its effects were witnessed by the population at large, would almost certainly have been a source of considerable alarm at some time during the medieval period. It is an interesting question, therefore, whether it is possible to identify when such an event occurred. Was the first fragmentation witnessed perhaps in late Roman times, and did its effects possibly reach some kind of peak during the Dark Age?

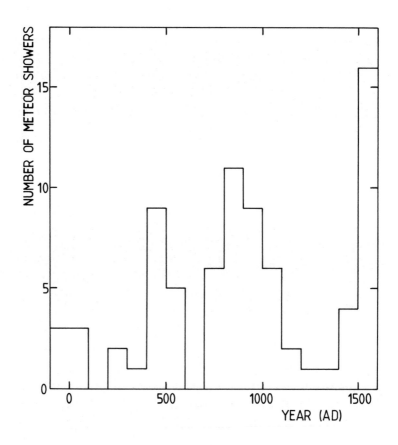

Figure 4.5: The incidence of meteor showers between the first century BC and the sixteenth century AD based on Chinese records (Tian-shan 1977). There have probably been at least two significant surges in meteor shower activity, namely 400–600 AD and 800–1000 AD; those that may have occurred immediately before 100 AD and after 1500 AD may be underestimated and overestimated respectively, due to their remoteness and comparative proximity in time.

To answer such questions, it is not necessary to rely on historical evidence alone. It is known, for example, from accurate calculations of the former orbits of meteors that a significant unknown body in the Taurid complex was probably disintegrating during the period in question (Whipple & Hamid 1952; *cf.* Section 17.1.4, p.397). In fact, at the time of the Dark Age there was greatly increased shower activity in several meteor streams, though it is not known whether these events are correlated with a single major fragmentation. Moreover, the final break-up of Comet Biela in 1845 could well have been a much weakened version of what was entailed, since the incidence of its showers in particular has been traced back at least to the early part of the sixth century AD (Klinkerfues 1873). Indeed, during the early stages of this body's fragmentation, possibly in the fourth and fifth centuries, the latter when the Dark Age was at its most intense, it is conceivable that the earth experienced some quite major bombardments, with effects on the ground similar to that of the more isolated twentieth-century Tunguska event (*cf.* Whipple 1930, Krinov 1963, Clube & Napier 1989b).

Direct attributions of destruction to the fall of fire from heaven (in Nennius; see Morris 1980), and corresponding references to the 'fire of righteous vengeance' and to its widespread, devastating effects (in Gildas; see Winterbottom 1978), general ruin, official cries for help, mass migration and the like, certainly deserve more attention in relation to such phenomena than they have so far received (Clube 1989b,c; *cf.* Myres 1986). Moreover, a contemporary global climatic recession may well have occurred at about the same time, whose locally adverse effects seem to have been noticed on a world-wide scale as well (Grove 1988). In northern Europe too, a contemporary fall and subsequent rise in sea-level may have played a significant rôle in the repopulation and later depopulation of the Low Countries, encouraging widespread migrations on an exceptional scale.

Such effects may provide direct examples of the kind of relationship between the earth and sky that was apparently well known to the much earlier generations of Sumerians and Babylonians: it would then be hardly surprising that the alternative Aristotelian world-view should once again have been seriously doubted and perhaps even overthrown at the start of the Dark Age. Indeed, amongst the European population at large there was a general return to early pagan beliefs at this time, whilst Christian views about the nature of the world retreated to earlier more primitive notions harking back to ancient Babylonian or Hebrew doctrines (Cohn 1957). Nevertheless, more orthodox Christian views were not entirely lost, and did indeed eventually prosper. The picture that emerges, therefore, is one of continuing confusion in response to the sky! Indeed, it is possible that we gain some understanding as to why the Aristotelian trend took so long to mature. In practice, any contrary view would probably have coincided with periods of social change and political turmoil, whilst it was only during periods of comparative calm — when records of celestial phenomena were generally preserved — that the Aristotelian world-view was progressively reinforced.

4.1.3   NEO-PLATONISM ECLIPSED

The advance of orthodox Christian doctrine is in fact mirrored by the fate of neo-Platonism, which reached some kind of pre-eminence during the fourth through to the sixth century AD. During the European renaissance, many years later, these neo-Platonist doctrines were to fall into disrepute and eventual oblivion. Nevertheless, it is possible now to trace their more or less continuous tradition from the ancient Near East, through the mystery religions of the Orphics and the Pythagoreans to Plato himself, and from thence through his famous academy and its various vicissitudes until their final rather obscure dissipation amongst the thoughts of early European scientists such as Bruno, Kepler, and — perhaps surprisingly — Newton. The Platonist tradition, with its gnostic and heretical overtones, was indeed eventually to be actively suppressed by the Christian Church, but we can gather something of its astronomical traditions from the voluminous writings of Proclus, who headed the neo-Platonist school during the fifth century AD.

As one might expect (see Chapter 2), Proclus specifically rejected Aristotelian and Ptolemaic teachings, particularly the idea of epicycles and any notion that the planets were attached to rotating crystalline spheres. He in fact maintained, as we now believe, that planets moved in orbits, whilst admitting some controversy over whether the centre of motion should be the earth or the sun. What is of interest, however, are his unequivocal remarks concerning the existence of invisible stars that revolve along with the planets in orbits of their own. Such groupings were evidently looked upon as angels and demons led by gods, and it was said of these stars that they were sometimes visible and would at other times disappear, by virtue of their hidden fires. This knowledge is said by Taylor (1816, 1820, 1825), who first translated the works of Proclus, to be indeed 'the grand key to the theology of the ancients', and it is clear from the frequent references to Plato's *Timaeus* that the cosmology included the expectation of future catastrophic returns, these being governed by the circulation of invisible stars in conjunction with their divine leaders, the planets. It was evidently this thesis of the ancients, harking back to Babylon, which the Christian Church, with its supposedly superior Aristotelian world-view, subsequently sought to suppress.

The Platonist school in Athens was finally eclipsed only a century or so after Proclus, but neo-Platonist doctrines did not immediately disappear. Indeed, during the post Dark Age centuries of the so-called Holy Roman Empire, such doctrines were to be officially espoused by the Church itself (see Section 4.2). With the benefit of hindsight, however, one now sees the Platonist and Aristotelian points of view gradually becoming less clearly defined, with the Church doing very little to stimulate rational debate about cosmology or the nature of the world, and if anything actively discouraging a questioning, critical approach to such things. The Bible, for example, contains many statements about cosmology and the nature of the universe over and above the ideas contained in Genesis (*e.g.* Eccles., 1:4; Joshua, 10:12; Psalms, 19:6; Isaiah, 38:8; 1 Esdras, 4:34; *cf.* Koestler 1968, part 2). These strongly suggested, to some at least, that the sun orbits the earth, while the latter was described as a flat, motionless body lying exactly at the centre of things. Such statements — 'gospel truth' — were usually interpreted literally, as evidence equal in quality to direct observations, and consequently could only be properly understood within the framework of an Aristotelian cosmology in which the known world (the earth) lay permanently at rest in the centre. Indeed, the early Christian motto: 'Do not examine, only believe', was ultimately a powerful deterrent to the spirit of free enquiry (Jeans 1947), and it is perhaps hardly surprising that the Church should have embraced for its own a geocentric view which lay comfortably in accord with the homocentric beliefs of the Christian faith.

4.1.4   PERSISTENT DOGMAS

The Dark Age seems eventually to have provided fertile ground for Aristotelian thinking to become once again firmly locked into the main body of Christian teaching, causing the Church to be seen later as the bearer of a rigid, canonical doctrine which persisted almost unchanged for a thousand years. It might seem, then, that comets were generally understood during this period to be no more than rare atmospheric illusions or flaming stars, fuelled by fires at the top of the atmosphere and driven by violent winds generated by the moving, crystalline spheres beyond.

However, many writers of the period, such as Isidore of Seville (*c.*560–636) and the Venerable Bede (673–735) continued to maintain that comets were harbingers of disaster, the latter explaining in *De Rerum Natura Liber:* 'Comets have always been regarded as a warning of portentous events' (Colgrave & Mynors 1969, p.556; *cf.* Jones 1975, p.216). Elsewhere Bede gives another illustration of the fear inspired by comets, writing (*loc. cit.* p.557): 'In the year of our Lord 729, two comets appeared around the sun, striking great terror into all beholders

... One was the forerunner of the day and the other of the night, to indicate that mankind was threatened by calamities both by day and by night.' Previously, Gregory of Tours (c.541–594), writing in De Cursu Stellarum (Dalton 1927, p.526), had distinguished two types of comet which might presage a disaster: 'When it seems to have a flaming diadem, it portends the death of a king. When it has a long ray like a sword, glowing red, and spreads its hair abroad darkly, it announces ruin to the country.'

This period was also notable in seeing the rise in the east of a second world religion, namely Islam. Founded by the prophet Mohammed in the seventh century, the new religion and its devotees quickly spread over much of south-eastern Europe and continental Asia, finally conquering Alexandria and completing the destruction of its great library in 642 AD. The initial wave of expansion made the Arab people masters of a large, loosely-knit empire ranging from India in the east to Spain and the Atlantic coast of Morocco in the west. However, once the momentum of the initial wave of conquest had been dissipated there began a period of relative calm, allowing the founding of important new centres of learning and the conditions to be established in which subjects such as astronomy, mathematics and medicine could be nurtured and slowly allowed to develop.

The Arabs thus became the first to revive the ancient astronomical traditions of Greece, translating many surviving manuscripts and making new and careful observations of the stars. In this way an important body of astronomical data was assembled and preserved for future generations, later to be transmitted to the western world. However, since there was no real understanding of the true nature of comets and the other heavenly bodies (cf. Section 2.2.3, p.18), nor even of the correct shape or place of the earth in the cosmos, it is quite possible that much of the original emphasis may have been misplaced or lost in the translation of the ancient records. Nevertheless, the renaissance of observational astronomy as part of Arabian culture was a crucial development (e.g. King 1957) without which the revival of European astronomy might never have taken place.

Indeed, neo-Platonist views of meteoric phenomena survived in medieval Europe more or less unchanged until well beyond the eleventh century. The only reference to comets in Byrhtferth's Manual (1011), for example, simply says: 'There is a star called a comet. When it appears it betokens famine or pestilence or war or the destruction of the earth or fearful storms' (Crawford 1929, p.133); and even this, it seems, is directly derived from a passage in Isidore's *Etymologiae* (Bonser 1963), written four hundred years before. In this way, it is likely that neo-Platonist views would have persisted much longer had it not been that Islamic culture began to filter into Europe by way of the Iberian peninsula, bearing with it a 'new' Aristotelian view of comets. It is ironic, however, that the cultural renaissance of the thirteenth century, associated with the foundation of the first universities in Europe at Paris, Bologna and Oxford, should have brought with it something of a regression in the general understanding of the nature of comets.

4.2   Meteoric alarm

4.2.1   SLOW AWAKENING

It was only after 800 AD that Europeans gradually emerged from the turbulence of the Dark Age and advanced towards a more civilized way of life. Progress was still halting, however, and often interrupted by setbacks and obstacles, including those of famine, disease and war. The latter not only frequently divided the leading nations and principalities of Europe but also opened deep rifts between the opposing religious forces of Christendom and Islam. Indeed, by the eleventh century, the Christian Church was re-establishing its central power and there is evidence again that renewed meteoric activity in the sky may have played a significant rôle.

Thus the conflict with Islam came to a head during the eleventh century, just as the fireball flux recorded by the Chinese came to a peak. Moreover, it is known that Pope Urban II instigated the First Crusade in November 1095 at the so-called Council of Clermont, in France, following the appearance of massive meteor storms. These meteor showers, which were observed throughout Europe, apparently generated widespread eschatological expectations which, at least to the extent that they expressed a popular view of the Final Judgement, were evidently to recur in much the same form until at least the time of the Reformation (*cf.* Figure 4.6, p.88).

Twelfth century historians, for example, make it clear that these responses arose as a result of 'great earthquakes in divers places', and of 'stars in the sky [that] were seen throughout the whole world to fall towards the earth, crowded together and dense, like hail or snowflakes' (*e.g.* Riley-Smith 1986; *cf.* Clube 1989b). It was also stated that 'a short while later, a fiery way appeared in the heavens; and after another short period half the sky turned the colour of blood'. Not only did the earth encounter a meteor swarm, therefore, but there are also hints that suitably sized dust particles may have been rapidly dispersing through their associated meteor stream into the zodiacal cloud. Although the difficult task of identifying where past Tunguskas may have exploded (producing 'earthquakes') has not yet been undertaken, the historical record is remarkably specific and the public response is not in doubt. Indeed, it has been suggested (Riley-Smith, *loc. cit.*) that Urban's crusade and the nationwide church-building programmes towards the end of the eleventh century are best regarded as the climacteric of a temporarily restored general viewpoint according to which divine agencies would 'taketh away kingdoms and changeth times'. The belief that celestial agencies used 'weapons' to terminate nations, thereby transferring 'divine kingship' to the leader of a surviving nation, is of course a very old idea, reaching back at least to Sumero-Babylonian times.

Such evidence places the Greek scientific revolution clearly in perspective, showing that ideas about the cosmos extant from four or five thousand years ago in Babylon were still very much in vogue a thousand years ago in Europe, even within the Christian Church. However successfully the Greek revolution in science was transplanted into the Roman empire, therefore, and thence into Islamic teaching, it is now clear that there was no such advance elsewhere. The chaotic situation in early medieval Europe was evidently not conducive to the development of new concepts in physics and cosmology, let alone thoughts about astronomy or the nature of comets!

Indeed, the most important single requirement in attempting to form a realistic view of comets and meteoric phenomena is the preservation of accurate records of past apparitions. Such records, even inaccurate ones, throughout the medieval period and especially during the Dark Age were the single most conspicuous item in short supply. Here and there throughout Europe city states and aspiring nations would survive long enough to maintain useful calendars and chronicles of events, but in the end only the Christian Church acquired sufficient stability and longevity to become a successful repository of past knowledge. However, even here disinterested scholars with the capacity and circumstances to interpret the knowledge accurately were few and far between, and the habit of systematic rational analysis sustained by appropriate academic institutes and universities took centuries to revive.

4.2.2   OFFICIAL VIEWS

By the twelfth century, the fireball flux was in decline. Whatever eschatological rationale could be drawn upon by the Christian Church to sustain its crusading tendency was now deprived of its more visible support, whilst the Islamic faith continued to flourish, nurtured perhaps by what seemed to be a more relevant (Aristotelian) doctrine. Itinerant scholars appear to have been the main agents for a reversal of European thought, and the Christian Church seems only then to have been moved to present itself as the bearer down the ages of an orthodox Aristotelian view of the world.

However the change came about, challenges to the newly established order remained few and far between, despite the often glaring discrepancies between observations and predictions based on Aristotelian concepts. Roger Bacon (1214–1292), for example, in his *Opus Tertium* (1267), was one who strongly argued against a slavish devotion to Aristotle's writings (Stimson 1917), but such protests went unheeded. Rather than question the geocentric world view, with its assumed 'perfect' circular movements of the sun and planets about the earth, astronomers instead preferred to introduce various *ad hoc* features into their calculations. This led to a model of the solar system which was quite unwieldy, and the problem of precisely predicting the phases of the moon or the positions of the planets became an increasingly arduous task.

For these reasons, and also because comets tended in any case to be unpredictable and erratic in their behaviour, the motions and appearances of comets went largely unrecorded in Europe. An excellent review of the sparse European literature on comets for the period up to about 1400 has been given by Hellman (1944), while Thorndike (1950; *cf.* Jervis 1985) has systematically collected texts on comets from a variety of authors in the thirteenth and fourteenth centuries, and has translated into English the reviews by Albert the Great (*c.*1193–1280) and Thomas Aquinas (1225–1274). However, despite the undoubted achievements of these medieval authors in other spheres of activity and their influence in furthering Aristotelian views generally, neither appears to have added anything very significant to the subject of comets.

What therefore appears to have been a decline in *official* interest in comets had the effect of giving new life to Aristotle's teaching, with the result that the latter remained in the vanguard for a nearly unbroken period of fifteen hundred years. The decline amounted almost to a dereliction of duty amongst professional astronomers, or at the very least to a continuing failure on the part of their masters to understand the importance of keeping a professional eye on our astronomical surroundings. This has left a gap in our knowledge of cometary and meteoric phenomena which has never been completely filled. Most of our present information concerning comets from this time has only later become available from translations of Chinese records. These observations, however, were not always recorded with great scientific accuracy or attention to detail, and even here the data at the time seem mostly to have served the purely astrological purpose of marking some prodigious event.

It is clear that Aristotle's theory can be easily criticized with the benefit of hindsight, but it is equally important to realize that the arguments used in its favour were often not particularly unreasonable. For example, the Greeks and those who adopted their ideas did imagine, quite correctly, that aurorae, rainbows, parhelia and the like were confined to the earth's atmosphere. Thus, although the arguments were never entirely logical, and sometimes revolved around erroneous observations, what was undoubtedly needed at the time was a specific demonstration that comets did indeed exist beyond the sublunary zone. This is not to suggest that the atmospheric dogma of Aristotle was really defensible, but such an observation would have provided a significant check on the validity of the Aristotelian concept, which by the fifteenth century had become a serious obstacle to further progress.

In fact, the problems inherent in using naked-eye observations to determine whether comets lie beyond the moon provide a good illustration of the kind of practical difficulty, quite apart from any purely doctrinal objection, which might have been encountered by any at this time who might have wished to follow the Greek Apollonius Myndus in developing an alternative celestial theory. These practical problems were of such a magnitude that it was not until the second half of the sixteenth century that the required accuracy in observation was achieved, and even then (see p.93) only by the exceptionally gifted observer Tycho Brahe.

4.2.3   POPULAR OPINION

However, despite the evident lacuna in official and intellectual circles concerning the importance of comets, there was no such blind spot elsewhere. The population at large persisted in regarding them as definite celestial portents, to be treated with a good deal of fear and superstition (*e.g.* Hellman 1944), and comets continued to be associated in the public mind with all manner of natural and man-made disasters.

Accordingly, whilst cloistered academics insisted on the atmospheric qualities of comets, the clerics in the pulpit, in much closer contact with the masses, were more likely to find themselves upholding comets as celestial signs. Disaster, not least the Last Judgement, was a popular concern in the public mind, and there can be little doubt that the Church (or organized religion in all its manifestations) came perilously close to dissembly over the issue of comets. On the one hand, the expert would present sweet Aristotelian reason itself and would argue merely for an atmospheric vision; on the other, with a possible hint of privileged inside knowledge of the heavens, he would present a face of terror with the unashamed purpose of frightening the populace into a state of moral rectitude!

Despite the more lurid portrayals of doomsday encouraged by this kind of fanaticism, a reasonably realistic view of the conceivably catastrophic effects of meteoric phenomena was a persistent undercurrent in human affairs. Depictions of the Last Judgement, such as that of a Greek sixteenth-century fresco in the Dionysiou monastery on Mount Athos (Figure 4.6), indicate the survival of remarkably clear perceptions of the consequences, albeit divinely ordained, of a meteor swarm containing fireballs massive enough to induce earth tremors. The important point to be recognized, therefore, is that in spite of the reassuring view of meteoric phenomena upheld over the centuries *within* the Church, something more akin to the Babylonian perception of comets and their débris continued to be fostered at lower levels in society. An analogous situation can be seen in the

Figure 4.6: Depiction of the Last Judgement. This illustrates a comet-inspired day of reckoning from a Greek sixteenth-century fresco in the Dionysiou monastery on Mount Athos. Taken from an illustrated guide by Kadas (1987).

Ein sehr erschröcklich Gesicht vnd Wunderzaichen/welches geschehen ist
worden zu Bamberg vnd Liechtenfels/ Anno M. D. LX. den XXviij. Decembers.

Figure 4.7: Illustration of the Bamberg fireball of 28th December 1560, taken from Bischoff (1986).

survival of pagan beliefs for many centuries in spite of attempted suppression by the Church (Huxley 1980).

Indeed, from time to time events in the sky did occasionally occur which needed to be gainsaid. An example from the period in question will illustrate the point (Figure 4.7; Bischoff 1986): 'A very terrifying apparition and sign of wonder ... has been seen in Bamberg and Liechtenfels. In the year 1560, on the twenty-eighth of December, [this apparition] was seen in the sky which first had its beginning over the Eberssberg in Franconia, and rose directly over Zeyl, and then from Zeyl [moved] towards a little town called Elpmann, and after that advanced along the valley towards Bamberg, and stopped still there for a long time so that everyone was terrified and thought that the whole city was on fire ... and then everyone saw how the whole sky was red with fire, and in the red glow some stars in the bright sky, and two clouds standing opposite each other, and out of each cloud white lines crossing over each other, like long spears. Also, people saw swords shining in the clouds and there was a terrible roaring, as if they heard two armies fighting one another.' It is, of course, impossible to be absolutely sure what this account entails, an auroral effect perhaps; but several long meteor trails ending in fireball explosions, or the results of a single massive explosion, are within the bounds of possibility as well.

Although an immense gulf now divided the dawning consciousness of medieval Europe from the world of ancient Babylon, the tenuous strands of belief linking comets with meteoric events and frightening spectacles in the sky had somehow managed to persist unbroken down the centuries. The survival of such a persuasion, at odds with all conventional teaching for such a period of time, has never yet been fully explored or properly explained (cf. Bischoff 1986), and would still be enigmatic were it not for the new insights that are now emerging concerning our changing astronomical environment (cf. Section 2.2.3, p.18; Section 17.1.4, p.397). Indeed, this style of thinking has been so ingrained at the popular level from the earliest times, that the first appearance of Halley's comet in the present century was still thought by many to herald the end of the world! An interesting collection of postcards and other memorabilia associated with the 1910 apparition of Halley's comet has been put together by Etter & Schneider (1985), illustrating the ease with which, even in the twentieth century, it has been possible to exploit this latent fear and concern over comets.

In this way, just as the curtain begins to rise on the present scientific era, comets were being regarded paradoxically both as unimportant atmospheric illusions and as crucial events in the celestial calendar. The scene was set for important changes in understanding, changes which were eventually to shatter the classical beliefs and lead to the slow generation of a new paradigm.

5

Scientific calm

"If I have seen further, it is by standing on the shoulders of giants."

Sir Isaac Newton.

5.1 Renaissance

It was against this background of a growing, but largely un-
voiced recognition of serious difficulties with the conventional
Aristotelian dogma and of recurring bursts of meteor activity,
that during the fifteenth and sixteenth centuries Europeans such
as Toscanelli (1397–1482), Apian (1495–1552), and Fracastoro
(1483–1553), began to observe the heavens with something approaching scientific care. To the casual observer, comets give an
illusion of almost total unpredictability. Many of their characteristics change rapidly with time, their movements on the sky
appear to bear no relation to the ecliptic and the times of their
arrival are random. But Apian and others carefully recorded
their varying properties and motions, and in this way gained an
important new insight: that comet tails always point away from
the sun (Abetti 1954, pp.54–61; Jervis 1985). This fact had been
known to Chinese astronomers at least seven hundred years before (Biot 1843), but its independent discovery in early sixteenth
century Europe marked a significant new advance. Although
such observations did not immediately generate new ideas about
the nature or origin of comets, a previously unpredictable phenomenon had now been shown to yield to close study. At last
there was hope that continued observations might lead to further
progress.

This reward, together with a growing appreciation and understanding of ancient Greek astronomy (especially after 1453,
when the anticipated conquest of Constantinople by the Turks
led to a great exodus of scholars towards Italy), produced a
gradual shift in outlook: away from a dogmatic, uncritical ac-

ceptance of Aristotelian science, towards a more open, questioning approach. In particular, there was now a greater awareness of the principle that experiment and careful observations might be used both to guide progress and to settle debate. In another sphere of activity, for example, it was no coincidence that this period also saw the beginning of a series of major explorations of our own globe: the discovery of North America by Columbus and the first circumnavigation of the world by Magellan.

5.1.1   DECLINE OF ATMOSPHERIC IDEAS

The decline of the atmospheric theory of comets, after persisting almost unchanged for two millennia, is inextricably linked with the gradual overthrow of Aristotelian cosmology. As is well known, this advance is principally associated with the name of Copernicus (1473–1543), though it is certain (*e.g.* Stimson 1917, Jeans 1947, Koestler 1968, p.194 *et seq.,*) that Nicolas of Cusa (*c.*1400–1464) and others had, to a degree, anticipated his approach. Copernicus's work *De Revolutionibus Orbium Coelestium,* published in the year of his death, developed the radical viewpoint that the main difficulties associated with understanding the motions of the planets could be removed simply by adopting a heliocentric model of the solar system.

The initial Church reaction to this idea was rather muted, more indicative, perhaps, of a strongly held scepticism than of open hostility. But although the Catholic Church originally regarded the idea as scarcely worth serious consideration, Protestant leaders were less sanguine. Martin Luther, for example, is reported to have described Copernicus as this 'new astrologer', saying (Stimson 1917): 'The fool will overturn the whole science of astronomy. But as the Holy Scriptures state, Joshua bade the sun stand still and not the earth.'

But once the idea had begun to attract converts and its wider implications were appreciated (the earth moves and is no longer at the centre of things), a powerful and extreme Catholic reaction set in. Giordano Bruno (1548–1600), for example, an early advocate of the heliocentric theory, not only taught that the sun was at the centre of the solar system but also recognized that the stars in the heavens, without parallax, must be inconveniently far away. He was thus led to consider displacing even the sun from the centre of this larger stellar universe. However, Bruno was eventually tried and burnt at the stake in 1600; while Galileo (1564–1642) was later tried and forced under threat of torture to deny the heliocentric theory in 1633. Indeed, *De Revolutionibus* and other books dealing with the heliocentric concept were promptly banned by the Church, a futile act of religious censorship which persisted even as late as 1757. A scholarly account of this disturbing episode in the development of science has been written by Stimson (1917).

Curiously, even before the argument had really begun, a conclusive observation had been made which should have settled the issue. In 1577, careful observations by Tycho Brahe (1546–1601) of a bright comet which appeared in that year (see Figure 5.1) allowed him to calculate that this body had to be at least four times further away than the moon. Comets could therefore no longer be arbitrarily assigned to the sublunary zone, which implied that the associated cosmological view ought also to have changed to incorporate the fact, particularly the discovery of motion and time-dependent phenomena in the supposedly unalterable celestial spheres above the moon. This observation, together with the contemporaneous findings of other undisputed variations in the same supposedly unchanging heavens (Tycho's supernova of 1572, the stellar variables Mira Ceti and P Cygni, discovered in 1596 and 1600 by Fabricius and Janson respectively, and Kepler's supernova of 1604), should have rapidly led to the demise of the Aristotelian dogma.

However, the progress of science is never straightforward, and the atmospheric theory of comets, along with the geocentric point of view, continued to find strong support. Although some authors stoutly defended the older ideas for many years, others were rapidly convinced of the need for change, and the year 1600 may therefore be taken as broadly marking the start of a period

Figure 5.1: The comet of 1577, taken from the Shajâtname and Shamailname manuscripts, Istanbul University Library T.6043 V-12 and T.1404 V-58 respectively. Courtesy of Professor M. Dizer, Kandili Observatory.

when atmospheric and celestial theories of comets were clearly identified and began to be openly debated in terms which are now recognizable as scientific.

The celestial theory naturally became associated with the Copernican doctrine, but perhaps surprisingly the converse was not always the case. For example, although Galileo had been

tried for defending the heliocentric picture, he vehemently opposed the celestial theory of comets. In particular, he denied
the relevance of the observations by Tycho and others which
showed that comets had a negligible parallax, and went on to
argue, following the classical tradition (*cf.* the views attributed
to the Pythagoreans and Stoics), that comets were simply atmospheric 'illusions', along with aurorae, haloes, mock suns and
sun pillars (*e.g.* Drake & O'Malley 1960). (Modern descriptions
of some of these atmospheric phenomena are given, for example,
by Minnaert 1954 and Walker 1980.) If comets were indeed produced either by reflection or refraction of sunlight in the earth's
upper atmosphere, then one might argue quite justifiably, as
Galileo did, that observations of a null parallax proved nothing!

However, the celestial nature of comets was defended by Kepler (1571–1630), most famous for his discovery of the laws of
planetary motion, who furthermore confirmed that their tails
always pointed away from the sun. In 1618, while attempting
to explain observations of this phenomenon in the three comets
which appeared in that year, he concluded, far in advance of his
time, that the tails must be produced by some kind of solar radiation. He wrote (Caspar 1959, p.302): 'The sun's beams pass
through the body of a comet and instantaneously take something of its matter with them in their path away from the sun.'

Thus, although the Copernican theory was not accepted by
the Church and the celestial nature of comets was still not universally recognized, by the start of the seventeenth century many
with a more enlightened viewpoint had already begun to rule out
the atmospheric theory. Progress in cometary astronomy now
began to focus on mechanistic ideas and concepts, this time
based upon a conviction that the appearances and motions of
comets could be best understood from the celestial viewpoint.

5.1.2   First theories of orbits

While this fundamental change in the general understanding of
the physical nature of comets was taking place, the protagonists

of the new celestial theory had a variety of different ideas about cometary orbits (*e.g.* Rauffner 1971).

Tycho Brahe, perhaps the first to accept the celestial hypothesis, argued that comets probably moved on circular orbits about the sun beyond that of Venus. This view seems to have been previously suggested by Regiomontanus (Lalande 1792), and in fact harked back to the ideas of the Italian Pythagoreans (Section 3.2.3, p.62). Indeed, Tycho even went so far as to suggest that a comet's movement might be 'not exactly circular but somewhat oblong' (Singer 1943), this possibly being the first unequivocal proposal that any celestial body might move in a path other than circular. Furthermore, the idea that comets moved on heliocentric orbits beyond that of Venus appeared to offer a ready explanation of the fact that comets are most often observed when relatively close to the sun, either before dawn or just after sunset. However, Tycho had not yet developed a truly heliocentric world view, and although he believed (like the Greek Heracleides, see p.57) that Mercury and Venus orbited the sun, he argued that the sun and the other planets also revolved around the earth.

An alternative suggestion, that comets moved in greatly elongated ellipses, was put forward as early as 1610 by Sir William Lower, one of Thomas Harriot's correspondents (Armitage 1966, Johnson 1968), and at about the same time by Henry Percy, Earl of Northumberland. Kepler, on the other hand, believed that comets came from interstellar space and calculated that they moved under constant acceleration along straight, rectilinear paths. These possibilities were further elaborated by a number of authors in the second half of the seventeenth century, in particular by Robert Hooke (1678), who in 1665 considered that a wide variety of possible motions might in principle explain observations of the bright comet seen during 1664; while several other astronomers, notably Giovanni Borelli (1608–1679) and Hevelius (1611–1687), also appear about this time to have obliquely suggested a parabolic orbit for the same comet (*e.g.* Pannekoek 1961, p.268; Armitage 1966, p.164).

In this way, Hevelius is often credited as being among the first to postulate a parabolic orbit for comets (*e.g.* Barker 1767, p.3; Russell, Dugan & Stewart 1926, p.410), although one should note that in fact there was nothing in the arguments he put forward which necessarily suggested that the sun should be placed at the focus of the conic section (Armitage 1966). Nevertheless, the proposal was essentially correct, and both Dörffel, a Saxon contemporary of Hevelius, and Flamsteed, the first Astronomer Royal of England, were subsequently able to show that the parabolic hypothesis was consistent with observations of the great comet which first appeared in 1680.

5.1.3   FIRST PHYSICAL THEORIES

It was also during the early seventeenth century that the scientific debate as to the physical constitution of comets began. Tycho Brahe, for example, believed that comets were 'exhalations' from the planets (Von Littrow & Encke 1835); while Kepler (see Caspar 1959) considered that comets populated the heavenly air in great numbers, 'like whales in the ocean', and proposed that they formed out of the celestial air or fires by a process described as 'thickening' (*cf.* Section 3.1.4), rather analogous to one of spontaneous creation.

Clerke (1908, p.52), on the other hand, records an alternative proposal made about the same time, soon after sunspots had first been noted on the surface of the sun. According to this idea, it was suggested on the 'slag' theory of sunspots that the cindery refuse from the great solar conflagration might occasionally be thrown off from the sun in the form of visible comets. The coincidence, in 1618, of three bright comets and a sun which appeared to be almost devoid of spots seemed briefly to lend support to this idea.

Hevelius, however, was the first to attempt to construct a proper model. Though he had shown using parallax arguments that comets could not lie in the earth's atmosphere, he was un-

Figure 5.2: Seventeenth century sages discussing the origin of comets. This shows the three main contenders: atmospheric phenomena lying in the sublunary zone; bodies ejected in spiral paths from Jupiter or Saturn, subsequently to pass the earth in a parabolic orbit; and denizens of interstellar space passing the earth in straight lines. Taken from the titlepage of *Cometographia* (Hevelius 1668), courtesy of the John Rylands University Library, University of Manchester.

able to break completely with ancient Greek traditions and the atmospheric theory as advocated for example by Galileo. He reconciled these beliefs by proposing that comets originated in the atmospheres of the major planets, and suggested in particular that they originally formed as 'vapours' which he assumed to condense near the planet's surface. These were then swept up by violent whirlwinds and eventually ejected from the planet's atmosphere to produce an observable comet. This body was then believed to move in a parabolic orbit until the vapours out of which it was made finally dispersed (e.g. Barker 1767). A rather similar theory was also promoted at about the same time by Cassini (1680), in which comets were assumed to form from the exhalations of other stars. The debate at this time as to the origin of comets is rather nicely summarized by Figure 5.2, which shows three sages keenly discussing the course of the bright comet shown in the sky.

5.2   Age of Enlightenment

5.2.1   COMETS OF 1680 AND 1682

Flamsteed's discovery that the great comet of 1680 had a parabolic orbit proved, however, to be a major turning point. This comet was observed before perihelion in 1680, and again after perihelion in 1681, and since there is evidence that Newton (1642–1727) had already formulated his theory of planetary orbits by this time, it often comes as a surprise to learn that he did not immediately include the orbit of this body as an example of his universal law in action. Instead, Newton objected to Flamsteed's discovery on the ground that it must have been two separate comets moving along distant rectilinear orbits (e.g. Westfall 1980, pp.391–395).

This recalls Kepler's suggestion that comets were interstellar bodies moving in straight lines, but Newton was also motivated by a reluctance to believe that his 'clockwork' solar system could be upset by celestial 'missiles'. At this point, of course, no-one had any idea of the true masses of comets, though their generally portentous appearances seemed to imply huge size and destructive capability. Newton thus missed an important opportunity to bring comets into his theory, and unnecessarily upset Flamsteed by casting doubts on the precision of his work.

In the event, however, Newton was soon proved wrong: another bright comet appeared the following year (1682), and Halley (1656–1742) was one of the first to realize that it could be on the same elliptical orbit as that followed by the comets of 1456, 1531 and 1607, which had fortunately been well observed by Toscanelli, Apian and Kepler respectively. Halley was also aware that Newton had developed his theory to encompass elliptical orbits, and was foremost in recognizing the potential importance of a *universal* law of gravity extending to comets. Halley now prevailed upon the reluctant Newton to publish his work, and even went so far as to pay for the first edition of *Principia* out of his own pocket, so keen was he to facilitate the prediction of the 1682 comet's next return towards the end of 1758. As is now well known, this famous prediction was completely vindicated on Christmas Day 1758, when the amateur astronomer Palitzsh — a farmer living near Dresden — first detected the comet, almost a month before it was recovered by a professional astronomer (Messier) on 21 January 1759.

Newton, however, had been caught on the wrong foot: not only was he conscious of the opposition on continental Europe to the new law of gravity, because it carried connotations of 'action at a distance' and seemed to lack a solid physical basis, but he also had to admit his error over the 1680 comet. Moreover, he had to stand by while his acolyte Whiston used Halley's erroneous period for this comet, 575 years, to infer a history of close encounters of the comet with the earth, one of which had marked Caesar's death and another which had supposedly been responsible for the biblical Flood (Stecchini 1984).

5.2.2   REJECTION OF CATASTROPHISM

As a radical student of biblical history and a secret unitarian amongst trinitarians, Newton was already in the business of questioning conventional Christian wisdom. He too interpreted the Old Testament in catastrophic terms with cometary overtones, and doubted whether the New Testament testimony could be sustained. These facets of Newton's world-view, which are now known to us through his many unpublished works, are still not commonly mentioned in scientific circles, but it is not without reason that Newton has been described as far more than simply the first rationalist of the scientific age (Keynes 1947): he was also 'the last of the magicians, the last of the Babylonians and Sumerians, the last great mind which looked out on the visible and intellectual world with the same eyes as those who began to build our intellectual inheritance rather less than ten thousand years ago.'

Newton attached great importance to the subject of biblical chronology explored by Whiston, and he even acquiesced while Whiston extended his theories to make pronouncements about the nature of the godhead. But when these led Whiston to be branded a heretic and subsequently dismissed from his post, Newton cautiously downplayed the more blood-curdling ideas about celestial missiles. The argument that comets were too small to give rise to frequent planetary encounters was still in the future, so Newton felt obliged to emphasize (irrationally) their providential rather than catastrophic character, as well as their ability to bring new life and fuel to stars and planets! The overriding consideration, in fact, was to avoid confronting a prevailing state of protestant opinion, in which even to discuss events in nature or the bible which might be connected with 'first causes' ran the risk of being seen as a heretic.

The intention at the time was obviously to dissociate Newtonian theory from biblical catastrophism and other presumed miraculous effects, and above all to emphasize the rôle of comets in establishing the law of gravity. As is well known, Newtonian theory was strongly supported by later developments in planetary dynamics largely in the hands of continental mathematicians, but in spite of subsequent nineteenth and twentieth century attempts to associate the advance of astronomical theory exclusively with an understanding of planetary motions, it is clear that comets played a vital rôle in the initial development of Newton's theory of gravity. It is also clear that by an occasional skilful turn of phrase, designed to avoid conflict with the growing Anglo-Graeco-Christian vision of the universe, a rather specific non-catastrophist view of comets was also generated (*e.g.* Clube & Napier 1986a).

The period immediately following Newton and Halley cannot therefore be described as relentlessly scientific. For example, even Newton, towards the end of his life, was prepared to concede that comets might occasionally fall into the sun with associated catastrophic effects on the earth (Arago 1855, p.651), while in 1745 Buffon (see ter Haar & Cameron 1963) proposed a model for the formation of the whole planetary system involving the collision between a comet and the sun. According to this idea, such a collision would lead to the ejection of a huge mass of material, some of which might eventually condense to form the observed planets. However, Buffon's theory, described in his *Histoire Naturelle,* nowhere mentioned theology, and he was finally obliged to retract his hypothesis in the resulting clerical storm. Thus, these essentially catastrophist ideas about comets ran into severe opposition in both England and continental Europe, while others began assiduously cultivating Newton's later rather metaphysical views on comets until they eventually solidified into a kind of teleological dogma.

Newton's disciples and successors indeed concentrated upon highlighting the benign, almost purposeful actions of comets in the cosmos. Comets consequently were believed to supply the 'most subtle and active parts of our air, upon which the life of things chiefly depends' (Pemberton 1728, p.202), or to comprise a 'pure elementary fire, of absolute necessity for the life and being of all things' (*cf.* Hill 1754, Costard 1767). One can see in

these ideas an element of the old Platonic notion of world-soul
or *logos* (see Guthrie 1962, p.419 *et seq.*), and the general idea
soon proved to have an almost hypnotic appeal to cosmologists.
For example, a century after Newton, in 1790, Sir William Herschel (1738–1822) was presenting a world-view in which stars
and planets were inhabited by living things, and where comets, in moving from one stellar system to another, provided the
means by which stars and planets could replenish their losses
(Schaffer 1980).

5.2.3   UNIFORMITARIANISM

Newton's public stance thus exerted a deep influence on those
who came after, and there followed a definite tendency amongst
astronomers to eschew speculation in the field of catastrophism
in favour of the apparent increasing control over the natural
world which the new mathematical physics and beliefs about
comets brought in their wake. This is not to say, however, that
everyone became exclusively anti-catastrophist so far as comets
were concerned, despite the débâcles represented by the Whiston and Buffon episodes. In particular, the idea of close encounters or impacts by comets persisted for many years amongst the
continental philosophers, the French astronomer Laplace, for example (see *Oeuvres Complètes de Laplace 1835*, cf. Jones 1988),
writing in his famous treatise *Exposition du Système du Monde*
that if a comet were to approach the earth, 'The seas would
abandon their ancient positions ... most of the human race and
the beasts of the field would be drowned in the universal deluge,
... [and] entire species would be annihilated'.

In geological science too, the arguments over catastrophism
continued into the nineteenth century. The debate was fuelled
by the work of Cuvier, one of the founders of modern palaeontol-
ogy, who considered that the biblical Flood, which was widely
supposed to date back five or six thousand years, had simply
been the most recent of a succession of catastrophes that had
visited the earth. Construction work in Paris had revealed that

geological strata differed abruptly from one to another, with the fossilized remains of sharks, for example, in one layer contrasting sharply with those of reindeer in another. On this basis Cuvier inferred that six great catastrophes had struck the earth during its history, each associated with one of the days of creation and subsequently followed by an epoch of generation of new species.

Opposing this catastrophist school, however, especially after the revived interest in meteor showers during the first half of the nineteenth century (Section 6.1.3, p.110) had subsided, were the uniformitarians. In 1830, the Scottish geologist Sir Charles Lyell, developing on the work of his predecessor Hutton, published his *Principles of Geology*, an elaborate and influential study based on what was by this time an increasingly precise knowledge of the geological map of Europe. Lyell convincingly argued that the discontinuities uncovered by Cuvier were merely regional, and he showed in consequence that the geological record had no need of catastrophism. Accordingly, the uniformitarians concluded that the geological condition of the earth could be entirely explained by the gradual operation over many years of the same slow inexorable forces that were currently observed to shape its surface layers.

This fundamental division of beliefs, which can be traced back to the time of Newton or even earlier, continued even into the late nineteenth century. While Lyell's work exerted a powerful influence on the debate, it took the publication of Darwin's *Origin of Species* in 1859, in which the changing development of life forms was also seen to be the result of a long, slow uniformitarian process, to break the older moulds of thought. Finally, then, with the theory of evolution, the predominantly English 'Enlightenment', with the work of Newton at its apex, came to imply an extraction of the most perfect features of Hellenism and Christianity, and to encompass a new 'scientific' view of comets in which catastrophism played no part.

6

Comprehensive views

"What we know is minute; what we are ignorant of is vast."

Laplace.

6.1 Comets and thunderstones

6.1.1 CHANGING INTERESTS

The continued survival of the uniformitarian view in geology
and biology during the late nineteenth and twentieth centuries,
specifically excluding any catastrophic rôle for comets, would
on the face of it appear to correlate with the lack of any significant meteor showers during the period in question! Although
there is a widespread view amongst many geologists and biologists that the uniformitarian view is likely to be correct, it is
clear from an understanding of past astronomy that the extreme
uniformitarian view may well be a child of its time, merely a natural development of the earlier public *persona* adopted by Newton in order to avoid confrontation between his other scientific
ideas and the Protestant Church. We return to the important
question of catastrophism later in this book (see Chapters 16
and 17), but in the meantime there is no doubt as to the general attitudes that developed in cometary science during the late
nineteenth and twentieth centuries. Broadly speaking, the view
emerged that comets were essentially harmless, that a general
understanding of their behaviour would be best achieved without reference to any possible past interaction with the earth,
and that their significance even for understanding more general
solar system processes was generally minute. Moreover, we increasingly see a growing scientific trend towards the complete
separation of the subject from the historical record.

Thus, whilst the Renaissance is now seen as marking the first serious reversal for Aristotelian science and the Age of Enlightenment is seen as bringing in the Newtonian paradigm, the nineteenth century was a period of consolidation. In physics, for example, the success of Newton's law of gravity now increasingly led minds towards the problem of the supposed mechanical aether, the all-pervading medium that was believed to transmit light and the force of gravity; while in the earth sciences, since the astronomical environment had at last been rendered harmless, attention was directed towards the slow evolutionary processes in geology and biology which were believed to produce the stratigraphic and fossil records.

These developments, attributable in part to Newton's deliberately ambiguous views on comets (Section 5.2.2, p.101), in fact created new demarcations in science whose boundaries were in future years to become increasingly rigid. A self-regulatory preference emerged, therefore, for the development of theories within each separated scientific discipline that did not intrude upon these artificial boundaries, and as a consequence ideas which crossed the interdisciplinary boundaries gradually became more difficult to initiate.

Indeed, with solar system and cometary astronomy now apparently under control, and with none of their manifestations having to cross the boundary with either earth sciences or the earth itself, the interests of astronomers increasingly turned to higher things: the world of stellar astronomy and the problem of understanding the fixed stars. This encouraged rapid progress in these fields, and led to growing interest in observations of the faint patches of light called nebulae, most of which turned out to be groups of distant stars or gas clouds, though a few, those that moved, would sometimes turn out to be comets.

Progress in instrumental and observational techniques during this period, however, did lead to the discovery of new comets at an ever increasing rate. Although this eventually allowed the problem of cometary origin to be tackled by statistical techniques, the growing number of known comets initially proved something of a distraction to astronomers. Not only did these bodies exhibit a wide variety of forms and physical structures, which cried out for an explanation, but they also had to be carefully observed in order to determine and classify their various orbits. However, as the century progressed the problems of cometary dynamics were gradually displaced from their former pivotal position in the development of mechanics. In fact, it is fair to say that astronomy as a whole also suffered in this respect, though this was partly offset by the eventual rise of astrophysics as an independent discipline. Moreover, the application of the new astrophysical arguments to cometary questions eventually produced significant strides in explaining the general appearances of comets, especially the development and evolution of the coma and the two kinds of tail. An excellent review of this branch of the subject has been presented by Brandt & Chapman (1982), while in Chapter 18 we briefly summarize the current observational situation, making particular reference to recent new puzzles and constraints coming largely from observations of Halley's comet.

Despite these advances in understanding the physical processes which determine how comets evolve under the influence of the solar radiation, the first half of the nineteenth century saw only very limited interest in the question of the origin of comets. This led to a situation in which progress in this area became increasingly out of step with advances in other fields of astronomy, and in which ideas about cometary origin came to reflect the views of an ever smaller number of individual scientists. This inevitably caused the subject to become unreceptive to new ideas, and eventually led to a distinct tendency for important results in other fields to be ignored. As the nineteenth century developed, therefore, despite a number of significant advances in astronomy as a whole, it seems that the feeling of generally increasing mastery over nature that characterized the nineteenth-century approach to physical science had become so ingrained that cometary research, as a discipline, virtually ceased to have any significance at all.

6.1.2 Meteoritic impact

A good example of the reluctance of nineteenth century scientists to accept unwelcome observational results is given by the birth of meteoritic science. The celestial nature of comets was already well-established by this time, and leaving aside a few notable suggestions to the contrary (*e.g.* Halley 1714, Pringle 1759, Rittenhouse 1783) prevailing ideas about the origin of meteors and meteorites were still firmly set in the dogma of Aristotelian science.

According to this picture, meteors were viewed as atmospheric phenomena, conceivably related to lightning or aurorae, while meteorites were usually explained as no more than ordinary terrestrial rocks that had been struck by lightning! Although the former Babylonian and ancient Greek beliefs about these phenomena were by now well known, the dominant scientific attitude to such views was one of disbelief, being well summarized by a memorandum from the Paris Academy of Sciences dated 1772, which concluded (Krinov 1960, p.9): 'The falling of stones from the sky is physically impossible.'

The strength with which this opinion regarding the possibility of celestial missiles was held can be judged from the fact that even after the meteorite Barbotan had fallen in France in 1790, witnessed by the local mayor and city council, the physical chemist Berthollet could write: 'How sad it is that the entire municipality enters folk tales upon an official record, presenting them as something actually seen, while they cannot be explained by physics nor by anything reasonable' (*cf.* Krinov *loc. cit.*, Olivier 1925, p.5).

It was against this background of almost arrogant disbelief, that in 1794 the Czechoslovakian lawyer Chladni presented the results of an investigation surrounding the falls of several meteorites. He concluded (*e.g.* Chladni 1798) that the evidence overwhelmingly supported the idea that meteorites must be extraterrestrial in origin, and that their flight through the atmosphere was the primary cause of the luminous phenomenon known as

Figure 6.1: Illustration of a meteor storm, or great shower of shooting stars. Taken from Ball (1893).

a fireball. Clearly anticipating a sceptical response, he wrote (Krinov 1960, p.11): 'However, few are willing to believe that in cosmic space, in addition to the larger cosmic bodies, there are many small aggregations of coarse material particles. But this disbelief is of an illusory nature and is based not on any theory, but simply on prejudice.'

This pioneering study was followed by a detailed chemical and mineralogical investigation by Howard (1802), which showed that meteorites were definitely of a type of body distinct from other terrestrial rocks. Although this should have spelled the end of the Aristotelian viewpoint, the conclusion that they came from beyond the earth was still not accepted.

However, the following year, at around 1.00 p.m. on 26 April, a bright fireball was observed to explode and produce a great shower of stones which fell in the neighbourhood of the village of L'Aigle, in Northern France. This fall was of such a magnitude that it was reportedly witnessed by thousands (Zimmer 1916), and the Paris Academy directed that the distinguished natural scientist Biot should conduct a full investigation. The results of this inquiry, read before the Institute in July 1803 (Biot 1807), generally confirmed the authenticity of the phenomenon, and the doubts of Europe's leading intellectuals about falls of meteorites from the sky were at last set aside. Meteoritic science was thus inaugurated, though it was still many years before Chladni's suggestion of a cosmic origin was finally agreed.

Nevertheless, despite the rapid advance in meteoritic science, largely attributable to the efforts of Chladni, Howard and Biot *and* to a chance surge in the number of reported meteorite falls at the time (Burke 1986), the related question of the origin of meteors remained unresolved. As chance would have it, however, the greatest historical display of the Leonid meteor stream was witnessed on 13 November 1833 (*cf.* Figure 6.1). This shower was observed throughout the United States of America, such that 'one thousand meteor flashes [were] counted every minute'; and according to another eye-witness: 'the stars fell, and fell, thick as snow coming down in a snow storm' (Olivier 1925, p.26).

6.1.3   COMETS AND METEORS LINKED

These events could not fail to attract scientific attention, and in a detailed report of the phenomenon published shortly afterwards, Olmsted and Twining (Olmsted 1834a,b) seem to have been the first to draw a causal connexion between comets and meteors. This suggestion was followed soon afterwards by the investigations of Quetelet (1837), Erman (1839a,b) and Drach (1841), but it was another generation before the physical connexion between comets and meteors was finally accepted. For example, John Herschel's treatise on astronomy in 1842 makes no mention of the topic, and it was only after similar arguments had

Figure 6.2: Donati's comet as seen from Paris on the 5th of October 1858, taken from Guillemin (1877).

been independently put forward around 1860 by Reichenbach (1858), Kirkwood (1861, 1872) and Schiaparelli (1866, 1867) that the conclusion seemed secure (*e.g.* Lockyer 1890, p.143; Olivier 1925, p.50; Hughes 1982a). This 'hint' of a connexion between comets and meteors was regarded by Lockyer (1875, p.80) as 'one of the greatest discoveries in late years in the science of astronomy.'

The extraordinarily slow progress of this field during the first half of the nineteenth century contrasts strongly with advances made in other areas of science and astronomy, and gives some indication of the perceived importance of solar system and cometary astronomy in relation to other subjects. The late eighteen-fifties, however, stimulated in particular by the appearance of a great comet — Donati's — in 1858 (see Figure 6.2), saw a temporary revival of interest in cometary astronomy, and the study of meteor streams and their connexion with comets also became a popular topic for investigation.

The year 1866, for example, saw a conclusive demonstration by Schiaparelli to the effect that the differential attraction of the sun on the particles in a cometary dust cloud should cause the material to disperse around its orbit (see Olivier 1925, p.221). This provided a physical basis for the observed connexion between the orbits of some comets and meteor streams, and, by implying that comets evolved into meteor streams, contributed to the gradual reawakening of interest in the origin of comets that occurred in the second half of the century.

Progress in this field, however, was still very slow, and at first the discovery that the end product of cometary disintegration was principally dust seems merely to have further reduced any lingering scientific concerns about any possible danger posed by comets! Indeed, with the exception of certain exaggerated fears (especially in France, see Figure 6.3) about the effects of a cometary collision with the earth (*cf.* Peirce 1859), comets were now frequently believed to exert a beneficial, almost salubrious influence. This indicates the persistence of the prevailing Newtonian viewpoint at this time, an attitude which also appeared to

Figure 6.3: French cartoon purporting to show the disastrous effects of a cometary collision with the earth.

be vindicated by the great commercial success of the favourable 'comet' wines of 1811 and 1858!

6.2   Celestial theory established

6.2.1   KANT'S THEORY

If the upshot of Newtonian theory had been to render the earth apparently safe from the effects of comets and so remove them from the forefront of astronomical research, it is not altogether true there was no scientific interest in the origin of comets. Indeed, the first steps towards an understanding of their origin in a solar system setting had already been taken in the eighteenth century. Following Newton, as we have seen, much effort had been devoted to problems of dynamical astronomy particularly in relation to the orbits of planets and comets, whilst the rapid improvement in the design and construction of telescopes around this time meant that for the first time many faint 'telescopic' comets were discovered. This period also saw a growing awareness of the general properties of the solar system, a high point being Kant's concept (1755) of its formation from an extended diffuse protosolar nebula.

Kant believed (see Ley 1968, pp.83–90) that notwithstanding their different physical appearances and kinds of orbit, comets should be considered as basically similar to planets, and maintained that the apparent differences in their properties could be fundamentally attributed to a different place of origin (further from the sun) in the original nebula. In particular, he argued that the orbital eccentricities and the masses of the bodies formed in the nebula would tend to increase outwards, and it was anticipated that comets should therefore have masses at least comparable to those of the largest planets. At large distances, however, comet growth would be limited by the much longer time required to accrete large bodies, both because the density was expected to be lower in the tenuous outer regions of the nebula and because the orbital periods were longer. Kant proposed, therefore, that in reality numerous smaller particles would form instead of one huge mass.

Kant's nebular hypothesis was the first in which a serious attempt was made to understand the motions of all the bodies in the solar system within the context of a single physical theory based on Newtonian principles. However, his suggestion that comets belonged to the solar system went against the prevailing teleological spirit of the times, and most astronomers remained more inclined to regard comets as interstellar bodies, weaving their way purposefully amongst the stars. Nevertheless, Kant's proposal was an important first step, because it raised fundamental new questions, and laid the foundations for subsequent developments (see Chapter 10) based on the idea that comets were indeed formed within a primordial protosolar cloud.

6.2.2   WHENCE COME COMETS?

During this time knowledge about a relatively large number of comets continued to accumulate. This arose, as has been mentioned, partly from the discovery of new 'telescopic' comets, and also from improved translations of Chinese records which gave information about bright naked-eye comets of the past.

By the close of the eighteenth century these developments had combined to produce a new consensus as to the nature of the cometary phenomenon. Comets were now believed to be definitely celestial bodies, which although quite different from planets in their appearances and in the shapes and inclinations of their orbits, were clearly similar in the crucial characteristic that they too were 'gravitating' bodies. How far one could reliably extend Newton's law of gravity was still a moot point, but the return of Halley's comet to perihelion during March 1759, roughly as predicted, gave the new viewpoint considerable scope.

It should be noted, however, that the existence of periodic comets, already touched upon by some Greek ideas, was at this time still questioned. Indeed, the few periodic orbits which were sometimes claimed as such were frequently interpreted as either coincidences or exceptions. The available observations were often insufficient to allow a parabolic orbit to be distinguished from a highly eccentric ellipse, and it could plausibly be argued that in reality all comets had parabolic or slightly hyperbolic orbits and only ever made one passage past the sun.

In this respect, the modern 'solar system *vs.* interstellar' debate about the origin of comets, using evidence derived primarily from cometary orbital characteristics, has *its* origin in the latter half of the eighteenth century. Those who argued for an interstellar theory (e.g. Cole 1823) not only emphasized the ambiguity of the observations but also the many points where observations demonstrated differences between comets and planets, both in their general physical appearance and in their orbital types. However, proponents of a solar system origin (*cf.* Kant) denied that the observations were ambiguous, and quoted apparently clear-cut examples of periodic comets, like Comet Halley.

In 1770, a clear indication that the dispute would not be settled by these kinds of qualitative argument was provided by Lexell's comet (discovered by the great comet hunter Messier), which passed close to the earth in that year. The observations were impossible to understand if a parabolic orbit was assumed, but it was discovered soon afterwards that they could be readily explained by an elliptical orbit with a period of only six years (Grant 1852, p.105).

Unfortunately, at least for the supporters of a solar system origin, the comet was never again seen, and it was subsequently shown that successive close encounters with Jupiter had first 'captured' it into a short-period orbit from a nearly parabolic type and then ejected it again into an orbit of much longer period. An interesting account of the discovery and orbital evolution of Lexell's comet has been given by Chambers (1909, p.86). Recent calculations (Carusi *et al.* 1986) indicate that it will next return to perihelion about 2061, but with a perihelion distance somewhat beyond Jupiter.

Lexell's comet thus showed the need for caution. One could not interpret orbital elements simply at face value, because time and the likelihood of planetary interactions were other important factors affecting the evolution of comets which had a bearing on their places of origin. This comet was also the first to have a good limit placed on its mass. By arguing that its close passage to the earth had not perceptibly affected the earth's motion, Laplace (1805, p.230) demonstrated that the comet's mass must be less than 1/5000 that of the earth, or smaller than 10^{21} kg. Although the implications of a direct encounter of the earth with a body of this size do not seem to have been much discussed at this time, the discovery certainly appeared to reduce cometary masses to minuscule proportions, despite their huge volume and apparent bulk. This inevitably had some influence, albeit illogical (see Chapter 17), in further diminishing fears about the possibly catastrophic effects of collisions of comets with the earth.

In this way, by the beginning of the nineteenth century it had become accepted that comets were harmless celestial objects. Their conformance to Newton's laws indicated an essentially 'gravitating' physical nature, but the precise way in which they were connected to other kinds of astronomical body, such as stars, planets and nebulae, was still unknown. Evidence that some comets had periodic orbits strongly indicated a solar system origin, but the example of Lexell's comet, and the totally different appearances of most comets and planets suggested otherwise. Indeed, since the majority of cometary orbits were very nearly parabolic in form, there was a strong implication that perhaps their place of origin was located beyond the sun's sphere of influence, in the depths of interstellar space.

The year 1800 thus became something of a turning point in the history of cometary astronomy. Not only had the two-thousand year old debate 'atmospheric vs. celestial' now come to an end, but within the space of just two centuries it had been transformed into a new understanding and a new question: 'solar system or interstellar?' A summary of the nearly thirty cometary theories which had been proposed up to about this time can be found at the end of this chapter in Table 6.1 (see p.127). Although echoes of these early ideas can often be found in many modern theories of comets, progress from this time on has become almost independent of the ideas originally held on the subject by the first astronomers.

This epoch therefore marks the transition from an earlier stage of qualitative understanding to one in which Man's attempt to understand the nature and origin of comets has become increasingly dependent upon arguments which are detailed and technical in character, and which have to rely on the most accurate astronomical observations. In this sense, from about 1800 the *history* of cometary astronomy ceases to be of any real importance in the detailed development of the subject, though its significance — as we have seen — for a full understanding of the implications and long-term evolution of comets remains immense.

6.3   Interstellar picture

6.3.1   NEBULAR HYPOTHESIS

So far as the question of the origin of comets is concerned, discussions in the nineteenth century may be said to have begun in earnest with the completion by Laplace in 1805 of his monumental work *Mécanique Céleste*. This study attempted to incorporate all the discoveries then known concerning the astronomy of the solar system. The ideas it contains, which apparently were developed quite independently of Kant's cosmogony, clearly exerted a powerful influence on the direction of solar system studies at this time, and even now lie very close to the heart of modern solar system astronomy.

Laplace followed Kant's approach in first emphasizing the principal regularities of the observed solar system, especially the central dominance of the sun and the strange fact that the planets have nearly coplanar, almost circular orbits. He argued that these striking regularities could be best explained by postulating a physical model based on the collapse and contraction of an initially slowly rotating primordial gas cloud. This theory is now called Laplace's 'nebular hypothesis'.

The original slow contraction of the nebula gradually led to a tendency for the cloud to spin faster and faster, much as a ballet dancer might execute a pirouette, and it eventually developed a flattened, rapidly rotating configuration. This was now rotating so fast that mass and angular momentum began to be shed from its rapidly spinning equator, and it was assumed that this mass loss would occur through the intermittent ejection of successive

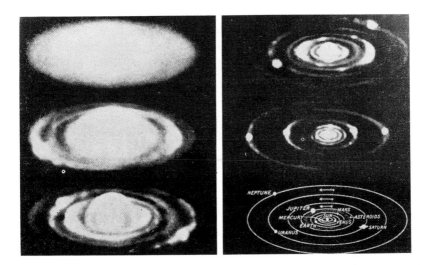

Figure 6.4: Schematic illustration of the formation of the solar system according to Laplace's nebular hypothesis. Taken from Whipple (1964b).

rings of gas. These then cooled, and were believed ultimately to form the observed sequence of planets. Most of the mass, however, remained in the central body, which gradually evolved to form a slowly rotating spheroid much like the present sun, the general sequence of events being illustrated in Figure 6.4.

Laplace's nebular hypothesis soon became the accepted model for the origin of the solar system, and remained in vogue for most of the century. However, although it provided an excellent framework on which to interpret the principal regularities of the observed solar system, it did not readily explain comets, especially their highly eccentric orbits and the fact that they appeared to come almost randomly from all directions on the sky.

This information had been known to Kant some fifty years earlier (who had certainly believed it possible to incorporate it into a solar nebula model), but Laplace now argued that a common origin for comets and the rest of the solar system was ruled out. In this way, he separated the origin of comets from the origin of the other bodies in the solar system, and advocated an interstellar origin for the former. Like Kepler before him (Section 5.1.3, p.97), Laplace therefore argued that interstellar space was populated by an extremely large number of comets.

6.3.2   LAPLACE'S INTERSTELLAR THEORY

At first sight, Laplace's suggestion was in complete accord with the observations. He argued, for example, that if the sun were at rest with respect to the population of interstellar comets, one should expect to see an overwhelming excess of nearly parabolic or weakly hyperbolic orbits, as observed. Similarly, provided that the interstellar comets were distributed uniformly throughout interstellar space, they should arrive more or less randomly from all directions, again as observed.

But some comets (such as Comet Halley) were known to have orbits of a closed, elliptical type. These could not readily be incorporated into either the nebular hypothesis or the interstellar picture, and Laplace was consequently led to introduce an *ad hoc* 'planetary capture' mechanism to account for these orbits.

The idea was originally inspired by observations of Lexell's comet some forty years before. Laplace now argued that a few interstellar comets with nearly parabolic orbits would inevitably suffer substantial perturbations due to rare, close encounters with one or other of the planets. Although Lexell's comet had admittedly not become a permanent member of the short-period comet population in this way, the observation did at least demonstrate that such a process could in principle occur, and astronomers generally accepted the idea as a viable explanation for the few periodic comets then known.

In this way, while the main regularities of the solar system were well explained by the nebular hypothesis, the orbital properties of comets were now perceived to be so different from those of planets as to require an interstellar origin for comets. Not only was such a view in good general agreement with the available observations, but, just as importantly it seems, it was also consistent with the prevailing intellectual spirit of the times. As we have seen (*cf.* William Herschel's cosmology, p.103), this strongly indicated an interstellar origin for comets, and Laplace's arguments were quickly adopted, for this reason as much as any other, it seems, by the larger astronomical community.

In the detailed development of his theory, Laplace also introduced two further important concepts: the solar 'sphere of action', and the 'zone of visibility'. The first was necessary in order to specify the region within which solar gravity could significantly modify the orbits of the interstellar bodies, while the second was required to explain why comets are only seen within a relatively small distance of the sun. On general grounds, it is clear that the radius of the sphere of action should be roughly half the distance between stars, and Laplace adopted a value of about 10^5 AU for this parameter, where 1 AU denotes the mean distance of the earth from the sun. The zone of visibility, on the other hand, corresponding to the region within which the sun was capable of producing visible emissions from the surface of a typical comet, was taken to have a radius of only 2 AU in order best to represent the observed behaviour of comets.

These assumptions were important ingredients in Laplace's explanation for the observed near-parabolic excess of comets. Their significance can be judged from the fact that even now the sphere of action plays a major rôle in determinations of the probable number and extent of comets in the sun's domain, while the idea of the zone of visibility is still the principal selection effect that must be considered in discussions of which comets might become accessible to direct observation.

The dynamics of interstellar comets beyond the sun's sphere of influence were subsequently investigated by Cole (1823), who concluded that interstellar comets must always lie within the sphere of action of one or another of the so-called 'fixed' stars. He also demonstrated how, in particular cases, perturbations by such stars might sometimes allow a comet to pass from one stellar system to another. However, it was almost a hundred years before the effects of stellar perturbations on cometary orbits were next seriously contemplated, apparently first by Burgatti of the University of Bologna (see Armellini 1922), in the context of a stellar eruption theory of comets (*cf.* Section 7.2.3, p.140), and then by Armellini (1922) and Fessenkov (1922).

Whereas Burgatti and Fessenkov seem to have started from much the same position as Cole in relation to the stellar velocities in space, assuming the stars to be essentially at rest, Armellini clearly recognized the importance of the solar motion (see next Section), and even seems to have anticipated in some respects the important effects of the overall distribution of galactic matter, namely the galactic tide (see Section 12.3, p.259). These early studies of stellar perturbations on comets were followed by Öpik (1932), in a study in which the stars were explicitly allowed to move with respect to the solar system, producing a situation where the more slowly moving long-period comets would experience a sequence of nearly instantaneous 'impulsive' perturbations of their orbits as the stars flew past the sun.

It is interesting to note that although Laplace's planetary capture mechanism for periodic comets was generally accepted, there were still some during the early nineteenth century who considered that this seemingly *ad hoc* explanation for periodic comets was unnecessary. Cole, for example, argued that the detailed discrepancies between the observed and predicted times of the perihelion passages of Halley's comet implied that the observations could not simply be explained by the periodic return of one body. On this view, which assumed that all comets moved in nearly parabolic orbits, the few apparent examples of periodic orbits were explained simply as the result of chance coincidences!

6.3.3   IMPORTANCE OF SOLAR MOTION

However, the acid test of Laplace's hypothesis of an interstellar origin for comets is whether or not the sun is moving through the supposed interstellar field of comets. Indeed, the principal assumption behind Laplace's explanation for the strong parabolic excess was that the sun had no motion with respect to the interstellar medium. If this assumption had been dropped, the parabolic excess would immediately have been converted into a strong hyperbolic excess, not observed.

As it turned out, in a study completed several years before the appearance of Laplace's theory, William Herschel (1783), building on earlier work by Mayer in 1760, had analyzed the motions of nearby stars on the sky and had already concluded that the sun did move (Grant 1852, p.555). Twenty-two years later, just as Laplace was publishing his first work on comets, Herschel again considered the problem, and confirmed his original result, albeit arriving at a somewhat different direction for the sun's motion.

Although these results were broadly consistent with those of other investigators at the time (cf. Prevost 1783; Grant loc. cit.), the evidence for the solar motion was strongly criticized by both Biot and Bessel as being of doubtful statistical significance. When Laplace (1816) finally considered the detailed predictions of his theory for the relative number of elliptical, parabolic and hyperbolic comets, he thus neglected the solar motion. In doing this, it is difficult to believe that he was entirely unaware of its considerable importance for his theory, especially in view of an admittedly obscure paper by Gauss (1815) appearing to draw attention to the fact (see Clerke 1908, p.370; Schiaparelli 1890). However, in ignoring the effect, he appears to have made neither the assumption nor its consequences explicit. The apparent success of Laplace's interstellar hypothesis was thus based right from the start on a questionable, and (as it was later shown) completely false premise.

6.4 Solar system developments

6.4.1 COMETS AND ASTEROIDS

A second important observation concerning Laplace's theory, also made at about the time that he was finalizing his ideas, was the discovery by Piazzi and Olbers, in 1801 and 1802 respectively, of the first minor planets: Ceres and Pallas.

In fact, Ceres was originally described by Piazzi as a star-like comet, recalling William Herschel's mistaken belief when he first discovered Uranus in 1781, that this body too was a comet. At first it appeared that the suggestion would be vindicated, as Herschel (1802) noted that Ceres was sometimes found to be embedded within a faint, transient coma, giving it the appearance of an almost defunct comet, while Schröter observed that both Ceres and Pallas were often surrounded by a faint, variable nebulosity (Brewster 1821, pp.88,91). Herschel (1805) later recorded the same phenomenon in the case of the third minor planet Juno (discovered by Harding in 1804), though no trace of a coma was found by either of them about the fourth, Vesta, discovered by Olbers in 1807.

Although these suggestions of a faint, transient nebulosity associated with the minor planets have since been repeated on a number of occasions, notably relating to 14 Irene (Hind 1851), 182 Elsa, 224 Oceana and 899 Jocasta (Bobrovnikoff 1931), and recently again in the case of 2 Pallas (Kapkov 1984), a definite confirmation of the effect has proved elusive. Even at the beginning of the nineteenth century, observers could not agree whether the apparent atmospheres about the first three minor planets were a real phenomenon, and it was soon accepted that the new bodies did not generally share the attributes of comets. Herschel (1802) therefore proposed that they should be called 'asteroids'.

The discovery of the asteroids upset the underlying simplicity of Laplace's nebular hypothesis, since it implied that at least some solar system bodies must have formed originally in orbits which were not only significantly non-circular, but which also had relatively high inclinations, taking them well beyond the zodiacal limits. As we have seen, by 1807 the number of known asteroids had risen to four, but, as with the solar motion, Laplace appears to have treated them mainly by omission, making no attempt to resolve the potential contradictions that they introduced for his nebular hypothesis for the origin of the main bodies in the solar system.

6.4.2   LAGRANGE'S PLANETARY THEORY

The minor planets were not ignored by everyone, however, and Olbers (1802) soon speculated that they might be fragments of a much larger planet which had once existed between Mars and Jupiter (Arago 1858, p.487), blown to pieces by the action of internal forces or the impact of a comet. An extension of this idea, intended to explain comets, was subsequently published by the mathematician Lagrange in 1814, a year after his death. Lagrange considered that the disruption of a planet could be a very probable event, and evaluated the explosive force necessary to put fragments of the planet into a typical cometary orbit. In particular (cf. Brewster 1821), he proposed that some comets might originate on the larger planets (such as Jupiter or Saturn) as a result of gigantic explosions.

Although this idea does not seem to have been analyzed in any great detail, the proposal was an important development. For example, Lagrange was a respected authority, certainly in the same league as Laplace, so others could not lightly dismiss his views; and secondly, by reintroducing a solar system hypothesis for the origin of comets, he rekindled the flagging solar system vs. interstellar debate. Moreover, whereas Lagrange's theory (cf. Hevelius, Section 5.1.3, p.97) implied that comets were made of essentially the same stuff as planets, Laplace's theory made no definite predictions in this area. In fact, the new theory highlighted the inadequacy of Laplace's ideas in this respect: whereas he had explained the provenance of comets, he had essentially ignored the related question of how they were formed.

In this way, the start of the nineteenth century saw the emergence of two distinct theories of cometary origin. The first, that of Laplace, postulated an origin in interstellar space, while the second, due to Lagrange, proposed a violent origin in events on the surfaces of planets. The detailed presentation of Laplace's ideas seems to have successfully avoided any discussion of difficult or potentially awkward observations for his theory, for example the existence of asteroids and their connexion with comets, and the importance of the solar motion in determining the predicted distribution of captured comets. But perhaps the most curious part of the affair was that belief in the interstellar theory seems to have increased directly in relation to the success of the nebular hypothesis for the origin of the planetary system, which had failed even to address the issue of comets! Lagrange's planetary explosion theory was in many ways equally speculative, but it did at least contain the provocative suggestion that comets were still being formed — even at the current epoch — by continuing processes involving potentially observable events, namely explosions on planets.

It seems that at this time there was little to choose between the two propositions: both were *ad hoc* in nature, and neither was sufficiently developed to allow a definitive observational test to be made which might have discriminated between the two ideas. Although science hardly ever advances in a perfect fashion, it still comes as something of a surprise, given the nature of the evidence, to realize how quickly the majority of astronomers appear to have swung behind Laplace's interstellar viewpoint.

A variety of extraneous factors almost certainly contributed to this conversion: the prior death of Lagrange, the questionable occurrence of planetary explosions and the connotations of this idea with catastrophism, not to mention Laplace's pre-eminent position in solar system astronomy and the excellent Newtonian credentials of the latter's interstellar theory. By such a route, whatever the relative merits of the several factors involved, the

Theory and type		Originator	Date
Earthy bodies akin to planets	(C)	Babylonians	c.2000 BC
Fiery atmospheric phenomena	(C)	Babylonians	c.2000 BC
Jets from fiery hoops	(C)	Anaximander	c.575 BC
Burning clouds	(A)	Xenophanes	c.550 BC
Planetary conjunctions	(C)	Anaxagoras	c.450 BC
Rare sighting of a planet	(C)	Pythagoreans	c.450 BC
A kind of planet	(C)	Hippocrates	c.430 BC
Reflected sunlight	(A)	Pythagoreans	c.430 BC
Chains of rocky bodies (stars)	(C)	Diogenes	c.430 BC
Chains of unseen planets	(C)	Artemidorus	c.400 BC
Fiery atmospheric phenomena	(A)	Aristotle	c.350 BC
Reflections from high clouds	(A)	Heracleides	c.350 BC
Influx of the sun into clouds	(A)	Metrodorus	c.330 BC
Celestial bodies	(C)	Apollonius	c.330 BC
Stellar conjunctions	(C)	Zeno	c.300 BC
Stars enveloped by cloud	(C)	Strato	c.290 BC
False images of stars	(A)	Panaetius	c.130 BC
Violent, fiery winds	(A)	Böethus	c.100 BC
Fiery celestial body	(C)	Seneca	c.50 AD
Exhalations from planets	(C)	Tycho	c.1600 AD
Interstellar bodies	(C)	Kepler	c.1600 AD
Reflected sunlight	(A)	Galileo	c.1600 AD
Vapours ejected from sun	(C)	Anon.	c.1620 AD
Vapours ejected from planets	(C)	Hevelius	c.1680 AD
Vapours ejected from stars	(C)	Cassini	c.1680 AD
Bodies akin to planets	(C)	Halley, Newton	c.1680 AD
Bodies akin to planets	(C)	Buffon, Kant	c.1760 AD
Interstellar bodies	(C)	Laplace	c.1800 AD
Result of planetary explosion	(C)	Lagrange, Brewster	c.1810 AD

Table 6.1: Chronological table of 29 cometary theories up to about the middle of the nineteenth century. Type code (C) denotes a broadly 'celestial' theory, while (A) denotes one rooted in the 'atmospheric' ideas introduced by the Greeks.

early nineteenth century saw the start of an extended period in which the interstellar hypothesis became accepted by most workers in the field, and laid the foundation upon which much of the modern subject of cometary origin has been built.

7

Complicating factors

"There are three kinds of lies: lies, damned lies, and statistics."

Disraeli.

7.1 Laplace under fire

7.1.1 SOLAR MOTION PROBLEM

The importance of Laplace's neglect of Herschel's solar motion has already been mentioned (Section 6.3.3, p.123). Although the solar motion was finally shown to be a real phenomenon in 1837 by Argelander (Grant 1852, p.556), it was many years before the wider astronomical community appreciated that the results contained serious implications for ideas about the origin of comets.

After Gauss (*cf.* Clerke 1908, p.370; Schiaparelli 1890), the first authors to raise the topic directly in the cometary context appear to have been Mohn (1860) and Carrington (1860a,b; 1863). These researchers realized that were the sun moving through the interstellar field, one should expect to see an excess of comets arriving from the direction towards which the sun is moving, rather in the same way that rain tends preferentially to strike the front windscreen of a moving automobile. Carrington, in particular, expected to discover an excess number of comets with perihelia in the direction opposite to the solar motion, and carried out an analysis of the orbits of 133 known comets with nearly parabolic orbits in order to determine the size of the effect. Surprisingly, he found that the perihelia were distributed more or less randomly on the sky, and though he accepted that the result was probably confused by uncertain selection effects influencing the reliability of the statistical sample, he argued that if these could be ignored the result indicated that the sun had no motion with respect to the interstellar field. An essentially similar result was found by Mohn.

However, although Carrington was inclined to argue against the solar motion, Schiaparelli, also around 1860 (see Richter 1963, p.147), finally put the argument the right way round, and emphasized the sensitivity of Laplace's predicted parabolic excess to his neglect of the solar motion. Accepting that the sun's motion with respect to the other stars was real, he concluded that the observations of cometary orbits implied that the sun must be very nearly at rest with respect to the cometary field. Schiaparelli therefore proposed that the sun was surrounded by an almost comoving comet cloud, and argued that comets (at least at the present time) were definitely part of the solar system (*cf.* Peirce 1849).

Despite the logic of Schiaparelli's argument, Laplace's nebular hypothesis and his interstellar origin for comets were so firmly entrenched that the conclusion was not accepted for another thirty years! Indeed, there seems initially to have been little enthusiasm even for contemplating the possibility. For example, in a review of cometary origins written more than a decade after Schiaparelli's original point was made, Newton (1878) briefly alluded to the solar motion in the following way: 'Professor Schiaparelli by introducing (improperly, as I am sure he will concede) the motion of the sun in space was led to decide against a foreign origin for comets.'

Laplace's interstellar theory was sustained in this way quite erroneously for many years, and it is not generally recognized as having been finally overthrown until almost the end of the century, when Fabry (1893), in a detailed investigation for his thesis, both generalized and independently confirmed Schiaparelli's principal results.

7.1.2   ANISOTROPY PROBLEM

Schiaparelli was not the first to attempt to persuade astronomers that Laplace's calculations had left out an essential feature. Almost as soon as the ideas behind the interstellar theory had become known, Bode (1812) presented a preliminary analysis of the distribution of the directions of cometary perihelia on the sky, while the general question of whether comets come equally from all directions (as assumed by Laplace) or instead from one or another preferred direction or plane on the sky was later taken up by investigators such as Brorsen (1852), Lardner (1853), Mohn (1860), Carrington (1860a,b) and Hoek (1865; 1866a,b; 1868).

The latter author, in particular, concluded that while the aphelion points were distributed more or less uniformly over the sky, their detailed distribution showed a distinct tendency towards clustering. He suggested that this implied that comets must move through interstellar space in groups, and argued that the individual groups might be broken up upon entering the solar sphere of action, in such a way that the separate comets making up a group would appear in the zone of visibility over a relatively short space of time.

Cole's (1823) work, implying that interstellar comets would always be within the sphere of action of one star or another, would have made this thesis difficult to support, but by this time his arguments had been largely forgotten. Nevertheless, Hoek's discovery was not easy to reconcile with Laplace's concept of a uniform distribution of interstellar comets, and the result, along with other difficulties for the theory, appears subsequently to have been quietly ignored.

7.1.3   Capture problem

Throughout this period, the number of comets with known orbits was steadily increasing, and many examples were now found in which the orbits were definitely elliptical. For example, while in 1790 only 78 comets (including 7 sightings of Halley's comet) had been recorded with sufficient accuracy to allow the assumed parabolic orbit to be calculated (Lalande 1792), a hundred years later the number of known comets had increased more than threefold to around 270 (Chambers & Chambers 1889). Of these, 20 were classified as definitely periodic (11 had been observed on more than one occasion), 43 were elliptical, and the remainder (more than 200) were either parabolic or weakly hyperbolic (6 or 7 cases). The 'periodic' comets thus constituted a significant fraction of all known comets, and it became increasingly hard to explain them all by Laplace's suggestion of an unlikely close encounter with one of the planets.

An indication of the rapid rise in the number of known comets is given in Figure 7.1, which shows the number of discoveries of comets per decade (including recoveries of periodic comets) taken from the catalogue of Marsden (1982). This catalogue contains 102 discoveries of comets prior to 1680, while the total number up to the end of May 1982 is 1109. These sightings represent 710 individual comets, of which 121 are 'periodic' (*i.e.* with an orbital period $P < 200\,\mathrm{yr}$), while 589 have parabolic or nearly parabolic orbits (*i.e.* with $P > 200\,\mathrm{yr}$).

Apart from the rising proportion of periodic comets amongst the rapidly increasing number of comets as a whole, several other lines of evidence also suggested that the comets of short period should perhaps be treated differently from the parabolic group. For example, they mostly moved in elliptical orbits not greatly inclined to the ecliptic, and with predominantly direct motions. This strongly suggested a solar system origin (Peirce 1849), while the orbits were also undeniably similar to those of the asteroids, which likewise began to be discovered in increasing numbers after about 1845. Indeed, the apparent orbital connexions between short-period comets and asteroids (*cf.* Section 6.4.1, p.124) led Alexander (1851) to propose that both kinds of body originated in the disruption of a single, large object.

It was also possible to group the known short-period comets into 'families', in which a particular period or aphelion distance was associated with one or another of the major planets (see Figure 8.2, p.157). This feature of the short-period orbits, first noted by Hind (1850), had led to Alexander's (1850) suggestion that cometary families might arise as a result of the break-up or disruption of a large comet due to a close encounter or collision

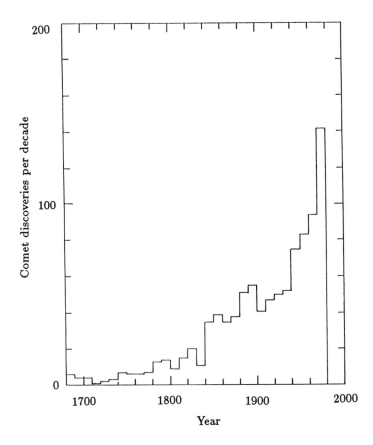

Figure 7.1: The number of discoveries of comets, including recoveries of periodic comets, per decade for the years 1680–1980.

with one of the planets. The statistical evidence for cometary families was subsequently made much more secure by Roller (1870), who presented a list of nearly two-dozen periodic comets which seemed in some way to be associated with the orbits of Jupiter, Saturn, Uranus or Neptune.

By contrast, the largest group of comets, comprising long-period and nearly parabolic orbits, had orbits that were vastly larger than the scale of the planetary system, and which were distributed almost randomly about the plane of the ecliptic (Figure 8.1, p.154). For these reasons, astronomers began to regard the comets with short orbital periods as a separate cometary group which might merit a quite different explanation for their origin.

By this time there were also a number of arguments, first set out by R.A. Proctor around 1870 (Olivier 1930, p.211), which indicated that Laplace's planetary capture theory could not quantitatively explain the proportion of observed short-period comets. In a series of articles (e.g. 1884), this author showed that Laplace's hypothesis was simply too unlikely an event to account for the increasingly large number of short-period comets, and concluded that they must originate within the solar system itself. He also argued, from the apparently short lifetimes of these comets against physical decay, that they must be continually formed in the planetary system. These factors led to a gradual revival of interest in Lagrange's planetary explosion theory. It was not clear whether all comets should have a planetary origin, but the number of short-period comets together with their orbital correlations with the planets suggested that at least some comets might arise this way.

However, a possible alternative explanation of the number of short-period comets was soon suggested by Bredichin (1889). Following Alexander (1850), this author proposed that the strong tidal force associated with the planetary capture event might cause a single progenitor comet to split up into several pieces (cf. Kresák 1981a,b). Examples of split comets were already known, and the suggestion raised the interesting possibility that perhaps the whole population of short-period comets might be explained as the result of several generations of such events (cf. Section 17.1.4, p.397). There were also several grounds for regarding the planetary explosion idea with a certain amount of suspicion: not only did it appear to be an unlikely proposal, especially in view of the probable physical constitution of the planets and the likely evolution of any presumably hot explosion products, but the whole idea smacked of catastrophism.

For these reasons, although Proctor's quantitative arguments against the capture theory were later to be substantiated many times (*e.g.* Newton 1891, 1893, Russell 1920; *cf.* Section 8.2.3), his conclusions were never generally accepted.

Despite this, however, Proctor's arguments did have some lasting value: they contributed to a growing awareness amongst astronomers that there was a problem with the origin of comets, particularly with those of shorter period, and they revived interest in Lagrange's planetary explosion theory, which represented an example of an alternative solar system hypothesis for cometary origin. Moreover, the difficulties with the number of short-period comets, first highlighted by Proctor, were eventually to be used by astronomers in the twentieth century as the starting point for a number of important new theories and suggestions (*e.g.* Section 13.3.4, p.296), both about the nature of comets and their likely distribution within the solar system. Nevertheless, leaving these points aside, Proctor's arguments appeared to have little immediate impact, and most astronomers at the time continued to accept Laplace's planetary capture theory as the most convincing explanation for the existence of periodic comets, and his interstellar theory to explain the underlying flux of nearly parabolic orbits.

7.1.4   LAPLACE REJECTED

It is interesting to reflect upon the reasons why the astronomical community ignored Proctor's arguments. They show, for example, that by this time cometary theories were being judged not only on purely astronomical criteria (such as orbital considerations), but also on physical criteria, such as whether explosions of sufficient violence could really occur on planets, and on whether the explosion products would necessarily recondense to form comets. By the end of the nineteenth century, however, the growing problem of the origin of short-period comets was soon to be eclipsed by an even greater difficulty, namely the realization that the larger, parabolic group was itself probably not interstellar.

This significant change in outlook occurred around 1890, stimulated by the researches of Schiaparelli and Seeliger (*e.g.* 1890) and by the publication of Fabry's thesis in 1893. This led to the rapid acceptance of Schiaparelli's former arguments about the importance of the solar motion, and the long-overdue conclusion that the 'parabolic' comets were also permanent members of the solar system quickly followed. Laplace's original mostly intuitive objections to a solar system hypothesis now seemed suddenly to carry less weight, and the arguments were soon turned around (*cf.* Kant 1755) so that the parabolic group might provide clues as to the conditions which must have prevailed at the time of formation of the solar system!

The end of the nineteenth century thus saw the start of an era in which both conventional theories relating to the properties of the solar system, the nebular hypothesis for the formation of the sun and planets and the interstellar hypothesis for comets, were in a state of considerable difficulty. The majority of astronomers were now arguing, following Kant, that comets had always been part of the solar system, though they still had no inkling as to how the original solar nebula had managed to produce such disparate bodies as planets and comets, moving respectively in nearly circular and highly elliptical orbits.

However, the quickening pace of astrophysical research did give astronomers some grounds to hope that future theoretical progress might soon cast some light on the problem. This stance was vindicated in the last year of the old century when Moulton (1900) finally showed that Laplace's nebular hypothesis was untenable on dynamical grounds. In later work by See (1909), this time following an argument apparently first made by Babinet (1861), it was also pointed out that the nebular hypothesis could not be made to work, as the present angular momentum of the solar system was far too small to have allowed the outer planets Uranus and Neptune to have formed as a result of equatorial mass loss from a disc rotating at break-up speed. These arguments put the final nail in the coffin for Laplace's interstellar ideas, and with the opening of the new century, astronomers began once again to look with renewed interest at fresh possibilities both for the origin of comets and for the origin of the solar system.

7.2   Solar system confusion

7.2.1   SURVIVAL OF THE FITTEST

The conviction that comets belonging to the parabolic group were definite members of the solar system was soon strengthened by the work of Strömgren (1914). This author, following Thraen (1894) and Fayet (1906), found that after allowing for the effects of known planetary perturbations, those comets with apparently hyperbolic orbits had in every case 'original', unperturbed orbits which were elliptical, and therefore originally bound to the solar system.

However, there was no strong argument for supposing that the protosolar nebula had only produced comets with nearly parabolic orbits, and it was therefore assumed at this time that comets must originally have been present with all kinds of orbit. Indeed, the ones with shorter periods would by now have made so many revolutions that they would have long since disintegrated, and it was argued, therefore, that the observed parabolic excess was simply an astronomical example of Darwinian 'survival of the fittest' (Crommelin 1910). At this time, of course, the existence of *some* comets with relatively short orbital periods was still being attributed to Laplace's planetary capture mechanism, now assumed to operate on marginally closed nearly parabolic orbits rather than ones which were just hyperbolic.

In general, the periodic comets move in a predominantly direct sense associated with the plane of the ecliptic, and the Darwinian argument was soon extended to incorporate this fact. Those nearly parabolic orbits which had originally small inclinations to the ecliptic were more likely to suffer strong gravitational interactions with the planets, and therefore had a much greater probability of being captured. In this way, although the fundamental difficulty with the efficiency of the capture process remained, it did provide a form of natural selection which might account for the excess of direct orbits that was observed amongst the short-period comets (Russell et al. 1926, p.414).

The early years of the twentieth century were thus a period that saw the development of a broad consensus as to the origin of comets. The larger group, making up the parabolic excess, was believed to have originally formed together with the sun and planets at an early stage of evolution of the solar nebula. Although the original distribution of these orbits was not known, it was essentially irrelevant to the argument, the only requirement being the initial existence of a substantial number of bodies in extremely long-period orbits. Subsequent Darwinian selection acting on this unknown distribution of orbits would then inevitably produce a situation in which the comets that remained would be the ones of longest period, i.e. those which had not yet made enough revolutions to have disintegrated.

7.2.2   SHORT-PERIOD COMETS

While this feeling about the origin of the long-period group was gaining ground, attention returned to the problem of the origin of the short-period comets. In particular, the question of whether these really were produced by the conventional planetary capture mechanism or by some other, possibly more exotic mechanism, became an important point for discussion. For example, a variation on Lagrange's planetary explosion hypothesis which enjoyed some brief favour was the suggestion by Chamberlin (1901), dating back at least to Kirkwood about 1860, that comets might be created as a result of the tidal disruption of asteroids which happened to pass within the Roche limit of one or another giant planet (cf. Alexander 1850, 1851, Hirst 1950). Throughout this period, therefore, the difficulties with the efficiency of the planetary capture mechanism remained (e.g. Russell 1920), and authors such as Crommelin (1929) continued to argue strongly that such problems with the standard viewpoint were so great that the planetary explosion theory should be given serious consideration.

An important parameter for both these theories of the origin of short-period comets was the rate of injection of new comets into the system. This was usually estimated from the observed number of such comets and their mean rate of change of brightness, giving a net loss of short-period comets on the order of one per century, this being the required injection rate assuming that the population is in a steady state. Crommelin concluded that this injection rate presented insurmountable difficulties for the planetary capture theory as an explanation of the observed number of short-period comets, but went on to argue that the figure was small enough that, given the supporting evidence for volcanic activity on the planets (the great red spot on Jupiter and the white spots on Saturn), the alternative planetary explosion theory should certainly not be rejected out of hand.

One should remember that at this time, the beginning of the twentieth century, it was still generally believed (cf. Anaxagoras!) that the sun and planets were basically similar kinds of body, both cooling on a thermal, Kelvin-Helmholtz timescale on the order of a few $\times 10^7$ years. Planets, being smaller than the sun, had cooled sufficiently to form solid surfaces, though all except the smallest were still believed to have liquid cores (e.g. Wilde 1910).

Furthermore, the identification of comet 'families' was another observation which could be used as evidence for a planetary origin for the short-period comets. At this time the reality of such groups was usually accepted without question, and further investigations into the orbits of medium-period comets even led to much interest in the idea of possible trans-Neptunian planets (e.g. Forbes 1880a,b, 1909; Todd 1880, Pickering 1911). Such work received additional support from analyses then also underway regarding anomalies in the positions of the outer planets (Pickering 1909; cf. Duncombe & Seidelmann 1980).

However, the difficulty of generating a sufficiently intense volcanic explosion to eject material into a cometary orbit remained (*cf.* Section 14.2.1, p.321). Even if it was agreed that this was in principle possible (*cf.* the modern photographic evidence for volcanic activity on Io, *e.g.* Morrison 1982, Nash *et al.* 1986), there still remained the severe problem of explaining how the hot explosion products could subsequently recondense into the meteoric particles which comets were then believed to comprise.

In fact, although it was usually assumed at this time that the condensation problem could somehow be overcome, in line with the assumptions then being made in the various 'tidal' theories proposed at the same time for the origin of the planetary system (*e.g.* Chamberlin 1901, Moulton 1905, Jeffreys 1916, 1918, 1929; Jeans 1917, 1919; see Figure 14.2, p.322), it was subsequently proved that this was certainly not possible (Spitzer 1939). When it was also shown (Russell 1920) that all the suggested comet families, with the possible exception of Jupiter's, were probably spurious statistical artefacts, another plank in the support of the planetary explosion theory was removed, and most astronomers after this date ceased to regard the suggestion with anything other than a strong degree of scepticism.

7.2.3   SOLAR THEORY

One important comet family was the sun-grazer group, comprising comets with perihelia lying just above the surface of the sun. Here it was natural to suggest a solar origin (*e.g.* Schaeberle 1893, Chamberlin 1928, Brydon 1945), and in this case the existence of explosions of sufficient violence could not be denied. Moreover, there was growing spectroscopic evidence which showed independently that comets were made of basically solar-type material. Indeed, this kind of evidence had already been used as long ago as the eighteen-seventies (*e.g.* R.A. Proctor 1873, p.147) to argue that comets were probably formed by expulsions of matter from the surfaces of other stars (*cf.* Section 5.1.3, p.97).

However, there were several difficulties with this theory. First, if comets were indeed formed on the sun, they must all have orbits that originally had perihelia deep inside the solar interior — providing a celestial example of the general rule that 'what goes up must come down'. In order for such comets to avoid falling back into the sun it was necessary to appeal in an *ad hoc* way to unlikely close planetary encounters, in order to give the comets sufficient angular momentum to miss the sun on their first return. Although several sun-grazers had been observed, there were at this time no records of a comet actually hitting the sun, although this has now been witnessed a surprising number of times in more recent years (*e.g.* Weissman 1983a, St. Cyr 1988a,b). Indeed, the recent rate of arrival of sun-grazers has suggested to some that we may now be 'overdue' for yet another really bright apparition of a large fragment of the original sun-grazing comet (Bortle 1989)!

A second difficulty was the general problem of explaining how the hot solar ejecta had managed to recondense into the solid meteoric particles which presumably comprised comets. And finally, even granting the existence of sufficiently large planetary perturbations and the possibility of recondensation, it was very hard to see how the theory could be extended to incorporate the vast majority of comets, *i.e.* those which had relatively large perihelion distances and nearly parabolic orbits.

In summary, therefore, even assuming a solar origin for sun-grazers and a planetary origin for the other periodic comets, the dominant group of near-parabolic comets remained essentially unexplained. In order to account for the existence of bodies in these kinds of orbit, advocates of the planetary and solar theories usually retreated to one or another form of the solar nebula hypothesis, which clearly weakened their general case. Although it was repeatedly pointed out that the planetary capture theory could not work quantitatively (*e.g.* M. Proctor 1926), the lure of identifying a common origin for all comets proved irresistible, and the nebular hypothesis for the parabolic group and the planetary capture theory for periodic comets continued to be the most generally acceptable picture (*e.g.* Newcomb 1910, Proctor & Crommelin 1937).

7.3   Debate widens

7.3.1   AGE OF SOLAR SYSTEM

Throughout this period significant advances were being made in the study of stars and stellar evolution (*e.g.* Russell 1925). In particular, it was recognized that the accepted age of the sun ought to be increased at least a hundredfold, at last bringing astronomically determined estimates of the age of the solar system into line with the ages independently determined for meteorites and the earth using radiometric or geological dating techniques. Planets could no longer be regarded simply as cool sun-like bodies, and this result, together with Russell's work in 1920 showing that cometary families were mostly spurious, further increased the already severe difficulties associated with the planetary explosion theory.

Following the work of Tisserand (1889), Fayet (1911) and Newton (*e.g.* 1893), Russell (1920) continued to investigate the planetary capture theory. He confirmed that this theory failed to produce sufficient short-period comets, but now offered suggestions as to where the simple theory might have gone wrong.

Among these, perhaps the most important single factor which confused the statistics was believed to be the possibility of planetary perturbations subsequent to the initial capture event (*cf.* Pickering 1911). Other effects which might increase the predicted number of comets included the possibility of capture by numerous small perturbations, somewhat analogous to a 'diffusion' process, capture by the resistance of a dense interplanetary medium and the hypothetical action of some other kind of 'nongravitational' force. Agreeing that the direct capture of a comet in the manner of Lexell's comet was a very improbable event, he also revived the suggestion of Alexander (1850) and Bredichin

(1889) that tidal disruption at the point of closest planetary approach might cause a new short-period comet to split into many smaller ones.

By the end of the nineteen-twenties, therefore, it was generally agreed, despite the lack of proof, that the short-period comets must almost certainly be derived from the observed long-period or near-parabolic flux of comets by a process essentially equivalent to the planetary capture mechanism. However, although this capture theory seems to have been widely accepted, the revised age of the solar system now had important implications for the assumed origin of the parabolic group. In particular, the apparent rate of cometary disintegration meant that even comets with an initial orbital period as great as a million years would by now have completed so many revolutions that they should long since have decayed. The Darwinian argument which previously had so well explained the parabolic excess could thus be turned round to demonstrate that we should not expect to see any comets at all!

7.3.2   RECENT CAPTURE?

This paradox led Bobrovnikoff (1929a,b) to introduce a modified form of Laplace's interstellar hypothesis. Following Nölke (1909), he argued in particular that the sun's present family of comets might have been captured relatively recently (*i.e.* about a million years ago) during passage of the solar system through a dense cloud of cometary or meteoric material. The present direction of the solar system through space, away from the star-forming clouds in Orion, lent some support to this hypothesis, as too did the indirect evidence of the lack of fossil meteorites on the earth. This suggested that comets had only been part of the solar system during comparatively recent times, and the present lack of any strongly hyperbolic orbit was taken to indicate that the most recent cometary capture episode had now finished.

However, a potentially serious difficulty with the hypothesis was that, following Laplace, the interstellar comets were assumed to be captured as a result of planetary perturbations. Since a sufficiently close planetary encounter to allow direct capture from a strongly hyperbolic initial orbit was an extremely unlikely event, it was necessary to postulate the existence of an extremely dense interstellar comet cloud (*cf.* Section 15.2.1, p.344). Nevertheless, if the presence of such a cloud was accepted, it was in principle possible to capture enough comets. Moreover, the simple assumption that the capture episode had finished (consistent with the sun's present position in the Galaxy) could be used to explain the observed lack of any significantly hyperbolic orbits.

Thus, Bobrovnikoff opened a new chapter in the solar system *vs.* interstellar debate. Although the theory appeared to be a somewhat *ad hoc* invention, relying upon the presence of hypothetical, dense interstellar clouds of comets (not observed) and rather special timing for the most recent capture event, the problem of explaining the survival of long-period comets for the great age of the solar system seemed to force one towards such a viewpoint. Bobrovnikoff's theory is also notable for introducing, for the first time, the idea that we might now be living at a privileged epoch so far as long-period comets were concerned. Of course, such capture events might still recur during the lifetime of the earth, but this was the first modern indication of a possible lack of long-term uniformity in the immediate astronomical environment.

7.3.3   Öpik's solution

The weak link in Bobrovnikoff's argument for an interstellar origin of comets was, of course, the assumption that all primordial comets disintegrated at approximately the same rate, namely that derived from the decay of observed short-period comets within the zone of visibility. Since comets are mostly inactive at larger distances from the sun, it was conceivable that many cometary bodies might survive at sufficiently large distances for at least the revised age of the solar system. This suggested that the real problem to be solved was how to arrange for these comets, initially lying beyond the zone of visibility, to be perturbed into orbits taking them sufficiently close to the sun to be seen.

In an important paper published a few years after the appearance of Bobrovnikoff's work, Öpik (1932) recognized this possibility, and showed furthermore that stellar perturbations (*cf.* Section 6.3.2, p.122) acting on the orbits of the comets of longest period would inevitably cause their perihelia to drift systematically towards larger, 'safer' values. Due to the random nature of the process, some comets would have their perihelia perturbed towards smaller values, and it was thus possible to envisage a primordial solar system hypothesis for cometary origins, provided that there were sufficient comets in store, as it were, with orbits of large perihelion distance.

Such comets would be safe from disintegration for at least the age of the solar system, and the random effects of stellar perturbations might then be invoked to reduce their perihelia into the zone of visibility, thereby providing a steady source of new comets from which to resupply the old (Öpik 1932). Öpik thus anticipated, in several important essentials, the later hypothesis of Oort (1950; see Chapter 9), which has subsequently formed the basis of much theoretical cometary research during the past forty years. In particular, Öpik's suggestion implied that it was in principle possible to retain a primordial solar system hypothesis for the origin of comets.

However, Laplace's second argument for an interstellar origin for comets, namely the apparently isotropic distribution of the parabolic of orbits on the sky (bearing no relation to the ecliptic), now also began to figure in the debate (*e.g.* Russell 1935, p.126). Several workers, following the earlier leads of Bode, Carrington and Hoek among others (Section 7.1.2, p.130), had performed increasingly sophisticated analyses of the distributions of the directions of the perihelia and aphelia of the parabolic group (*e.g.* Pickering 1911, Jantzen 1912, Eddington 1913, Oppenheim 1922, Bourgeous & Cox 1934), and although the data were still patchy and incomplete, possibly due to ill-understood observational selection effects, all these authors succeeded in detecting small departures from complete isotropy.

Rather than correlating with the ecliptic, however, as one might have envisaged were comets to have a solar system origin, these results indicated that in fact the long-period and nearly parabolic comets had orbits which weakly correlated with either the galactic equator or the direction of the solar motion. This result — the 'galactic concentration' of Armellini (1922) — became an important additional reason for seriously contemplating the interstellar hypothesis.

The mid nineteen-thirties, then, were years in which several independent lines of evidence began to converge so as to rekindle the solar system *vs.* interstellar debate (*cf.* Larmor 1935a,b,c; Crommelin 1935). Although Eddington (1913) had offered a solar system interpretation of the aphelion clustering of long-period comets (in terms of a non-uniform distribution of material in the protosolar nebula) and Armellini had also discounted the weak departures from uniformity, others now preferred to interpret the anisotropy in terms of an interstellar origin. Moreover, given that the short-period comets were ultimately derived in some way from the long-period group (but see Vsekhsvyatski 1935, and Orlov 1939 for alternative views; *cf.* p.149), attention began to focus on the question of the origin and source of this important 'parent' population of comets.

The relative merits of the two suggested sources of comets were quite finely balanced. On the one hand, if comets were truly primordial solar system bodies, the problem of their short lifetimes, as compared with the age of the solar system, seemed to force astronomers into the uncomfortable position of having to postulate an exceedingly large number of unobservable cometary bodies in orbits of large perihelia, simply in order to explain the relatively few comets that had been seen.

Alternatively, if comets were interstellar in origin, not only did one then have to postulate rather special and precise 'timing' for the most recent capture event, but it was also necessary to accept the existence of extremely dense interstellar clouds of comets, in order for the relatively inefficient planetary capture mechanism to trap a sufficient number. Although several alternative capture mechanisms were also suggested at around this time, for example by Nölke (1936; see Richter 1963, p.149; *cf.* Nölke 1908) and Corlin (1938), relying on the nineteenth century idea that interstellar space or the outer solar system might contain a dense resisting medium, perhaps associated with the hypothetical aether or the observed zodiacal cloud, these too seemed often arbitrary and unrealistic.

In this way, both the solar system and interstellar hypotheses seemed to depend on many *ad hoc*, and by implication implausible, assumptions and conditions (e.g. Russell 1935, p.43). Although additional circumstantial evidence could be brought to bear on each point of view, the only sure conclusion seemed to be (Russell *loc. cit.*, p.128): 'Comets remain one of the greatest enigmas of all.'

8

Enigma variations

" 'Tis all in pieces, all coherence gone."

John Donne.

8.1 Diverging paths

8.1.1 VIOLENT EJECTION

The following decade, up to about the middle of the twentieth century, was one in which the provenance of long-period comets remained largely undecided, although these years did finally see opinions on the origin of short-period comets settle into almost complete unanimity. There was general agreement by this time that short-period comets must originate through a process of dynamical capture by Jupiter, although several notable authorities in the Soviet Union, for example Orlov and Vsekhsvyatski (pronounced Vssessviatsky), held out strongly against the trend for many years (*e.g.* Vsekhsvyatski 1962, 1966, 1972, 1977).

The former author (Orlov 1939) had earlier proposed that certain detailed structures in cometary dust tails could be explained simply by assuming that comets occasionally collided with meteoric débris in the solar system, the collisions being so violent that they led to the explosive ejection of small cometary fragments and dust from the nucleus. Indeed, it was suggested that the same mechanism might also produce the observed clustering of cometary aphelia; namely, as a consequence of cometary break-up following impacts with the larger 'meteorites' in interplanetary space, the fragments subsequently evolving to form observed comet groups and pairs (*cf.* Hoek 1865; and p.130).

Given such evidence for collisions between cosmic bodies, Orlov then argued that the occasional collision of an asteroid and a large meteorite might disrupt the former body into many fragments which could then be identified with observed comets.

149

He thus concluded that Lagrange's hypothesis for the origin of comets was 'more probable than other hypotheses'.

Vsekhsvyatski, on the other hand, approached the problem from the then more conventional standpoint of the inefficiency of the Jupiter-capture process for the origin of short-period comets. This author, a cometary specialist working in Kiev in the Ukraine, continued to argue for Lagrange's planetary explosion theory right up to the time of his death in 1984. In particular, following the earlier discussions of Proctor and Crommelin (e.g. M. Proctor & Crommelin 1937), he continued to draw attention to the acknowledged short lifetimes of periodic comets ($\approx 10^3$ yr), which meant not only that these comets must be recently formed within the confines of our own solar system (e.g. Vsekhsvyatski 1930), but also that Laplace's proposed capture mechanism could never explain their observed number.

His first investigations, around 1930 (see Richter 1963, p.152 and references therein), followed these former authors in presenting a model based on volcanism on Jupiter and Saturn. However, in later work around 1950 the theory was modified to allow for comet formation on the satellites of these planets. This change was introduced chiefly in order to counter a severe problem with the earlier version of the theory, namely how to explain the ejection of comets from the surfaces of the giant planets. This difficulty was aggravated by the great escape velocities from Jupiter and Saturn (about 60 and 35 km s^{-1} respectively), and also by the strong resistance posed by their dense atmospheres.

Vsekhsvyatski's name is also associated with the attempt to extend the planetary explosion theory to explain all comets, including those with nearly parabolic orbits. In this respect he tackled a difficulty with the theory which previous workers had preferred to ignore, since the observed continuity in the physical properties of short and long-period comets meant that it became increasingly difficult to maintain that the two different classes of comet, differing only in orbital characteristics, had completely separate modes of origin.

However, this extension of the theory exacerbated the problem of understanding how planets could eject sufficient material to explain observed comets. The mass which planets now had to expel was much greater than had formerly been thought, and required a much greater explosive force for its ejection. Observations of the present number of comets combined with their apparent rates of decay suggested (e.g. Vsekhsvyatski 1977) that the total mass which now had to be removed from the planets during the age of the solar system was on the order of 10^{-3}–$10^{-2}\,M_\odot$, where $1\,M_\odot$ denotes the solar mass. This figure seemed so large that most astronomers found it difficult to accept the idea.

The required mass loss from the planets or their satellites, amounting to between one and ten times the mass of Jupiter, was so great that it effectively undermined any residual plausibility which the explosion hypothesis might have retained. For instance, it meant that the energy source for the explosions was unlikely to be ordinary volcanism, and Vsekhsvyatski (e.g. 1966, 1977) increasingly emphasized the similarities of the planetary explosion idea to related cosmogonical concepts which had then recently been introduced in other fields of astronomy. Thus, the planetary explosion theory became implicitly linked with other kinds of explosion hypothesis, for example that of Ambartsumian (e.g. 1958, 1960, 1965) for explaining the genesis of compact stellar associations, galaxies and active galactic nuclei.

8.1.2   DESPERATE MEASURES

The assumptions of the planetary explosion theory thus gradually diverged from those of more conventional viewpoints, and it became increasingly difficult to identify common ground from which discussions and proper scientific debate could advance. Eventually, the physical difficulties mentioned above, especially those concerning the problem of how planetary bodies might eject sufficient material with sufficient energy to explain observed comets, became the main reason leading to rejection of the idea. In any case, it was not obvious that bodies with the dimensions and icy constitution of comets would be a natural product of the eruptions; *cf.* Chapter 19.

However, Vsekhsvyatski himself remained a firm believer in the overall physical picture, and continued to emphasize the difficulties which the prevailing capture theory encountered in trying to explain the observed number of short-period comets. Although the planetary explosion theory is almost certainly mistaken, it is nevertheless worth noting that arguments based on the idea did lead Vsekhsvyatski to make several significant predictions: the outflow of molecular material from young stars (*e.g.* Vsekhsvyatski 1977; *cf.* Lada 1985); the presence of rings of meteoroidal material around planets such as Jupiter (*e.g.* Struve 1960, Vsekhsvyatski 1962); and volcanism on the Galilean satellites of Jupiter, the latter long before the phenomenon was discovered on Io in 1979 after analysis of television pictures taken by Voyager I (*e.g.* Morrison 1982). More recently, indirect evidence has also been presented for volcanic activity on Europa (Cruikshank 1988).

As we have seen, support for the planetary explosion idea was scarce in the nineteen-thirties, and with the passage of time the theory has gradually fallen completely into disrepute. It is fair to conclude that Lagrange's original conception of a planetary origin for short-period comets has now finally died, although modern variations on the theme are still sometimes reintroduced by a minority of authors (see Section 14.2.1, p.319). These have frequently been advanced for many of the same reasons as those which first inspired the original suggestion, particularly the association of short-period cometary orbits with asteroids and the major planets (*e.g.* Figure 8.2, p.157), and the continuing difficulty in explaining the observed number of short-period comets (*e.g.* Whipple 1957, Joss 1973a, Delsemme 1973, Mendis 1973, Fernández 1980a, Fernández & Ip 1983a,b; Napier 1983; *cf.* Section 13.3.4, p.296). None of these features of the short-period comet population has yet been completely explained in terms of the capture of *observed* comets with nearly parabolic orbits passing through the zone of visibility.

8.2   Van Woerkom's paradox

The next significant step occurred in 1948, with the almost simultaneous publication of two influential papers, by van Woerkom and Lyttleton respectively. These works primarily concentrated on the question of the origin of long-period comets, and both introduced important new ideas and arguments. In the remainder of this chapter we describe each in some detail, beginning with van Woerkom's study.

8.2.1   STATISTICAL RESULTS

Van Woerkom (1948) was the first to present a detailed investigation of the effects of planetary perturbations on the orbits of long-period comets (cf. Russell 1920). In particular, he concentrated on determining the statistical, or most probable, effect of planetary perturbations on the observed orbits, especially in relation to the relative number of ellipses vs. parabolae and the proportion of direct vs. retrograde orbits.

It has already been remarked that the principal observations which theories of cometary origin must accommodate are the following: first, why long-period comets come in nearly equal numbers from all directions on the sky (cf. Fernández 1980b, 1981; Delsemme 1985), in particular in such elongated, nearly parabolic orbits; and secondly, why the orbits of short-period comets have mostly small inclinations to the ecliptic and show such strong associations with the planetary system.

The first of these statistical results is presented in Figure 8.1. This illustrates the distribution of the inclinations of 589 nearly parabolic and long-period ($P \geq 200\,\mathrm{yr}$) comets observed up to the end of May 1982, and compares it with that expected for an assumed isotropic source. Although the observed distribution is broadly consistent with the assumption of isotropy, there is, rather surprisingly, a slight excess of retrograde orbits ($i > 90°$). This excess could be slightly reduced if comet groups, such as the Kreutz sun-grazer family (e.g. Porter 1952, Table 9; Marsden

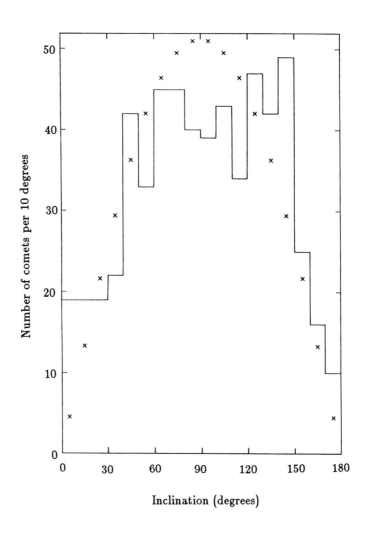

Figure 8.1: Distribution of the inclinations of 589 long-period comets. Crosses denote the levels of the equivalent histogram for a completely isotropic source.

Range of $1/a$ (AU^{-1})	N	Range of $1/a$ (AU^{-1})	N
0.000–0.002	177.0	0.012–0.014	1.0
0.002–0.004	10.0	0.014–0.016	1.5
0.004–0.006	8.0	0.016–0.018	1.5
0.006–0.008	7.0	0.018–0.020	4.0
0.008–0.010	2.5	0.020–0.022	2.0
0.010–0.012	6.5	0.022–0.024	0.0

Table 8.1: Observed numbers of comets from 1850–1936 in equal intervals of $1/a$, after van Woerkom (1948, Table 5).

1967), were counted as a single comet instead of several, but most of the excess, if real, probably has another cause. These data were taken from the catalogue of Marsden (1982).

The second significant observation relating to the long-period comets is the parabolic excess. This is most simply illustrated by a table of the observed number of long-period comets divided into equal intervals of $1/a$, the reciprocal semi-major axis. This defines a very important statistical result known as the '$1/a$ distribution', which we present in Table 8.1 using data drawn from van Woerkom's Table 5. This clearly demonstrates the preponderance of nearly parabolic orbits amongst the two hundred or so well-observed long-period comets discovered from 1850 to 1936. In particular, note the relative height and extreme narrowness of the 'spike' in the distribution near the parabolic limit $1/a = 0$. This peculiar feature of the $1/a$ distribution — the near-parabolic excess — provides what is perhaps the most fundamental observational constraint which theories of cometary origin must address.

Finally, the short-period comets (usually defined to have periods less than 200 years) have strong orbital associations with the planetary system. In addition to having mostly direct orbits of relatively small inclination to the ecliptic ($i \lesssim 30°$), their aphelia Q are found to correlate strongly with the mean radius of Jupiter's orbit. We illustrate the latter result, again following van Woerkom (*loc. cit.*, Figure 1b), in Figure 8.2.

This confirms the strong connexion between short-period comets and Jupiter; but of almost equal interest in this diagram is the weaker indication of a link with the other major planets: Saturn, Uranus and Neptune. This correlation was first suspected by Hind (1850) and Roller (1870), and the implications of 'families' of short-period comets possibly associated with the major planets have since been the subject of many detailed investigations (*e.g.* Forbes 1880a,b, 1909; Pickering 1911, Schütte 1949, Öpik 1972).

Russell (1920) and others (*e.g.* Wilson 1909) had noted that the association of cometary aphelia with one or other of the major planets seems to be without secure foundation, since most short-period comets (excepting the members of Jupiter's family) actually pass no closer to their governing planet than would be expected for a completely random distribution of orbits. (This, for example, is the case with Halley's comet which though part of Neptune's family actually never comes closer than 9 AU to this planet; Crommelin 1907.) However, despite this indication that the apparent clusters of aphelia are spurious, a curious feature of the diagram is that the original groupings have persisted despite a near-doubling of the data set.

In particular, the group with aphelia in the approximate range 50–90 AU seems especially prominent, a result which has frequently been cited as indicating the presence of another massive planet, Planet X, lying some distance beyond the orbit of Neptune (*cf.* Pickering 1911, 1919, 1928, Schütte 1949). Although the statistical significance of these groups is difficult to assess, the apparent clusters of aphelia are clearly an important observation which theories of cometary origin and their dynamics should attempt to explain. A modern interpretation of these data has now been given, for example, by Carusi & Valsecchi (1987) and Carusi *et al.* (1987).

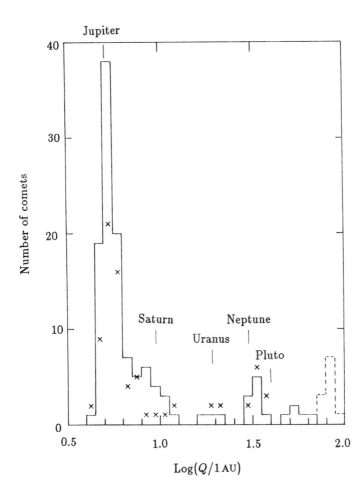

Figure 8.2: Distribution of the aphelia Q for short-period comets. Crosses denote the levels of the histogram for the 77 comets plotted by van Woerkom, while the solid line refers to the 121 periodic comets given by Marsden (1982). The dashed line shows 11 orbits with aphelia less than 100 AU but periods greater than 200 years.

8.2.2   EFFECT OF JUPITER

In his investigation, Van Woerkom concentrated on determining the effect of Jupiter's perturbations on the evolution of long and short-period comets. First, he confirmed that a typical long-period or nearly parabolic orbit was extremely unlikely to experience a sufficiently close planetary encounter to lead directly to capture into a short-period orbit: the probability may be compared with the chance of bringing down a bird by firing a random shot at the sky. This led him to emphasize the relative importance of the weaker, but more numerous, distant planetary encounters, and he showed that these would inevitably produce small, but cumulatively significant changes in a comet's orbital energy during each passage through the planetary system.

The question of whether a comet loses or gains energy during its passage through the planetary system depends largely on whether it happens to pass in front of, or behind, Jupiter in its orbit. Since this is an essentially random process, an arbitrary long-period comet has an almost equal chance of gaining or losing energy during each perihelion passage, while the amount of the energy exchange is usually small compared with the typical orbital energy of a periodic comet. The net effects of Jupiter's perturbations thus much more closely resemble a stochastic process analogous to diffusion, than the sharp, sudden orbital change described by the capture process.

It is usual to represent the changes in specific orbital energy $E = -GM_\odot/2a$ by the equivalent variations in the value of a comet's reciprocal semi-major axis $1/a$. In this way, the perturbations by Jupiter on a representative set of random, nearly parabolic orbits may be described by a quantity $\Delta(1/a)$, whose mean absolute value per revolution was shown by van Woerkom to be on the order of 10^{-3} AU^{-1}. The amount of this change, which we shall loosely describe as the 'energy change' may perhaps be better appreciated by comparing the resulting change in velocity (typically $\lesssim 1\,\mathrm{km\,s^{-1}}$) with the comet's initial orbital speed, usually on the order of 20–50 km s^{-1}. The exact size of the perturbation, however, depends on the precise geometry of the encounter, and also on orbital parameters such as the comet's perihelion distance q and its inclination i with respect to the ecliptic.

Subsequent work has considerably refined van Woerkom's early results (see, for example, Kerr 1961, Lyttleton & Hammersley 1964; Everhart 1968, 1969; Yabushita 1972a, 1983c; Weissman 1978; Fernández 1980b, 1981; Nakamura 1981, Duncan et al. 1987). These studies, especially the comprehensive investigation by Everhart, show that for small values of the absolute energy change $|E|$ per revolution the distribution of energy changes can often be approximately represented by a symmetrical bell-shaped curve resembling a Gaussian distribution. In the case of larger energy changes, however, which mostly occur as a result of moderately close encounters with one or other of the major planets, the true distribution of the energy changes decreases much less steeply than predicted by a simple Gaussian distribution, and in fact falls off roughly as $|E|^{-3}$ up to some maximum value of the energy change (e.g. Everhart 1968). This dependence can also be inferred from equation (8.3) below, and in general it is this part of the distribution of energy changes which dominates the orbital evolution of comets that suffer a very large number of encounters (Everhart 1977, Stagg & Bailey 1989).

Although the exact shape of the curve is rather complex (and in fact generally departs at some level of approximation from exact symmetry; Everhart 1969, Oikawa & Everhart 1979, Nakamura 1981), and depends also on both the perihelion distance and inclination (see Everhart 1968 and Stagg & Bailey 1989 for details), it is often useful to have a relatively simple expression which reproduces the order of magnitude of the random perturbations that are most frequently experienced. Most authors have assumed for simplicity that the exact distribution of perturbations can be approximated by a simple Gaussian distribution, and have allowed for the variations in their characteristic size versus perihelion distance and inclination by letting the dispersion of the Gaussian, σ_E be a function of q and i. Of

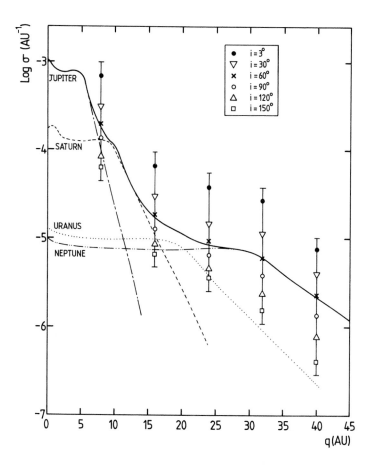

Figure 8.3: The variation of σ_E due to planetary perturbations as a function of perihelion distance and inclination. The solid line shows the dispersion in $1/a$, which we denote by $\sigma_E(q)$, for a random distribution of inclinations, while the vertical bars indicate the range of values for comets with different initial inclinations. The dashed and dotted lines show the individual contributions by each of the major planets.

course, in the present situation, in which the distribution of energies falls off roughly as $|E|^{-3}$ for large values of $|E|$, defining a 'typical' dispersion is not easy, as the true dispersion formally diverges. (In effect, this means that in the long run the single closest encounter usually dominates.) Nevertheless, taking into account the number of planetary encounters that a comet of a given q and i will usually experience, finite values of σ_E can be defined and may be approximately described (e.g. Bailey 1984a, Weissman 1978) by expressions of the form

$$\sigma_E(q) \simeq 10^{-3} \exp(-q/a_J) \qquad (8.1)$$

or

$$\sigma_E(q, i) \simeq (718 - 125.5\tilde{q} + 164c + 9.88\tilde{q}^2 + 282c^2 + 27c\tilde{q}) \times 10^{-6} \qquad (8.2)$$

where, $a_J = 5.2\,\mathrm{AU}$ is the semi-major axis of Jupiter's orbit, $\tilde{q} = q/(1\,\mathrm{AU})$, $c = \cos(i)$ and the units of σ_E are AU^{-1}. We note that although the detailed derivation of equation (8.2) is strictly dependent on the assumption $q \lesssim 4\,\mathrm{AU}$, the values of σ_E derived from equation (8.1) are approximately correct (within a factor of about 3) out to perihelia of order $40\,\mathrm{AU}$. At such distances, however, as shown in Figure 8.3, the principal perturbations are due to Neptune, and no special significance should be attached to the appearance of Jupiter's semi-major axis in this rough expression.

For completeness, we show in Figure 8.3 values of the dispersion of the planetary perturbation function calculated directly from the parameters listed in Tables II and III of Everhart (1968). These data, calculated by Dr. C.R. Stagg, were obtained by assuming that the distribution of energy changes has a sharp cut-off at a dimensionless energy corresponding, in Everhart's notation, to setting $U_d = U_m$. The interested reader is advised to consult the papers by Everhart (1968, 1969) for further details. This figure not only shows the trend in σ_E vs. q for a distribution of initially nearly parabolic orbits with random inclinations, but also illustrates the relative individual contribution by each of the major planets and the spread in σ_E values for comets of differing inclinations. We see, for example, that Jupiter dominates up to about $q = 8\,\mathrm{AU}$; Saturn dominates for q in the range 8–15 AU; Uranus and Neptune are of comparable importance up to about 22 AU; while beyond this, the distribution is dominated by Neptune. There is also a broad spread in σ_E vs. inclination, with the result that comets of low inclinations but large perihelia ($q \simeq 40\,\mathrm{AU}$) are affected similarly in terms of energy changes to those of higher inclination and much smaller perihelia ($q \simeq 15\,\mathrm{AU}$).

8.2.3   SHORT-PERIOD COMETS AGAIN

Van Woerkom's analysis of Jupiter's perturbations led him to draw several far-reaching conclusions about the possible origin of comets, and he exhaustively discussed (and even eliminated!) the various possibilities. On the question of the origin of short-period comets, he first verified that the planetary capture theory did indeed predict too few such comets compared with the observed influx of long-period and nearly parabolic orbits. The discrepancy amounted to a factor of at least 20, which, despite the uncertainties in the argument, proved difficult to eliminate entirely.

The basis of the calculation was the following. The observed isotropic flux of long-period comets brighter than an absolute magnitude $H_0 = 10$ (about 40 times fainter than Halley's comet), corresponded to the arrival of about 28 comets per annum with perihelia within Jupiter's orbit. This figure was based on extrapolating the observed flux of comets (within the zone of visibility) to Jupiter's orbit, and included a factor of 4.5 to allow for incompleteness in the observed record, caused by various kinds of selection effect. (Incidentally, the absolute magnitude of a comet is the apparent magnitude it would have if seen from the earth and placed at a nominal distance of 1 AU from the earth and the sun; cf. equation 18.1, p.426).

The capture theory then predicted that a fraction F_c of these comets would be turned directly into short-period orbits with semi-major axes smaller than a, where (Russell 1920)

$$F_c \simeq \frac{4}{3} \left(\frac{M_J}{M_\odot} \right)^2 \left(\frac{a}{a_J} \right)^2 \tag{8.3}$$

Here, M_J is the mass of Jupiter (about $10^{-3} M_\odot$), $a_J \simeq 5.2\,\text{AU}$ is the semi-major axis of its orbit, and the approximation is valid for $a \gtrsim a_J$.

Setting $a = 50\,\text{AU}$, allowing a rather generous definition of a short-period orbit, showed that only about 1 comet in 10^4 should be directly captured. About 1% of these would have periods less than that of Jupiter (*i.e.* $a < a_J$, corresponding to $P < 12\,\text{yr}$), so the probability that a random new comet would be directly turned into a member of Jupiter's cometary family (Figure 8.2) is only about one in a million.

Lastly, since van Woerkom estimated that only $\simeq 40\%$ of the initial captures would be permanent (*loc. cit.*, p.471), the net rate of increase of the short-period comet population ($a < 50\,\text{AU}$) would be about $28 \times \frac{4}{3} \times 10^{-4} \times 0.4 \simeq 1.5 \times 10^{-3}\,\text{yr}^{-1}$. However, observations of the loss and decay rates of short-period comets indicated that they were disappearing at a rate of about 3 per century, greater than the rate of supply by a factor of at least 20. It thus appeared that the capture process was unable to sustain the observed number of short-period comets.

Russell (1920) had concluded that the discrepancy was most simply resolved by assuming that the excessive number of short-period comets was largely produced by the effects of cometary disruption induced by the action of Jupiter (*cf.* Alexander 1850, Bredichin 1889), but van Woerkom now investigated the alternative planetary explosion theory, which at this time was being strongly advocated by Vsekhsvyatski. Although he agreed that in principle the main orbital properties of short-period comets could be explained by such a hypothesis, van Woerkom now went further and investigated whether Vsekhsvyatski's then recent extension of the idea to explain *all* comets was tenable.

Unfortunately (at least for proponents of the explosion theory), the answer was in the negative. Van Woerkom proved, in fact, that unless the explosions were favourably directed Vsekhs-vyatski's theory should predict three times as many direct orbits as retrograde (*loc. cit.*, Figure 9). This was quite at variance with the observations of long-period comets (Figure 8.1, p.154), and he therefore concluded that the explosion theory could be used, at best, only to explain short-period comets.

It was now clear that even leaving aside the physical problems with the explosion theory, it could never provide a satisfactory explanation for the dominant group of long-period comets. Moreover, since the observed continuity in properties between long and short-period comets seemed to suggest that all comets had an essentially similar mode of origin, van Woerkom was therefore led to conclude that the planetary explosion idea, even for short-period comets, should be rejected.

Thus, van Woerkom's study had apparently ruled out all explanations for short-period comets: the capture theory was unable to explain their total number, assuming a steady-state population had been achieved; whilst the explosion theory completely failed to accommodate the long-period group. However, he did not entirely reject the capture hypothesis, and instead proposed several ways by which the size of the discrepancy might be reduced.

First, a severe difficulty with reliably determining the steady-state balance of short-period comets is that the result depends crucially on the observed disintegration rate or lifetime of such comets. This problem is aggravated by uncertain instrumental and observational selection effects, and by the fact that short-period comets clearly differ, one from another, in their intrinsic physical properties. The difficulty of determining the true number of short-period comets is also further complicated by the likelihood that the observed population might be a biased sample, including, for example, a few intrinsically faint comets that were discovered by chance during brief episodes of major outburst or flaring.

A second, related complication is that whereas periodic comets tend on the whole to be relatively faint objects, they do have more than one chance of being detected. By contrast, long-period comets with periods vastly greater than the historical timescale over which comets have been recorded, only ever have one chance of being seen. The result of this period-dependent selection effect is that, other things being equal, short-period comets are more likely to appear in the observational record.

A third effect is provided by the fact that the capture process may affect any comet with perihelion distance within Jupiter's orbit. But, because Jupiter lies well outside the normal zone of visibility for comets, the influx of parabolic and long-period comets in its neighbourhood could be much larger than that which would naïvely be expected from a simple extrapolation of the observed cometary flux.

Lastly (cf. Russell 1920), van Woerkom noted that a few comets had been observed to break up during their passage through the planetary system. It was therefore possible to envisage a modified form of the capture theory, in which an exceptionally massive progenitor comet of originally long period might occasionally break up to produce a whole family of 'daughter' comet nuclei, each of relatively short period.

Thus, provided that one was prepared to make certain additional assumptions, the apparent discrepancy between the observed and predicted number of short-period comets could in principle be resolved. On this basis van Woerkom next turned to consider the more fundamental question: the problem of the origin of the progenitor long-period group, whether solar system or interstellar.

8.2.4   LONG-PERIOD COMETS

Here, the problem was how to explain the observed distribution of $1/a$ values shown in Table 8.1 (p.155), particularly the near-parabolic excess and the subsequent slow decrease in comet numbers. Van Woerkom's primary contribution was to realize that the accumulation of small perturbations in $1/a$ at each revolution might be described by a process analogous to diffusion.

In this way he obtained a relatively simple model for the evolution of the $1/a$ distribution, and assuming a constant flux of incoming nearly parabolic orbits, was able to solve the relevant diffusion equation and predict the shape of the $1/a$ distribution as a function of time.

The situation is analogous to the conduction of heat along a metal bar. When the tip of the bar is first placed in a fire, only the end nearest the flames is heated, and the temperature profile resembles that of the $1/a$ distribution in Table 8.1, showing a sharp decline away from the 'hot' end, $1/a = 0$. However, if the end of the bar remains in the fire, the temperature profile gradually flattens out and becomes much smoother, eventually reaching an equilibrium in which the whole bar is probably too hot to handle. In this analogy, the distribution of temperature along the bar corresponds to the number of comets observed per unit interval of $1/a$, while the constant heat of the fire corresponds to the steady influx of nearly parabolic orbits with $1/a$ close to zero.

Writing the root-mean-square change in $1/a$ per revolution as σ_E (Section 8.2.2, p.161), van Woerkom showed that the equation to be solved has the form

$$\frac{\partial \nu}{\partial t} = \frac{1}{2}\frac{\sigma_E^2}{P(x)}\frac{\partial^2 \nu}{\partial x^2} \qquad (8.4)$$

where $\nu(x,t)$ is the number of comets passing perihelion per unit time with a given $1/a$-value, $P = 2\pi(GM_\odot)^{-1/2}a^{3/2}$ is the orbital period and $x \equiv 1/a$.

Here van Woerkom ignores any possible loss of comets by disintegration or decay during the diffusion process (corresponding, in the analogy, to the assumption of a well-lagged metal bar). Since it could also be shown that a comet in a nearly parabolic orbit will usually take only about a million years to evolve by diffusion into one with semi-major axis less than $100\,\mathrm{AU}$, during which time it might typically complete only about a hundred revolutions, van Woerkom believed that the 'no-decay' assumption was a good first approximation. Observations of short-period comets, for example, gave no evidence for significant changes in brightness over such a relatively small number of orbits.

The diffusion process could thus be seen as a mechanism for slowly converting 'new' nearly parabolic orbits into 'old' comets of relatively short period, as exemplified by the observed members of Jupiter's cometary family. The whole process was usually completed within a few million years, after which time the original comet would be destroyed by the cumulative effects of solar heating.

It should be emphasized, however, that cometary diffusion is not entirely a one-way affair. For every comet which diffuses all the way down to a short-period orbit, there are many more that will ultimately be ejected by Jupiter's perturbations into hyperbolic orbits, eventually to be removed from the confines of the solar system. In this way, viewed on a timescale greater than a few million years, the net effect of the planets (principally Jupiter) on incoming nearly parabolic orbits is to remove completely all incoming orbits, either by capture and subsequent decay or by ejection into interstellar space.

The solution of equation (8.4), assuming a constant influx of nearly parabolic orbits, was shown by van Woerkom to be

$$\nu(x,t) = B(1 + 4D\sqrt{x}/t)\exp(-4D\sqrt{x}/t) \qquad (8.5)$$

where B is a normalizing constant and the diffusion coefficient $D = 4\pi(GM_\odot)^{-1/2}/\sigma_E^2$. The form of this expression shows that after a time t very much longer than the characteristic diffusion time $t_D = 4D\sqrt{x}$ (roughly a million years for $x \simeq 10^{-2}\,\mathrm{AU}^{-1}$) the predicted $1/a$ distribution ought to evolve into a quasi-steady form with nearly equal numbers of comets in equal intervals of $1/a$ (cf. the metal bar analogy). This predicted behaviour is completely contrary to the sharp decrease and slow subsequent decline illustrated in Table 8.1.

In this way, van Woerkom showed that the predicted steady-state $1/a$ distribution completely disagreed with observations, unless the diffusion process was somehow still at an early stage.

But this would imply that comets had been subject to the diffusion process at most for a few million years, which not only ruled out a primordial solar system model, but also eliminated the possibility of steady comet capture from a diffuse interstellar field.

Van Woerkom's study thus compounded the difficulties (see Section 7.3.1, p.142) of explaining how primordial comets could survive for the age of the solar system. Even if comets were somehow to survive physical disruption indefinitely, it was clear that they would still be eliminated from the solar system within a time much shorter than its age by the action of relatively straightforward dynamical processes. The long-period comets could neither have originated, nor could they remain, in their observed orbits.

One possible solution to the problem was to assume that long-period comets had somehow been formed originally in orbits with perihelia well outside the range of Jupiter's orbit. In this case, the expected mean change in $1/a$ per revolution would be smaller (equation 8.1), which in turn would lead to a much longer diffusion time t_D. However, if such comets were to be brought into the observable region, they would necessarily have to experience planetary perturbations in order to change their perihelion distances, and these would inevitably act so as to broaden the observed $1/a$ distribution, flattening it in a way quite inconsistent with observations. Van Woerkom therefore reluctantly concluded that comets could not have had a solar system origin.

8.2.5   THE PARADOX

This led him finally to consider the interstellar hypothesis. Here, there were two extreme cases: continuous capture from a diffuse interstellar field of comets, as Laplace had originally envisaged; or recently-finished capture from a dense local concentration of comets, as proposed by Bobrovnikoff (1929a,b).

Strictly speaking, the first case (which had recently been

erroneously reintroduced by Daghlian 1937) had already been eliminated by the argument based on the $1/a$ distribution, since any process which operated on a timescale substantially longer than a few million years would inevitably tend to produce a much flatter $1/a$ distribution than observed.

Nevertheless, van Woerkom still considered the possibility, and confirmed Schiaparelli's conclusion that in order to avoid a strong hyperbolic excess (not observed) it was necessary on the model to postulate not only that the sun was moving through the interstellar field with a remarkably small relative velocity ($\lesssim 1\,\mathrm{km\,s^{-1}}$) but also that the comets themselves had to have an extremely small velocity dispersion (loc. cit., Table 6). This seemed a most unlikely combination of circumstances, especially as such a comet cloud, moving so nearly exactly with the sun, would almost certainly be quickly disrupted by perturbations from passing stars or the galactic differential rotation. Although the generally flattened, rotating structure of the Galaxy had by this time been appreciated for about twenty years (Oort 1927a), this seems to have been the first hint of its potential significance for theories of cometary origin (cf. Armellini 1922).

However, the position with regard to Bobrovnikoff's interstellar hypothesis hardly seemed any better. Planetary capture, necessary in order to convert originally hyperbolic orbits into elliptical types, was such a rare event that an exceptionally dense comet cloud had to be postulated in order to trap a sufficient number; and even then it would only work if the relative velocity and velocity dispersion of the cloud were both kept extremely small (loc. cit., Table 7). These arguments combined to eliminate the interstellar hypothesis.

Van Woerkom had thus arrived at an impasse. By assuming that all comets had essentially the same origin he had ruled out the planetary explosion hypothesis, whereas arguments based on the $1/a$ distribution and the efficiency of the capture mechanism also eliminated both the primordial solar system hypothesis and the possibility of capture from an interstellar field. If these arguments were accepted, comets should not exist!

The time was ripe for new ideas, and when, almost simultaneously with the appearance of van Woerkom's paper, Lyttleton (1948) presented a completely new theory for cometary origin, highlighting a possible loop-hole in the above argument, it seemed that there might be much to be said for the new idea.

8.3   Lyttleton's accretion theory

8.3.1   ACCRETION PROCESS

Lyttleton's proposal was a novel variant of the interstellar hypothesis. He emphasized the presence of large numbers of interstellar dust clouds in the Galaxy and the fact that comets appeared to be mere aggregations of small meteoric particles similar to the dust observed in interstellar space, and argued that one could make a direct link between the two classes of body. In particular, he argued that if the sun were to pass through an interstellar dust cloud with relative velocity V, its gravitational field would act to focus the hyperbolic trajectories of the dust grains on to the axis of symmetry described by the sun's past path through the cloud. This process is illustrated in Figure 8.4.

The concentration of grains towards the axis of symmetry inevitably produced an enhanced rate of dissipative grain-grain collisions on the axis, and he calculated that depending on precisely where the collisions occurred, a fraction of the original kinetic energy of the grains relative to the sun could be radiated away. It was thus possible for the originally hyperbolic orbits of the grains to be converted into bound elliptical types, thereby allowing the grains to be captured by the solar system. In this way, Lyttleton predicted that interstellar dust grains could be captured by the solar system in the form of a dense accretion stream, having an axis directed parallel to the sun's past path relative to the dust cloud.

Capture would only occur, however, if the collisions were sufficiently violent to dissipate the excess hyperbolic energy of

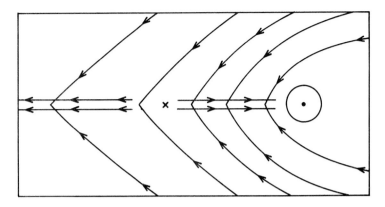

Figure 8.4: The mechanism of Lyttleton's accretion theory. Here, X denotes the position of the neutral point (at a distance $r_0 = 1.25\,GM_\odot/V^2$; Lyttleton, 1953a), while the circle about the sun shows the relative size of Jupiter's orbit for the representative case of $V = 5\,\mathrm{km\,s^{-1}}$.

the grains, corresponding to the relative speed V of the cloud at infinity. This meant that capture could only affect those particles which happened initially to pass quite close to the sun, and therefore with trajectories that crossed the accretion stream within a critical heliocentric distance r_0. The size of r_0, the so-called 'neutral point' of the stream (dividing regions of inflow from outflow), depends on the exact physical parameters of the interaction and on how the stream is originally set up. Nevertheless, it can readily be shown (e.g. Lyttleton 1953a) that r_0 is always on the order of the accretion radius R_A, given by

$$R_A = GM_\odot/V^2 \tag{8.6}$$

For $V = 10\,\mathrm{km\,s^{-1}}$ this is only about 9 AU, suggesting that encounters with interstellar clouds will not usually produce comets in very long-period orbits, but if V is relatively small (less than about $1\,\mathrm{km\,s^{-1}}$) initial orbits with semi-major axes up to $\approx 10^3$ AU might in principle be produced.

The theory's detailed development also showed that the density in the accretion stream should correspond to a steady-state mass per unit length of the order of

$$\mu = 2\pi\rho\,(GM_\odot/V^2)^2 \qquad (8.7)$$

where ρ denotes the ambient density of the interstellar dust cloud. The speed of the inflowing material in the stream can also be calculated at any point, and may be shown to be approximately equal to the free-fall speed of a particle dropped from the neutral point towards the sun. In practice, the flow speed will be a little less than this, due to the outward momentum imparted by new dust grains entering the stream. In general, therefore, one would normally expect that any comets which formed in the stream would have semi-major axes $a \lesssim R_A/2$.

The inspiration for this new idea came from the realms of stellar astronomy, referring particularly to the investigations of Hoyle & Lyttleton (1942) and Bondi & Hoyle (1944) concerning stellar evolution. These authors had originally proposed the accretion mechanism as a means by which old, evolved stars might develop a structure comprising an outer layer of light, relatively pure hydrogen lying on top of an inner core of denser material of higher molecular weight containing the end-products of nuclear burning. It appeared that the presence of such a chemical composition discontinuity was necessary in order to explain the evolution of ordinary stars into red giants (*e.g.* Bondi & Bondi 1950), and though the details of the accretion process in relation to stars were somewhat different from the situation now proposed by Lyttleton to explain comets, it seemed that the general process must be one which actually occurred in Nature.

The theory was notable too in that it was the first simultaneously to address both aspects of the question of cometary origin: where they come from and how they are made, the last most often being ignored. Moreover, in appealing to a conceptually simple model for comet formation, the theory naturally lent itself to subsequent detailed studies, and in this way stimulated a large body of research.

Nevertheless, despite this apparently auspicious start, there were several difficulties which had to be overcome before the theory could be regarded as providing a viable explanation of observed comets. First, assuming that a steady-state accretion stream could indeed be set up, it had to be shown that comet-like bodies would necessarily form in the inflowing material. Secondly, contrary to the requirements for red-giant formation, it was important to show that the newly-formed comets would in fact *not* fall on to the sun. Moreover, the problem ought properly to include consideration of a gas-and-dust cloud, rather than a pure dust cloud as envisaged by Lyttleton. Thirdly, because the accretion stream departs strongly from spherical symmetry, any protocomets formed therein would tend to have aphelia which clustered strongly towards particular regions of the sky. Thus, it had to be shown why observed comets appeared to be distributed so nearly randomly (*cf.* Figure 8.1, p.154). Finally, one had to explain how the $1/a$ distribution acquired its present peculiar form (Table 8.1), and why, in particular, so many comets appeared to come from distances far greater than that, R_A, of the neutral point.

8.3.2 CONDENSATION PROBLEM

In order to account for the formation of comets in the accretion stream, Lyttleton assumed that in reality the flow would contain numerous small-scale irregularities and inhomogeneities. These, he suggested, could ultimately be attributed to slight variations in the density of the original cloud, and their effect on the stream would be to act as local centres of attraction for the production of small condensations or protocomets.

As the stream flowed in towards the sun, the picture for comet formation thus resembled the break-up into drops of a thin stream of water from a tap. By requiring that a small element of the stream (of length d, say) should be able to contract by self-gravity against the disruptive tidal gravitational field of the sun, he found that the length d of the protocomet had to be smaller than a certain limit, d_{max}, given by

$$d_{max}(R) \simeq 2(\mu R^3/M_\odot)^{\frac{1}{2}} \qquad (8.8)$$

where R is the distance of the point in question from the sun.

The maximum mass of the condensations should thus satisfy $m_c < \mu \, d_{max}$. Substituting for μ from equation (8.7) and setting $R \simeq R_A$, we find that this reduces to

$$m_c \lesssim 4\sqrt{2} \, \pi^{3/2} \rho^{3/2} G^{9/2} M_\odot^4 \, V^{-9} \simeq 10^{17} \, (1 \, \text{km s}^{-1}/V)^9 \, \text{kg} \quad (8.9)$$

where the numerical coefficient assumes $\rho = 10^{-22} \, \text{kg m}^{-3}$ (*cf.* Lyttleton 1953a).

This expression shows that the maximum mass of any cometary condensations which the accretion stream might produce is extremely sensitive to the assumed value of the velocity V of the sun with respect to the dust cloud. In particular, we note that unless V is quite small, the accretion theory has difficulty in explaining even the average cometary mass ($\approx 2 \times 10^{14} \, \text{kg}$, *e.g.* Fernández 1982a), let alone that of the largest members of the cometary population.

Allowing for the gradual decrease in R during the time needed for collapse to occur, the above limit on d, and hence m_c too, ought probably to be taken as somewhat less than the above values, but in any case it did appear that the stream might separate into a number of discrete segments as it fell in towards the sun. Lyttleton therefore suggested that these condensations should be identified with observed comets, and since at this time (1948) comets were still frequently considered to be swarms of meteoric dust (*e.g.* Russell *et al.* 1926, p.442; Watson 1948), this prediction was regarded as a major success of the theory.

8.3.3 ANGULAR MOMENTUM PROBLEM

A more difficult problem, however, was how to arrange for the newly-formed comets to gain enough 'sideways' motion to avoid falling into the sun. Here, Lyttleton discussed three main possibilities: first, that the protocomets were perturbed by a passing star on their approach to the sun; secondly, that they might suffer a close encounter with one of the planets; and thirdly, that the accretion stream as a whole might have some net angular momentum. This was thought to arise inevitably as a consequence of the existence of planets in the solar system since, depending on the relative positions of the planets in relation to the sun, the barycentre (or centre of gravity) of the solar system, towards which the stream would be initially directed, might sometimes lie just outside the solar surface.

Lyttleton (e.g. 1948, 1953a, 1963a) considered the last of these possibilities to be the most important, and at the time his argument seems generally to have been accepted (e.g. Bondi 1953, McCrea 1953, Richter 1963, p.150). However, it is easy to show that this mechanism cannot work because, even under the most favourable circumstances, the perihelion distances of all comets formed in the stream would lie deep within the solar interior. Whipple (1963) and Öpik (1966a) both mention this difficulty with the accretion theory, and even Lyttleton (e.g. 1968a, p.166) later appeared to accept that his original solution to the problem was inadequate.

Although it was not immediately recognized, therefore, the angular momentum problem could in principle only be resolved by appealing to unlikely close encounters between the newly formed comets and other massive bodies (such as stars or planets) or by making substantial modifications to the original accretion scheme. For example, Gething (1951), McCrea (1953) and Lyttleton (1968a) all developed the idea that underlying irregularities in the surrounding cloud might ultimately generate the required deviations from exact axial symmetry, but in this case the assumption that a steady-state accretion stream would develop became much harder to justify (Gething 1951).

Moreover, if inhomogeneities were really an essential part of the process, it seemed much less likely that significant amounts of hydrogen could fall on to other stars (Gething 1951). This therefore removed one of the major independent arguments in favour of the theory (cf. Bondi 1953). In this connexion, Lyttleton's theory also made no mention of the effects of gas-dynamical processes on the development of the accretion stream. When these are taken into account, it is not at all certain that a simple accretion stream would ever be set up (*cf.* Öpik 1966a).

Setting these criticisms aside, however, the angular momentum of observed comets has continued to be a major difficulty for the accretion theory to overcome. Lyttleton (*e.g.* 1975) has subsequently considered other ways by which comets might gain sufficient angular momentum to have perihelia on the order of a few astronomical units, but the theory has never been properly developed to take full account of this difficulty.

8.3.4   DIRECTIONAL DIFFICULTIES

Finally, assuming that observable comets do somehow originate in the accretion stream and that they do get endowed with sufficient angular momentum to avoid plunging into the sun, it is still necessary to explain how they came to be distributed more or less isotropically in space, with such a concentration of orbital energies towards the parabolic limit.

With respect to the first of these observations, Lyttleton (*e.g.* 1948, 1953a) believed that the general isotropy could be explained by appealing to many past encounters of the solar system with interstellar clouds. However, in accepting this possibility no complete explanation of the observed $1/a$ distribution was provided, except possibly that it might be due to a combination of observational selection effects (*e.g.* Lyttleton 1953b, 1974).

But if planetary and stellar perturbations had managed to randomize the long-period cometary orbits in a way consistent with observations, it would also be necessary to take account of van Woerkom's argument (see also Kendall 1961), which implied that the observed sharply-peaked $1/a$ distribution (Table 8.1) could certainly not result from such a process. Moreover, unless the relative sun-cloud velocity V is taken to be very small, the distance of the neutral point from the sun (roughly $GM_\odot/V^2$) is far too small for the theory to accommodate the preponderance of very long-period comets in the observed sample.   Aust &

Woolfson (1973) have subsequently pointed out that sufficiently small values of V are, in fact, impossible to achieve, since the self-gravity of any substantial gas cloud would cause the sun always to pass through the cloud itself with a significant speed at least of order several $km\,s^{-1}$.

In continuing to develop the accretion theory, Lyttleton (e.g. 1963b, 1968b, 1970, 1974, 1985) has largely ignored these difficulties, and instead has confined his attention almost exclusively to criticizing alternative explanations of the problematical $1/a$ distribution (cf. Section 9.1.5, p.192). In the eyes of contemporary astronomers, on the other hand, these difficulties for the accretion theory are not by any means peripheral, and represent a very serious problem for the underlying picture. Although the theory was undoubtedly timely and astrophysically relevant, therefore, it has so far failed to provide any lasting solution to the issues it was set up to resolve.

8.3.5   END OF AN ERA

In this way, by the end of 1948 the paradoxical rejection by van Woerkom of all existing theories had apparently been superseded by a new interstellar hypothesis: Lyttleton's accretion theory. At first, there were no completely secure arguments against the idea, and one might generally have expected it to expand into the vacuum which had arisen. However, the model was never generally accepted, and instead, just thirteen months after publication of van Woerkom's paper, the solar system vs. interstellar debate received a push in another direction.

This occurred with the publication in 1950 of a new solar system hypothesis by the Dutch astronomer Oort. This was specifically geared to explaining the peculiar $1/a$ distribution and the parabolic excess. Oort's paper, which was to dominate the field for more than three decades, is generally regarded as a 'classic', both in its scope and influence, and it is appropriate therefore that we should discuss it at some length.

The year 1950 thus marks a significant watershed in the history of cometary astronomy. The many new concepts and ideas generated about this time combined in large measure not only to lay the foundations for many recent developments in the subject but also to anticipate the directions of much modern research. Oort's paper therefore closed the door on a half-century of uncertainty on cometary origins, and cleared the way to a hopeful new era of rapid advance and understanding.

9

Primordial cloud

"You can do only one thing well at a time."

J.H. Oort.

9.1　Birth of a theory

Oort's proposal was simply that the solar system is surrounded by a huge primordial swarm of comets, containing around 10^{11} average-sized cometary nuclei moving in orbits extending more than halfway to the nearest star. This hypothesis appeared in January 1950, and the general picture seems to have had such immediate and widespread appeal (*cf.* Merton 1951) that it was quickly accepted by the astronomical community as providing the basis of a model on which the remaining problems of cometary origin might be overcome.

The logic of Oort's (1950) argument may be broadly separated into four strands: proof that the solar system is surrounded by a huge cometary cloud; discussion of the importance of stellar perturbations in determining the cloud's structure and evolution of the long-period orbits within it; interpretation of the $1/a$ distribution on this model; and lastly, addressing the important question of the cloud's origin, the presentation of a theory of comet formation based on the idea of a common origin for all bodies in the solar system.

In this section, we first review these various aspects of Oort's paper, highlighting their relative strengths and weaknesses, and then briefly introduce the other major concepts and ideas on cometary origin which were proposed at about the same time. The period around 1950 thus lays the ground for a more detailed discussion of theories of cometary origin up to the present day.

9.1.1   OORT'S IDEA TAKES SHAPE

Oort began by considering the data for 19 long-period comets for which so-called 'original' orbits had been calculated. An original orbit is one for which the effects of known perturbations have been rigorously subtracted from the observed motion, so that the inferred orbital elements provide an accurate description of the comet's motion before it first entered the planetary system.

Although the original orbits of these comets are among the most accurate available, it is important to realize that they can never be entirely free from error. For example, though they all include corrections for the known effects of planetary perturbations, it is exceedingly difficult to make accurate estimates of the various non-gravitational forces which also affect comets. These arise principally as a result of the 'jet-reaction' on the nucleus, caused by the ejection of gas and dust from the comet around perihelion passage. Only a handful of long-period comets have been sufficiently well observed for the effects of non-gravitational forces to be incorporated into the detailed determination of the original orbit.

The original values of $1/a$ determined in this way provide the principal raw data on which discussions of the immediate provenance of a comet may be based. Oort found that of the 19 then most accurately known original orbits (mean errors less than 100×10^{-6} AU^{-1} in $1/a$), more than half had original $1/a$ values less than 50×10^{-6} AU^{-1}. Furthermore, none had $1/a$ greater than 750×10^{-6} AU^{-1}.

The degree of concentration of these comets towards the parabolic limit was even harder to explain than van Woerkom's $1/a$ distribution (Table 8.1, p.155): even one revolution through the planetary system should have broadened the peak by an amount of order $\sigma_E \simeq 1000 \times 10^{-6}$ AU^{-1}, greater than the whole range covered by the original $1/a$ values of Oort's 19 comets. The conclusion was inescapable: the majority of the 19 comets with well-determined orbits must never have previously passed through the inner planetary system.

Range of $1/a$ (10^{-6} AU^{-1})	Number of comets
−50–0	2
0–50	8
50–100	4
100–150	1
150–200	1
200–250	1
250–500	1
500–750	1

Table 9.1: Distribution of original $1/a$ values for 19 accurately known orbits, after Oort (1950, Table 1).

The exact distribution of these 19 original $1/a$ values is shown in Table 9.1 (*cf.* Sinding 1948), which shows that more than half of the sample must have come from distances in excess of 4×10^4 AU, or more than half a light-year! Oort pointed out that the mean value of $1/a$ for the ten comets making up the first two rows of the table corresponded to a value of the major axis of order 10^5 AU, thus giving the first direct indication that the home of the comets extends nearly halfway to the nearest star. The two comets with slightly negative $1/a$ values, (*i.e.* with apparently weakly hyperbolic original orbits), are probably the result of observational error or the neglect of non-gravitational forces.

The problem of explaining the parabolic excess was now more acute than ever. First, following van Woerkom, Oort rejected the idea of an origin in interstellar space, and therefore was led to concentrate on the primordial solar system hypothesis. Although the extreme narrowness of the 'spike' in the $1/a$ distribution posed great difficulties for this theory, Oort

Figure 9.1: Globular cluster Messier 13 in Hercules. This illustrates the appearance of the Oort cloud as if viewed from outside. Note the roughly spherical shape and the rapid rise in the density towards the centre.

was now foremost in realizing that the observations might be explained if one could identify a process which scattered previously invisible comets of large perihelion distance into orbits that passed close to the sun, through the zone of visibility.

Three possibilities were discussed: planetary perturbations, resistance of a dense interplanetary medium, and stellar perturbations. The first had already been rejected by van Woerkom, since such perturbations would also greatly increase the spread of the $1/a$ distribution, contrary to observations. The second, that of a hypothetical resisting medium, seemed equally implausible, and in any case would not have the desired effect: it would preferentially reduce the aphelia, leaving the perihelia relatively unchanged. The last possibility however, that of stellar pertur-

bations, seemed more promising. In this way Oort rediscovered
the potential importance of stellar perturbations for the evolution of long-period cometary orbits, and his subsequent analysis
both extended and confirmed that of Öpik (1932).

Oort's hypothesis had thus taken shape. The original $1/a$
values indicated that most long-period comets come from a vast
region of space extending to distances at least of order 10^5 AU
from the sun, while the overall isotropy of the cometary population indicated that the comet swarm must be almost spherical.
A schematic representation of the Oort cloud as if viewed from
outside is shown in Figure 9.1.

The orbital periods of these comets ranged up to at least
30 Myr, during which time there was a reasonable probability
that one or more neighbouring stars would pass, by chance,
through the region of the cloud. The effect of such stellar encounters, while individually lasting only a relatively short time
(10^4–10^5 yr), was to give each comet a small impulse, or change
in velocity, amounting typically to a few metres per second. Such
a small impulse could never significantly change the orbital energy of a comet (and hence its $1/a$ value), but due to the 'lever-
age' effect of the comet's distance from the sun a significant
angular momentum change *could* occur.

Two effects combined to produce a sensitive dependence of
the change in angular momentum per revolution on a comet's
semi-major axis. First, the length of the 'lever' was simply
proportional to the length, $2a$, of the orbit; and secondly, the
strength of the impulse depended on the distance of the closest
approach of a star to either the sun or comet. Other things
being equal, the comets of longest period would experience the
largest number of stellar encounters per revolution, so the closest stellar passage during a single orbit would be smallest for
these comets of longest period. Thus, not only would the comets of greatest semi-major axis receive the largest cumulative
change in velocity during a single orbital period, but this velocity change also acted as if on a lever of longer average length. In
this way, the effect of stellar perturbations on cometary orbits

was found to increase sharply with the value of the semi-major axis. In particular, Oort's detailed results showed that comets with $a < 3 \times 10^4$ AU were relatively 'safe' from such effects, while those with $a > 3 \times 10^4$ AU would suffer significant changes in perihelion distance.

In this way, whereas van Woerkom had shown that planetary perturbations would systematically remove comets from the zone of visibility on the relatively short timescale of a few million years or so, the losses could be recuperated provided there were enough comets in orbits of sufficiently long period ($a \gtrsim 3 \times 10^4$ AU) and large perihelia ($q \gtrsim 15$ AU) that stellar perturbations could efficiently drive them into the inner planetary system. Oort's cloud was thus established. Not only did it provide a ready explanation of how to maintain a more or less steady flux of 'new' nearly parabolic orbits, thereby explaining the narrow spike of the $1/a$ distribution, but it also retained the attractive physical assumption of a primordial solar system origin. The general picture was clearly similar to the ideas which had been contemplated previously by Schiaparelli and others during the nineteenth century (e.g. Peirce 1849; cf. Young 1898), and then later by Armellini, Öpik and Russell during the nineteen-twenties and thirties; but Oort was nevertheless the first to quantify the hypothesis and put it on to a firm footing.

9.1.2 DETAILED MODEL

In essence, on the Oort cloud hypothesis one envisages a spherically symmetrical cloud of comets, with the sun at centre, in which the velocities of the comets are directed almost completely randomly. The outer radius of the cloud was estimated to be on the order of $R_0 \simeq 2 \times 10^5$ AU, and since the orbital velocities were randomized by the effects of stellar perturbations the cloud was assumed to contain comets with almost all orbital types, ranging from examples of nearly circular orbits (both direct and retrograde) to ones of almost parabolic form. In this respect, the structure of the overall model has close similarities to a spherical gas cloud, or perhaps more accurately (since comets hardly ever collide with each other), a spherical star cluster like the globular cluster shown in Figure 9.1.

In addition to spherical symmetry and isotropy of the velocity distribution, Oort had to make one further assumption in order to completely determine the model. This concerned the assumed distribution of orbital energies within the cloud, or equivalently the distribution of comets in the imaginary three-dimensional velocity space associated with each point in the cloud at a distance r from the sun. Such an assumption was necessary in order to evaluate the relative number of comets at each heliocentric distance r and the radial variation in the cometary number density $n_c(r)$.

The analogy of a gas cloud in equilibrium under solar gravity may help to clarify the need for this requirement. In such a case a little thought shows that the density distribution of a very cold gas should be quite different from that of a similar mass of gas confined to the same volume at a higher temperature. In particular, a cold gas will tend to settle much lower down in the potential well, giving a strong enhancement of the gas density near the centre, while a hot gas will tend to be much less centrally condensed. In the same way, a model of the Oort cloud in which the comets have large orbital energies (corresponding to a 'hot' velocity distribution) will tend to be less centrally condensed than one dominated by comets in more tightly bound orbits. Thus, the density distribution of the comet cloud is inextricably linked with the distribution of the cometary velocities within it.

As a simple first approximation to the velocity distribution, Oort suggested that it should have a form such that the comets at any heliocentric distance r should be distributed uniformly in velocity space, up to a maximum value

$$v_{\max}(r) = \left[2GM_\odot\left(\frac{1}{r} - \frac{1}{R_0}\right)\right]^{1/2} \tag{9.1}$$

corresponding to the speed of free-fall of a comet dropped from the cloud's outer edge R_0 to the given radius r. Although this approximation is unlikely to be strictly accurate at all radii, especially close to R_0 (cf. Serafin 1988), this assumption allowed several simple, yet powerful results to be derived.

Since the cloud is in dynamical equilibrium (not expanding or contracting) with an isotropic velocity distribution, one may use the usual law of hydrostatic balance for gases to determine the cloud's internal density distribution $n_c(r)$. The law of hydrostatic equilibrium may be written in the form

$$\frac{dP}{dr} = -\rho\,g \tag{9.2}$$

where $P(r) = \frac{1}{3}\rho\overline{v^2}$ is the effective kinetic 'pressure' of the comets treated according to the kinetic theory of gases, $\rho(r) = n_c m_c$ is their density as a function of radius, and $g = GM_\odot/r^2$ is the inwardly directed gravitational acceleration at r. For the particular velocity distribution assumed by Oort (a uniform density of comets in velocity space up to v_{max}), it may readily be shown that the mean-square velocity dispersion $\overline{v^2}(r) = \frac{3}{5}v_{max}^2$. This can be substituted into equation (9.2) and the result then used to determine the cometary number density $n_c(r)$.

In this way (cf. Bailey 1983a), Oort showed that the number density of comets could be written in the form

$$n_c(r) = A\left(\frac{R_0}{r} - 1\right)^{3/2} \tag{9.3}$$

where the normalizing constant A, proportional to the total number of comets, may be determined by comparing the predicted near-parabolic flux with that observed. This equation shows that the density distribution in Oort's original model is approximately a power law: $n_c \propto r^{-3/2}$ ($r \ll R_0$).

Comparing the predicted near-parabolic flux with that observed (essentially the rate of addition of new comets to the observed 'spike' in the $1/a$ distribution), gave $A \simeq 10^{-5}\,\mathrm{AU}^{-3}$, assuming the cloud's outer radius was $R_0 \simeq 2 \times 10^5\,\mathrm{AU}$ (Oort

1950, equation 24). Another choice for the outer radius of the cloud would give a different value for the normalizing constant, A, since it may be shown (Bailey 1983a) that the latter is proportional to $R_0^{-3/2}$.

The total number of comets can now be obtained by integrating equation (9.3) over the entire volume of the cloud contained within the radius R_0. This gives $N_0 \simeq \pi^2 A R_0^3/4$, which reduces to $N_0 \simeq 2 \times 10^{11}$, using Oort's value for the outer radius. The form of the cloud's density distribution (equation 9.3) indicates that in this model, although the density increases inwards, the majority of comets lie in weakly bound orbits concentrated close to the outer radius R_0.

In order better to appreciate the dimensions of the Oort cloud, it is sometimes helpful to think in terms of a scale model. If the size of the earth's orbit were reduced to that of a typical football pitch, with the sun at centre, the observed comets would appear to come as if from distances of order 10^4 km; that is (seen from Europe) as if from Australia. If we recall that the cometary velocities are directed completely randomly, a little thought will persuade one that the chance of any one comet at such a distance having a velocity pointing sufficiently close to the sun to be seen must be extremely small, a result which goes some way to explaining why such a huge number of hypothetical comets ($\approx 10^{11}$) is needed on Oort's model simply in order to explain the observed cometary influx (≈ 1 per annum).

In this way, Oort's model provided the basis for explaining the observed influx of nearly parabolic orbits, thus overcoming van Woerkom's primary objection to a primordial solar system hypothesis. Moreover, since the flux of new, nearly parabolic orbits within 15 AU of the sun was only on the order of 10 per annum, even if these were completely removed from the cloud (as indeed seems likely, due to planetary perturbations or decay), the total number of comets lost, even over the whole age of the solar system, would still be only a relatively small proportion of the whole. Thus, a primordial cloud, if it existed, appeared able to survive for the age of the solar system.

9.1.3   STELLAR PERTURBATIONS

However, in addition to shuffling the perihelion distances of the long-period comets, stellar perturbations also introduce small, random changes in the cometary binding energies or $1/a$ values. Although these changes in $1/a$ are certainly negligible from the standpoint of significantly broadening the observed $1/a$-distribution (*e.g.* Le Poole & Katgert 1968), they nevertheless do have important long-term effects.

These are primarily of two kinds: first, a tendency to systematically transfer energy to the orbiting comets, leading to a gradual expansion of their orbits and hence to removal of comets to interstellar space; and secondly, a steady shuffling of the cometary energies in a random fashion, leading to net loss of comets by a gradual accumulation of energy analogous to a random walk. This process is negligible on the timescale of a typical orbital period, but integrated over the age of the solar system it has an overall effect comparable in size to the first.

The evolution of the cometary energies under the influence of external stellar perturbations can thus be likened to the profit of a gambler playing with loaded dice. In the long run, though some comets will gain and others lose, the average orbital energies will gradually increase, ultimately leading to the removal of comets beyond the outer boundary R_0.

The source of the two effects may be understood by considering the change in kinetic energy of comet after it has received a small impulse Δv due to a random stellar perturbation. If the comet's initial velocity is v, that after the impulse will be $v + \Delta v$. Hence, the change in kinetic energy may be written in the form simply

$$\Delta E = \frac{1}{2}(v + \Delta v)^2 - \frac{1}{2}v^2 = \frac{1}{2}(\Delta v)^2 + v.\Delta v \qquad (9.4)$$

Since the directions of v and Δv are uncorrelated, the second term averages to zero, while the first (usually smaller) energy change always has a positive sign.

In this way, the cumulative effects of stellar perturbations, both systematic and random, raise the important question of whether the weakly-bound comets which dominate the conventional 1950-model of the Oort cloud can survive as permanent members of the solar system. This is a crucial, potentially fatal criticism of the model, and the possibility led Oort to make a detailed study of the rate at which stars gradually transfer energy to the comets in the cloud.

9.1.4 ENERGY TRANSFER RATE

Oort's analysis of the effect of stellar perturbations used the 'impulse approximation', in which both the sun and comet are assumed to be relatively at rest during the rapid passage of a nearby star. If we consider a star of mass M_* passing the sun with velocity $\mathbf{V}_*$, with impact parameters $\mathbf{b}$ and $\mathbf{d}$ with respect to the sun and comet respectively (using the notation of Bailey 1983a), the net change in the velocity of the comet referred to the sun is given by

$$\Delta\mathbf{v} \equiv \Delta\mathbf{v}_c - \Delta\mathbf{v}_\odot = \frac{2GM_*}{dV_*}\,\hat{\mathbf{d}} - \frac{2GM_*}{bV_*}\,\hat{\mathbf{b}} \qquad (9.5)$$

where $\hat{\mathbf{b}}$ and $\hat{\mathbf{d}}$ are unit vectors directed towards the points of closest approach of the star to the sun and comet respectively. This expression enables the 'tidal' influence of stellar perturbations on the sun-comet system to be calculated.

The mean energy transfer rate, $\dot{\varepsilon}_*$, may be obtained by squaring equation (9.5), multiplying by the frequency of each type of encounter, summing over all possible encounters and averaging the result around a representative orbit with semi-major axis a and eccentricity e. The details of the calculation are rather complicated, but assuming the orbit in question has $e \simeq 1$ the results of Oort (1950) and those of later authors (e.g. Shteins & Sture 1962, Nezhinskij 1972, Yabushita 1972b, Yabushita et al. 1982, Bailey 1983a, 1986a,b; Weinberg *et al.* 1986, Hut & Tremaine 1985) may be closely approximated by a relatively simple expression of the form (Bailey 1986b,c)

$$\dot{\varepsilon}_* = \frac{4\pi G^2 M_*^2 n_*}{V_*} \begin{cases} (a/a_c)^2 & a \leq a_c \\ 2\ln(a/a_c) + 1 & a \geq a_c \end{cases} \tag{9.6}$$

Here a_c is a parameter given by $a_c = b_{min}\sqrt{12/7}$, where $b_{min} = (2\pi n_* V_* T)^{-1/2}$ is the minimum expected impact parameter for a stellar encounter during a time T, and n_* is the mean number of stars per unit volume averaged along the solar orbit during the same time.

The values of the parameters entering this expression are usually assumed to be $n_* \simeq 0.1\,\mathrm{pc}^{-3}$, $M_* \simeq 0.7\,M_\odot$, and $V_* \simeq 20\text{--}60\,\mathrm{km\,s}^{-1}$ (*e.g.* Oort 1950, Sekanina 1968, Rickman 1976, Weissman 1980a, Bailey 1983a). However, the recent compilation of local stellar densities by Bahcall & Soneira (1980) gives $\langle n_* M_*^2 \rangle \simeq 0.03\,M_\odot^2\,\mathrm{pc}^{-3}$, and if this is increased by a factor of order 4/3 for use in the above formula (to allow for the effects of close binaries amongst the field stars; Rickman 1976, Fernández 1980b), we obtain $\langle n_* M_*^2 \rangle \simeq 0.04 \pm 0.01\,M_\odot^2\,\mathrm{pc}^{-3}$. Adopting this average value for $n_* M_*^2$ in equation (9.6) together with a mean relative velocity $V_* \simeq 30\,\mathrm{km\,s}^{-1}$ thus gives a value for the mean stellar energy transfer rate at $a \simeq 10^5\,\mathrm{AU}$ of order $10^{-13}\,\mathrm{m^2 s^{-3}}$, averaged over the age $T = 4.5 \times 10^9\,\mathrm{yr}$ of the solar system. The total net relative velocity change of such a comet is thus on the order of 170 m s^{-1}, rather larger than the range 110–150 m s^{-1} often quoted (*e.g.* Weissman 1980a, 1985a).

A rough estimate of the semi-major axes of comets that are likely to be significantly affected by stellar perturbations during the age of the solar system may now be obtained simply by multiplying the mean energy transfer rate by the age of the solar system and comparing it with the energy $GM_\odot/2a$ needed to unbind an initial orbit with semi-major axis a. Equating this value of a to $R_0/2$ thus gives a rough estimate of the outer radius of a primordial cloud.

This kind of argument was used by Oort to show that the outer boundary of the comet cloud was on the order of $R_0 \simeq 2 \times 10^5$ AU, but in a footnote to his original article, prompted by van Woerkom's comments, it was remarked that this first estimate should be revised downwards to about 10^5 AU. Allowing for a further factor of 3/2, due to Oort's use of 3×10^9 yr for the age of the solar system, would produce a final figure for the cloud's outer radius R_0 of around 6.5×10^4 AU, substantially less than the usually quoted value of 2×10^5 AU! This reduced value, however, is in good agreement with that obtained on the same basis from equation (9.6).

In concluding this discussion, we mention that (following Oort) this calculation ignores the effect of the second, 'random walk' term in the expression for ΔE. Later work (*e.g.* Clube & Napier 1982a, Bailey 1983a, 1986a) has shown that in fact the second factor cannot be entirely ignored, and that when this is included, slightly smaller values still are obtained for the outer 'radius' of the cloud (see Section 12.2, p.254).

This work has shown, therefore, that the overall effects of stellar perturbations on the stability of the cometary cloud over the age of the solar system may now be rather more important than Oort originally envisaged, though we emphasize that Oort never intended that his detailed model should be used for anything other than a simple illustration of the hypothetical cloud's properties. Moreover, since the determination of a cloud 'radius' in this way is itself fraught with difficulties (for example, it immediately raises the question of the cloud's evolution, and what one means by the 'edge' of the cloud), the Oort cloud's apparently rather smaller size should not by itself be taken as an overriding objection to the model. Nevertheless, the result does cast some doubt on the likely survival of the majority of comets in Oort's original model, and raises the question of whether a realistic *primordial* comet cloud can indeed survive for the age of the solar system. This is a currently very active area of study, and we return to some of the arguments which have been raised in Chapter 12.

9.1.5 ORBITAL ENERGY DISTRIBUTION

Having shown that a primordial cloud could plausibly survive
for the age of the solar system, at least at an order-of-magnitude
level, Oort next considered the detailed shape of the $1/a$ distribution. Here it was reasonable to assume that the distribution
should have relaxed to a steady-state form, because the diffusion
timescale due to planetary perturbations is very much shorter
than the age of the solar system. However, he now argued that
effects due to cometary disruption and decay should also be
included. Van Woerkom had believed that these effects were
negligible, but Oort was convinced that the detailed shape of
the $1/a$ distribution, particularly the slow decline towards larger
$1/a$ values, indicated that disruption must be a major factor.

Assuming that the $1/a$ distribution is indeed constant in time,
the number of comets scattered by planetary perturbations from
any particular $1/a$ value to all other values must equal the number of comets scattered from all other $1/a$ values back to the
particular $1/a$ value in question, allowing for the injection of new
comets from the Oort cloud and the possibility of removal of old
comets by physical decay or disruption. In this way, conservation of comet number leads to an expression for the steady-state
$1/a$ distribution $\nu(1/a)$ which takes the form of a relatively simple integral equation. Following Bailey (1984a), this may be
written in the approximate form

$$\nu(x) = \nu_{inj}(x) + \int_0^\infty (1 - k)\,\nu(y)\phi_{pl}(x - y)\,dy \qquad (9.7)$$

where ν_{inj} describes the annual influx of 'new' nearly parabolic
orbits from the Oort cloud, k is the assumed constant probability
of disruption per revolution and $\phi_{pl}(\Delta)$ describes the probability per revolution that a planetary perturbation will produce a
perturbation of size Δ in $x \equiv 1/a$.

At large $1/a$ values ($x \gtrsim 2\times10^{-3}$ AU^{-1}, corresponding approximately to $a < 500$ AU), the direct injection of new comets from
the Oort cloud is completely negligible. In this circumstance,
using the approximation that planetary perturbations are small

compared with the values of $1/a$ under question, it may be shown (Oort 1950) that the solution of equation (9.7) involves an approximately exponential decrease in the $1/a$ distribution, i.e.

$$\nu(x) = C \, \exp(-bx) \qquad (9.8)$$

in rough agreement with observations. In this equation, C is a constant whose value depends on the total number of comets in the distribution and

$$b^2 = \frac{2k}{(1-k)} \frac{1}{\sigma_E^2} \qquad (9.9)$$

As before, σ_E denotes the root-mean-square change in $1/a$ due to planetary perturbations over one orbit.

Combining this solution with that of the exact integral equation at small $1/a$ values (equation 9.7) thus enabled Oort to compare the predictions of his model with observations over the whole range of x. This comparison (taken from Oort's Table 8) is shown here in Table 9.2.

Oort adopted a mean disintegration probability per revolution given by $k = 0.019$, based on data from observed comet splittings, but he also argued that such evidence as was available from other comets, particularly those of short period (such as Encke's comet), indicated that the intrinsic spread in k values could be very large. In this way, while some comets might have an extremely low disruption probability, others could be quite fragile. In the light (or dark!) of these uncertainties, he concluded (see Table 9.2) that except for the first row of the distribution the predicted steady-state $1/a$ values were in excellent agreement with observations.

Thus, except for the parabolic excess, Oort's model could explain the entire $1/a$ distribution. However, in order to keep this conclusion in perspective, we should emphasize that the 'parabolic excess' remained the dominant feature of the $1/a$ distribution, and that there is a sense therefore in which the introduction of comet splittings, though both interesting and likely on other grounds (they are indeed observed!), may have placed the cart before the horse in this particular context.

Range of $1/a$ (AU^{-1})	Observed	$k = 0.019$	$k = 0.003$
0.0000–0.0005	2.400	0.4800	0.340
0.0005–0.0010	0.300	0.2200	0.180
0.0010–0.0020	0.160	0.1800	0.170
0.0020–0.0040	0.090	0.1200	0.150
0.0040–0.0100	0.046	0.0350	0.084
0.0100–0.0200	0.014	0.0040	0.031
0.0200–0.0400	0.004	0.0001	0.006

Table 9.2: Comparison between the observed $1/a$ distribution and that predicted for two values of the disruption probability per revolution k, after Oort (1950, Table 8). The tabulated values represent the number of comets per 50×10^{-6} AU^{-1}.

9.1.6 FADING PROBLEM

In effect, one may take the view that cometary splitting, and hence fading, are aspects of a comet's evolution that can be expected on general physical grounds to change with a comet's evolutionary age. However, the precise value of the disruption probability per revolution cannot readily be determined from observations, nor can one easily calculate the form of its probable variation with $1/a$. Oort had therefore effectively introduced a free parameter, or fading function, into his model, the exact form of which could not be predicted except by using observational constraints based on the $1/a$ distribution. This clearly introduced a degree of circularity into the argument for a primordial comet cloud; but nevertheless, if the original steady-state Oort cloud hypothesis is accepted, one can in principle not only explain the whole $1/a$ distribution but also 'predict' the form of the fading function (cf. Bailey 1984a).

In particular, the comparison between theory and observation indicated a discrepancy near the parabolic limit of about a factor of five in comet numbers (Table 9.2). This existed despite the fact that the model included a mechanism (stellar perturbations) by which a steady influx of 'new' nearly parabolic orbits would always be produced. However, if the predictions of the model were scaled to the observed $1/a$ distribution at large $1/a$ values (*i.e.* towards shorter period orbits), the spike near $1/a = 0$ was not nearly high enough.

Within the context of the model, therefore, one could argue that the discrepancy merely indicated that the 'wrong' choice had been made for the fading probability for new comets. In fact, Oort suggested that this was quite likely to be the case, since it could be argued that comets which approached the inner solar system apparently for the first time would generally be expected to have a greater capacity to develop large, luminous envelopes than comets which had suffered a greater number of returns. In this way, the 'new' comets might be anomalously bright and therefore perhaps more easily discovered.

But if the theory was to fit observations, about 80% of new comets which happened initially to undergo 'favourable' planetary perturbations (*i.e.* which ultimately would return to the inner planetary system) would have to be so faint on their second and subsequent returns as not to be seen (*e.g.* Oort & Schmidt 1951). This implied a greater degree of fading per revolution for these new comets than any which had previously been inferred from observations. Although some preliminary evidence soon came forward (Oort & Schmidt 1951) which indicated that the dynamically 'new' comets might indeed differ physically from the dynamically evolved population with larger $1/a$ values, the presence of significant differences between the two classes of comet is still unresolved (*e.g.* Donn 1977, Whipple 1978a).

This difficulty with the steady-state model of the Oort cloud is now known as the 'fading problem' (*cf.* Whipple 1957, 1962; Everhart 1979, 1982; Yabushita 1983a, Kresák 1984, Bailey 1985a, and references therein). Many attempts have since been made to justify the high degree of fading per revolution required for new comets in order for the steady-state interpretation of the observations to be valid, but none has yet been shown to arise as a quantitative prediction of a particular model of the cometary nucleus. Nevertheless, setting aside this rather unsatisfactory introduction of an assumed strong fading for new comets, Oort's investigation had confirmed that in principle the basic comet-cloud model could quantitatively explain the main statistical features of observed cometary orbits. He now completed his paper by turning to the important question of the cloud's origin.

9.1.7 FORMATION PROBLEM

In concentrating on the question of where comets come from, rather than how they are made, Oort had both simplified and complicated the problem of cometary origin. His answer to the first part was 'from a huge cloud of comets'; but this immediately begged the question of how the comets themselves were formed, and how, having formed, the comet cloud itself was created.

Clearly, due to the extremely low density of material in the outer parts of the cloud, or indeed any reasonable solar nebula, it was exceedingly difficult to envisage a mechanism by which comets might have condensed *in situ* at distances of order 10^5 AU from the sun. Oort therefore argued that comets probably originated in the first instance deep within the planetary system.

In particular, though he stressed the tentative nature of the proposal, he suggested (*cf.* Olbers and Lagrange) that comets and asteroids might have originated as a result of the explosion of a hypothetical terrestrial planet which had once existed in the region now occupied by the present asteroid belt. On this view, since asteroids at this time were often regarded simply as devolatilized comets (*e.g.* Leuschner 1927, Bobrovnikoff 1931; *cf.* Section 6.4.1, p.124), the original explosion might have generated a huge number of active cometary bodies.

Having thus 'explained' the formation of comets, Oort turned to consider whether such a model could produce comets with orbits similar to those currently observed. In particular, he considered two extreme possibilities, the main difference between them depending on the assumed strength of the original explosion.

In the first, Oort suggested that the explosion had been so violent that cometary fragments might have been ejected immediately into orbits comparable with the present dimensions of the Oort cloud. These orbits would then have been subject, on an orbital timescale, to the randomizing effect of stellar perturbations, and a significant fraction of the initially bound outwardly moving comets would be scattered into orbits of larger perihelion distance in the manner first suggested by Öpik (1932). However, the probability of placing comets directly into the Oort cloud by this means (a single gigantic explosion) could only be reasonably high if one was prepared to accept extremely fine tuning for the initial energy of the explosion.

On the other hand, if the original explosion had been less energetic, it was possible to assume that the comets might have been scattered into the Oort cloud by the cumulative effect of Jupiter's perturbations. On this mechanism, essentially the inverse of the diffusion process described by van Woerkom, cometary orbits would gradually become more and more elongated, until eventually stellar perturbations would again scatter their perihelia outside the region of planetary influence. This possible building process for the origin of the Oort cloud is schematically illustrated in Figure 9.2.

However, on an orbital timescale, stars are only able significantly to change the perihelia of those comets with extremely elongated orbits, corresponding roughly to semi-major axes $a > 2.5 \times 10^4$ AU (*i.e.* $1/a < 40 \times 10^{-6}$ AU^{-1}) and orbital periods greater than 5 Myr. Since only those comets with $a \gtrsim 2.5 \times 10^4$ AU would be 'saved' by stellar perturbations from ejection into interstellar space by the cumulative effect of planetary perturbations, any comet cloud formed in this way should have an inner boundary corresponding roughly to a semi-major axis of about this order of magnitude (see Öpik 1973 for a more detailed estimate of the 'inner edge' of the comet cloud). Furthermore,

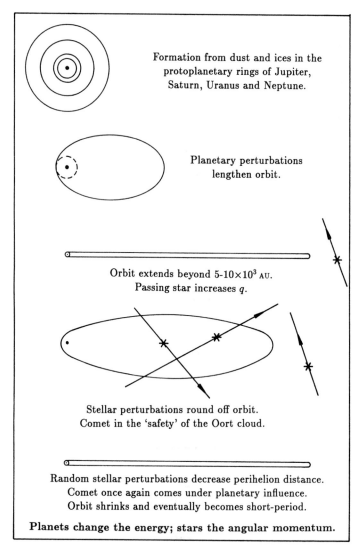

Formation from dust and ices in the
protoplanetary rings of Jupiter,
Saturn, Uranus and Neptune.

Planetary perturbations
lengthen orbit.

Orbit extends beyond 5-10×10^3 AU.
Passing star increases q.

Stellar perturbations round off orbit.
Comet in the 'safety' of the Oort cloud.

Random stellar perturbations decrease perihelion distance.
Comet once again comes under planetary influence.
Orbit shrinks and eventually becomes short-period.

Planets change the energy; stars the angular momentum.

Figure 9.2: A possible mechanism for forming the Oort
cloud.   Planetary perturbations gradually increase the
cometary semi-major axes until stellar perturbations eventually scatter the perihelia out of the planetary region, allowing the comets to be placed into the Oort cloud in orbits
unaffected by further planetary perturbations. The reverse
process allows observed comets to be produced from the
Oort cloud.

since Jupiter produces random changes in $1/a$ on the order of 10^{-3} AU^{-1}, the net efficiency of placing comets into the cloud would be expected to be $\simeq 40 \times 10^{-6}/10^{-3} \approx 1/30$. Thus, even neglecting further loss of comets from the cloud by stellar perturbations (which as we have seen is a rather poor approximation; Section 9.1.4), the total number of comets which were originally required in the asteroid belt would have to be $\approx 10^{13}$, just to explain the $\simeq 2 \times 10^{11}$ now inferred for the present cloud population (cf. Section 11.2, p.243). Although these attempts at explaining the formation of the comet cloud clearly indicate the difficulty of the task, in view of the genuine uncertainty in knowledge concerning the detailed structure of the early solar system, the explosion hypothesis could not be immediately ruled out.

Oort's seminal paper had thus demonstrated that a primordial solar system hypothesis for cometary origin was indeed viable. In particular, the hypothesis had the advantage that it could explain, at least in principle, the main statistical features of the observed comets, particularly the steady influx of nearly parabolic orbits and the overall shape of the $1/a$ distribution.

However, several important difficulties for the model had also been identified. Of these, the two most serious seemed to be firstly that it only explained the exact shape of the $1/a$ distribution by postulating strong fading (not directly observed) for new comets and by assuming a wide spread in the disintegration rates for other long-period comets; while secondly, the problem of the formation of comets and the cloud itself still remained to be worked out in detail.

Concerning the latter point, the fundamental difficulty was how to devise an efficient mechanism for placing primordial comets into the extended, weakly-bound orbits which seem mostly to characterize the comet cloud. For example, if comets were scattered into this region by the perturbations of Jupiter, about 10^{13} comets had initially to be present in the region of the asteroid belt, almost certainly requiring too great a total mass for the model to be viable.

It is perhaps worth noting at this point Russell's (1935, p.43) adverse opinion on the requirements of a primordial solar system model for comets: 'The chief difficulty about this hypothesis is that it demands the existence of an enormous number of comets of large perihelion distance.' By 1950, however, the climate within astrophysics had changed to the extent that this kind of caution was not generally considered a sufficient reason for rejecting a theoretical proposal, speculative as it might seem.

9.2   Other developments

9.2.1   WHIPPLE'S DIRTY SNOWBALL

At the same time as Oort was proposing his comet-cloud concept, Whipple (e.g. 1949, 1950a,b; 1951) was developing a radically new model for the structure of the cometary nucleus. For nearly a hundred years, ever since the link between comets and meteor streams had been reliably established, the apparent cometary nucleus had been regarded by most authors as comprising a swarm of dust grains, or meteors, resembling a very rarefied 'sandbank'. On this model, the activity of comets was attributed partly to the release of gas which had been adsorbed on to the dust particles, and partly to the effects of mutual intergrain collisions. In the accretion theory the latter process was believed to be dominant (e.g. Lyttleton 1953a, p.111), thereby explaining both why a comet became more active near perihelion and why the size of the coma often appeared to shrink as the comet approached the sun.

According to Whipple, however, the comet nucleus consisted instead of a discrete ball of ices and meteoric material, resembling a 'dirty snowball' a few kilometres across. Under the influence of solar heating the more volatile species would undergo sublimation and stream away from the comet in gaseous form, carrying with them the less volatile ices and meteoric dust.

This model had three main advantages over the 'sandbank' alternative. First, it could more readily account for the 'abnor-

HMC COMPOSITE IMAGE

IMAGES 3457,3475,3480,3491,3496,3500

Figure 9.3: Giotto image of Halley's comet, taken with the Halley Multicolour Camera on 13th March 1986. Courtesy of Dr. H.U. Keller.

mal' non-gravitational forces which were known systematically to affect a number of short-period comets. Secondly, it could easily explain the calculated gas production rates for comets (suggesting an intrinsic ratio of order unity for the masses of volatile and nonvolatile species, cf. Delsemme 1982); and lastly, it explained why comets continued to produce copious quantities of gas and dust over many revolutions, and how the members of the sun-grazing group had managed to avoid complete disintegration at perihelion.

Although it was argued by some (e.g. Lyttleton 1972, 1977; O'Dell 1973; Fellgett 1977, 1985) that the nucleus might not exist and that the dust-swarm model might fit the observations equally well, many astronomers accepted Whipple's model as a working hypothesis and no longer considered the earlier picture. Historically, of course, the current view, in which comets contain a discrete central body (strikingly confirmed by the Giotto images of Halley's comet in March 1986; see Figure 9.3), antedates the dust-swarm hypothesis by a considerable margin. A detailed review of the relative merits of each model has been given by Whipple (1963).

9.2.2 Kuiper's solar nebula

The period around 1950 was also one in which a number of authors (*e.g.* Whipple 1948, Edgeworth 1949, Kuiper 1949, 1951a,b; Urey 1952) were undertaking detailed theoretical investigations into the origin of the solar system. These studies were broadly based on developments of the nebular hypothesis, and concentrated particularly on the expected evolution of a disc-like protoplanetary cloud with a total mass of around $0.1\,M_\odot$.

Kuiper showed that on this picture one could begin to understand the distribution of planetary sizes, and even made the specific prediction that the most likely bodies to occur in the nebula beyond Neptune should be comets. It was argued that these would form by the condensation of 'snowflakes' of icy compounds, which would subsequently undergo coagulation by collisions, first to form 'snowballs', with sizes of order tens of centimetres (after about $10^5\,\mathrm{yr}$), and then fully-fledged cometary nuclei, with sizes of order kilometres after about $10^9\,\mathrm{yr}$ (*cf.* equation 10.3, p.214). This general picture evidently has much in common with the ideas first put forward around the middle of the eighteenth century by Kant (*cf.* Section 6.2.1, p.113).

The composition of comets on Kuiper's model, based on theoretical condensation sequences for a protoplanetary nebula of typical cosmic abundances, was predicted to be primarily frozen volatile compounds (*cf.* Whipple 1949). In particular, these included molecules such as methane (CH_4), water (H_2O), ammo-

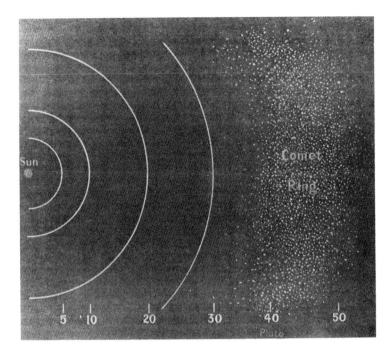

Figure 9.4: Schematic illustration of the primordial comet belt surrounding the planetary system, predicted by Kuiper's theory of the protosolar nebula. After Whipple (1964b).

nia (NH_3), cyanogen (CN) and carbon monoxide (CO), and it may be noted that Kuiper's suggestion seems to have been made quite independently of Whipple's new model for the comet nucleus (e.g. Kuiper 1951a, p.363). Kuiper saw Whipple's work as strongly confirming the general validity of his own arguments, and he argued that a self-consistent model of the solar nebula could be developed in which large numbers of bodies resembling those of Whipple's icy-nucleus concept would indeed be formed on the outskirts of the protoplanetary system.

It remained only to explain how primordial comets, formed at the edge of the protoplanetary disc, might be ejected into the Oort cloud. Here, Kuiper modified Oort's use of Jupiter's perturbations, and suggested that because Pluto moves in an eccentric orbit which eventually 'sweeps' the whole region of space between 38 and 50 AU, its perturbations would sooner or later scatter all comets initially formed in this region into Neptune's sphere of influence. Neptune, and the other planets to a lesser extent, would then complete the process by ejecting a fraction of these comets into the zone at large heliocentric distance where stellar perturbations were effective, thereby trapping comets into the 'safety' of the Oort cloud in orbits extending to distances greater than 2.5×10^4 AU.

Pluto's ability to scatter a large number of comets towards Neptune obviously depends on its mass, and at this time it was generally thought (e.g. Kuiper 1950) that this was in the range $0.1–1\,M_\oplus$, where $M_\oplus$ denotes the mass of the earth. Kuiper believed that the proposed dynamical mechanism for producing the Oort cloud should work provided that Pluto's actual mass was not very much less than this value. Unfortunately, however, recent observations of Pluto and its satellite Charon have shown that their total mass is only about $1/400\,M_\oplus$ (e.g. Harrington & Christy 1981), thus casting considerable doubt on the feasibility of this aspect of Kuiper's cometary model.

Lastly, since the disturbing force of Pluto is negligible beyond about 50 AU, Kuiper made the important prediction (cf. Edgeworth 1949, Whipple 1964, 1972a) that a primordial cometary 'belt', analogous to the asteroid belt between Mars and Jupiter, should probably still exist on the outskirts of the planetary system. This is illustrated in Figure 9.4.

9.2.3   OORT CLOUD ESTABLISHED

In summary, therefore, in the space of just a few years not only had two completely different theories of cometary origin emerged, but so too had two completely different theories of cometary constitution. Whipple's icy nucleus model naturally became associated with the ideas implying an origin of comets within the primordial solar system, and the concepts developed by van Woerkom and Oort then enabled one to show how it might be possible for such comets to be stored in the 'deep freeze' of the Oort cloud for the necessary four and a half billion years, before reappearing as seemingly 'new' comets apparently passing through the planetary system for the first time.

However, the nineteenth century picture of comets as little more than a dense concentration of meteoric particles had received strong support from Lyttleton's accretion theory, and it could also be argued that the complicated processes required for cometary 'storage' were then unnecessary, since the sun probably passed through a suitable interstellar dust cloud every ten million years or so (Lyttleton 1953a, p.96). The random directions of the perihelia of long-period comets could be understood on this model by assuming that there had been many past encounters of the sun with dust clouds (e.g. Bondi 1953), and it was also argued in favour of the theory that current theories of stellar evolution indicated that the accretion process must actually be realized.

At first it seemed that there was little to choose between the two ideas. Each appeared equally likely: one being bound up with the formation of the planets, the other with the evolution of the stars; and each could apparently explain the gross statistical features of comets and their general physical appearance. However, it soon became clear that most astronomers favoured an origin for comets within the solar system, and though Lyttleton continued to argue for many years in favour of the accretion theory, there were few who supported him.

There were several reasons for this. First, it should be remembered that more people were actively involved in the former theory and therefore had some interest in its support (cf. Whipple 1953). The influence of a scientific 'establishment' of this kind could never sustain an obviously wrong theory, but in a debate such as this (cf. Lyttleton 1950, 1952a,b; Whipple 1976, pp.16–17) its effect should not be minimized. Other instances where an establishment view of comets has prevailed despite the argument being finely balanced, are provided by the solar system vs. interstellar debate of the nineteenth century, and the difficulty with the number of short-period comets highlighted by Proctor and Vsekhsvyatski. In both these cases the arguments used to 'prove' the standard model eventually turned out to be suspect, but whereas Laplace's interstellar theory succumbed to attack, the idea that short-period comets were fundamentally derived from the background long-period flux had much greater resilience (though even this is now being questioned). Evidently, the progress of science is not always either as rational or as rectilinear as commonly believed!

Secondly, using the ideas developed by van Woerkom and Oort, Kuiper had now shown that one could solve the problem which had defeated Laplace: namely, how a common origin for all the bodies in the solar system might be possible. Set against this significant advance, the alternative idea of an interstellar origin for comets seemed much less attractive.

Lastly, as we have described (e.g. Section 8.3.2, p.173), there were also a relatively large number of unsolved problems concerning the detailed theoretical development of the accretion theory, and several observations which this theory could not explain as easily as the other: the detailed shape of the $1/a$ distribution, the presence of comets with large perihelia, and, particularly associated with the model of the nucleus, the systematic orbital changes presumed to be caused by non-gravitational forces.

Moreover, although McCrea (1953) had shown that in a sufficiently non-uniform cloud both the angular momentum of comets and the $1/a$ distribution might be understood if the formation of an accretion stream could be shown to occur in such a case, the theory was never extended in this way; and at the time it was even stated by some (e.g. Bondi 1953) that such modifications to the theory were unnecessary.

In this way, although Lyttleton (e.g. 1964, 1968c, 1974) has continued to criticize Whipple's icy nucleus model, Oort's comet-cloud hypothesis and the conventional interpretation of the $1/a$ distribution, his arguments have been largely rejected (e.g. Le Poole & Katgert 1968, Bailey 1977, Marsden 1977). We also refer the interested reader to other work (*e.g.* Kendall 1961, Öpik 1966a, Aust & Woolfson 1973, Wallis 1978) in which various detailed aspects of the accretion theory and the arguments used in its support have been criticized.

By the early nineteen-fifties, therefore, the solar system *vs.* interstellar debate had apparently come to a rather strong conclusion. Although several areas of potential difficulty had already been identified for the new theory, it now seemed almost certain that comets were fundamentally solar system bodies, possibly formed by processes of condensation and accumulation in the outer regions of a cold protoplanetary disc. The model also appeared intellectually satisfying, since not only did it provide the basis for a unified interpretation of comets, but it also connected observed phenomena (comets) occurring deep within the solar system with events (stellar perturbations) proceeding near the edge of the sun's sphere of action. While planetary perturbations were thought initially to scatter comets into the Oort cloud, subsequent stellar and planetary disturbances acted together to produce the observed $1/a$ distribution. A feeling arose amongst professional astronomers not directly concerned with cometary research, that a subject which was not of primary interest anyway had at last been hammered into reasonably coherent shape by the combined researches of Oort, Whipple and Kuiper. The scene was set for a final period of consolidation and a tying up of loose ends.

10

Planetesimal picture

"If it is not true, it is a happy invention."

Anon.

10.1   Growth of a paradigm

10.1.1   PERFECTING OORT'S CLOUD

The ideas of Oort, Whipple and Kuiper had thus combined into
a rather formidable alliance. Whereas Oort had convincingly
demonstrated that the solar system must be surrounded by a
huge cloud of comets, comoving and presumably coeval with the
sun and planets, the researches of Kuiper and Whipple showed
how the whole comet-cloud hypothesis could be neatly tied into
a modern picture of the origin of the solar system. The ideas
introduced by these authors soon led to general acceptance of
the view that comets are primordial solar system bodies; and it
has since often seemed that there was only one remaining issue
of substance to be resolved: namely, the origin of the Oort cloud
itself.

The situation in which theories of cometary origin have developed during the past thirty years or so may thus be described,
albeit superficially, as one in which the majority of cometary specialists have concentrated more or less exclusively on the conventional solar system hypothesis, whilst a few mavericks, left
much to their own devices, have occasionally sought to throw a
spanner in the works wherever possible in the form of alternative ideas, variously described as dubious, ingenious or obviously
unacceptable. However, it would be misleading to take such an
account too literally, for several of the new suggestions have indeed been developed to beyond the level of mere speculation
and may yet prove to be important points of departure for the
future advancement of the subject.

In these circumstances, it is helpful to depart slightly from our previously strict chronological order, and collect the theories under discussion into a number of distinct and clearly identifiable types. In this chapter and the following Chapter 11 we therefore concentrate on the important class of modern theories that can be broadly described as representing the standard primordial solar system viewpoint. We begin by reviewing those theories (principally due to Öpik and Safronov) in which the starting point is taken as a conventional low-mass ($\simeq 0.1\,M_\odot$) protoplanetary disc and in which (following Kuiper) comets are subsequently explained as the inevitable result of the aggregation of dust grains initially present in such a system. In Öpik's theory, the planetary masses are assumed to be given more or less a *priori*, being primary condensations, whilst comets form somewhat later by accretion in the remaining disc. In Safronov's theory, on the other hand, the comets form first as planetesimals, the latter then aggregating to form planets. These ideas, including their more recent embellishments, currently represent the central core and mainstream development of the subject up to the present day.

The following Chapter 12 extends this review to include the important question of Oort cloud evolution, laying particular emphasis on the effects of the recently discovered 'galactic' perturbations of the Oort cloud, especially those due to giant molecular clouds in the disc of the Galaxy and the galactic tide. These previously unrecognized perturbers of the Oort cloud have led to a growing problem so far as the survival of the standard model is concerned, and this in turn has led to the consideration of previously unforeseen problems: namely, have the observed comets become unbound from a cloud of shorter period orbits closer in (a massive inner core hypothesis), or have they been recently captured from further out (an interstellar capture picture)?

These issues are explored in the ensuing Chapters 13 to 15. First (Chapter 13), we describe a burgeoning group of solar system theories, which although less well developed than those grouped around the standard solar system hypothesis, may yet prove to contain a physically more realistic description of the early evolution of a protosolar nebula, especially in that they allow more naturally for the inclusion within the Oort cloud of a massive inner core. These variations on the underlying theme of a conventional nebular hypothesis have been largely stimulated by radio and far-infrared observations of dense molecular clouds and regions of active star formation, which we describe in the first part of Chapter 14. In particular, they approach theories of *comet* formation from the vantage given by theories of *star* formation, assuming that the latter process is a relatively inefficient one naturally involving a great deal of 'wastage' of the initial collapsing material of the protostellar cloud. These cometary theories, which are now primarily associated with the names of Cameron, Biermann and Hills, may be contrasted with the 'standard' model in taking as their starting point an initially more massive protoplanetary disc ($\simeq 1\,M_{\odot}$) or protosolar nebula.

Chapter 14 goes on to review a variety of more recent new observations of star-forming regions, and introduces a number of less easily classified solar system theories that attempt to explain comets. Then, in Chapter 15, we consider more recent arguments which again indicate that renewed attention should once more be given to one or another version of the interstellar hypothesis. These six chapters together complete our historical review of the origin of comets, and set the scene for our concluding discussion of cometary catastrophism (Chapters 16 and 17) and the impact of this and other subjects (*e.g.* the recent space missions to Halley's comet) on current theories of cometary origin, finally summarized in Chapters 18 and the concluding Chapter 19.

Returning to the present chapter, therefore, we begin by describing the conventional low-mass solar nebula hypothesis, in which comets are assumed to be primordial solar system bodies formed somewhere on the outskirts of the protosolar or protoplanetary nebula. According to these ideas, comets (or the particles of which they are made) are initially formed by a process of accumulation rather analogous to the growth of raindrops or snowflakes in clouds in the earth's atmosphere. We begin this review by discussing the important work of Öpik, whom we previously met (p.145) in connexion with the effect of stellar perturbations on a hypothetical primordial comet cloud.

10.1.2   ÖPIK'S VIEW

Öpik was born in Estonia in 1893, but his scientific work — which spanned a prodigious range — was mostly carried out in Ireland, Germany and the United States (Wayman & Mullan 1986). He was first associated with the Armagh Observatory in Ireland in 1948 and remained there until his death in 1985. It was there that he developed his theories of the origin of the solar system, and where he completed his most important investigations into the origin of comets.

These studies are best represented by an important series of papers published over a ten-year period during the nineteen-sixties and seventies (e.g. Öpik 1966a, 1970, 1973, 1975), by which time he was well past the age at which most would be considered to have passed their prime! Öpik's efforts to explain the formation of both comets and the Oort cloud within a primordial solar system framework often dwarfed those of his contemporaries, and his work can rightly be counted as amongst the most comprehensive individual attempts yet made to explain the origin of comets and the Oort cloud within a single, all-embracing framework.

Öpik began, following Kuiper and others, by adopting a so-called 'minimum-mass' protoplanetary nebula ($\simeq 0.1\,M_\odot$), calculated simply by correcting the observed planetary masses up to approximate solar abundances. He subsequently attempted to show that bodies resembling observed comets would inevitably form in such a disc of material, and that their dynamical evolution would necessarily be such as to generate the observed Oort cloud.

This ambitious programme led him to make a detailed assessment of the various questions and difficulties which beset this kind of theory. Although he eventually concluded that the suggested solar system hypothesis for the origin of comets was indeed viable, provided that comets formed no further out than the Jupiter-Saturn zone of the nebula (*i.e.* $r \simeq$ 5–10 AU), his work will probably have most enduring significance for the problems it raised rather than for those which it may (or may not) have overcome.

Öpik was thus foremost in attempting a comprehensive discussion of the assumptions underlying the Kuiper-Oort-Whipple hypothesis for cometary origin: how quickly could comets form in the protoplanetary disc; how rapidly were they scattered out towards the Oort cloud; what proportion would eventually finish up in the cloud; and what initial mass was necessary in order to explain the observed influx of long-period comets? Since these questions are fundamental to this whole class of theory (and many others too), it is convenient to describe Öpik's ideas in the context of these practical problems.

10.2   Attention to detail

10.2.1   ACCUMULATION PROBLEM

The first difficulty which must be overcome in nebular theories of this type is that of forming structures the size of observed comet nuclei within the age of the solar system. Öpik's estimate of this timescale, however, differed substantially from the earlier determination by Kuiper (despite their broadly similar physical assumptions concerning the protoplanetary disc), and he argued strongly against Kuiper's detailed picture of comet formation on the periphery of the planetary system. In order to identify the source of such a difference, it is helpful first to consider the main factors which govern the rate of growth of the largest members of a population of dust grains undergoing collisional coalescence.

If we consider a grain with radius a_{gr} and internal density ρ_{gr}, the rate of increase of its mass $m_{gr} = \frac{4}{3}\pi\rho_{gr}a_{gr}^3$ is given simply by the rate of collisions of this grain with other members of the population, multiplied by the mass of the colliding grains and the probability ξ_c that they should stick upon collision. Introducing m_f and n_f to denote the mass and number density of the background 'field' population of grains, this reduces to

$$\frac{dm_{gr}}{dt} = \xi_c n_f \sigma_c v_{\rm rel} m_f \tag{10.1}$$

where $\sigma_c = \pi(a_{gr} + a_f)^2$ is the grain-grain collision cross-section and $v_{\rm rel}$ is the mean relative velocity.

This expression may now be simplified in two ways. First, assuming that the mass density of large grains is relatively small compared with that of the field population, we may write $n_f m_f = \rho_d$, where ρ_d is the local smoothed-out density of dust in the nebula. Secondly, since we are interested in the growth of grains up to the size of typical cometary nuclei, a_{gr} is expected to be much larger than the value a_f for the average grain in the population, so $\sigma_c \simeq \pi a_{gr}^2$. The grain-growth equation can thus be rewritten in the approximate form

$$\frac{dm_{gr}}{dt} \simeq \xi_c \, \pi a_{gr}^2 \rho_d v_{\rm rel} \tag{10.2}$$

which implies

$$a_{gr} \simeq \frac{1}{4} \xi_c (\rho_d / \rho_{gr}) v_{\rm rel} \, t \tag{10.3}$$

where we have assumed that the initial radius of the grains is negligible compared with their value at the final time t.

This shows that the largest particles in the distribution grow at a rate proportional to ρ_d / ρ_{gr} multiplied by the mean relative velocity and the sticking probability per collision. Assuming an origin for comets at about the distance of Neptune, the assumptions made by Kuiper and Öpik as to each of these factors were quite similar (i.e. $\rho_d \approx 10^{-12}\,{\rm kg\ m^{-3}}$, $\rho_{gr} \approx 10^3\,{\rm kg\ m^{-3}}$, and $v_{\rm rel} \approx 10^2\,{\rm m\ s^{-1}}$); they differed, however, in the important question of the sticking probability ξ_c. Here, Kuiper assumed that grains with icy mantles would stick with almost unit probability (i.e. $\xi_c = 1$; cf. Cameron 1973, Arnold 1977, Morfill et al. 1978), while Öpik adopted a much lower value ($\xi_c = 0.05$; *cf.* Cora-dini *et al.* 1977, Greenberg *et al.* 1978). Not surprisingly, their conclusions about the likelihood of significant grain growth were significantly different!

The choice of a realistic value for the sticking probability was thus of crucial importance in determining the rate of grain growth in the protoplanetary nebula. In particular, whereas Kuiper (*cf.* Section 9.2.2, p.202) calculated that kilometre-sized bodies could easily be formed in the Uranus-Neptune zone (and beyond) within a time on the order of 10^9 years, Öpik's assumption in this respect ($\xi_c = 0.05$) led to the opposite conclusion.

For example (see Öpik 1973, Table II), the latter author estimated that even in the case of comets originating in the Uranus zone of the protoplanetary nebula ($r \simeq 20\,\mathrm{AU}$) the time for grains to grow to a diameter of ten kilometres would exceed the age of the solar system. Further out, the timescale was even longer, ranging up to more than 4×10^{10} years for a presumed origin of comets in Neptune's zone — greater than the age of the universe! These arguments led Öpik firmly to rule out the possibility of forming comets in the outer regions of a protoplanetary disc.

Closer to the sun, however, the background density of neb-ular material was expected to be much higher. According to Öpik's theory (*loc. cit.*, p.320), ρ_d could be estimated by spreading roughly half the mass M_{pl} of the governing planet at helio-centric distance r over a ring of width $\Delta r = 0.2r$ and thickness $\Delta z = 0.1r$, giving

$$\rho_d \simeq \frac{1}{2} M_{pl} / 2\pi r \Delta r\, \Delta z = \frac{25}{2\pi} \frac{M_{pl}}{r^3} \qquad (10.4)$$

Thus, the density of material in the Jupiter-Saturn zone of the nebula was much greater than that in the Uranus-Neptune zone. Moreover, it could also be argued that the mean rela-tive velocities of dust grains would increase inwards, this time at a rate roughly proportional to the circular velocity at r, *i.e.* $v_{\mathrm{rel}} \propto r^{-1/2}$. In this way, Öpik concluded that cometary bodies

should accumulate at a much faster rate in the inner regions
of the nebula, and for a presumed origin at Jupiter's distance
($\simeq 5\,\mathrm{AU}$) he estimated that bodies with diameters up to ten
kilometres would form within only a few million years. Öpik
therefore rejected Kuiper's suggestion of comet formation on
the outskirts of the planetary system, and argued instead for an
origin in the neighbourhood of Jupiter's zone of the nebula.

10.2.2   EJECTION PROBLEM

Having confirmed that comet formation by coagulation of dust
grains in the protoplanetary nebula was feasible, at least in the
regions associated with the proto-Jupiter and the proto-Saturn,
the next problem was to eject comets into the Oort cloud. This
involved a careful study of the processes by which cometary
orbits are altered by the accumulation of random planetary perturbations, and also required a detailed assessment of the rate
at which stellar perturbations effected placement of long-period
comets into the relative safety of the Oort cloud.

The purpose of Öpik's investigation was two-fold: first, to
determine how quickly Jupiter, Saturn and the other planets
might remove comets from the inner planetary region to the Oort
cloud; and secondly, to evaluate the proportion of such comets
that would eventually finish up in stable long-period orbits safe
from the disruptive effects of planetary perturbations and solar
heating.

With regard to the first question, if the suggested scheme for
comet formation was at all valid it is clearly necessary that the
ejection timescale should be less than the age of the solar system. Öpik (1973, Table XIX) showed that this condition could
be met if comets formed in either the Jupiter or Saturn zones of
the nebula, but calculated that the timescale was too long if comets originated further out. This result was used (*e.g.* Öpik 1970;
1973, p.382) as an additional strong argument against the suggestion that comets initially condensed in the Uranus-Neptune
zone of the nebula, although we note that his estimates in this

respect are about an order of magnitude too large. The later results of Fernández (1978) and others now indicate a timescale of about 10^9 years for the ejection of comets by Uranus and Neptune, rather shorter than the age of the solar system.

However, whatever the exact time required to eject comets, it is also necessary that the newly formed cometary nuclei should survive as active comets whilst planetary perturbations scatter them into the Oort cloud. This illustrates another important area of difficulty for this general class of theory, since the strength or otherwise of this constraint depends on how rapidly comets are assumed to disintegrate as a function of perihelion distance. Since there is still no agreement as to how quickly *observed* comets disintegrate, the adoption of a particular law for the disintegration of newly formed comets with perihelia beyond Jupiter's distance (*i.e.* outside the usual zone of visibility) is bound to be both controversial and conjectural.

For example, a variety of studies (*e.g.* Delsemme 1982) have shown that the observed output of gas and dust from a cometary nucleus is largely determined by the rate of sublimation of water ice, a quantity which decreases rapidly beyond a few astronomical units of the sun. This has led several authors (*e.g.* Delsemme 1973, Rickman & Froeschlé 1980, Weissman 1980b) to conclude that the lifetime of comets with perihelia beyond Jupiter's orbit is essentially infinite. In this case the ejection timescale, however long, would be much shorter than the corresponding disintegration time (for $q \gtrsim 5$ AU), and the problem of explaining how active comets could be placed in the Oort cloud whilst retaining their initial propensity for activity would not arise.

However, Öpik argued that cometary disintegration would in practice be significant out to much larger heliocentric distances (*e.g.* Öpik 1973, equation 13.16 and pp.382–383). For example, it seemed obvious (*cf.* Section 9.2.2, p.202) that a realistic cometary nucleus would in fact contain a significant proportion of substances more volatile than ordinary water ice, including molecules such as carbon dioxide, ammonia and methane. Since these ices were expected to sublimate at much lower temperatures than that associated with water ice, mass loss should occur even while the comet was well beyond the usual zone of visibility.

Moreover, a few comets are known to emit substantial quantities of gas and dust at large heliocentric distances (ranging up to about 9 AU). These examples give direct evidence for cometary decay beyond the usual limits, and it is worth remembering also that Halley's comet, presumably a highly evolved body, was observed to emit gas and dust at the considerable distance of $\simeq 6$ AU (Wyckoff et al. 1985). This evidence for cometary decay at relatively large distances has been strengthened by recent observations of Comet Bowell (1982 I), a dynamically new comet with semi-major axis $a \simeq 3 \times 10^4$ AU probably approaching the inner solar system from the Oort cloud for the first time. On the outward leg of its journey, the coma of this comet was detectable out to distances greater than 13 AU from the sun (Meech & Jewitt 1987), a record now broken by Comet Černis whose coma has remained detectable to at least 15 AU (Meech 1989).

Öpik thus believed that mass loss should occur even at substantial heliocentric distances. Furthermore, although the highly volatile species were generally reckoned to comprise only a relatively small fraction of the total nuclear mass, he considered that there would still be a certain tendency for the sublimation of these molecules to induce further mass loss in the form of less volatile ices and dust, much in the same way as the sublimation of water ice at smaller distances leads to loss of the non-volatile 'dust' component of the nucleus.

In this way, Öpik argued (cf. Rickman & Vaghi 1976, Rickman & Froeschlé 1980, Kresák 1984) that the physical lifetime in revolutions of a comet nucleus of initial radius R_c and perihelion distance q could be represented by a function proportional to $R_c q^{1/2}$, given approximately by

$$N_{\mathrm{rev}} \simeq 500 \,(R_c/1\,\mathrm{km})(q/1\,\mathrm{AU})^{1/2} \qquad (q \lesssim 60\,\mathrm{AU}) \qquad (10.5)$$

For example, while a comet of radius $R_c = 1$ km and perihelion distance $q = 1$ AU might survive for 500 perihelion passages (in reasonable agreement with the estimates of other authors), a similar comet with $q = 25\,\mathrm{AU}$ would probably survive for only about five times the number of revolutions.

The disintegration lifetime determined in this way could now be compared with the predicted number of revolutions required for planetary perturbations to place comets in the Oort cloud. Initially, this comparison (Öpik 1973, Table XIX) gave a rather surprising result: the former timescale was considerably shorter than the latter for *all* sites of cometary origin! Moreover, if Uranus and Neptune had dominated the ejection process, the timescale for building the cloud must have been at least 10^9 years. This leads to a potentially severe problem for the theory, namely how genuinely active comets, rather than (say) devolatilized cores or deactivated dust-balls, might be successfully placed in the Oort cloud.

Öpik took this as further compelling evidence against the idea of forming observed comets in the Uranus-Neptune zone of the nebula (or beyond), but argued that an origin in Jupiter's zone was still possible. However, in order to maintain this hypothesis he was forced to assume that a mechanism had operated at an early time which had greatly reduced the effective intensity of the sun's radiation field at Jupiter's distance for at least the few million years necessary for Jupiter to populate the Oort cloud with 'live' comets.

Although this was an unexpected conclusion, it could be argued in its favour that the presence of the asteroid belt between Mars and Jupiter, and the existence of the terrestrial planets Mercury, Venus, Earth and Mars, proved that the early solar system must once have contained a vast amount of absorbing dust within Jupiter's orbit. Moreover, the proposal received indirect support from an analysis by Kopal (1971) of the light curve of the peculiar variable star Epsilon Aurigae, which, it was suggested, might be explained in terms of stellar eclipses by one or more rings of dust roughly distributed about the star in a common plane. Nevertheless, if this was the correct explanation for the survival of comets long enough to populate the observed

Oort cloud, the dense 'shield' of dust must have persisted for at least a million years.

In this way, albeit at the expense of introducing an apparently *ad hoc* intervening screen of dust to shield comets against disintegration due to solar heating, Öpik had shown that it was quite possible in principle for planetary perturbations (primarily those of Jupiter) to eject active comets into the Oort cloud in the time available. It now remained to address the question of the efficiency with which the cloud could be populated.

10.2.3   PLACEMENT EFFICIENCY

This problem proved much simpler to tackle, and (as we have already seen in relation to Oort's theory; see p.199) the probability that a given comet might be ejected into the Oort cloud with a semi-major axis in the range $2.5 \times 10^4 – 10^5$ AU may be approximately determined by comparing the range of binding energies described by such orbits (corresponding to $\simeq 30 \times 10^{-6}$ AU^{-1}) with the typical perturbation in $1/a$ introduced by the scattering agent. Since Öpik had argued that ejection would only proceed fast enough if it was caused by Jupiter's perturbations, the value of $\Delta 1/a$ was on the order of 10^{-3} AU^{-1} (*cf.* equation 8.1, p.161), so the net placement efficiency was expected to be around 1/30.

Öpik's detailed estimates of this efficiency factor, assuming that comets originated in Jupiter's zone of the nebula, led in fact to a net placement efficiency of about 0.024 (*loc. cit.*, Table XIX, *cf.* Section 11.2, p.243). In other words, for every thousand comets initially present in Jupiter's region of the protoplanetary nebula only about twenty four would be successfully scattered into orbits characteristic of the Oort cloud. In this way, the original mass of comets in Jupiter's zone had to be at least forty times the present mass of the Oort cloud. This estimate of the initial-to-present cometary mass is certainly too low, due to the neglect of losses from the cloud since its time of formation, but even a factor of forty could not easily be ignored. Öpik was therefore led finally to consider another important problem with this general class of theory: namely, how to reconcile the present mass of comets in the Oort cloud with the relatively low mass assumed for the adopted protoplanetary nebula.

10.2.4   MASS OF THE OORT CLOUD

The total number of comets in the 'observable' part of the Oort cloud (corresponding roughly to semi-major axes $a \gtrsim 2 \times 10^4$ AU) may be obtained by combining the observed influx of dynamically new comets with an internally consistent mathematical model of the cloud. Such a model should relate the total number of observable comets (those with small perihelia) to those that are not seen on account of their larger perihelion distances, and clearly depends in detail on the assumed origin of the cloud. In effect, such a procedure connects the observed near-parabolic flux of comets, for example one per annum with $q \leq 1.5$ AU, to the total number of comets in the whole cloud. For Oort's model of the cloud, the observed flux gave a total population for the whole comet cloud of about 2×10^{11}.

Of course, such a figure is of little use unless one also specifies the limiting magnitude to which one is counting comets. For example, a flux of one comet per annum with perihelion distance less than 1.5 AU corresponds roughly to the flux of comets brighter than an absolute magnitude $H_0 \simeq 9$, rather fainter than the brightness of Halley's comet ($H_0 \simeq 4$–6). Oort's (1950) model of the comet cloud thus contained about 2×10^{11} comets each somewhat smaller than Comet Halley.

In this way, the mass of the Oort cloud depends on two factors. First, on the detailed cloud model (*i.e.* on the cometary number density and velocity distribution), which in turn depends on the assumed site of comet formation (*e.g.* in the planetary region or elsewhere); and secondly, on the purely observational question of the observed flux of comets down to a particular absolute magnitude and the mean cometary mass to the same limiting brightness. Not surprisingly, the uncertainties allowed by such factors give scope for wide variations in the mass of the Oort cloud as determined by different investigators!

For example, whereas Oort (1950) adopted a mean mass per comet of about 10^{13} kg and derived a total cometary mass of order 0.3 $M_\oplus$, Öpik's initial estimate of the same quantity (*loc. cit.*, p.317) was around 740 $M_\oplus$. This was two thousand times larger than Oort's estimate, and clearly of such a size that planetary perturbations, even by Jupiter, would have to be rejected as a viable means of populating the cloud. The total mass of comets in Jupiter's zone of the nebula would then have been almost 0.1 $M_\odot$, far greater (when abundance constraints are included) than the whole mass of the disc! This apparent contradiction led Öpik to investigate ways by which the current mass of the Oort cloud might plausibly be reduced, and he identified three sources of potential error.

The first of these concerned the assumed model of the comet cloud. As has already been mentioned, the details of such a model are closely connected to the proposed site of comet formation, in particular to whether comets originate within the planetary system ($r \lesssim 50$ AU, say) or beyond. In Öpik's theory, comets predominantly accumulated in the Jupiter-Saturn zones of the protoplanetary disc, and it was therefore predicted that their initial orbits in the Oort cloud would have eccentricities of order unity, *i.e.* $e \simeq 1$. Although stellar perturbations would tend rapidly to round off these initially nearly parabolic orbits, it would nevertheless take some time before the final distribution of eccentricities began to approach that expected, namely $f(e) = 2e$, for the random distribution of velocities assumed by Oort.

Thus, Öpik's model of the comet cloud contained an excess of high-eccentricity orbits compared with that of Oort and a corresponding deficit of near-circular types. Other things being equal, therefore, Öpik's model could produce a greater flux of comets through the observable region, and Öpik therefore argued that Oort's figure of $\simeq 2 \times 10^{11}$ comets should be reduced by a factor of almost three, to around 7×10^{10} (*loc. cit.*, p.353).

A second way by which the total mass of comets in Öpik's model could be reduced also became apparent when it was realized that on this model (which differed in several respects from that of Oort) the total number of comets should increase as the 7/2-power of the cloud's outer radius (*cf.* equation 9.3). Since Öpik in fact estimated that comets would be removed from the region of planetary influence by stellar perturbations when their semi-major axes first began to exceed about 5000 AU (*cf.* Duncan *et al.* 1987), he strongly argued for a smaller size for the cloud as a whole. Assuming this was of order 10^4 AU (*loc. cit.*, p.353), twenty times less than Oort's adopted radius, this too could potentially lead to a much reduced total mass.

Thirdly, Öpik emphasized the large practical uncertainties involved in determining the mean mass per comet, and showed in particular (*loc. cit.*, p.390) how his first estimate of this quantity might easily have been too large by a factor of about sixteen. This first estimate, referring to comets brighter than an absolute magnitude $H_0 = 8$, was of order 8×10^{15} kg (*loc. cit.*, Table 1); but when the reduction was made the mean cometary mass was found to be about 5×10^{14} kg, in reasonable agreement with more recent determinations (*e.g.* Fernández 1982a).

In this way, by a somewhat judicious choice of parameters, Öpik finally concluded (*loc. cit.*, p.395) that the cloud's present mass was probably about $1.5 \, M_\oplus$, and that it required an initial cometary mass in Jupiter's zone of the protoplanetary disc of only $\simeq 60 \, M_\oplus$. This mass, now being much less than that of Jupiter itself, no longer seemed to pose a severe difficulty for the model, though it is still worth emphasizing that the adopted mean cometary mass remained extremely uncertain (*cf.* Section 18.1.2, p.432), while he had also made no allowance for the inevitable removal of comets from the cloud since its time of formation. Öpik thus finally decided that an origin for comets in the Jupiter ring of the protoplanetary nebula was indeed possible.

10.2.5   CONFIDENCE GROWS

In summary, although the detailed development of Öpik's theory does appear to contain several inaccuracies and inconsistencies, his work was the first to be developed to a level significantly more precise than one of a simple order-of-magnitude estimate. His final conclusion, that comets formed in the neighbourhood of Jupiter and no further out, seemed to be supported by detailed calculations, though (as we have seen) the theory was not entirely free from difficulties, even on its own terms. In the event, however, Öpik's theory fell rather rapidly out of favour, partly (it seems) because it did not automatically explain the origin of planets as well. Since this aspect of the theory has not since been pursued in any detail, it cannot be said that Öpik's line of enquiry is completely finished. However, the theory has now been overtaken to such an extent that in many modern reviews of the origin and dynamics of comets (*e.g.* Weissman 1985a,b) the suggestion is often not mentioned at all, it usually being simply *assumed* that icy bodies with the nature of observed comets could never form in a region as close to the sun as Jupiter's zone of the nebula.

Indeed, the period immediately following publication of the paper by Öpik (1973) was notable in that it marked the beginning of a significant change in outlook amongst many solar system cosmogonists: from an older view in which comets were regarded as a mere by-product of the formation of the sun and planets, to a new picture in which comets were seen to be crucial. By the late nineteen-seventies, therefore, most mainstream solar system cosmogonists had altered their way of thinking to such an extent that it became seen as vital that any *complete* theory of the origin of the solar system should attempt also to explain the origin of comets and planets together, something which the earlier approaches of Kuiper and Öpik had conspicuously failed to address.

The stimulus for this relatively sudden change in outlook came during the late nineteen-sixties, with the publication of an important new solar system theory called the 'planetesimal hypothesis', by Safronov (*e.g.* 1969) and co-workers in the Soviet Union. However, after initially meeting some resistance from cosmogonists in other countries, it was later adopted and developed by a number of groups particularly in the United States (*e.g.* Greenberg *et al.* 1978), who eventually found the assumptions underlying the theory both attractive and compelling. The rapid advance of the planetesimal hypothesis at this time may also be associated, of course, with the increasing ease with which the power of the electronic computer could be turned to dynamical problems of cometary origin and the growth of protoplanets. In particular, the new theory seemed to be ideally suited to a Monte Carlo approach, involving a statistical investigation of the accumulation and growth of planetesimals, and it quickly became a popular theory amongst dynamicists.

10.3   Planetesimal theory

10.3.1   EARLY DISC FORMATION

Safronov's planetesimal theory (*e.g.* Safronov 1967, 1969, 1972, 1977) drew on the earlier cosmogonical ideas of Schmidt, Gurevich and Lebedinski in the Soviet Union during the post-war period up to 1950 (see ter Haar & Cameron 1963), and following these former authors Safronov also adopted a low-mass protoplanetary disc, this time with an initial mass of about $0.05\,M_\odot$. Indeed, this assumption and other ideas based on the planetesimal picture have tended to dominate recent discussions of the formation of planets within a low-mass protoplanetary nebula, and, by the same token, this picture has exerted great influence on cometary theories as well.

Safronov's fundamental approach (*e.g.* Safronov & Ruzmaikina 1978, 1985; Horedt 1979, Ipatov 1987) has been essentially to follow the evolution of the particulate matter in the disc from first principles. Initially, he assumed that the gravitational collapse of the protosolar nebula would lead first to the formation of a massive central body resembling the present sun, surrounded by a dense, rapidly rotating gaseous disc. This was expected to have an initial structure dominated by the presence of powerful turbulent motions, themselves probably generated by a variety of non-steady processes originating in the original collapse of the protosolar cloud.

Within a short time, however, the initially strong turbulence in the disc was predicted to undergo a rapid decline in intensity. This was primarily due to the presence of efficient damping and dissipation mechanisms in the protoplanetary disc, a consequence of the relatively high densities of both gas and dust, and because no further sources of strong turbulence could be identified. Safronov therefore argued that the residual turbulence in the original protoplanetary disc would rapidly die away, in much the same way as the motions of a vigorously stirred bath decay, leaving a cold, dense, quiescent disc comprising material moving predominantly in nearly circular orbits about the sun. The timescale for the turbulence to dissipate completely was estimated to be on the order of a thousand years, roughly a dozen orbital periods at the distance of Uranus.

Safronov thus proposed that at an early stage of solar system evolution, the ready-formed sun would find itself surrounded by a dense, cold protoplanetary disc with a total mass on the order of $0.05 M_\odot$. The assumed lack of turbulence in the disc indicated that any internal motions would be subsonic, and generally smooth and laminar in form. Under these circumstances, any small dust grains entrained in the gas would have extremely small random velocities, and Safronov concluded that the dust would slowly settle under gravity towards the disc's equatorial plane of symmetry, in much the same way as sand eventually settles to earth after a violent wind or sandstorm.

The sedimentation of the dust through the gas gradually led to a growing concentration of dust in the equatorial plane of the protoplanetary disc, and eventually to the formation of a thin, dense dust layer within the main disc resembling the filling of a sandwich or a 'disc-within-a-disc'. In fact, because grains of different sizes suffer different drag forces or resistance while moving through ambient gas (*cf.* equation 13.2, p.285), they will tend to settle towards mid-plane at slightly different rates. In this way, although the random velocities of the grains in the quiescent disc were thought generally to be negligible, grains of different size were nevertheless expected to drift past one another, allowing the possibility that, given the relatively high dust density within the disc, they would undergo frequent collisions. Safronov was therefore led to suggest that moderately large grains, or even bodies the size of small comets, might accumulate by collisional grain growth within a reasonably short time. These bodies were called 'planetesimals', meaning 'very small planets'.

10.3.2   GROWTH OF PLANETESIMALS

The initial growth rate of such bodies was rather faster than had previously been estimated by Kuiper and Öpik, the principal difference arising from the higher dust density near the disc's mid-plane as a result of sedimentation. Safronov also assumed (*e.g.* Safronov & Ruzmaikina 1978), along with Kuiper, that small ice-covered grains would stick to one another with a relatively high sticking probability on the order of 1/2. However, whatever the precise value of this factor, it was also recognized that the formation of solid bodies of significant size could be augmented, or even overtaken, by the occurrence of a local gravitational instability in the disc. This would cause the central dust layer to fragment into a large number of unstable blobs having characteristic sizes and masses that depended only on the local velocity dispersion of the dust in the disc and on the angular velocity

$$\Omega(r) = (GM_\odot/r^3)^{1/2} \qquad (10.6)$$

at their distance r from the sun.

This instability, which occurs in any rotating disc of gravitating material when the internal velocity dispersion falls below a critical value which depends on the local surface density, plays an important rôle in many planetesimal theories of this type. In particular, not only are the masses and radii of the first bodies which form at a distance r from the sun then reasonably well determined by the theory, but the mechanism offers an independent way of predicting the masses of cometary nuclei without making additional assumptions about the mean sticking probability per collision.

The nature of the local gravitational instability, often described as the 'Goldreich-Ward' instability, though many authors prior to Goldreich & Ward (1973) had previously described the mechanism (e.g. Edgeworth 1949), can be approximately understood by considering the balance of forces on a small, circular region within the main disc. If such a region is to undergo gravitational collapse, it is clearly necessary that it should be large enough for self-gravity to overcome the tendency for pressure forces to push it apart. Moreover, it must also be small enough for self-gravity to dominate the centrifugal repulsion produced by its overall rotation. The latter effect is illustrated, for example, by the inertial forces experienced on a rapidly turning roundabout when clapping hands or bringing together outstretched arms.

If the mass and radius of such a sub-region of the disc are denoted by M and R respectively, the first condition can be approximately described by the requirement that any particle in the disc moving with the root-mean-square velocity V_d of the dust grains should remain gravitationally bound to the subdisc, i.e. $GM/R \gtrsim V_d^2$. Similarly, the second condition (that gravity should be stronger than centrifugal repulsion) requires $GM/R^2 \gtrsim R\Omega^2$.

Substituting $M = \pi R^2 \Sigma$ into these two expressions, where $\Sigma(r)$ is the surface density of the disc at a distance r from the sun, one finds that the sub-disc will collapse if its radius R simultaneously satisfies

$$R > R_1 \simeq V_d^2 / \pi G \Sigma \qquad (10.7)$$

and

$$R < R_2 \simeq \pi G \Sigma / \Omega^2 \qquad (10.8)$$

This approximate result may be refined by more detailed analyses using perturbation theory (e.g. Safronov 1960, Toomre 1964, Goldreich & Lynden-Bell 1965a,b; Goldreich & Ward 1973), and the overall result may be simply summarized by the statement that a rotating disc is stabilized on small scales by pressure and on large scales by rotation.

Thus, in a protoplanetary disc in which turbulence is negligible, as the relatively heavy dust particles settle towards the equatorial mid-plane of the system and the grain-grain velocity dispersion gradually declines, a situation eventually develops in which the critical radius R_1, below which pressure stabilizes the disc, falls below that, R_2, above which angular momentum is important. In this way, one may approximately determine the size of the first unstable fragments by setting $R_1 = R_2$.

This shows that gravitational instability inevitably occurs in a dust disc of velocity dispersion V_d whenever the local surface density exceeds a critical value on the order of $\Sigma_{\rm crit} = V_d \Omega / \pi G$. Substituting this value of Σ into the expressions for R_1 or R_2 allows the radius of the first unstable fragments to be determined, i.e. $R_{\rm crit} \simeq V_d/\Omega$; while the critical mass of the first gravitationally unstable condensations may be estimated from

$$m_{\rm crit} = \pi R_{\rm crit}^2 \Sigma_{\rm crit} \simeq \frac{V_d^3}{\Omega G} = \frac{\pi^3 \Sigma^3 r^6}{M_\odot^2} \qquad (10.9)$$

This equation is in good agreement with estimates of $m_{\rm crit}$ often quoted by other authors (e.g. Greenberg 1984), though we note that the results of more detailed analyses (e.g. Wetherill 1980, Sekiya 1983) indicate that the numerical coefficient in the relation should be increased by about an order of magnitude.

In physical terms, this equation tells us that if the dust velocity dispersion falls sufficiently for the dense dust disc to undergo local gravitational instability, the initial masses of the bodies that form will depend only on the local heliocentric distance r and the disc surface density at this point. Safronov argued that the bodies so formed would have many of the characteristics of observed cometary nuclei, and that these bodies, or 'planetesimals' as they are called in the theory, would subsequently aggregate into the observed planets.

In order to determine whether such a picture for the origin of comets may be valid, it is first necessary to enquire whether the predicted masses of the planetesimals do lie roughly in the range expected from observations. This depends on an estimate of the surface density of the nebula at heliocentric distance r, discussed for example by Weidenschilling (1977a) and others. Following Öpik (1973) and Wetherill (1978) we here assume simply that the surface density $\Sigma(r)$ of the dust disc in the neighbourhood of a growing protoplanet can be written in the form

$$\Sigma(r) \simeq \frac{1}{2} M_{pl}/2\pi r \,\Delta r \qquad (10.10)$$

In this expression, it is assumed that at a representative time roughly half the mass M_{pl} of the governing planet at r remains in the dust disc, distributed in the form of small grains spread over an annular region of width Δr in the radial direction.

Inserting particular numerical values into equation (10.10), i.e. $M_{pl} \simeq 10^{26}$ kg (for Neptune) and $\Delta r \simeq 10$ AU (to describe the width of Neptune's accretion zone), gives $\Sigma(30\,\text{AU}) \simeq 1\,\text{kg m}^{-2}$. Equation (10.9), which we emphasize is only valid provided that the dust velocity dispersion is small enough for gravitational instability to occur (i.e. $V_d \lesssim \pi G\Sigma/\Omega \simeq 0.2\,\text{m s}^{-1}$ for the above parameters), then implies $m_{\text{crit}}(30\,\text{AU}) \approx 10^{17}$ kg. This shows that the predicted mass of the first gravitationally unstable blobs to form in the disc is indeed in a range which can be associated with cometary masses, while the radius of such a body, assuming that it collapsed to form a single cometary nucleus with internal density $\rho_{gr} \simeq 10^3\,\text{kg m}^{-3}$, is about 30 km.

Lastly, we note that if the width Δr of the planet's zone of influence is taken to be proportional to r (as it is in Öpik's theory, where $\Delta r = 0.2\,r$; cf. equation 10.4, p.215), the above expression for the mass of a typical comet can be shown to be proportional to the cube of the mass of the governing planet at

r. Writing Δr in the form $\Delta r = k\, r$, we have (equation 10.9)

$$m_{\mathrm{crit}} \simeq \frac{1}{64k^3} \left(\frac{M_{pl}}{M_\odot}\right)^3 M_\odot \qquad (10.11)$$

These arguments taken together show that a low-mass, quiescent protoplanetary disc of the type considered by Safronov is expected eventually to break up into a large number of planetesimals. The sizes of these bodies naturally depend on the exact parameters of the system and on their distances from the sun, but in general are expected to be in the approximate range 1–100 km. Safronov therefore concluded that the planetesimals in the outer regions of the disc could indeed be identified with observed cometary nuclei.

10.3.3   PLANETARY PROBLEMS

Safronov next considered the processes by which planetesimals might aggregate into observed planets while at the same time scattering the remaining débris in the disc out of the solar system to form the Oort cloud. First, he showed that the random growth of planetesimals in the disc would eventually allow one planetesimal to become much larger than the rest. This dominant member of the distribution was identified with the growing protoplanet or planetary embryo, and was subsequently expected to grow rapidly by accretion of any neighbouring planetesimals and, if it were massive enough, by the infall of any remaining gas.

At the same time, however, any bodies not immediately accreted would be gradually scattered by the growing perturbations of the new planet into systematically larger or smaller orbits. Those that happened to be scattered outwards were eventually ejected from the solar system or placed into highly eccentric orbits with semi-major axes greater than 10^4 AU characteristic of the Oort cloud. Once in these orbits it could be assumed that stellar perturbations would efficiently raise their perihelia out of the original protoplanetary region, thereby allowing comets finally to be placed into the 'safety' of the Oort cloud.

Safronov's theory thus forged a strong link between the origin of comets and the wider question of the growth and origin of the outer planets. Indeed, since on this theory comets came first, the outer planets Uranus and Neptune might perhaps be regarded simply as huge amalgamations of comets, no more than giant snowballs! A particular consequence of this idea is that whereas Kuiper and Cameron (*e.g.* 1962), and even Öpik had implicitly assumed that Jupiter, Saturn, Uranus and Neptune would initially experience an early phase of rapid growth (as now seems to be required by observations of the dust discs around young stars; *cf.* Section 14.1.4, p.311, Strom *et al.* 1989), Safronov recognized that the new planetesimal picture implied a rather extended period of slow accumulation for the outer planets, on the order of 10^9 years or possibly even longer.

In order to illustrate this difficulty for the planetesimal picture, one may estimate the rate of growth of the dominant planetesimal (or protoplanet) by use of an equation essentially identical to equation (10.2). In fact, the only real difference between this and the previous situation (p.214) arises because it is now necessary to include the gravitational attraction of the growing body. This causes the effective collision cross-section of the protoplanet, of mass M_p and radius R_p, to be enhanced above the geometric value πR_p^2 by a factor $(1 + 2\theta)$. Here, following Safronov, we have introduced the notation $\theta = GM_p/R_p v_{\mathrm{rel}}^2$, *i.e.* $\theta = \frac{1}{2} v_{\mathrm{esc}}^2/v_{\mathrm{rel}}^2$, where v_{esc} is the escape velocity from the planet's surface. Assuming that every planetesimal which strikes the protoplanet will stick (*i.e.* $\xi_c = 1$), equation (10.2) becomes

$$\frac{dR_p}{dt} = \frac{1}{4}\left(1 + 2\theta\right)\frac{\rho_d}{\rho_p} v_{\mathrm{rel}} \qquad (10.12)$$

where ρ_p denotes the internal density of the growing planet.

The numerical value of this expression thus depends on the assumed smoothed-out density ρ_d of planetesimals in the disc. In general, if the relative velocities v_{rel} are assumed to be randomly orientated, the average component of velocity perpendicular to the disc's equatorial plane will be on the order of $v_\perp \simeq v_{rel}/\sqrt{3}$. Moreover, it is straightforward to show (for example, by considering the equation of motion of a particle at a height z above the disc) that the semi-thickness of the disc is given by an expression of the form $h \simeq v_\perp/\Omega(r)$. Substituting $\rho_d = \Sigma/2h = \Sigma\Omega/2v_\perp$ into equation (10.12), we finally obtain

$$R_p = \frac{\sqrt{3}}{8}(1 + 2\theta)\frac{\Sigma\Omega}{\rho_p}t \qquad (10.13)$$

Inserting the values $\theta \simeq 4$, $\rho_p \simeq 10^3\,\text{kg m}^{-3}$, $\Sigma \simeq 1\,\text{kg m}^{-2}$ and $r \simeq 30\,\text{AU}$ (appropriate to the distance of Neptune) into this expression, we find that the time required for the planet to grow to a radius $R_p \simeq 10^4\,\text{km}$ is on the order of 10^{11} years(!), far greater than the total time available (cf. Safronov 1967, 1969; Wetherill 1978, Safronov & Ruzmaikina 1978, Greenberg et al. 1984).

10.3.4 GENERATION OF THE OORT CLOUD

The excessively long timescale for the growth of the major planets posed a severe difficulty for the planetesimal picture. Not only did it undermine the idea as a viable explanation of observed planets, but it also meant that the proposed mechanism for the origin of comets was placed in jeopardy. The process of ejecting comets to the Oort cloud depended on gravitational interactions with the giant planets, but if the formation of these bodies were to be significantly delayed, then so too would be the origin of the Oort cloud.

A second difficulty with Safronov's theory in relation to comets concerned the predicted efficiency with which the growing planets would scatter comets into stable orbits with large semi-major axes. As with Öpik's theory, it was expected that the net efficiency of such a process might be very low, but Safronov's

Planet	Ejected mass ($M_\oplus$)	Emplaced mass ($M_\oplus$)
Jupiter	100	0.2
Saturn	80	0.4
Uranus	50	0.6
Neptune	60	1.3
Total	290	2.5

Table 10.1: The cometary mass ejected by the giant planets into hyperbolic orbits and the total mass placed in the Oort cloud (2–8×10^4 AU), after Safronov (1972, Table 1).

determination of the overall effect suggested extremely low values indeed, on the order of $\simeq 0.002$ if Jupiter's perturbations were primarily responsible (Safronov 1972, Table 1). This was at least ten times smaller than had been previously estimated by Oort and Öpik; while if Neptune was held to be the principal perturber, a net efficiency of about 0.02 was claimed.

A selection of Safronov's results is shown here as Table 10.1, which shows that the net efficiency for producing the Oort cloud (here defined to comprise orbits with semi-major axes in the range 2–8×10^4 AU) was only on the order of 1%, substantially less than that estimated by previous authors. If these figures were correct, an initial cometary mass on the order of 300 $M_\oplus$ would be required to explain even a cometary mass in the Oort cloud as small as 2.5 $M_\oplus$. This table also shows that most of the hyperbolic ejection can be attributed to the effects of Jupiter, while most comets which end up in the Oort cloud are ejected by Neptune.

It could be that the apparent discrepancy between Safronov's results for the placement efficiency and those of other authors is partially explained by the fact that comets seem to have been counted as 'ejected' by Neptune if they had first been fed inwards to shorter orbital periods before finally being removed by the much stronger perturbations of Jupiter and Saturn (Safronov 1972). However, assuming that Safronov's figures are broadly correct (but see the discussion in Section 11.2, p.243), the relatively large mass of ejected material could in fact be turned to the advantage of the theory. It was thus possible to argue that the problems of the total initial mass of comets in the protoplanetary nebula and the difficulty of explaining how the outer planets had formed in a reasonable time were related, and could simultaneously be overcome by supposing that the initial protoplanetary disc had indeed originally contained a great mass of material.

In this way, by making suitable adjustments to the assumed surface density of the disc at Neptune's distance (*i.e.* increasing the value of Σ by about an order of magnitude), and allowing the possibility that the random velocities of the planetesimals could have been somewhat smaller than had first been estimated (thereby increasing the parameter θ in equation 10.12 by a factor of 2–3), the overall timescale for the formation of Neptune could be reduced to around 10^9 years (*e.g.* Safronov 1972, Safronov & Ruzmaikina 1978; *cf.* equation 10.13). Although this now implied an initial cometary mass in the Uranus-Neptune zone of about $300\,M_\oplus$ (roughly ten times the combined mass of the present planets in this region), one could now form planets and comets, and populate the Oort cloud in the time available. Moreover, if the placement efficiency was as low as Safronov had claimed, the suggestion of a huge initial mass of comets in the protoplanetary disc had the added advantage (*cf.* Section 10.2.4, p.221) that it was in principle possible to accommodate a current mass of comets in the Oort cloud on the order of 1–$10\,M_\oplus$.

Safronov's suggestion that the initial cometary mass must have been greater than the total observed mass of the planets was the first explicit recognition of the potentially crucial importance of comets to understanding the origin of the solar system. Previously, as we have seen, comets had been considered as mere 'by-products' of planet formation, and therefore as relatively minor players in the overall scheme; but from this time on the rôles were reversed: comets being increasingly seen as fundamental, the next most important thing to the sun in terms of mass, and planets as mere by-products of comet formation!

11

Standard model

"There now seems to be more value in eliminating theories than in proposing them."

S.J. Weidenschilling.

11.1 Formation problem

Safronov's planetesimal picture for the origin of comets provided an attractive scenario within which to explain observations of comets and the solar system. However, apart from relying on a specific model for the evolution of the protosolar nebula (see Morfill & Völk 1984, Lin & Papaloizou 1985, Cameron 1985, and Hayashi *et al.* 1985 for alternative theories of this general type), the particular suggestion so far as comets were concerned clearly involved some rather fine tuning. For example, the problem of the timescale of planet formation seemed to require that the original nebula was much more massive than the sum of the observed planetary masses — though not so great as to vitiate the assumption of a low-mass protoplanetary disc. It was also necessary to show that an efficient mechanism did indeed operate to remove just the right amount of material from the region of the observed planets, whilst simultaneously placing the appropriate amount of material into the Oort cloud so that, after allowing for subsequent losses due to stellar perturbations, the observed near-parabolic flux could be explained.

Later work on the standard model, adopting a low-mass, quiescent protoplanetary nebula, has tended to focus on one or another of these general difficulties. For example, Hills (1973) gave independent arguments for the formation of comets in the Uranus-Neptune zone of the nebula, and estimated that comet-like bodies might accumulate at this distance from the sun in around 10^8 yr (*loc. cit.*, Table V), with a timescale for the final accumulation of the outer planets of about 2×10^9 years,

237

almost half the age of the solar system. On the other hand, Safronov's assumption of a much higher dust surface density in the Uranus-Neptune zone of the disc led to the difficulty that the former rather good agreement between the masses of observed comets and the value of m_{crit} (equation 10.9, p.229) was now spoilt. The masses of the first planetesimals to form at about Neptune's distance from the sun were now at least a thousand times larger than that of a typical comet, thereby casting doubt on the validity of the original identification of planetesimals as both observed cometary nuclei *and* as the building blocks of the outer planets.

In this chapter, we briefly review the main results of these recent investigations into topics primarily associated with the planetesimal picture: the processes leading from dust to planetesimals, and the formation and evolution of the Oort cloud itself.

11.1.1   PLANETESIMAL SIZES

The problem of the formation and early growth of planetesimals in the protoplanetary disc has been discussed by a large number of authors during the past decade (*e.g.* Adachi *et al.* 1976, Weidenschilling 1977b, 1980, 1987; Biermann & Michel 1978, Coradini *et al.* 1981, Sekiya 1983, Greenberg *et al.* 1984, Nakagawa *et al.* 1981, 1983, 1986, Yamamoto & Kozasa 1988, Nakano 1987, 1988; Weidenschilling *et al.* 1989). This work has generally shown that, especially in its initial stages, grain growth is a complex process involving competition between several important physical effects. Problems include determining the motions of grains of different sizes past one another; the question of coagulation or fragmentation of grains as a result of mutual collisions; tidal dissipation of the planetesimal motions during close encounters with one another; the differential settling of grains of different sizes towards mid-plane and the timescale of this process; and the aggregation of the largest grains, 'snowballs' or planetesimals by gravitational instability or some other process when their surface density near mid-plane reaches some critical value.

For example, important arguments *against* the usual gravitational instability picture for combining small dust-grain aggregates in the protoplanetary disc into larger bodies have recently been given by Weidenschilling (1987) and associates. However, if one does accept this general picture as a mechanism for comet formation, a possible way of resolving the dilemma posed by the excessive initial mass of planetesimals might be to assume the largest grains will rapidly settle towards mid-plane. This could allow the local gravitational instability, when it occurs, to affect only a relatively small proportion of the overall surface density, perhaps as low as $\approx 10^{-2} \Sigma$ (Greenberg *et al.* 1984). In this way, one might reconcile the apparent need for a higher total surface density with the requirement to form planetesimals with masses similar to those of observed comets. Indeed, some have argued that some such process *must* have occurred, since gravitational perturbations by the more massive planetesimals in the distribution would otherwise have tended to increase the velocities of the first-formed cometary bodies in the Uranus-Neptune zone to such an extent that they would have been destroyed by collisions long before Neptune became large enough to begin populating the Oort cloud (Greenberg 1985). However, Nakano (1988) has recently argued that observations of the β Pictoris circumstellar dust disc are incompatible with any reduction of the theoretical value of m_{crit} by more than a factor of about 50.

It may be necessary on this picture, therefore, to explore alternative explanations to non-homologous sedimentation of grains as a way of overcoming the problem of the excessive initial mass of planetesimals. In particular, rather than directly identifying planetesimals with cometary nuclei, one might instead assume that they are simply by-products of the physical and dynamical evolution of the first-formed planetesimals. For example, a gravitationally unstable region of original mass m_{crit} might undergo a hierarchy of fragmentation events during its contraction (e.g. Biermann & Michel 1978), or the subsequent process of ejection of planetesimals to the Oort cloud by close gravitational encounters with the growing planets might lead to repeated fragmentation of the initially loosely bound nuclei (*cf.* Öpik 1973). None of these qualitative suggestions has yet been closely examined, however, nor have they yet been shown definitely to explain the mass spectrum of observed comets.

11.1.2 SCATTERING RATES

Setting these difficulties with the 'physics' of comet formation aside, the remaining investigations into the planetesimal picture have tended to focus on the apparently simpler question of the dynamical evolution of an initial population of planetesimals assumed to be present in the outer protoplanetary disc. Among the first to consider this problem in detail were Ip (1977) and Fernández (1978).

These authors discussed the problem of the gravitational scattering of planetesimals, initially assumed to lie in nearly circular orbits, by the major planets Jupiter, Saturn, Uranus and Neptune, assuming that these planets had essentially their present masses and orbits. Ip showed that on the order of 60% of the comets or planetesimals initially in Neptune's ring would be scattered inwards to the control of another planet, ultimately to be either ejected or accreted (or, presumably, dissipated by solar radiation as a short-period comet). In the case of bodies initially in the Uranus zone, only 10% were ejected by Uranus or remained in its vicinity, while the majority (this time almost 80%) were again transferred inwards eventually to be captured or finally ejected by Jupiter or Saturn. These results may be compared with Everhart's (1977) numerical study of the capture of short-period comets, which showed that about 60% of the comets initially under the gravitational influence of Uranus were eventually transferred inwards to the control of Saturn, while about 50% of those initially under Saturn's influence were eventually transferred to Jupiter. These studies taken together suggest that between 60% and 70% of the planetesimals initially present in the Uranus-Neptune zone of the protoplanetary disc will probably be scattered inwards, to an eventual fate (probable ejection) governed by Jupiter or Saturn.

Fernández's (1978) study, on the other hand, was directed towards establishing the fate of the ejected comets, and at last gave a convincing demonstration of the greater efficiency of Uranus and Neptune in relation to Jupiter and Saturn at producing comets with orbits in the 'safety' of the Oort cloud. (This result had of course been anticipated by Kuiper, Safronov and Öpik on the ground that the outer planets produced much smaller energy changes per revolution than Jupiter or Saturn.)

In particular, Fernández (1978, Table 1) showed that for his preferred assumptions the ratio of the number of comets injected into nearly parabolic orbits to those ejected hyperbolically was about 0.018, 0.060, 0.30 and 0.45, for Jupiter, Saturn, Uranus and Neptune respectively. Here we should mention that Fernández's definition of 'nearly parabolic' in this context corresponded to a range of $1/a$ roughly equal to $2 \times 10^{-4}\,\mathrm{AU}^{-1}$, about five times greater than that $(3.75 \times 10^{-5}\,\mathrm{AU}^{-1})$ considered by Safronov (1972) as producing effective placement in the Oort cloud. Fernández's figures may therefore be approximately interpreted as referring to the production of comets with semimajor axes $a \gtrsim 5\,000\,\mathrm{AU}$.

A later study by Fernández & Ip (1981) addressed nearly the same problem and incorporated several technical improvements to the early models. In particular, they improved the treatment of the relatively weak, though more numerous, 'diffusive' encounters that had formerly been ignored, and they allowed for a period of extended growth of Uranus and Neptune by starting these planets with smaller initial masses, equal to 10% of their present values. From this investigation, it was concluded that the above figures for the production ratio of nearly parabolic to hyperbolic orbits should be revised upwards to 0.03 and 0.16 in the case of Jupiter and Saturn respectively, whilst the equivalent figures for populating the Oort cloud with comets from the Uranus-Neptune zone increased by factors of order 4–6 to the values 1.3 and 2.6 for Uranus and Neptune respectively. Put another way, whereas $\approx 65\%$ of the comets initially in the Uranus-Neptune zone would probably be scattered inwards, to a fate largely determined by Jupiter or Saturn (based on the results of Ip and Everhart), the remaining 35% (scattered outwards) were successfully placed in the Oort cloud with efficiencies of order 57% (1.3/2.3) and 72% (2.6/3.6) for Uranus and Neptune respectively. In a similar way, the efficiencies with which Jupiter and Saturn ejected comets to the Oort cloud were 3% and 14% respectively.

Subsequent studies (*e.g.* Fernández & Ip 1983a, 1984; Greenberg *et al.* 1984, Greenberg 1985) have included a number of more complicated physical effects into these models, and have generally drawn attention to a wide variety of possible predictions (and difficulties) with the general picture. For example, the inclusion of gas drag and the effects of collisions with the smallest particles in the disc will probably cause the motions of the smaller comets to be more efficiently damped, allowing the larger ones to be preferentially ejected to the Oort cloud. On the other hand, the obliquities of the orbits of Uranus and Neptune and their axial inclinations to the ecliptic suggest that the accretion of large planetesimals, perhaps with masses as large as $1\,M_\oplus$, may have occurred during the later stages of the formation of the outer planets. It is not known whether the Oort cloud now includes any bodies of lunar size or greater, and most astronomers usually assume (or hope!) that the cometary mass function does not extend that far.

These recent investigations into the formation of the Oort cloud in the context of the planetesimal hypothesis, while leading to a growing number of models of ever increasing detail and complexity, have not yet achieved the hoped-for universal agreement among theorists. Nevertheless, the conclusions drawn by various authors do overlap in several important respects, especially concerning the efficiency of the formation of the Oort cloud and the timescale on which it is built. In particular, planetesimals formed in a given protoplanetary zone appear to have a probability rather greater than a half of being scattered inwards to the control of the next inner planet (*cf.* Fernández 1980a); and the timescale for the formation of Uranus and Neptune (whose perturbations are most effective at generating the Oort cloud) is typically in the range 2×10^8 to 10^9 years.

11.2   Producing the Oort cloud

11.2.1   EFFICIENCY FACTOR

The question of the efficiency of the formation of the Oort cloud is crucial to theories of this general type, and it is therefore worth describing a simple model of cloud formation which takes these conclusions into account. Thus, following Fernández (1978), we may assume that the total mass eventually ejected from the zone of each giant planet is a constant factor f (to be determined) times the mass $m_{s,i}$ of solids and condensibles now associated with each major planet ($i = 1, 2, 3, 4$ for Jupiter, Saturn, Uranus and Neptune respectively). These masses are only approximately known, and we here assume $m_{s,1} = 45\,M_\oplus$ (Jupiter), $m_{s,2} = 30\,M_\oplus$ (Saturn), $m_{s,3} = 12\,M_\oplus$ (Uranus) and $m_{s,4} = 14\,M_\oplus$ (Neptune). These values may be compared with the present total masses of the planets ($317.7\,M_\oplus$, $95.2\,M_\oplus$, $14.5\,M_\oplus$ and $17.1\,M_\oplus$ respectively), and also with detailed models of their internal composition and structure (*cf.* Podolak & Cameron 1974, Podolak & Reynolds 1985).

We also follow Fernández & Ip (1981) in assuming that of the planetesimals ejected outwards from each protoplanetary zone, 3%, 14%, 57% and 72% are successfully placed in the Oort cloud (corresponding to semi-major axes in the approximate range 5×10^3–10^5 AU) by the perturbations of Jupiter, Saturn, Uranus and Neptune respectively. Lastly, although it is undoubtedly an oversimplification to represent the complex dynamical interactions between planetesimals and protoplanets by means of a single transfer probability, the results obtained by a number of authors during the past decade (*e.g.* Ip 1977, Everhart 1977,

Shoemaker & Wolfe 1984a, Duncan *et al.* 1988) are all broadly
consistent with the statement that about 65% of the comets or
planetesimals in each planetary zone are scattered inwards to
the control of the next planet.

On this simple model of Oort cloud formation, 65% of the
planetesimals in Neptune's zone (with an initial total mass of
$14f\,M_{\oplus}$) will be scattered inwards to the temporary control of
Uranus, while about 25% (0.35×0.72) are scattered to the Oort
cloud, the remaining 10% (0.35×0.28) being directly ejected
into hyperbolic orbits. Applying the same procedure to Uranus,
Saturn and Jupiter in turn, allowing for augmentation of the
planetesimal masses in each zone by inward scattering of bodies
from further out, finally gives the results shown in Table 11.1.
The original mass of the Oort cloud may thus be estimated to be
on the order of $10f\,M_{\oplus}$, while the net placement efficiency for
planetesimals initially in each protoplanetary zone is of order
1%, 5%, 20% and 25% for Jupiter, Saturn, Uranus and Neptune respectively. This gives an overall efficiency for forming
the Oort cloud of order 10%. The remaining 90% of comets
that are lost divide into two roughly equal groups which are either ejected hyperbolically or scattered inwards (ultimately to
be lost into short-period orbits, ejection or decay). The fact that
these placement efficiencies are broadly in line with those previously estimated by Oort, Öpik and others, strongly suggests
that Safronov (see Table 10.1) underestimated the net formation
efficiency of the Oort cloud by about an order of magnitude.

In order to determine the parameter f on this model, and
hence estimate the actual planetesimal masses required in each
zone, we have to compare this original Oort cloud mass with
constraints implied by observations. A recent model of the Oort
cloud (Bailey & Stagg 1988) suggests that the present mass
of comets brighter than absolute magnitude $H_0 = 16$ is about
$14\,M_{\oplus}$. This must be less than the original mass, due to evolutionary losses over the age of the solar system, and if we conser-
vatively assume that the present mass is about half the original
value we obtain an original mass for the Oort cloud of order

Region	M_{init} $(fM_\oplus)$	M_{aug} $(fM_\oplus)$	M_{in} $(fM_\oplus)$	M_{hyp} $(fM_\oplus)$	M_{Oort} $(fM_\oplus)$
Neptune	14.0	14.0	9.1	1.4	3.5
Uranus	12.0	21.1	13.7	3.2	4.2
Saturn	30.0	43.7	28.4	13.2	2.1
Jupiter	45.0	73.4	47.7	24.9	0.8
Total	101.0		47.7	42.7	10.6

Table 11.1: The fate of the planetesimals ejected by the giant planets and the formation of the Oort cloud. M_{init} is the initial mass of solids assumed in each protoplanetary zone, M_{aug} represents the initial mass augmented with that transferred in from zones further out, M_{in} is the mass transferred inwards to the control of the next planet, M_{hyp} is the mass directly ejected to hyperbolic orbits by each planet, and M_{Oort} is the mass ejected to the Oort cloud. In the case of Jupiter, M_{in} is eventually lost either by hyperbolic ejection or physical decay. All masses are expressed in units of $fM_\oplus$, where $f \simeq 2\text{–}10$.

$30\,M_\oplus$, indicating $f \simeq 3$. The total initial mass of planetesimals is therefore required to be about $300\,M_\oplus$. Such a figure is broadly consistent with the estimates independently obtained by Fernández & Ip 1983a, 1984), though it must be emphasized that the proportion of primordial comets that might survive for the age of the solar system is not securely known (see Section 12.2, p.254), and larger values of f (and hence larger original masses) may turn out to be necessary (cf. Section 18.1.2, p.432).

The uncertainties in these kinds of estimate are still too large to allow firm conclusions to be drawn concerning the overall validity of the planetesimal hypothesis, but the argument provides an interesting illustration of how the planetesimal picture is now tightly constrained by a number of independent lines of argument. In particular, it is clear that a successful model must now explain (a) how the observed planets can be formed fast enough to eject comets on a reasonable timescale; (b) how the cloud had just the right initial mass that, after evolution, the observed cometary flux is produced; and (c) how studies of the long-term evolution of the cloud and the predicted cometary flux can be reconciled, for example, with observations of the long-term cratering record on the surfaces of the earth, moon and other planets (*cf.* Shoemaker & Wolfe 1982). We return to this important last question in Chapter 17. Moreover, since it is not immediately obvious that all these requirements can be met simultaneously within the planetesimal picture, the detailed predictions of this type of model are now looked upon with growing interest as possibly providing a firm basis for testing — and even ruling out — the theory.

11.2.2   FORMATION TIMESCALE

As already noted, another general conclusion implied by these recent investigations is that the timescale for the accumulation of Uranus and Neptune is typically in the range 2×10^8–10^9 years. This means that the formation of the Oort cloud will be necessarily delayed until these planets have attained a reasonable fraction of their final masses. The generation of the Oort cloud is therefore a long drawn-out affair on the planetesimal picture, and it is quite possible that its growth would not have been completed until well after the sun had emerged from its (presumed) parent molecular cloud and local star cluster.

An important consequence of this extended period of growth for the outer planets, particularly in relation to the more rapid formation of the inner planets, is that the late stages of lunar cratering (the 'late heavy bombardment'; *e.g.* Wetherill 1975, Fernández & Ip 1981, 1983a; Shoemaker & Wolfe 1984a) may be explained as a result of impacts of planetesimals scattered inwards from the Uranus-Neptune zone to the inner solar system. Indeed, it is possible that the existence of water and other volatile material on the inner planets — even life itself — may be attributed in part to the impacts of cometary bodies ultimately derived from the Uranus-Neptune zone of the protoplanetary disc (e.g. Ip & Fernández 1988, and review by Weissman 1988); while an indication that the planetesimal mass function might have extended up to quite large values ($\approx 0.1\,M_{\oplus}$) is provided by recent interpretations of the early history, for example, of the planet Mercury (e.g. Stewart 1988) and of the formation of the moon (Newsom & Taylor 1989).

By this stage in the search for a broad understanding of the origin of comets, therefore, one cannot fail to be impressed by the large number of investigators who have been involved in attempts to perfect the planetesimal picture as an explanation both for the origin of protoplanets and for the formation of the Oort cloud itself. To the onlooker, who may not be deeply involved in the enquiry, the sheer weight of astronomers devoted to the task is perhaps enough to convince him that the end of the tunnel is in sight: there is a sense, then, in which this picture of the Oort cloud and the associated origin of comets has come to be regarded as standard. On the other hand, to the participant perhaps more acutely aware of the many loose ends that remain to be tied, there is also a sense in which progress with the 'standard model' has, after thirty years, become disappointingly slow. After so much attention, one is bound to ask whether this pattern of progress (as we have described in Chapters 9–11) relates as much to the availability of well-drilled intellectual talent and computer capacity intent on a single theme, as it does to the manner in which uncertain details of cometary cosmogony have yet to be resolved.

In fact, as we show particularly in the following Chapters 14 and 15, throughout the period in question there was a growing phalanx of astronomers who, suspecting that the problems with the standard model were more deep-seated than are generally assumed, speculated whether more profitable lines of enquiry should not be considered. Whilst such speculations enabled one to see, with perhaps much greater clarity, the weaknesses and strengths of the standard model, they also created a climate of opinion in which there was a readiness to pit new astronomical observations, seemingly unrelated at first, against the prevailing paradigm. We shall see, in fact, that two major developments in the late nineteen-seventies did eventually make their mark. First, an increasing knowledge of the cratering record on planetary surfaces; and secondly, a growing awareness of potentially destructive influences on the Oort cloud, forces which had previously not been recognized, and which may be ultimately traced to the clumpy nature of the interstellar material and to the sun's varying position in the Galaxy. It is to these harmful 'galactic' effects on the Oort cloud that we now turn.

12

Galactic upheaval

"Though the heavens be glorious, they are not all stars!"

Anon.

12.1 New perturbers

Despite the attention which has recently been given to the origin of comets on the planetesimal picture and the associated mode of formation of the Oort cloud, it is important to realize that an almost equal amount of effort has been directed also at the question of the *disruption* of the Oort cloud. At first sight it may seem perverse that the problem of the evolution of the Oort cloud should receive such attention when its *origin* remains controversial; but we do know that a cloud exists (we see comets coming from great distances), and the problem of the long-term evolution of cometary orbits is itself a question with far-reaching implications irrespective of the precise theory of the origin of comets (*e.g.* whether solar system or interstellar). It is for this reason, as much as any other, that investigators into the long-term evolution of the Oort cloud have tended to skirt around the difficulties associated with the cloud's primordial origin, and have usually started simply by postulating an initial distribution of ready-formed comets, with original orbits extending more or less to fill the whole of the current cloud.

As it turned out, the late nineteen-seventies and early eighties saw two significant advances in our general understanding of the processes affecting the evolution of the Oort cloud. Interestingly, both may be traced to unforeseen developments which occurred largely outside the field of cometary astronomy: first, the importance of molecular cloud perturbations, related to the discovery of massive gas clouds in the Galaxy by high-resolution radio surveys using emission from the carbon monoxide (CO) molecule; and secondly, the effect of the galactic tide, whose importance was recognized largely as a consequence of renewed interest in the idea that terrestrial catastrophism might be caused by a varying rate of cometary impacts fundamentally driven by galactic cyclicities (see Chapters 16 and 17). These developments have important implications for understanding the evolution and disruption of the Oort cloud, and it is appropriate that we should describe each in some detail.

The purpose of these evolutionary studies of course, at least within the framework provided by the standard model, is to determine the proportion of those comets originally created in a protoplanetary disc which might reasonably be expected to survive within the Oort cloud *in situ* for the age of the solar system. The result, skipping slightly ahead, is that the standard Oort (1950) model of the comet cloud cannot survive. As we have already indicated, this has stimulated growing interest in the development of alternative models, particularly whether the 'observed' Oort cloud is in fact derived dynamically from a massive inward extension of the primordial nebula, otherwise described as a 'dense inner core' of the Oort cloud; or whether it might recently have been captured during passage of the solar system through a dense molecular cloud or spiral arm. We take up some of these issues in the following Chapters 13 to 15, but here concentrate simply on the question of the cloud's dynamical evolution, looking first at the importance of molecular cloud perturbations.

12.1.1   Molecular clouds

The high-resolution carbon monoxide radio maps which first demonstrated the existence of massive concentrations of molecular gas in the Milky Way first became available from about the mid nineteen-seventies. They showed that a significant fraction of the mass of the interstellar medium is confined to a relatively small number of cold, massive gas clouds, each with a typical mass and radius of about $3 \times 10^5 \, M_\odot$ and 20 pc respectively, the total mass of the system being around $10^9 \, M_\odot$ (*e.g.* Sanders *et al.*

1984, 1985). The potential importance for comets of close passages past such massive nebulae was first appreciated at the end of the nineteen-seventies (e.g. Biermann 1978, Napier & Clube 1979, Clube & Napier 1982a, 1983) and, depending on factors such as the past history of the solar orbit in the Galaxy and the time-evolution of the molecular cloud system, there may have been as many as 5–15 penetrative encounters of giant molecular clouds by the solar system during its lifetime (e.g. Napier & Staniucha 1982, Bailey 1983a). Indeed, it was appreciated quite early on that the relative importance of these *penetrating* encounters with giant molecular clouds would be enhanced relative to grazing 'fly-by' encounters, due to the clumpy, rather than smooth, nature of the observed internal structure of the clouds; occasional passages of the solar system past exceptionally dense, concentrated 'substructure' within the cloud having a relatively more damaging effect (cf. Staniucha & Banaszkiewicz 1988, Wasserman 1988).

That such encounters may lead to the destruction of the conventional Oort cloud can readily be seen by evaluating the relative velocity change for a typical comet in Oort's 1950-model of the cloud. Thus (cf. equation 9.5, p.189), assuming the impulse approximation is valid, the relative velocity imparted to such a comet with semi-major axis a by a cloud of mass M is of order

$$\Delta v \simeq \frac{3GMa}{b^2V} \tag{12.1}$$

where b and V respectively denote the impact parameter of the cloud and its overall speed with respect to the sun (Hills 1981). Even a grazing encounter ($b = 20\,\mathrm{pc}$) at a representative velocity $V = 20\,\mathrm{km\,s^{-1}}$, with a giant molecular cloud of mass $M = 3 \times 10^5\,M_\odot$, will give a comet of semi-major axis $a = 5.0 \times 10^4\,\mathrm{AU}$ an impulse of order $\Delta v \simeq 120\,\mathrm{m\,s^{-1}}$, rather greater than the escape velocity at the corresponding aphelion distance for such a comet. Since such encounters are expected to have occurred at least several times during the lifetime of the solar system, they clearly have had a devastating effect on the extended, loosely bound system of comets originally envisaged by Oort.

12.1.2   GALACTIC DISC

In the same way that perturbations from passing stars and molecular clouds deflect comets in their orbits about the sun, so too it was recognized that the overall distribution of matter in the Galaxy may also produce a slight 'tidal' disturbance of the sun-comet system, causing small, but still significant long-term changes in the otherwise constant elliptical cometary orbits of large perihelia about the sun. The first to comment on the possible importance of the Galaxy in relation to cometary orbits seem to have been Armellini (1922) and van Woerkom (1948); subsequent investigators (e.g. Chebotarev 1964, 1965, 1966; Antonov & Latyshev 1972, Wyatt & Faintich 1971, Bailey 1977, Van Flandern 1978a, Ovenden & Byl 1978), although confirming that a marginally significant effect did exist, particularly in the outer parts of the Oort cloud (where the orbits of the longest period comets were shown to be significantly affected by the galactic tidal field, and where the surfaces of equal cometary density within the cloud were predicted to be definitely non-spherical), generally concluded that the Galaxy would be a relatively unimportant perturber of cometary orbits.

The situation changed rather suddenly around 1985, however, when, following discussions by Byl (1983) on perturbations by an assumed point-mass Galaxy and by Smoluchowski & Torbett (1984) on the three-dimensional shape of the Oort cloud under the influence of a more realistic galactic potential, a number of astronomers independently reinvestigated the importance of the galactic tide (Torbett 1986a,b; Morris & Muller 1986, Heisler & Tremaine 1986, Byl 1986). These authors seem to have realized almost simultaneously that the tidal effects of the Galaxy, especially those due to forces perpendicular to the plane, could no longer be ignored, and the rapidly developing understanding of cometary dynamics opened what may now be seen as a Pandora's Box of potentially important interactions between the Galaxy and the solar system, with many implications for processes both on earth and within the larger planetary system (see Smoluchowski *et al.* 1986, and Chapter 16.)

However, the effect of the galactic tide on the lifetime of the Oort cloud is more subtle than that formerly considered for the case of molecular clouds, for the tide hardly changes the cometary energies at all. In fact, its principal effect is simply to alter the orbital angular momenta in a more or less regular way, causing comets with initially small perihelia to move out to larger q-values, and those with initially large perihelia to move in towards smaller q-values, thereby taking them closer to the planetary system.

The ways that this affects the survival of cometary orbits are two-fold. First, since the orbital energy is almost unchanged, as the perihelion distance q decreases so the aphelion distance increases, and hence a comet of given semi-major axis may spend relatively more of its time at large heliocentric distance. Since the mean energy transfer rate due to stars and molecular clouds tends to increase rapidly with increasing distance from the sun, this means that, other things being equal, the galactic tide subjects all comets to a slightly increased net disruptive effect of external perturbations.

The second process is related to the rate of stirring up of the Oort cloud as a result of the changing perihelion distances of its constituent comets. Comets which might otherwise have been considered 'safe' from ejection by planetary perturbations are steadily reintroduced into orbits of small perihelion distance, from which they are either ejected into interstellar space or captured as short-period orbits subsequently to decay. Ultimately, this also depletes the Oort cloud, and it turns out that under some circumstances this process can be comparable in importance to orbit energization itself in reducing the population of the standard Oort cloud. The net effect of the galactic tide, as indeed for molecular clouds, is therefore to assist the overall disruption of the Oort cloud, with the important result that both these newly discovered perturbers of the Oort cloud combine to produce a substantial reduction in the net lifetime of the Oort cloud based on the standard model.

12.2   Oort cloud disruption

12.2.1   ENERGY TRANSFER RATE REVISED

The first attempts to determine the exact rate at which energy is transferred to cometary orbits in the Oort cloud were based on the belief that rapidly passing stars were the only important perturbers involved (Section 9.1.4, p.189). As we have seen, however, occasional passages by and through massive molecular clouds are also important, and the value of the mean energy transfer rate has therefore to be revised. As before, the primary goal of such calculations is to determine how quickly these various perturbing influences systematically remove comets from the solar system, thereby providing a way of estimating the overall rate of disruption of the comet cloud. These studies may then be used to estimate the number of comets which were originally necessary in the assumed primordial Oort cloud in order to explain those we now see.

As indicated by equation (9.6), the general expression for the mean energy transfer rate vs. semi-major axis, $\dot{\varepsilon}(a)$, can be divided into two parts. First, a term proportional to $M^2 n/V$, where M, n and V are the mean mass, number density and relative velocity of the perturbers in question; and secondly, a term that depends solely on the ratio a/a_c, where a_c is approximately 1.3 times the expected minimum distance of approach b_{min} of the perturbers to the sun during the time over which $\dot{\varepsilon}(a)$ is evaluated. If the perturbers are stars, and therefore very numerous, many will pass *through* the Oort cloud during the age of the solar system, so the semi-major axes of typical comets in the Oort cloud will generally satisfy $a \gg a_c$. In this case, the mean energy transfer rate depends only weakly (*i.e.* logarithmically) on semi-major axis, and can be approximated by a constant. Thus, the mean stellar energy transfer rate can be roughly described by $\dot{\varepsilon}_*(a) \simeq A_* =$ constant, where

$$A_* \simeq \frac{4\pi\, G^2 M_*^2 n_*}{V_*}\, I_* \approx 10^{-13}\ \mathrm{m^2\, s^{-3}} \qquad (12.2)$$

and I_*, to represent the slowly varying logarithmic function, is on the order of 10 for comets with orbits in the outer parts of the Oort cloud. If we adopt the formerly assumed mean values for $M_*^2 n_*/V_*$, i.e. $\langle M_* n_*/V_* \rangle \simeq 0.04\, M_\odot^2\ \mathrm{pc^{-3}}/30\,\mathrm{km\,s^{-1}}$, we have $A_* \simeq 10^{-13}\ \mathrm{m^2\, s^{-3}}$.

On the other hand, if the dominant perturbers are few and far between, as is the case for giant molecular clouds, then even the closest encounter during the age of the solar system will have an impact parameter many times greater than the size of the Oort cloud. Hence, for perturbers satisfying this constraint, we should evaluate the mean energy transfer rate in the limit $a \ll a_c$. Equation (9.6) now shows that the mean energy transfer rate varies roughly quadratically with semi-major axis, i.e. $\dot{\varepsilon}(a) \propto a^2$. In this case, therefore, we may write $\dot{\varepsilon}(a)$ in the approximate form

$$\dot{\varepsilon}_c(a) \simeq A_c\, a^2 \qquad (12.3)$$

where A_c is a constant (cf. Bailey 1986b) given in terms of $\rho = Mn$ and the age, T, of the solar system by

$$A_c \simeq 14\pi^2 G^2 \rho^2 T/3 \qquad (12.4)$$

Note that this expression for the mean energy transfer rate is now independent of the uncertain parameters M and V, and depends only on the total mass density ρ of the perturbers and on the time, T, over which the average is taken. (The mean energy transfer rate increases with T because the closest encounter during a given time interval always has a disproportionate effect, and as T increases, so the closest encounter become steadily closer, until eventually the assumption $a \ll a_c$ breaks down.)

In reality, of course, although such an expression might be used to describe perturbations of the Oort cloud by a rarefied population of point masses such as black holes (which have sometimes been introduced to explain the apparent 'missing mass' in the galactic disc), if one seeks to determine the perturbations of the Oort cloud by observed molecular clouds it is important to include the fact that these gas clouds have a finite size. Inevitably, although a significant fraction of the mass of such bodies may be confined to dense, compact subclouds, the finite sizes of the clouds have the effect of decreasing the overall mean energy transfer rate to a value somewhat less than that given by (12.4). Allowing for the finite extent of the clouds, therefore, and the likelihood of compact substructure within them, it can be shown (*cf.* Bailey 1986a, Hut & Tremaine 1985) that the mean energy transfer rate by molecular cloud perturbations is still given by an expression of the form of equation (12.3), but now with

$$A_c \approx \frac{4\pi G^2 M_{\mathrm{GMC}}^2 n_{\mathrm{GMC}}}{V_{\mathrm{GMC}}} \frac{3}{R_{\mathrm{GMC}}^2} \tag{12.5}$$

where $R_{\mathrm{GMC}} \simeq 20\,\mathrm{pc}$ is the r.m.s. radius of the giant molecular clouds and V_{GMC} is their mean relative velocity with respect to the sun. Introducing appropriate mean values of these quantities averaged along the mean solar orbit in the Galaxy during the age of the solar system (*e.g.* $M_{\mathrm{GMC}} \simeq 3 \times 10^5\,M_\odot$, $n_{\mathrm{GMC}} \simeq 40\,(\mathrm{kpc})^{-3}$, and $V_{\mathrm{GMC}} \simeq 20\,\mathrm{km\,s}^{-1}$; *cf.* discussion by Bailey 1986a), we finally obtain $A_c \simeq 10^{-44}\,\mathrm{s}^{-3}$. The total mean energy transfer rate by stars and molecular clouds may thus be approximately represented by

$$\dot{\varepsilon}(a) = A_* + A_c\, a^2 \tag{12.6}$$

where $A_* \simeq 10^{-13}\,\mathrm{m^2\,s}^{-3}$, $A_c \simeq 10^{-44}\,\mathrm{s}^{-3}$ and the semi-major axis a is expressed in metres.

12.2.2 OORT CLOUD HALF-LIFE

The importance of the mean energy transfer rate is that it allows the survival probability of cometary orbits in the Oort cloud to be evaluated, and provides a means of comparing the stability of orbits with different initial semi-major axes. For example,

the form of equation (12.6) shows that the mean energy transfer rate increases with increasing semi-major axis, and hence
demonstrates that the largest orbits — those with the least
binding energy — are proportionately more rapidly disrupted.
Since according to Oort's 1950 model of the comet cloud more
than half the comets lie at heliocentric distances greater than
7×10^4 AU (cf. equation 9.3), the time required to disrupt such
long period orbits is of great interest. Moreover, the particular
form of equation (12.6) shows that comets with semi-major axes
$a \gtrsim (A_*/A_c)^{1/2} \simeq 2 \times 10^4$ AU are, on the average, most affected
by molecular clouds, and experience a mean energy transfer rate
increasing as a^2.

Thus, once comets achieve semi-major axes greater than
about 2×10^4 AU, they gain orbital energy at an ever greater
rate (roughly proportional to a^2) and are rapidly lost from the
solar system into interstellar space. These results, together with
the fact that comets are *observed* to come from distances greater
than 2×10^4 AU (the whole of the 'spike' of the $1/a$ distribution is
produced by such comets), have thrown the question of the survival of such long-period comets for the age of the solar system
into sharp relief.

A detailed discussion of how one may use the above expression for the mean energy transfer rate to determine the half-life
of the Oort cloud is given in Appendix A.1 (p.483). Here, we
define the half-life of a cometary orbit of initial semi-major axis
a to be the time after which exactly half the initial number
of such comets are lost from the system; the results described
in the Appendix show that this is longer than the age of the
solar system (4.5×10^9 yr) only for those comets with initial orbits having $a \lesssim 10^4$ AU. In other words, the half-life of comets
with original semi-major axes of order 10^4 AU is on the order of
the age of the solar system, while the number of comets with
initial semi-major axes greater than 2×10^4 AU is seriously depleted after times of order 10^9 yr (cf. Wasserman 1988). The
observed long-period comets (which come from distances in the
Oort cloud greater than 4×10^4 AU) cannot then have been in

such long-period orbits for the age of the solar system, and must therefore have originated elsewhere, either closer in (in a dense inner core to the Oort cloud) or further out (in interstellar space, and so recently captured).

These recent analytic results on the evolution of the Oort cloud under the influence of both stellar and molecular cloud perturbations, together with inferences drawn from a number of more detailed Monte Carlo studies (see Appendix A.2, p.486, for a brief review), therefore strongly indicate that the majority of primordial comets that start with initial semi-major axes greater than about 10^4 AU are likely to have been lost from the solar system, although those beginning with semi-major axes less than 10^4 AU *could* survive (some of these by now having diffused outwards in radius so as to fill the whole of the conventional Oort cloud up to $r \simeq R_0 = 2 \times 10^5$ AU).

Obviously, the precise number of comets that are initially required in order to explain the number we now see is inextricably linked with the question of the original distribution of primordial comets. The survival and evolution of the Oort cloud for timescales comparable to the age of the solar system therefore provide important indirect constraints on theories which assume a primordial origin for comets. If the comets were initially concentrated in orbits having relatively small semi-major axes, it is possible that depletion effects might be quite small, so that the ratio of the original number of comets to the present number might be limited to a factor on the order of 2 or less. On the other hand, if the original comets mostly had orbits with $a \gtrsim 2 \times 10^4$ AU, the present number would then represent a relatively small fraction of those originally present, indicating the occurrence of substantial losses from the Oort cloud since its time of formation (*i.e.* an original-to-present mass ratio very much greater than 2). Indeed, whereas the planetesimal picture for comet formation predicts that the former of these possibilities is more likely to be closer to the truth, the initial proportion of comets in such tightly bound orbits could, in fact, have been so small that a more recent source of comets, such as a dense molecular cloud or nearby spiral arm, might have to be invoked (*e.g.* Clube & Napier 1982a).

12.3   Tidal influence

We now describe some of the detailed effects of the galactic tide on the Oort cloud, following the general approach developed by Byl (1986) and Heisler & Tremaine (1986). The effects of the galactic tide, as with any other tidal perturbation, are essentially produced by the varying intensity of the gravitational force at the position of the sun compared with that at the comet. In other words, a comet slightly displaced from the sun feels a slightly different galactic acceleration from the sun (owing to their slightly different positions in the Galaxy), and it therefore experiences a net 'tidal' force measured relative to the sun.

The problem of evaluating this perturbation may be conveniently divided into two parts. First, the determination of the overall gravitational field of the Galaxy, which allows an estimate of the gradient of the gravitational force in the solar neighbourhood; and secondly, the calculation of the solar orbit in the Galaxy. Once the tidal perturbation on the sun-comet system has been obtained, it is then relatively straightforward to predict the effects on cometary orbits (at least to first order) by using standard procedures of celestial mechanics. Interestingly, these techniques were first developed by authors such as Lagrange and Gauss around the beginning of the nineteenth century, originally for the purpose of studying purely solar system problems arising from observed planetary, asteroidal and cometary motions in an otherwise isolated potential almost entirely dominated by the sun.

12.3.1   TIDAL FIELD ASSESSED

The general shape of our Galaxy, a fairly typical spiral galaxy of type Sbc, is rather like that of its near neighbour M 31 (the Andromeda Nebula). This galaxy lies a mere 630 kpc away (about two million light years), and has the distinction of representing the most distant point that the unaided human eye can see: it is just visible with the naked eye as a faint luminous patch high in the northern sky. We show a photograph of M 31 in Figure 12.1, in an unusual print also showing (bottom left) the presence of Comet Holmes (1892 III); an enlarged negative image of the same comet is shown in Figure 12.2.   Turning our attention to the galaxy, we immediately recognize the two main characteristics of a spiral galaxy: a massive, central 'spheroidal' component (sometimes referred to as the 'bulge'), and an extended relatively thin 'disc' feature, in which hints of spiral-arm structure are just visible. Two further photographs of spiral galaxies resembling our own Galaxy seen at different orientations are shown in Figure 12.3.

In broad outline, therefore, our Galaxy may be thought of as roughly resembling a perfectly formed fried egg! It has a massive central bulge (containing about 10% of the total mass) and an extensive circular stellar disc. Superimposed on these generally axisymmetric components are the prominent spiral arms, which contain the most massive molecular clouds in the system and are the observed sites of formation of the most massive stars in the Galaxy. These spiral arms are usually considered to arise as a result of streaming motions of stars and gas clouds moving in a weakly modulated spiral gravitational field produced by non-axisymmetric instabilities in the underlying stellar and gaseous disc of the Galaxy, although it should also be mentioned that this view is not universally held (*e.g.* Ambartsumian 1958, 1965; Clube 1988b). Be this as it may, in considering the effects of the galactic tide in this chapter, we now follow most authors in neglecting the spiral arms and concentrate on the underlying axisymmetric disc.

The assumption of axisymmetry greatly simplifies the mathematical analysis (see Appendix B, p.495), and in particular makes it convenient to introduce a galactocentric cylindrical coordinate system to specify the positions of bodies within the Galaxy. We may then represent the position of a star or comet

Figure 12.1: Photograph of M 31, the Andromeda Nebula, showing the general appearance of a spiral galaxy like our own. This photograph, taken on the 10th November 1892, also shows (bottom left) the nebulous image of Comet Holmes (1892 III). Taken from Barnard (1913).

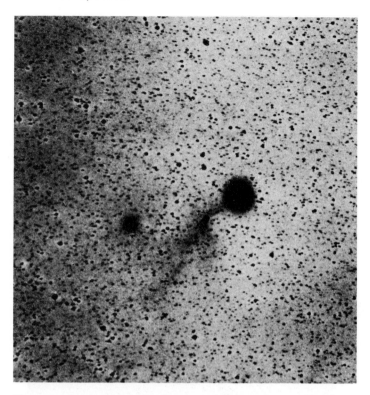

Figure 12.2: Enlarged negative image of Comet Holmes (1892 III), taken from Barnard (1913).

in the Galaxy by the vector $\mathbf{R} = (R, \Theta, Z)$, where R denotes the distance from the galactic centre projected on to the galactic plane, Θ is the angular variable measured in the direction of galactic rotation, and Z determines the height above the plane. The galactic potential ϕ_{gal} cannot then depend on the angular variable Θ (by symmetry), so we may write the gravitational acceleration of the Galaxy, $\mathbf{F}_{\text{gal}}$, in the general form $\mathbf{F}_{\text{gal}}(\mathbf{R}) = \mathbf{F}_{\text{gal}}(R, Z) = -\nabla \phi_{\text{gal}}(R, Z)$.

Thus, if we now define $\mathbf{R}_0 = (R_0, \Theta_0, Z_0)$ to be the galactic coordinates of the sun at some instant and let $\mathbf{R} = \mathbf{R}_0 + \mathbf{r}$ denote the coordinates of a comet with heliocentric position $\mathbf{r}$, the differential force between the comet and the sun — the galactic

Figure 12.3: Photographs of the spiral galaxies NGC 4565 (left) and M 81 (right), showing the thin disc-like structure and characteristic swirling arms typical of spiral galaxies like our own.

tide — is given by

$$\mathbf{F}_{\text{tide}}(\mathbf{r}, \mathbf{R}_0) = \mathbf{F}_{\text{gal}}(\mathbf{R}_0 + \mathbf{r}) - \mathbf{F}_{\text{gal}}(\mathbf{R}_0) \simeq (\mathbf{r}.\nabla)\mathbf{F}_{\text{gal}} \quad (12.7)$$

The form of this expression (*cf.* Byl 1983, 1986; Heisler & Tremaine 1986; and Appendix B.1) shows that the strength of the galactic tidal perturbation depends both on the separation of the sun-comet system (represented by the value of $\mathbf{r}$) and on the particular location of the sun in the Galaxy (represented by $\mathbf{R}_0$). To make further progress, therefore, we need to know the position of the sun in the Galaxy and the details of its orbit.

12.3.2   SOLAR ORBIT

Studies of the location of the sun in the Galaxy show that it currently lies relatively close to the galactic plane ($Z_0 \lesssim 10\,\mathrm{pc}$) at a distance of order $R_0 \simeq 8.5\,\mathrm{kpc}$ from the galactic centre. In terms of the photograph of NGC 4565 shown in Figure 12.3, we are currently close to the mid-plane of symmetry and about two-thirds the way out along the disc.

Of course, the sun cannot be exactly at rest in the Galaxy, and its present motion is, in fact, dominated by a strong circular component of velocity about the galactic centre, with a speed on the order of $220\,\mathrm{km\,s^{-1}}$. Superimposed on this predominantly circular motion, which is also that experienced by most of the sun's near neighbours in the galactic disc, is the so-called 'peculiar' solar velocity. This may be represented by a vector $\mathbf{V}_\odot$, with components currently of order $(10, 15.4, 7.8)\,\mathrm{km\,s^{-1}}$ directed respectively towards the galactic centre, parallel to the circular velocity and perpendicular to the galactic plane. In galactic coordinates this corresponds to motion towards a galactic longitude $l \simeq 60°$ (see Figure 12.4) and roughly 30° out of the plane towards the north galactic pole. This direction, incidentally can be viewed from the northern hemisphere on any summer's evening, as it lies in the constellation of Hercules ($\alpha = 18^{\mathrm{h}}, \delta = 30°$), roughly half-way between the bright stars Vega (α Lyrae) and Ras Alhague (α Ophiuchi), almost exactly opposite the molecular clouds in Orion.

The fact that the magnitude $V_\odot$ of the sun's peculiar motion is so much less than that of the underlying circular orbit makes it possible to resolve the solar motion into three more or less independent components. The first, of course, is the underlying circular motion, with a speed on the order of $220\,\mathrm{km\,s^{-1}}$ and radius R_c estimated to lie in the range 7–$10\,\mathrm{kpc}$. This circular orbit may be thought of as roughly describing the mean motion of the sun, though such an assumption would have to be more carefully justified were the galactic motion of many stars in the solar neighbourhood confirmed as having a strong radial component (e.g. Clube & Waddington 1989a).

Superimposed on this basic circular orbit are two 'epicyclic' motions: one in the galactic plane, the other perpendicular to it. Determinations of the mean rotation velocity at the solar circle together with its variation with R and the solar velocity $V_\odot$ suffice to determine completely the periods and amplitudes of these small epicyclic oscillations.

Following standard procedures (e.g. Mihalas & Routly 1968), we may represent the in-plane epicyclic motion by a slow retrograde ellipse centred on the mean circular orbit. The galactocentric radial coordinate of the sun may then be written in the form

$$R_0(t) = R_c - \frac{u_0}{\kappa} \cos(\kappa t) \tag{12.8}$$

where κ, the so-called epicyclic frequency, corresponds to a period of about 1.7×10^8 yr (cf. the orbital period of the sun around the Galaxy, of order 2.4×10^8 yr), and u_0 represents the radial velocity of the sun (either inwards or outwards) at times when its galactocentric distance exactly equals R_c.

Following the same analysis, excursions of the solar orbit in the tangential direction (i.e. parallel to the underlying circular motion) also have a period $2\pi/\kappa$ and are given by

$$Y_0(t) = -\frac{u_0}{2B} \sin(\kappa t) \tag{12.9}$$

where the coefficient B denotes the second of Oort's constants A and B introduced by Oort (1927a). These are defined in terms of the 'circular' velocity $V_c(R)$ by

$$A = +\frac{1}{2} \left(\frac{V_c}{R} - \frac{dV_c}{dR} \right) \tag{12.10}$$

and

$$B = -\frac{1}{2} \left(\frac{V_c}{R} + \frac{dV_c}{dR} \right) \tag{12.11}$$

while the epicyclic frequency κ is given by

$$\kappa^2 = 4B(B - A) \tag{12.12}$$

Observations discussed by Kerr & Lynden-Bell (1986) suggest that $R_0 = 8.5 \pm 1.1\,\text{kpc}$, the circular velocity is $V_0 = 222 \pm 20\,\text{km}\,\text{s}^{-1}$, and at this point in the Galaxy

$$A = +14.4 \pm 1.2 \;\; \text{km}\,\text{s}^{-1}\,\text{kpc}^{-1} \qquad (12.13)$$

$$B = -12.0 \pm 2.8 \;\; \text{km}\,\text{s}^{-1}\,\text{kpc}^{-1} \qquad (12.14)$$

These values indicate $\kappa = 35.3 \;\text{km}\,\text{s}^{-1}\,\text{kpc}^{-1}$ (*i.e.* about $1.1 \times 10^{-15}\,\text{s}^{-1}$), and together with $u_0 \simeq 14.4\,\text{km}\,\text{s}^{-1}$ imply that the excursions in the radial direction have an amplitude $u_0/\kappa \simeq 400\,\text{pc}$, while those in the transverse direction have an amplitude $u_0/|2B| \simeq 600\,\text{pc}$. Thus, the solar in-plane epicycle is an ellipse with semi-major axes of length $400\,\text{pc}$ and $600\,\text{pc}$ in the radial and transverse directions respectively. This motion is illustrated in Figure 12.4, where we also show for comparison the current projected positions of the principal molecular clouds in the sun's immediate neighbourhood, taken from Dame *et al.* (1987). In practice these objects also have their own peculiar motions relative to their local standards of rest, which themselves move with velocities $2A\,(R_c - R)$ parallel to $l = 90°$. Our knowledge of these various motions is such that the relative positions of the sun and these various features in the past are not established with great accuracy for times much more than about 10 Myr.

The motion of the sun perpendicular to the galactic plane may be obtained in an exactly similar fashion, and can be shown to be approximately simple harmonic in form, *i.e.*

$$Z_0(t) = A_\perp \, \sin(\lambda t) \qquad (12.15)$$

Here $A_\perp = v_\perp(0)/\lambda$ is the amplitude of the solar motion perpendicular to the plane, and the frequency λ is approximately equal to the galactic constant C, assuming a restoring force perpendicular to the galactic plane of the form $F_Z = -C^2 Z$. The parameter $v_\perp(0)$ represents the speed of the sun perpendicular to the galactic plane at the point $Z = 0$, and the galactic constant C (analogous to the Oort constants A and B) has the value

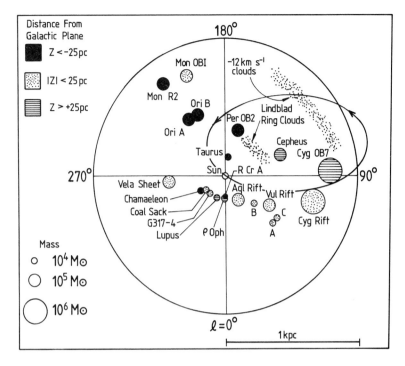

Figure 12.4: Distribution of molecular clouds in the solar neighbourhood, and the sun's epicyclic orbit (adapted from Dame *et al.* 1987). Note that the relative positions of the molecular clouds will change significantly during the $\simeq 170\,\mathrm{Myr}$ period of the solar epicycle.

$C \simeq 100\,\mathrm{km\ s^{-1}\ kpc^{-1}}$ (see p.498). For the present solar orbit, $v_\perp(0)$ is very close to the sun's present speed perpendicular to the plane, about $8\,\mathrm{km\,s^{-1}}$, so the current amplitude $A_\perp$ of the solar Z-oscillation is on the order of $80\,\mathrm{pc}$.

12.3.3   EFFECTS OF THE TIDE

The detailed effects of a known perturbing force on the elements of a cometary or planetary orbit are most simply obtained by solving a set of first-order differential equations known collectively as the Gaussian form of Lagrange's planetary equations.

These express the variations in semi-major axis, eccentricity, in-clination *etc.*, in terms of the other relevant orbital elements and the components of the perturbing acceleration (*e.g.* $\mathbf{F}_{\text{tide}}$) resolved along three mutually perpendicular directions. The interested reader is referred to Byl (1983) for the explicit form of these equations, or to almost any standard textbook on celestial mechanics (*e.g.* Brouwer & Clemence 1961, p.301).

We now follow Byl (1983, 1986) in representing the shape and orientation of a cometary orbit in space by the perihelion distance q, semi-major axis a, and orientation parameters b_p, l_p and α_p, which respectively denote the galactic latitude and longitude of the perihelion point and the angle (α_p) between the orbital plane and the polar great circle passing through perihelion. One can then express the Lagrangian planetary equations in terms of these new parameters, resolve the galactic tide into its appropriate components parallel to $\mathbf{r}$, transverse to $\mathbf{r}$ in the orbital plane, and perpendicular to the orbital plane, substitute the result into the planetary equations and integrate them to obtain the resulting small changes in orbital elements over one complete revolution. Finally, approximating the cometary orbit by a highly eccentric ellipse (so that $e \simeq 1$ and terms of order q/a and less can be neglected), and assuming for simplicity that only the dominant Z-component of the galactic tide is operative (*cf.* Appendix B.2, p.496), one obtains

$$\Delta q = \frac{5\pi\sqrt{2}}{GM_\odot} a^{7/2} q^{1/2} \left.\frac{\partial^2 \phi_{\text{gal}}}{\partial Z^2}\right|_0 \sin b_p \cos b_p \cos \alpha_p \qquad (12.16)$$

and

$$\Delta b_p = \frac{\pi\sqrt{2}}{GM_\odot} a^{5/2} q^{1/2} \left.\frac{\partial^2 \phi_{\text{gal}}}{\partial Z^2}\right|_0 (5\sin^2 b_p - 1) \cos \alpha_p \qquad (12.17)$$

(*cf.* Byl 1986, equations 15 and 17). Here Δq and Δb_p represent the changes in q and b_p over one complete revolution, while α_p may be shown to evolve rapidly to either 0 or 180° (giving $\cos \alpha_p = \pm 1$). The corresponding expression for Δa integrated over one complete orbit reduces to $\Delta a = 0$ if the radial components $(\partial/\partial R)$ of the galactic tide are ignored and stellar and molecular cloud perturbations are negligible, showing that in this approximation the tide introduces no change in the cometary energies.

An interesting feature of these equations, apart from the relatively large change in q which may occur from one revolution to the next, *i.e.*

$$\Delta q \approx 50(a/2 \times 10^4 \text{ AU})^{7/2}(q/100 \text{ AU})^{1/2} \text{ AU} \qquad (12.18)$$

is that both q and b_p are found to evolve cyclically. That is, starting from some small initial perihelion distance, q first increases to a maximum value (which in general can be a substantial fraction of the semi-major axis, indicating evolution to an orbit of only moderate eccentricity), and then decreases again. At the same time the galactic latitude, b_p, of the perihelion point cycles between plus or minus its original value or between its original value and the galactic poles. The period of these grand oscillations in the orbital elements depends on the initial value of the latitude of perihelion, and varies inversely both with the orbital period and the strength of the galactic tide, being given approximately (Byl 1986, Heisler & Tremaine 1986) by

$$P_{\text{osc}} \approx 3\text{--}10 \times 10^8 (a/2 \times 10^4 \text{ AU})^{-3/2} \text{ yr} \qquad (12.19)$$

These general features of the orbital evolution of typical long-period comets in the Oort cloud are illustrated for two particular initial orbits in Figure 12.5, adapted from Figures 2 and 3 of Byl (1986).

The galactic tide is therefore a significant influence in driving long-period comets into orbits of sufficiently small perihelion distance that they may become visible or captured by the giant planets. Nevertheless, it is important to emphasize that even on this picture perturbations by stars and molecular clouds must still be included. This is because were the randomizing effects of stars and clouds completely negligible, then nearly all the comets

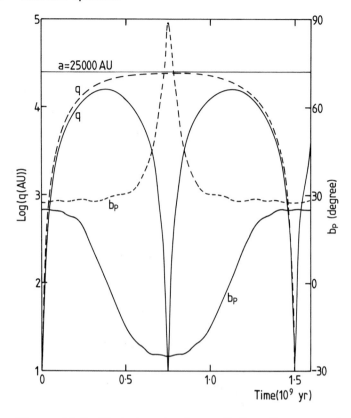

Figure 12.5: Variations in the perihelion distance and latitude of perihelion due to the galactic tide for initial orbits with $a = 2.5 \times 10^4$ AU and $b_p = 25°$ and $27.5°$ (solid and dashed lines respectively). Adapted from Byl (1986).

which might become visible (*i.e.* evolve into orbits with small perihelion distance) would in fact do so within a timescale on the order of P_{osc}. At perihelion they are nearly all either ejected from the solar system or captured into short-period orbits with limited physical lifetimes by planetary perturbations, and hence are removed from the Oort cloud. Thus, in order that comets should continue to be observable on timescales comparable with the age of the solar system, it is necessary to invoke the effects of stellar and molecular cloud perturbations, acting on timescales comparable to P_{osc}, to stir up the Oort cloud and replenish the supply of comets with orbits that will eventually achieve small perihelion distances.

An indication of the relative importance of stellar perturbations vs. these other effects can be found by comparing the *random* changes in q introduced by stars with the systematic effects of the galactic tide (cf. Fernández 1980b, Figure 6). As an example, we show in Figure 12.6 a comparison between the systematic change in perihelion distance per revolution due to the galactic tide (for orbits with $q \simeq 5\,\mathrm{AU}$ and $\sin b_p \cos b_p \cos \alpha_p \simeq 0.5$) with (i) the mean change in q for a typical molecular cloud perturbation ($M = 10^5 \, M_\odot$, $V = 20\,\mathrm{km\,s^{-1}}$ and impact parameter $50\,\mathrm{pc}$) and (ii) the r.m.s. variation in q calculated by Fernández (1980b) for typical stellar perturbations. This comparison illustrates the anticipated dominance of the galactic tide in affecting the angular momenta of highly eccentric cometary orbits, although occasional unusually close stellar or molecular cloud encounters, occurring only once in a large number of cometary orbits, would obviously have a much greater effect than the particular curves shown.

An important prediction from the theory of the galactic tide, assuming its effects are dominant in driving new comets into the inner solar system, is that the orbits of observed new comets should have orientation parameters consistent with a tidally driven evolution in the sense of decreasing q (see equation 12.16). However, a recent study by Yabushita (1988) has shown that this in fact is not the case, suggesting either that stellar or molecular cloud perturbations have been exceptionally strong during the past 5–10 million years (Yabushita 1989a,b), or (on an interstellar picture) that comets might have been recently captured from interstellar space and the tide has not yet had time to organize their orbits.

In this way, the recently discovered importance of the Galaxy on cometary orbits, including the effects of massive perturbers such as molecular clouds and the galactic tide, has initiated an era of rapid progress in understanding the main processes which

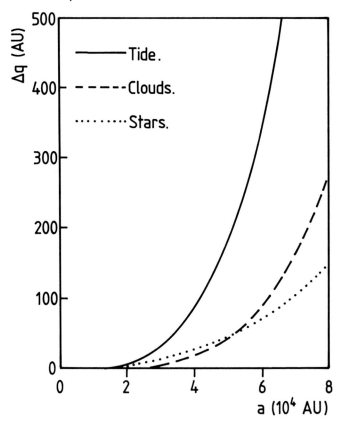

Figure 12.6: Comparison of the variation in perihelion distance per revolution induced by the galactic tide, a representative molecular cloud encounter, and the r.m.s. change per revolution due to stellar perturbations. See text for discussion.

drive new comets into the inner solar system. Indeed — perhaps for the first time — it has now been firmly established that there is a definite 'galactic' influence on the solar system. Whereas it had formerly been supposed that the Oort cloud was relatively stable in the presence of external perturbations, it is now clear that the standard Oort cloud, as modelled in 1950, is more or less completely disrupted on a timescale which is relatively short ($\lesssim 10^9$ yr) compared to its presumed age. Moreover, since some fraction of the terrestrial cratering flux must comprise comets, and the time-averaged cratering rate on the inner planets appears to be substantially unchanged during this period (or even increasing; cf. Baldwin 1985, and Figure 16.2, p.374), a new problem may now have emerged, namely how to *replenish* the region from which observed comets are seen to come without simultaneously contradicting the cratering record. To resolve this difficulty, one may in principle turn either inwards or outwards, considering replenishment from an unseen inner core of the Oort cloud (see Section 13.3, p.286) or by the capture of unseen comets possibly originating in other star and planet-forming regions in the Galaxy (cf. Chapter 15.2, p.344).

Although our present understanding of these questions is still very rudimentary, a measure of the significance of these new developments may be obtained from the fact that already the galactic tide and its various effects have been invoked to overcome a number of long-standing difficulties and anomalies in theories of cometary dynamics, such as the short-period comet problem (e.g. Bailey 1986c), the anisotropy of the directions of perihelia of the long-period comets (e.g. Delsemme & Patmiou 1986) and the possibility that variations in the strength of the galactic tide (due to the changing position of the sun in the Galaxy) might provide a mechanism by which significant quasi-periodic variations in the injection rate of new comets might be produced (e.g. Clube 1987a, Napier 1987, Clube & Napier 1989a; see Chapter 17). Whether or not any of these suggestions are eventually confirmed, the significance of the rôle played by massive perturbers and the galactic tide is not now in question.

13

Unexpected reserves

"Those who refuse to go beyond fact rarely get as far as fact."

Thomas Huxley.

13.1   Extending the nebula

Much recent cometary research has now been directed at the twin problems both of forming comets and the Oort cloud within the planetesimal picture and at the questions of Oort cloud evolution and its survival for the age of the solar system. Although final conclusions have yet to be reached, the present activity particularly in the field of Oort cloud evolution has undoubtedly been a major factor in calling into question the underlying assumptions of the standard model, especially in relation to the total original mass of comets. However, as we emphasized at the beginning of Chapter 10, the true pattern of progress since about 1950 has been much more complex than this rather simplified description might suggest, and a more balanced account of the subject's advance during this period ought certainly to include the fact that the assumptions underlying the standard model were never *generally* accepted.

Many of the alternative proposals to which astronomers are even now directing their attention were originally conceived, in fact, quite soon after Oort's basic model had been established, and it is only relatively recently that their comparative strengths and weaknesses have become more widely known and appreciated. In this way, although it is probably fair to say that most astronomers have tended to subscribe, at least passively, to one or another version of the planetesimal picture of cometary origin for the past thirty years or so, and may continue to do so, the superficial impression which is then often presented — of a steady, almost inexorable advance of the planetesimal hypothesis — would be misleading.

Alternative ideas for the origin of comets have been suggested at more or less regular intervals, albeit by a minority of astronomers, continuously since about 1950, and we describe many of these more radical 'solar system' and other hypotheses in the second part of the next chapter (see Section 14.2, p.317). Here, however, we concentrate on a particular subgroup of theories which, as a class, address themselves primarily to three crucial aspects of the planetesimal picture: namely, whether comets really were formed in a quiescent, low-mass protoplanetary disc; whether the initial size of the disc might once have been much larger than predicted by the standard model; and whether comet and planet formation were genuinely linked.

Our discussion of these theories and associated topics begins by returning to the early nineteen-sixties: to a point following the establishment of the Oort cloud, but preceding the development of what later became the 'establishment view' led in the main by the ideas of Öpik and Safronov. It was then, during the initial period of consolidation of the standard model, that the suggestion of a much more massive protosolar nebula (Cameron 1962) was first floated.

13.1.1   ARGUMENT FROM DESIGN

Cameron's studies seem primarily to have been motivated by the attempt to place theories of comet and planet formation into the wider context of star formation. He therefore emphasized the importance for solar nebula theories of the new observational results which were then beginning to emerge in relation to energetic activity associated both with young stars and regions of recent star formation. Subsequent events have served only to underline the importance of such 'stellar' connexions to theories of cometary origin (see Section 14.1, p.305), and it is now clear that Cameron's original approach began a line of argument which by no means has completely run its course.

Nevertheless, despite the obvious advantage of placing theories of comet formation into a more modern picture of star formation, the benefits of the broader view were soon lost by the qualitative nature of Cameron's ideas and the apparently reduced significance in the theory of comets *per se*. Cameron's ideas seemed once again to reduce comets to the status of a mere by-product (albeit within a new nebular concept involving a much more massive protoplanetary disc), and important details of the proposal, such as the precise mechanism of comet formation and the exact location of cometary origin in the more massive nebula, soon became much less certain and less developed than in any of the competing planetesimal pictures.

For example, whereas in Cameron's first model it was suggested that comets might form just beyond Neptune (*i.e.* at a heliocentric distance r on the order of 50–100 AU), in later work (*e.g.* Cameron 1973) it was proposed that they might originate much further out, depending in this case on unknown initial conditions describing the positions, masses, and angular momenta of hypothetical satellite nebulae which by then had also been introduced. On this theory, therefore, the existence of comets might (or might not) be important; and worse still, cometary bodies might conceivably have formed almost anywhere in the proposed nebula, provided the region was cool enough and at a sufficiently great distance from the sun, *i.e.* certainly beyond the orbit of Neptune.

In fact, Cameron's first paper, in 1962, was important for introducing two important new concepts for solar system theories: first, the idea of a relatively massive disc ($\simeq 1\,M_\odot$); and secondly, the suggestion that the destruction or 'dissipation' of this disc would eventually occur at an early stage of the system's evolution, due to an initial period of violent mass loss associated with a presumed 'T Tauri' phase of solar evolution. Indeed, it is now generally accepted that many stars of about the sun's initial mass probably do pass through a short-lived period of energetic mass loss associated with the very earliest stages of stellar evolution (*e.g.* Lada 1985, *cf.* Section 14.1, p.305), although the detailed mechanism of disc dissipation remains largely obscure.

In this way, while Kuiper, Öpik and Safronov were arguing on the basis of the observed *planetary* masses for a low-mass, so-called 'minimum mass' protoplanetary nebula, with a total mass (including hydrogen and helium) of no more than about $0.1\,M_\odot$, Cameron now approached the problem from the vantage provided by stellar evolution. In particular he argued that a rotating protostellar cloud would almost certainly collapse in the first instance to form a very massive nebular disc (*loc. cit.*, p.64), such that perhaps only half the original mass of the collapsing cloud would reside in the central object, leaving the remainder in the form of a massive circumstellar disc.

Such a view implied an initial protoplanetary disc with a mass on the order of $1\,M_\odot$, and Cameron maintained that during the evolution of such a system much of the 'excess' material would be expelled to distances well beyond that of Neptune. This led to the suggestion (*loc. cit.*, p.67) that if comets *could* form in the outer regions of such a disc, a very large number of such bodies might in principle be formed. However, at this time the potentially crucial importance of comets to theories of the origin of the solar system was not generally appreciated; moreover, since he seems in any case to have been primarily concerned with the question of the origin of the solar system, rather than with that of comets, Cameron gave no detailed discussion of the possible mechanisms of comet formation or of the ways in which such comets might subsequently be scattered into the Oort cloud.

Nevertheless, it was certainly implied that the origin of cometary nuclei and planets would occur relatively quickly in this sort of disc, if only because the early T Tauri phase of solar evolution was expected to dissipate the original protostellar cloud within a time rather less than a million years. This was much shorter than the timescale for particle growth previously obtained in the case of Kuiper's quiescent, low-mass disc structures, a difference which may be traced partly in Cameron's model to the strong 'turbulent' motions assumed to be present.

13.1.2   SATELLITE NEBULAE

Details of a specific calculation of this kind were published by Cameron & Pine (1973), while in an accompanying paper Cameron (1973) considered the problem of the accumulation of small particles in this kind of nebula. He argued first for a sticking probability of order unity for the inter-grain collisions (cf. Section 10.2.1, p.213), and concluded that the presence of strong turbulence in his model of the disc would lead to the rapid growth of larger bodies, ultimately producing planet-sized objects within a timescale of a few thousand years.

There were two main reasons why this accumulation time was so much shorter than that previously found by Safronov and others: first, the assumption that particle growth was dominated by relative velocities driven by turbulence, which led to much higher relative velocities amongst the dust particles than expected for a quiescent system; and secondly, because the disc itself was much more massive, the resulting disc surface density was also much higher.

Arguing on the basis of angular momentum conservation, he also concluded (loc. cit., pp.431–436) that several minor fragments of the original nebula, with masses on the order of 0.1 $M_\odot$, would probably separate out from the main flow during the initial collapse of the cloud. These were subsequently expected to evolve into 'satellite' discs, with individual radii on the order of 10^3 AU, orbiting the main mass at distances ranging up to about 10^4 AU from the sun.

Cameron (loc. cit., p.436) thus believed that it was most unlikely that a massive Oort cloud could arise as a result of the evolution of comets formed in the outer protoplanetary zone of the disc, particularly on his model of the disc, since this region was probably too hot to allow either the formation or survival of icy comet nuclei in the central part of the disc. He therefore proposed that the newly introduced satellite discs were the next most obvious site for comet formation. Applying a detailed theory of particle growth to the situation expected to apply in such discs implied that rapid growth of comet-sized bodies might occur within a time as short as 10^3 yr. The satellite discs were then assumed to be destroyed soon afterwards by the appearance of a nearby massive O or B-type star in the sun's local star cluster, thus leaving a cloud of comets formed as if *in situ*, orbiting the sun at distances $r \simeq 10^4$ AU in the general region of the present Oort cloud.

Subsequent rapid mass loss from the main protoplanetary disc during the sun's T Tauri phase of evolution would then lead to the removal of some of these comets, but the remainder, provided that they were in sufficiently tightly bound orbits, were expected to be left in orbits which would generally expand to fill the whole of the Oort cloud. In this way Cameron may be seen to have departed from a strictly 'solar system' interpretation of the primordial theory of the origin of comets, his work forming the basis of a new idea that although comets might be examples of bodies formed coevally with the sun and planets, they might in fact have originated in separate fragments of the parent protostellar cloud.

However, despite the apparent success and internal consistency of this new solar system hypothesis, the theory remained mostly at a qualitative level so far as comets were concerned, and no detailed estimates were given either of the size distribution of the comets which might form or their expected number. These, as we have seen, are crucial parameters in the success or otherwise of any theory of comet formation, and since he also made no attempt to determine the efficiency of generating the Oort cloud or the initial number density of comets about the sun, it is not possible to subject his ideas to the same close quantitative analysis which has been possible in the case of the 'planetesimal' theories of Öpik and Safronov.

In the same year, Donn (1973, 1976) suggested an important development of Cameron's satellite nebula hypothesis. In particular, he argued that comets might form in small, but completely separate fragments of the primordial interstellar cloud from which the sun itself had originated. In this way, although the formation of comets was now in principle completely separate from the detailed processes which formed the sun and planets, comets might nevertheless still be distant 'relatives' of the sun, in the restricted sense that they would have originated from the same interstellar source, having a common interstellar cloud as parent.

Donn was also the first to emphasize the potentially significant effect on the survival of a primordial Oort cloud of strong perturbations from nearby stars, which were presumed to have formed together with the sun in neighbouring parts of the original molecular cloud. In this way, he was led to suppose that there might in fact be two general classes of comet: one formed in the solar nebula, the other in separate fragments of the sun's parent interstellar cloud.

13.1.3 MASSIVE DISC

By this time one can begin to identify an increasing tendency to prefer an origin for comets outside the planetary régime altogether; and the following years saw further work along these general lines. For example, Cameron (1978) and Biermann & Michel (1978) both presented detailed models for comet formation in massive ($\simeq 1\,M_\odot$) protoplanetary discs, in which comets originated at large heliocentric distances, far beyond the central 'planetary' region of the discs.

Cameron also argued that a massive disc would inevitably be vulnerable to ring-like gravitational instabilities of a kind that would allow the rapid formation of the giant, gaseous outer planets. However, turbulence in the remainder of the disc, possibly driven by angular momentum mismatch of the still infalling material (*cf.* Safronov & Ruzmaikina 1985), was expected to cause a quick spreading and dissipation of the remaining disc according to the theory of viscous disc evolution that had recently been developed by Lynden-Bell & Pringle (1974). We note, however, that although Cameron included the infall of mass in this disc model, he ignored the effects of the accompanying angular momentum. Depending on the exact nature of the processes leading to infall of gas on to the disc, it is possible that radial motions in the disc driven by the associated angular momentum mismatch of infalling material might completely dominate any purely 'viscous' evolution (cf. Bailey 1982, 1985b).

According to Cameron's (1978) model, the radius of such a disc would be in the range 10^3–10^4 AU, with most of the mass lying well beyond the orbit of Neptune. He thus argued that comets could form in massive, extended discs at heliocentric distances on the order of 10^3 AU, and suggested that the actual process of growing comet nuclei in the outer parts of the disc would probably occur via the gravitational instability mechanism described by Goldreich & Ward (cf. Section 10.3.2, p.227).

Finally, he proposed that when infall eventually ceased the disc would probably become unstable to a period of temporary, rapid mass loss, which in turn would allow the comets originally formed at distances of order 10^3 AU to be ejected into the much larger orbits characteristic of the Oort cloud. The efficiency of this mechanism for placing comets in the Oort cloud obviously depends in detail on the precise way in which the main phase of mass loss occurs, but in principle the placement efficiency could be quite high (e.g. Dermott & Gold 1978). In this way Cameron (1978, p.22) seems to have been one of the first to suggest that the total mass of comets in the Oort cloud might be very much greater than the conventional value, which at this time was still widely estimated as being only of order $1\,M_\oplus$ (cf. Section 13.3, p.286).

Biermann & Michel (1978) presented a theory qualitatively similar to this, although they concentrated on a detailed analysis of the processes by which the grains sedimented through the gas and subsequently developed local gravitational instabilities. This, as in the planetesimal picture, was seen as the primary mechanism by which comet-sized bodies were formed in the massive disc. They confirmed the conclusions of earlier workers, such as Safronov, that the characteristic masses of the first marginally unstable regions of the dust disc tended to be somewhat larger than those of typical comet nuclei, and suggested in particular (*loc. cit.*, p.455) that the discrepancy might be overcome by further fragmentation of the dust blobs during their final phase of collapse.

However, the problem of explaining the observed mass of comets is more difficult than one of simply accounting for the size of an 'average' comet: the slope of the mass spectrum, and the upper and lower limits to cometary masses, must also be reproduced. In this case, although the theory now gave a much better estimate of 'typical' cometary masses, the inferred *upper* mass limit, $\approx 10^{15}$ kg, was about three orders of magnitude less than the size of the largest comets observed during historical times (*e.g.* Hughes & Daniels 1982; *cf.* Sections 17.1 and 18.1.2, pp.389, 432 respectively).

Biermann (1981) later returned to Cameron's earlier ideas of forming comets in satellite fragments of the protosolar nebula and emphasized the possible importance for cometary theories of the magnetic field configuration in determining the detailed fragmentation history of the cloud. The basic mechanism for forming comets, however, remained much the same as that calculated earlier by Biermann & Michel (1978).

13.2   New nebular theory

At about this same time, a completely new proposal for comet formation was made by Hills (1981), suggesting that comets might originate at large heliocentric distances during the early collapse phase of the protosolar nebula.

13.2.1   EFFECT OF RADIATION PRESSURE

The idea was analyzed in detail in several papers by Hills (1982) and Hills & Sandford II (1983a,b), who showed that radiation pressure acting on partially opaque clumps of dust in the collapsing cloud might under some circumstances quickly drive the grains together to produce kilometre-sized cometary nuclei in the cloud.

The principal problem was to show that protocomets of mass m_0 and initial radii $R_0 = (3m_0/4\pi\zeta\rho)^{1/3}$, where $\zeta \approx 10^{-2}$ is the dust-to-gas ratio by mass and ρ is the ambient gas density, would indeed collapse to form comet nuclei on a formation timescale, $t_{\text{form}} \simeq R_0/\Delta v_D$, less than that, $t_{\text{infall}} \simeq \pi(r_0/2)^{3/2}(GM_\odot)^{-1/2}$, on which the clumps of dust would fall into the sun. Here t_{infall} is the half-period of an orbit having a semi-major axis $a = r_0/2$, and $r_0 \approx 10^3$ AU is the assumed heliocentric distance at which comet formation by this mechanism may occur. Δv_D is the drift velocity of the dust grains towards one another, caused by the differential effect of radiation pressure acting across the clump.

Assuming that comet nuclei have about the same material density ρ_{grain} as their constituent grains, the final radius of any newly formed nucleus is $R_n = (3m_0/4\pi\rho_{\text{grain}})^{1/3}$. If the dust grains are assumed to have initial radii a_d and a space density $n_d = \zeta\rho/m_d$, where $m_d \equiv \frac{4}{3}\pi\rho_{\text{grain}}a_d^3$ is their mass, the initial optical depth across the protocomet may be shown to be of order

$$\tau_0 \simeq 2R_0 Q_{\text{abs}} \pi a_d^2 n_d = \frac{3}{2}\frac{R_n}{a_d} Q_{\text{abs}}(\zeta\rho/\rho_{\text{grain}})^{2/3} \qquad (13.1)$$

where Q_{abs} is the absorption efficiency factor. For representative values of the parameters (e.g. $R_n = 1$ km, $a_d = 0.3\,\mu$m,, $Q_{\text{abs}} = 1$, $\zeta \simeq 0.02$, $\rho \simeq 2 \times 10^{-15}$ kg m^{-3}, $\rho_{\text{grain}} \simeq 10^3$ kg m^{-3}; Hills 1982) this gives $\tau_0 \lesssim 10^{-3}$.

The relative inward drift velocity of grains inside a clump is then on the order of $\Delta v_D = \tau v_D$, where v_D is the overall drift velocity of the grains through the gas due to radiation pressure. This velocity may be determined by equating the force, F_{rad}, due to radiation pressure, to the resistance on the grains due to gas drag. This is given approximately (cf. Baines et al. 1965,

Draine & Salpeter 1979, Bailey 1987a,b) by

$$R_s = \frac{4}{3}\pi \rho a_d^2 v_D \bar{v} (1 + \frac{9}{16}\frac{v_D^2}{\bar{v}^2})^{1/2}$$

(13.2)

where $\bar{v} = (8kT/\pi\bar{m})^{1/2}$ is the mean molecular speed of the gas. Hills assumed that the intensity of the radiation field would be comparable to that from a point source of luminosity $L = 30\, L_\odot$ at a distance r_0, which gave

$$F_{\rm rad} \simeq \frac{L}{4\pi r_0^2 c}\pi a_d^2 Q_p$$

(13.3)

where $Q_p < 1$ is the efficiency factor for radiation pressure (cf. Fernández & Jockers 1983, Figure 40; Hills & Sandford II 1983a).

For $v_D < \bar{v}$ this argument gave $v_D \simeq (3LQ_p/16\pi r_0^2 c\rho\bar{v}) \approx 10^2$ m s^{-1}, which indicated relative drift velocities $\Delta v_D < 10^{-1}$ m s^{-1} and a timescale for comet formation on the order of

$$t_{\rm form} \simeq \frac{R_n}{\Delta v_D}(\frac{\rho_{\rm grain}}{\zeta\rho})^{1/3} \approx 10^3 \text{ yr}$$

(13.4)

This was indeed a little shorter than the time for infall from $r_0 \simeq 10^3$ AU, and it was concluded (Hills & Sandford II 1983a) that comet formation by this mechanism could occur.

Whether observed comets are formed by this mechanism, however, remains unclear, since the theory involves a number of uncertain factors and assumptions. Of these the three most important are first, the neglect of turbulent motions in the collapsing cloud, which if present might wash out the gentle inward drift speeds of the grains; secondly, the efficiency of the radiation-grain coupling, which could be severely reduced if the ambient, mostly optical or ultraviolet, radiation field had been degraded by dust absorption to longer infrared wavelengths; and lastly, the uncertain total number of comets which might be formed by this means and the fraction that would remain bound to the solar system in the Oort cloud after the growth of the sun and planets had been completed.

Hills's theory was an important advance, in that it described a quantitative mechanism for producing comet nuclei in the collapsing protosolar nebula, but further work remains to be done before firm conclusions regarding its validity can be drawn. For example, while the strong turbulence now known to be present in the environments of many young stars and protostars (*e.g.* Section 14.1.3, p.308) may prove to be an insuperable obstacle to this kind of process, the inclusion of other physical effects might significantly relax this and other general constraints on the theory (*e.g.* Cameron 1988). An appreciable rotation of the original cloud, for instance, would remove the requirement that comets form on a timescale less than that, t_{infall}, associated with the original collapse of the nebula, and it is also possible that other, more efficient, processes may act to drive dust grains together in a dense, collapsing cloud (*e.g.* Napier & Humphries 1986).

13.3   Massive inner core

A common feature of these alternatives to the conventional solar system hypothesis is that they break the link between comet and planet formation which had been so assiduously forged by the proponents of the planetesimal hypothesis and its various modifications. This gave theorists a much greater degree of flexibility, especially concerning the various kinds of cometary mass distribution which might reasonably be envisaged. Moreover, it is worth noting that these implied attacks on the standard model at this time, while still advocating what could be described as a 'solar nebula' picture, nevertheless contributed significantly to the growing climate of opinion during the nineteen-seventies in which more radical speculations about the origin of comets began to be made with increasing frequency. Indeed, even the primordial solar system hypothesis itself could eventually be seen as being called into question (*cf.* Section 15.1, p.335).

However, despite these somewhat iconoclastic associations of the massive disc and massive nebula ideas, the suggestion that the total mass of comets could be very large (*e.g.* Whipple 1975, Hills 1981) remained an extremely attractive proposition, possibly (it must be said) because the idea is so extraordinarily difficult to rule out! Comets are difficult to detect at the best of times; and by placing their nuclei at distances greater than about 50 AU, well beyond the region where solar heating is effective, the comets individually become virtually invisible. This feature of the massive protoplanetary disc picture soon became closely interlinked with the problem of survival of the primordial Oort cloud (see Section 12.2, p.254), and recent years have now begun to see the two kinds of argument coalesce into a vigorously expanding new viewpoint: namely, that the Oort cloud may contain a massive, hidden 'inner core'.

In this section we describe the main observational and theoretical constraints related to this question, and outline the various forms of 'dense inner core' hypothesis that have been proposed. It almost goes without saying, of course, that if the Oort cloud does contain a massive inner core, then comets probably do play a crucial rôle in the evolution of the protosolar nebula. Indeed, the effects of comets may then directly impinge on other apparently unrelated fields, ranging from theories of cosmology (driven, for example, by astronomical observations of galactic evolution and of variations in the far-infrared background radiation), to geological conceptions of the evolution of the earth, including terrestrial catastrophism and the likely biological response of plants and animals to a sudden influx of comets or cometary material hitting the earth (see Chapters 16 and 17).

13.3.1   COMET STORMS

Hills (1981) seems to have been the first to draw particular attention to comet *showers*, sudden enhancements of the cometary flux through the inner solar system, at least within the general context of a massive inner core hypothesis. In the context of the standard Oort cloud, significant variations in the cometary flux during close passages of the solar system to massive stars or nebulae (or even during passages through interstellar clouds of comets) were already recognized (*cf.* Oort 1950, Bobrovnikoff 1951, Bailey 1977, Napier & Clube 1979), as indeed was the distinction between relatively short-lived comet showers (10^6–10^7 yr) and more extended *episodic* variations in the comet flux on timescales of order 10^7–10^8 years, such as might arise during solar passages through spiral arms (Clube 1978, Napier & Clube 1979; *cf.* Chapter 17). Hills however emphasized that occasional encounters of the solar system with passing stars of relatively high mass, or low velocity or small impact parameter, would inevitably produce a much larger than average perturbation of cometary orbits in the Oort cloud. The effect of such encounters was to cause a significant enhancement in the number of long-period comets scattered into the inner solar system, thereby generating the appearance of a 'shower' of comets with perihelia less than that of the earth. In Oort's (1950) model, such variations in the new-comet flux were predicted to be relatively slight, but Hills now pointed out that theoretically more plausible models of the comet cloud (*cf.* Bailey 1983a) should contain many more bodies in orbits of shorter period, thereby allowing a greater likelihood of short-lived, very intense comet showers.

Obviously, the greater the number of comets with semi-major axes less than 2×10^4 AU, the greater the intensity of the resulting 'comet showers'; and on this basis (depending on both the impact parameter of the perturber and the assumed model of the comet cloud) Hills argued that a new-comet flux as high as one per hour might be anticipated during an intense comet shower. During such a storm ('comet blizzard' is perhaps a more apt description!), the night sky would be almost completely filled with comets, and it was suggested that the ensuing collisions of comets or their débris with the earth might have potentially catastrophic effects on terrestrial evolution. In this way, Hills appears to have been tempted to join the then burgeoning 'me too' brigade in relation to terrestrial catastrophism (variations on which were being strongly promoted by groups at this time on both sides of the Atlantic; e.g. Napier & Clube 1979, Alvarez et al. 1980), and he suggested that the effects of such a cometary bombardment, about 65 million years ago, might have been instrumental in causing the extinction of the dinosaurs, primarily through the impact of large bodies.

Independently of this work, stimulated in particular by the earlier studies of the disruption of a primordial comet cloud by molecular cloud perturbations (Napier & Clube 1979, Clube & Napier 1982a, Napier & Staniucha 1982), others now also argued that theoretically more plausible models of the Oort cloud should contain relatively more comets in a hypothetical 'dense inner core' within the conventional cloud (e.g. Van den Bergh 1982, Bailey 1983a). This suggestion was then simultaneously extended by Bailey (1983b,d) as a way of resolving several outstanding difficulties associated both with cometary theories and the dynamics of the outer solar system.

Hills's suggestion of comet showers, however, although not exclusively rooted in a massive inner core concept (cf. Bobrovnikoff 1951), has subsequently proved extremely fruitful, and a large number of authors (e.g. Heisler et al. 1987, Fernández & Ip 1987, Bailey et al. 1987, Bailey 1988a, Hut et al. 1987) have since investigated how perturbations of the Oort cloud by a variety of bodies (such as stars, molecular clouds, or even hypothetical 'dark matter') might lead to non-steady injection of comets into earth-crossing orbits and thence to significant terrestrial effects involving variations in the cratering rate and the rate of extinctions of species (see Chapters 16 and 17). Indeed, this connexion between comet showers and observable effects on the earth has even been turned around to provide important indirect constraints on the assumed properties of the dense inner core of the Oort cloud (e.g. Napier 1987, Stothers 1988, Bailey & Stagg 1988).

13.3.2   Nemesis notions

A particular suggestion made around this time, born from accounts by Raup & Sepkoski (1984) of the discovery of an apparently strict 26 Myr periodicity in the record of mass extinctions on the earth, was the idea that the sun might have a companion star, called 'Nemesis' (Davis *et al.* 1984; other proposed names included 'Kali', 'Indra', and even 'George'; *cf.* Hut 1986). An essentially identical idea was also proposed independently by Whitmire & Jackson (1984). These authors argued that if such a star were in a sufficiently eccentric elliptical orbit, it could periodically plunge through the dense inner regions of the Oort cloud and produce short-lived, intense showers of comets with orbits passing through the inner planetary region. The length of the hypothetical star's orbit was chosen so its period would match that seen in the terrestrial record, implying a semi-major axis of order 9×10^4 AU, and it was argued that associated mass extinctions of species might be caused by effects related to the impacts of comets on the earth. Moreover, analyses of the terrestrial cratering record also indicated a roughly constant 30 Myr periodicity (Rampino & Stothers 1984b, Alvarez & Muller 1984), and the idea of the importance of cometary impacts for the evolution of the earth rapidly gained in prominence.

The suggestion that Nemesis might thus produce periodic comet showers, and hence dominate biological evolution on the earth, proved to be both popular (in the broadest sense) and controversial. Its popularity gained much from the apparent simplicity of the dynamical scheme, and from the ease with which such an idea could be 'sold' to the general public through the mass-media; its controversy, particularly in scientific circles, had more to do with what many saw as the speculative nature of the proposal and, it must be said, the unconventional manner in which it and competing suggestions were often rapidly communicated both between individuals and to the public at large (see Maddox 1984, Hoffman 1988).

So far as the Nemesis idea itself was concerned, the controversy revolved around three main questions: (a) whether the geological record really provided firm statistical evidence for a regular periodicity of order 30 million years throughout the past $\simeq 250\,Myr$ (e.g. Hallam 1984a); (b) whether the supposed existence of a solar companion star is necessary, or even desirable, in order to explain such data (e.g. Clube & Napier 1984c); and (c) whether the model, as proposed, had been developed to a level of detail and internal coherence appropriate to the radical nature of the suggestion. Indeed, within a year of publication of the original idea, several authors had already drawn attention to the likely instability and a priori improbability of the assumed orbit of Nemesis (e.g. Clube & Napier 1984c, 1985b; Torbett & Smoluchowski 1984, Shoemaker & Wolfe 1984b; cf. Hills 1984, Hut 1984, Bailey 1984b), while others (Whitmire & Matese 1985, Matese & Whitmire 1986a,b) were already investigating an alternative proposal (cf. Tremaine 1986), this time involving the periodic production of short-period comets by a hypothetical 'Planet X', moving in an inclined orbit relative to a comet belt lying some distance beyond Neptune (cf. Section 13.3.3, p.293).

Later arguments concerning Nemesis have been concerned also with the reliability or otherwise of the evidence for periodicity in the terrestrial record (e.g. Rampino & Stothers 1984b, 1986b; Sepkoski & Raup 1986a,b; Clube & Napier 1986b; Hoffman 1985, 1986; Tremaine 1986; Patterson & Smith 1987, Heisler & Tremaine 1989, Stothers 1989); on the significance (or otherwise) of these data for the model; and on whether the dated terrestrial craters are more likely to have been made by comets or asteroids (e.g. Weissman 1985d). Taken together, these various arguments constitute an impressive list of difficulties for the so-called 'death star' picture, though Davis et al. (1985) and Hut (1986) have nevertheless mounted a spirited defence of the general model and its underlying methodology, whilst others (e.g. Pineault 1987) have investigated further detailed implications of the idea. Despite this, the particular questions raised (e.g. Clube & Napier 1984c, Weissman 1985c, Bailey 1986a) have not yet been answered. Specifically, a companion star with semi-major axis $a \simeq 9 \times 10^4$ AU would not survive in the galactic environment for more than a few revolutions (*cf.* equation A.2, p.486), and in any case companions with $a \gtrsim 2 \times 10^3$ AU are not found around stars of the sun's spectral type and age (Abt 1988). It seems doubtful, therefore, whether the proposed solar companion star will ever be found.

In spite of this rather negative assessment of the viability of the Nemesis proposal, the idea did have one important benefit so far as the origin of comets was concerned: it stimulated several independent investigators to reconsider the evolution of very long-period orbits in the Oort cloud, paying particular attention to the *combined* effects of stars, molecular clouds and the galactic tide (*e.g.* Bailey 1986a, Torbett 1986a, Weinberg *et al.* 1986). As we have seen (see Section 12.2, p.254), this work subsequently proved to be especially influential in helping to generate the current view that comets in the outer parts of the conventional Oort cloud — certainly those constituting the bulk of the Oort (1950) model — are highly unlikely to survive *in situ* for the age of the solar system.

In this sense, therefore, whether or not Nemesis exists, the idea has certainly played a significant indirect rôle in discussions of cometary origin, and it provides an interesting example of the sometimes unexpected ways that apparently speculative ideas can often advance understanding. Nevertheless, the seemingly insurmountable difficulties for the idea as a viable explanation of regular 30 Myr comet showers in the solar system do mean that most astronomers nowadays (amongst whom we include ourselves!) do not give the idea much time. Despite this (or perhaps because of it), proponents of the Nemesis notion have not been deterred from attempting to discover the predicted solar companion star by direct observational techniques, thereby aiming to settle the issue in their favour by perhaps the only remaining argument which all might agree would be conclusive (*cf.* Hut 1986). The discovery of Nemesis by such means would then rightly count as a formidable example of success in the face of adversity!

13.3.3 INFRARED FLUX

Leaving aside these questions related to comet showers and their possible links with terrestrial catastrophism, which we explore more fully in Chapter 17, a second important implication of the proposed 'inner core' models of the Oort cloud concerns the prediction of a significant far-infrared background flux. This possible observational test of the inner core picture was suggested by Bailey (1983c), shortly before the infrared satellite IRAS was due to fly, and the general idea has since been developed in more detail by a number of authors (e.g. Bailey *et al.* 1984, Jackson & Killen 1988).

At this point it is important to emphasize that 'the' inner core hypothesis, as commonly considered, is in fact a shorthand description for one or more of at least six independent 'inner core' hypotheses. We therefore distinguish two qualitatively distinct variations on the idea, and, within each of these, three different kinds of model for the cometary mass distribution. On the one hand, the inner core comets might be concentrated *very* close to the outer planetary system, in what we might call a 'compact' inner core, comprising comets moving at typical heliocentric distances on the order of 50–200 AU. Within such a picture, one can imagine cometary density distributions resembling (a) a torus, reminiscent of the present asteroid belt (*e.g.* Fernández 1980a); (b) a disc-like extension of the protoplanetary disc (*e.g.* Edgeworth 1949, Kuiper 1951a, Whipple 1964a,b, 1972; Mendis 1973); and (c) a more spherical distribution, analogous to the central core of an elliptical galaxy, similar to that suggested by Bailey (1983d) in order to explain certain observed discrepancies in the motions of the outer planets Uranus and Neptune.

Alternatively, the inner core comets could be much further out, but still well within the region ($r \gtrsim 10^4$ AU) usually associated with the conventional 'outer' Oort cloud. On this picture, the dense inner core would contain comets with typical semi-major axes in the range 10^3–10^4 AU, which we may call 'extended' inner core models, and continuing with our former designations we may again distinguish three types of model: (d) a further extension of the extended protoplanetary disc, perhaps analogous to the very extended dust discs seen around many main-sequence stars in the solar neighbourhood (*cf.* Section 14.1.4, p.311); (e) a conceptually rather similar structure, but this time formed by the gravitational scattering of large dust grains and planetesimals from the inner solar system by the growing major planets (*e.g.* Fernández 1985a), possibly flaring out in thickness to form a more spherical outer region which merges imperceptibly with the conventional Oort cloud; and (f) a much more spherical distribution, this time possibly merging both with the hypothetical compact spheroidal (or even triaxial) core at the centre and, at its outer edge, with the more spherical distribution making up the conventional Oort cloud.

Detailed investigations of the inner core hypothesis require a clear definition of terms; and to emphasize this point we show in Figure 13.1 a schematic picture of the six different proposed models. These, of course, are not mutually exclusive. For example, the planetesimal picture would predict (e), possibly with (a) ± (b) as well; while the problem of the survival of a primordial Oort cloud for the age of the solar system argues rather insistently for models of type (e) or (f), possibly together with one or other of (a) to (d), depending on the precise model. It is therefore important to investigate ways by which such comet clouds might be detected observationally and possibly distinguished from one another (*cf.* Bailey 1983b, Bailey & Stagg 1989).

Insofar as comets at large heliocentric distances inevitably absorb some proportion of the sun's radiation, which they re-emit at far-infrared or submillimetre wavelengths, each of these various manifestations of the inner core is potentially testable by observations. It turns out, however, that only those models with large numbers of comets lying within about 200 AU of the sun, *i.e.* the compact inner core models, are currently accessible to such tests, but there are nevertheless good grounds for

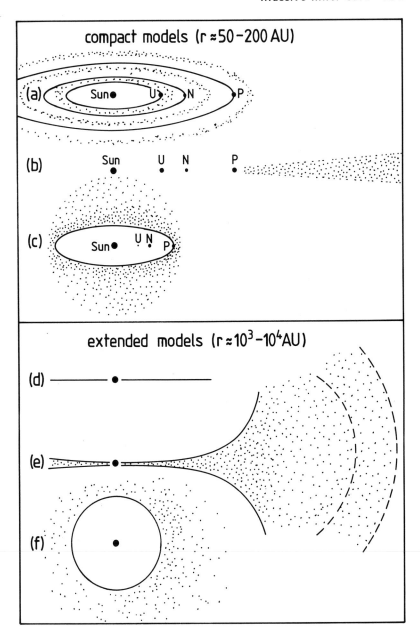

Figure 13.1: Schematic illustration of the six proposed variations on 'the' dense inner core hypothesis.

hoping that future observations may one day either confirm or rule out one or all of the ideas. In particular, we emphasize that the infrared astronomical satellite IRAS did observe a far-infrared background flux, which has variously been interpreted (*e.g.* Rowan-Robinson 1986) as evidence (a) for uncertainty in the absolute calibration of the instrument; (b) for a large and rapidly evolving population of so-called 'starburst' galaxies at cosmological distances comparable to those of quasars; and (c) even as the first hints of the predicted inner extension of the Oort cometary cloud!

None of the current measurements of this background radiation are yet conclusive, however, and further observational and theoretical work on these problems is keenly awaited. Needless to say, if comets (and their decay products or collisional débris; *cf.* Jackson & Killen 1988) really *do* produce detectable far-infrared background emission, the cosmological implications of the discovery would be profound. In the same way that infrared studies of galactic structure now have to contend with the brightness of the zodiacal cloud, cosmologists concerned with the more distant regions of the universe, including problems of galaxy formation and the earliest stages of the Big Bang, would then have seriously to consider the complex foreground structures introduced by comets and other solar system débris, *before* they could convincingly draw cosmological conclusions. There is perhaps no more recent example of the folly, in astronomical research, of becoming too narrowly based: to *assume* the infrared background is purely cosmological may be completely to miss the point!

13.3.4 NEW RESERVES

The difficulty of explaining the observed number of short-period comets, particularly the large number of bodies of relatively low inclinations belonging to the Jupiter family, has been a persistent problem in cometary cosmogony (see, for example, pages 131, 138 and 162). Indeed, despite a steadily growing understanding of the complicated dynamical interactions involved in the general capture process (*e.g.* Everhart 1968, 1972, 1973, 1976, 1977; Kazimirchak-Polonskaya 1972, 1976, 1985; Rickman & Vaghi 1976, Havnes 1972, Froeschlé & Rickman 1980, Carusi & Valsecchi 1985), which frequently involve a 'handing down' of comets from one outer planet to the next, rather than direct capture by Jupiter, the problem of explaining the total number of observed short-period comets has remained. In particular, following Everhart's (1972) detailed determination of the overall efficiency of the capture process, several authors (*e.g.* Joss 1973a, Delsemme 1973, Mendis 1973) emphasized that the apparent inconsistency in comet numbers could in principle be resolved either by postulating a much greater flux of long-period comets in the neighbourhood of Jupiter (greater, that is, than seemed possible by extrapolating the observed long-period flux), or by invoking an alternative source of short-period comets: namely, adopting a massive inner core hypothesis.

On this picture, therefore, short-period comets are no longer viewed necessarily as originating through planetary perturbations acting on the 'observed' long-period flux, but are instead considered more likely to come from an extended cometary disc or perhaps a more compact toroidal distribution of comets lying just beyond the orbits of Neptune and Pluto. The latter suggestion was later investigated by Fernández (1980a), who showed that provided the cometary 'disc' contained bodies of almost up to lunar size, perturbations from such masses might in principle scatter comets directly into the region of Neptune's influence (and thence indirectly towards Jupiter) at a sufficient rate to explain the observed number short-period comets. More recently, the same general idea (*cf.* Whipple 1964a, 1972a) has also been reintroduced by Duncan *et al.* (1988, 1989), on the theoretical basis of a long-term evolutionary study of original cometary orbits with initial perihelia in the Uranus-Neptune zone.

The latter authors suggested in particular that short-period comets are essentially the residue of the original population of planetesimals first formed in the Uranus-Neptune region of the protoplanetary disc. They argued against a parabolic source distribution with perihelia in the neighbourhood of Jupiter's orbit on the basis that the calculated periods of such captured comets did not correspond to the observations, while an isotropic source older than a few million years was ruled out on the ground that the captured comets, even if assumed to have the correct distribution of periods, were generally found to preserve their original inclinations. Thus, the observed flattened distribution of short-period comets (mostly belonging to the Jupiter family) towards the ecliptic plane was taken as a strong argument for an initially flattened source distribution, although a detailed mechanism for feeding comets from the Uranus-Neptune zone and beyond into planet-crossing orbits and finally into the observed short-period comet population is still required. Torbett (1989), for example, has suggested that perturbations by the four major planets may generate a 'chaotic zone' extending out to about 60 AU from the sun. It is possible, therefore, that comets whose semi-major axes lie within this zone may be perturbed, over the age of the solar system, into Neptune-crossing orbits, and thence into observable short-period orbits of the Jupiter family. In order to maintain the observed number of short-period comets in an approximately steady state, however, the chaotic outer zone has to feed comets into Neptune crossing orbits at a rate on the order of $0.15 \, \mathrm{yr}^{-1}$, which Torbett estimates would require a total disc population of order 10^9 comets.

In contrast to these suggestions, one can also show that a more spherically symmetrical dense inner core might resolve the problem of the observed numbers of short-period comets (e.g. Bailey 1983b, 1986c), although the precise degree of flattening of the Jupiter-family short-period comets might still be a problem for a strictly isotropic source. Indeed, in work originally motivated by the suggestion of Stothers (1988) that the terrestrial cratering record could constrain models of the inner core of the Oort cloud, Bailey & Stagg (1988) and Stagg & Bailey (1989) have emphasized that cometary capture from long-period comets originating in a hypothetical dense inner core of the Oort cloud might under some circumstances be *too* efficient. That is, rather than failing to produce too few short-period comets, the predicted long-period flux from an extended inner core model might produce too many captured bodies. The balance between observation and theory then provides useful constraints on the assumed properties of the dense inner core (Bailey & Stagg 1989), while the generally flattened distribution of short-period comets is then explained as being due largely or in part to the decreasing capture efficiency of comets with initial orbits of greater inclination, as emphasized for example in the numerical work by Everhart (1972, 1974).

The recent work by Stagg & Bailey (1989), then, shows that a dense inner core of the extended type, of the sort which might be predicted by the planetesimal picture and which might be occasionally disturbed by close stellar or molecular cloud encounters (thereby producing comet showers), cannot be taken to be arbitrarily dense. Although it is too soon to draw firm conclusions from these studies, a self-consistent model which is broadly consistent with the predictions of the planetesimal picture of cometary origin (*e.g.* Duncan *et al.* 1987) *and* which produces the observed number of short-period comets, is found to be roughly in agreement with observations.

These developments suggest, therefore, that the number of short-period comets may not be a great difficulty for the massive inner core concept. However, it is important to keep the problem in perspective, and while it has been argued by a number of authors that an inner Oort cloud or a cometary disc in the Uranus-Neptune zone (or beyond) is now *essential* to explaining the numbers and orbital elements of the observed short-period comets, it is also important to emphasize that the same data may be more simply understood by incorporating an element of time-dependence into the model: either on an orbital time-scale, for example due to a recently enhanced flux of long-period comets through the inner planetary system during the last few million years (*cf.* Section 15.1.3, p.339), or on a 'historical' time-scale, due to enhanced fragmentation of the few largest comets captured during the last twenty thousand years or so, corresponding to the latest stages of cometary evolution (*cf.* Clube & Napier 1982a).

The steady-state population of comets with small perihelia, for example, is known to be significantly contaminated by a transient population of comets of the Kreutz sun-grazer group, derived from the disintegration of an erstwhile giant progenitor (*e.g.* Kresák & Pittich 1978), while many observations of apparent 'pairs' and groups amongst both long-period and short-period comets, linking two or more comets to a single progenitor (*e.g.* Comets Neujmin 3 and Van Biesbroeck: Carusi *et al.* 1986; Comets Levy and Shoemaker-Holt: Marsden 1988; and Comets P/Machholz and 1491 I: McIntosh 1989), confirm the likelihood of fragmentation as an important effect. Öpik (1972), for example, has presented a detailed study of numerous possible cometary groups (*cf.* Whipple 1977); while we also note that bodies ranging in size up to some hundreds of metres across seem to have been ejected from the nucleus of Comet Wilson during its most recent apparition (de Pater *et al.* 1989). It is therefore possible that much of the discrepancy between the observed and predicted numbers of short-period comets might in the end be reduced by an improved understanding of the effects of cometary break-up and the indirect effects of observational selection and cometary decay. If such processes are eventually confirmed as significantly increasing the predicted number of short-period comets, the 'problem' of the short-period comets might indeed be a problem — this time for models of the inner core!

13.3.5   SHADOWS AND PLANET X

Further possible tests of the dense inner core suggestion, particularly of the compact inner core viewpoints, are also provided by the possibility that nearby comets might occasionally pass in front of distant stars (e.g. Bailey 1976, 1983b), thereby causing the starlight to become dimmed or perhaps even completely eclipsed, albeit for only a few tenths of a second. The discovery of transient stellar eclipses ('occultation astronomy') provides a novel and exciting way to probe the density distribution of boulders, asteroids and comet nuclei within a few thousand AU of the sun, though the instrumental techniques currently available for such studies make the chance of serendipitously detecting such an eclipse extremely remote. For representative models of the dense inner core, the eclipse probability is on the order of 10^{-8} per star per second per observer; the shadows are only as wide as the comet, at best. Nevertheless, it is an interesting speculation whether occasional observations of transits of mysterious 'dark' objects in front of the sun, moon and other bodies (e.g. Le Verrier 1860, Hind 1862, Kohler 1975, O'Sullivan et al. 1985, Olsson-Steel 1988a and references therein; cf. Houzeau & Lancaster 1882) might represent a more mundane illustration of the same general process.

Finally, it is possible that a compact inner core could be detected, provided it is not exactly spherically symmetrical, by its distorting gravitational effect on the orbits of the outer planets Uranus, Neptune and Pluto. It is not generally appreciated that modern dynamical models of the solar system — incorporating the best current determinations of the masses and orbits of all the known planets and asteroids — still do not successfully predict the positions of Uranus, Neptune and Pluto to an accuracy much better than about a tenth of an arcsecond over a ten-year period (e.g. Duncombe & Seidelmann 1980, Seidelmann et al. 1980, Anderson & Standish 1986). Such small discrepancies between theory and observation might appear completely negligible, and many argue that this is indeed the case; but the slight variations in the predicted motions of these outer planets can also be interpreted as indicating that the fundamental gravitational theory should be changed or as evidence for the elusive tenth planet: the hypothetical 'Planet X'. In this context, it is of course significant that Planet X has never been found, even by the sensitive IRAS infrared survey, and a possible resolution of the ensuing paradox might be that the unmodelled gravitational effects are produced by an assembly of bodies with much smaller masses: such as comets, occupying a comet belt (Whipple 1964a), comet disc, or spheroidal inner core of varying eccentricity (Bailey 1983d).

In future years, as the United States' spacecraft Pioneers 10 and 11 move ever further from the sun, precise radio tracking of their orbital paths will allow increasingly stringent tests to be placed on the gravitational field in these distant parts of the solar system, especially the important component of the force perpendicular to the ecliptic plane. Present constraints based on these observations indicate that the mass of comets in the hypothetical comet belt beyond Neptune is probably less than $5\,M_{\oplus}$ (Anderson & Standish 1986), while similar arguments based on the orbits of well-observed comets which penetrate to comparable distances provide an upper limit on the belt mass of order $1\,M_{\oplus}$ (Hamid et al. 1968).

13.3.6   CASE FOR A CORE

In summary, several independent lines of evidence have recently come together to suggest that the conventional Oort cloud may be dominated, in terms of mass, by comets comprising a 'dense inner core'. Although the arguments for the existence of an inner core are mostly indirect (the comets are so distant that they are almost invisible), it is important to emphasize that a number of variations on the usual primordial solar system hypothesis for cometary origin (e.g. the planetesimal picture, Cameron's idea of an extended massive disc, and Hills's suggestion for comet formation during the original collapse phase of the protosolar nebula) all *predict*, to a greater or lesser extent, the existence of one or another form of dense inner core of the Oort cloud.

The most direct arguments in favour of a dense inner core are first, that it provides an attractive way of replenishing the dynamically unstable outer Oort cloud for the age of the solar system; and secondly, that it may under certain restricted circumstances be capable of resolving the long-standing problem of the number of short-period comets. The dense inner core also offers a plausible explanation of the far-infrared background radiation possibly detected by IRAS; and conceivably could be the principal source of the gravitational perturbations which disturb the motions of the outer planets, results which were previously attributed to a hypothetical 'Planet X'. Finally, if comet showers do, in fact, affect the earth, then perturbations of an inner core of the Oort cloud are obviously a prime candidate for the cause of such events.

The suggestion that the Oort cloud contains a massive, dense inner core therefore provides a plausible means of resolving several outstanding difficulties associated with current understanding of the evolution of the earth and solar system. Indeed, the very idea can be attractively packaged as an almost inevitable evolutionary prediction of a number of popular solar system models, including the ideas of Cameron and Hills (cf. Marochnik & Mukhin 1988). The competing interstellar theories (see Chapter 15), on the other hand, do not necessarily require an inner core to exist. In fact, one could even go so far as to say that, on the interstellar hypothesis, the discovery of a massive inner core would be surprising to say the least. This particular distinction is a significant one, therefore, and it is hardly possible to overemphasize the importance of the hypothetical inner core of the Oort cloud for present theories of cometary origin. Indeed, it continues to stimulate debate and new theories, and has the long-term potential of becoming a kind of experimentum crucis for theories of the usual primordial solar system paradigm!

14

Changing perspectives

"I reckon there's more things told than are true,
And more things true than are told."

Rudyard Kipling.

14.1 Infrared view

14.1.1 EXTINCTION EXTINGUISHED

A completely separate line of enquiry in recent years has also led
to unexpected discoveries with potential relevance to cometary
origin. Thus, whereas comet researchers formerly tended to treat
the problem of cometary origin in isolation, often deliberately
overlooking the wider questions raised by observations of other
stellar systems, recent work — as emphasized by Cameron —
has now increasingly highlighted the relation of processes of *star*
formation to theories of *comet* formation. Originally, the lack of
secure data on other star-forming regions meant that the former
rather *laissez-faire* attitude could often be justified, at least on
a pragmatic basis, but recent observational advances have now
completely transformed the situation. These new observations,
driven particularly by rapid instrumental and technical progress
during the past decade, have provided many fresh and exciting
insights into star-forming regions throughout the Galaxy, and
their implications for theories of cometary origin are becoming
increasingly widely recognized.

For example, energetic outflows of material are now known to
be prevalent amongst many young stellar systems, to the extent
that they appear to be a quite fundamental phenomenon, yet
they usually gain little more than a passing mention on most
current theories of solar system formation, and none at all in
models of comet formation. Whether such processes should figure prominently in the final story about comets is still unknown,
but if we are to progress to a complete theory of the origin of

comets we should clearly attempt to place not only their dynamics, but also their cosmogony, in the wider galactic context. Two immediate questions, then, are first whether the star-forming environments now being revealed are compatible with the growth of comets, and secondly how peripheral or central are comets to the processes of star formation? Indeed, to what extent can we relate the theoretical protoplanetary discs described by Cameron and Safronov to the actual ones now being discovered; and how can we use observations to discriminate between the different theories?

The new infrared and millimetre technologies now available are starting to reveal the very early stages of star formation in previously impenetrable regions, such as the denser parts of the Orion Nebula (see Figure 14.1), and they provide important information on material orbiting other stars. The significance of the infrared spectral region, of course, lies mainly in the fact that star-forming regions are frequently hidden by many magnitudes of visual extinction, due to dust, and so cannot be seen using conventional optical techniques. However, the cool dust radiates conspicuously at longer wavelengths, and its temperature and spatial distribution in and around the star-forming region provide important clues as to the evolution and dynamics of such clouds. The infrared astronomical satellite IRAS has also yielded valuable new evidence. This instrument orbited the earth during 1983, and surveyed almost the whole sky with optics cooled to temperatures less than 5 K and with an impressive array of detectors sensitive to wavelengths around 12, 25, 60 and 100 microns. The discovery of cold circumstellar dust around many stars in the solar neighbourhood therefore became possible.

14.1.2   PROTOSTELLAR ACTION

The mechanics of star formation is still not fully understood (an optimistic statement!), but a provisional description of the process might run as follows. We start with a cool gas-and-dust

Figure 14.1: Star-forming region in Orion, showing many previously undetected stars. Courtesy of Royal Observatory, Edinburgh.

cloud, which may be rotating, containing molecular hydrogen and atomic helium together with a few percent by mass of heavier elements mostly locked up in the form of interstellar dust or as icy mantles on such dust. A dense, compact core forms in the cloud, of a few solar masses, with a temperature in the range 10–15 K and atomic hydrogen number density of order $n_{\mathrm{H}} \simeq 10^4$–$10^5$ cm^{-3}. Such a cold, dense region is unable to support itself against its own weight, and it begins to collapse. The collapse proceeds from the centre outwards, the layer where pressure support fails moving steadily outwards through the core at about the speed of sound. As the collapse proceeds, a stage is finally reached when the originally more distant material with the higher angular momentum is unable to reach the surface of the protostar, and it instead falls inwards on orbits which result in the formation of an accreting, growing disc, which also feeds material on to the core.

Eventually, when the mass of the developing protostar reaches a few tenths of a solar mass, the central core attains a temperature of order 10^6 K, and deuterium, a fragile, but relatively abundant element, begins to 'burn'. The onset of thermonuclear burning at the centre of the protostar rapidly brings the collapse of the protostar to a halt, and a strong stellar wind, ultimately energized by nuclear reactions in the core, begins to blow. Because of the effect of continuing infall, however, the stellar wind does not at first escape, but as time passes and the infall subsides, the wind is at last able to escape through the polar regions.

Initially, it seems that the opening angle of this 'bipolar' outflow is quite narrow, producing the appearance of 'jets', but it gradually expands as the infall declines until it eventually extends in all directions. At this stage the protostar may be regarded as a standard 'T Tauri' star, evolving along an evolutionary track on the Hertzsprung-Russell diagram towards higher temperatures and luminosities until it eventually reaches the hydrogen-burning 'main sequence'. Although an accretion disc might still exist at this time, its gas is later lost, leaving only a remnant dust disc around the newly formed main-sequence star. T Tauri stars are frequently the source of powerful stellar winds, and high-velocity outflows are such common features in young star-forming regions that they seem likely to be a normal part of at least the first ≈ 0.1 Myr of a star's life (*e.g.* Schwartz 1983).

14.1.3   COMETARY PROBLEMS

If this sequence of events is basically correct, we can attempt to associate the various stages of the process with specific protostellar objects and ask how friendly or hostile their environments would be to the formation of comets. For example, IRAS 1629 A is a cold, luminous object discovered in a dense molecular cloud in the constellation Ophiuchus (Walker *et al.* 1986). The object has only about a quarter of a solar mass, and has probably been collapsing for only a few tens of thousands of years. In terms of the above sequence it may therefore be a protostar in the very earliest stages of collapse preceding the development of high-velocity outflows and inflows. Even so, material within about 3000 AU of the object appears to be falling inwards with a speed of order $1\,\mathrm{km\,s^{-1}}$, and with a random 'turbulent' velocity dispersion of order $0.4\,\mathrm{km\,s^{-1}}$.

Simultaneously with this inflow is a high-velocity outflow, which takes the form of a double bipolar flow, involving four jets in all (Walker et al. 1989). The material in these outflows is clumpy, and has either been gradually accelerated to the observed velocity or is expanding as a result of an initial explosion. The infalling gas has a number density $n_H \approx 10^6\,\mathrm{cm^{-3}}$, which may be compared with a mean density of order $300\,\mathrm{cm^{-3}}$ for molecular clouds generally, and the turbulent velocity dispersion is sufficiently high (about 900 m.p.h.!) that one would probably expect collisions between any icy grains entrained within the gas to lead to their mutual destruction rather than coalescence (d'Hendecourt et al. 1982). It does not seem, therefore, that this very early stage of stellar evolution can be conducive to the growth of comets.

What may be a later stage in the process is exemplified by the young stars detected in the Orion molecular cloud at far-infrared wavelengths (see Figure 14.1). These stars have outflow velocities of order $100\,\mathrm{km\,s^{-1}}$, again with an apparently large internal velocity dispersion. At an apparently later stage again, HL Tau is a star of about $1\,M_\odot$ which seems to be viewed through a torus of gas and dust of radius $\simeq 2000\,\mathrm{AU}$ but uncertain mass ($\simeq 0.01\text{–}0.5\,M_\odot$), the latter values spanning the mass range of both the low-mass and high-mass protosolar nebulae described by Safronov and Cameron (cf. Sargent & Beckwith 1987, Weintraub et al. 1989). The material in this ring has a temperature of a few tens of degrees, and a number of ice 'signatures' have now been detected in the infrared spectrum (e.g. Cohen 1983). The properties of the gas and dust in this ring of material are not unlike those expected for the outer regions of the early solar nebula (cf. Pringle 1989), but again there are high-velocity jets, and the system appears to be permeated by a strong stellar wind. It is not yet certain, therefore, whether the extremely quiescent conditions that seem to be required for the aggregation of ice-covered dust grains into comets, at least on the planetesimal picture of comet formation, are being met, though there does seem to be a surprisingly large amount of material at relatively large distances from the central star.

A further problem facing the manufacturer who wishes to grow comets is the hazard of stellar flaring. A normal feature of the evolution of T Tauri stars is the so-called recurrent FU Orionis outburst. This typically involves an increase of the luminosity by a factor greater than 100, enduring over periods of several years. It seems possible that such outbursts might be driven by the infall of material on to a protostar (Hartmann & Kenyon 1985), and they could be associated with the underlying driving mechanism of bipolar outflows. The total energy involved in such an event is estimated to be more than 10^{38} J.

Herbig (1977, 1983) pointed out that FU Orionis outbursts during the sun's early T Tauri stage of evolution would have completely melted millimetre-sized dust particles in the inner solar system, and the same result will apply *a fortiori* to the icy mantles of such grains. The evaporation rate of water ice is known experimentally for a wide range of temperatures (*e.g.* Grim & Greenberg 1987), and one finds that even a single FU Orionis outburst in the primordial sun, of duration $\simeq 30\,\mathrm{yr}$, would have evaporated the icy mantles of unshielded grains out to 200 AU. Over the 10^5–10^6 year lifetime of the sun's presumed T Tauri phase, there may have been as many as 100 such outbursts, enough to evaporate (or more precisely, sublimate) comets of up to kilometre dimensions in circular orbits out to 100 AU, and comets of 10 km dimensions out to 80 AU, well beyond the planetary region (Napier 1987).

Since relaxed orbits in a protoplanetary disc would be expected to be approximately circular, any indigenous ice grains in the planetary region, and protocomets growing from them, would have to be shielded from the sun's radiation for the entire

T Tauri lifetime of the protosun. The growth of planetesimals to form planets, however, implies a relatively rapid phase of coagulation of dust particles and a subsequent clearing of small dust grains, thereby casting doubt on the efficiency of any long-term shielding of the solar radiation to form comets. Alternatively, even if protoplanets and protocomets are formed prior to the onset of the T Tauri phase (e.g. McCrea 1978, Clube 1988b), it would seem reasonable to expect that the surface ices at least will have undergone a good deal of processing in the presence of ionizing radiation, possibly affecting the relative isotopic composition, for example, to a quite considerable degree (cf. Section 18.2.3, p.446).

It has not yet been shown, then, that the turbulent outflows associated with protostars, and the violent flaring associated with the early phases of stellar evolution, are consistent with the cold, quiescent conditions apparently required for the growth of comets by coagulation of icy grains. Ices are indeed abundant in the outer solar system, but they might have been transported there from elsewhere. The compatibility of these new observations with traditional ideas concerning cometary growth in the solar nebula, especially those associated with the planetesimal picture (e.g. the settling of the dust to midplane within a quiescent disc), has yet to be demonstrated; both detailed modelling and further infrared observations of young star-forming regions are required to decide the issue. Indeed, it could even be argued that the whole process of quiescent settlement along the lines of the standard model is so implausible in the face of these observations that one ought to be looking for another process altogether!

14.1.4 REMNANT DISCS

At a later stage still, excess infrared radiation has also been detected from a number of relatively old main-sequence stars. This emission comes mostly from interstellar grains with temperatures in the range 40–140 K, and total luminosities on the order of 10^{-3}–10^{-6} L_*, where L_* is the luminosity of the central star. For comparison, the sun's zodiacal dust cloud currently has an infrared luminosity of about 10^{-7} $L_\odot$. Allowing for the difficulty of detecting such excess infrared emission, and for the fact that several of the stars with such an excess are more than 10^9 years old, it seems likely that a majority of ordinary main-sequence stars are surrounded by dust grains that are heated by the central star (*e.g.* Aumann 1988). In particular, the presence of such dust is not connected solely with *young* stellar objects, and relatively strong far-infrared emission has now been spatially resolved, for example, around four bright, otherwise ordinary nearby stars: namely, Beta Pictoris, Alpha Lyrae (Vega), Alpha Piscis Austrini (Fomalhaut) and Epsilon Eridani (*e.g.* Aumann *et al.* 1984, Aumann 1985, Norman & Paresce 1989). As a result of these observations it has been possible to construct models in which a dusty circumstellar disc is heated by the central star, and a particularly good example is provided by the A5 V star Beta Pictoris, whose main-sequence lifetime is about 2 Gyr.

In this system, visual observations demonstrate the presence of what appears to be an edge-on disc (*e.g.* Smith & Terrile 1984, Paresce & Burrows 1987). This optical disc, if such it is, is extremely flat (half-thickness $\lesssim$ 50 AU at the outer edge of the disc) and asymmetric (one branch extending at least 1150 AU from the star, the other 950 AU). Interestingly, these dimensions are not unlike those found in the cases of the young stellar systems IRAS 1629 A (about 3000 AU) and HL Tau ($\simeq$ 2000 AU) described above. Combined visible and infrared observations indicate that the radiation probably comes from 1–20 μm sized particles extending to an inner boundary of the disc some 5–15 AU from the central star (*e.g.* Telesco *et al.* 1988, Artymowicz *et al.* 1989). The particles are fairly bright, with individual albedos of order 0.7, although this does not allow one to discriminate between a mineral constitution or a composition made predominantly of water or ammonia ice. In either case, however, one has the problem of particle replenishment. Small ice particles would sublimate within hours at distances ranging up to $\simeq 40\,\mathrm{AU}$ from the central star, while refractory particles, such as silicates, would undergo mutually disruptive collisions in less than 5000 years at the inner edge of the disc, and within 10 Myr for nearly circular orbits at the outer edge.

These arguments show that the dust must be replenished on a timescale much less than the current age of the star, demonstrating the necessity for a continuing source of such material in the system. Of course, an obvious possibility is the disintegration of massive bodies such as comets, orbiting in elliptical paths of various eccentricities within the general region of the disc. Outgassing of solar system comets usually begins within about 2 AU of the sun, which is consistent, within the errors, with the 5–15 AU estimated inner boundary of the Beta Pictoris disc (*cf.* Section 10.2.2, p.218). Moreover, a single large comet recently thrown into an orbit of intermediate period might possibly account for the observed asymmetry of the edge-on 'disc'.

Further indirect evidence for the presence of large bodies in this system comes from observations made with the International Ultraviolet Explorer satellite (IUE), which showed that metal absorption lines in the star's ultraviolet spectrum are strongly variable, a result which has been attributed by Lagrange-Henri *et al.* (1988) and Beust *et al.* (1989) to the infall of planetesimals ranging in size up to some kilometres on to the surface of the star at a rate of order 10–100 per year. To achieve this, the planetesimal flux would have to correspond to that which bombarded the moon $\simeq 3.9\,\mathrm{Gyr}$ ago (*cf.* Section 16.2.2, p.373) and which presumably lasted $\simeq 800\,\mathrm{Myr}$, consistent with the main-sequence lifetime of Beta Pictoris.

However, if the dust is indeed supplied by collisions or the decay of planetesimals in such a system, the total mass of dust lost over the lifetime of the system would be extremely large, greater even than that of the giant planets. It may well be, then, that the existence of so much dust around old main-sequence stars, coupled with the need for rapid replenishment, is evidence for the existence of a massive ring of comets or planetesimals around many stars. Such a ring of material could be considered to be virtually immune to the perturbations of passing stars or molecular clouds, although if it were cometary and included relatively massive objects continually stirring it up, then one would expect a steady influx of intermediate-period comets to penetrate to within a few AU of the central star. Moreover, if a planetary system existed around the star, it could also act so as to feed these comets into an Oort cloud.

Far-infrared emission, at around 60 μm, has also been observed around the bright star Vega, and in this case appears to be coming from a disc observed almost face-on. This disc, which seems to have a central depleted zone with radius of order 20 AU, extends out to about 80 AU. It too could arise from the sublimation and disintegration of icy cometary nuclei and dust grains, again occupying a massive ring around the star, although the existence of such inner boundaries to the discs of systems where dust rings have been resolved could also be attributed to the presence of a supposed massive planet, dynamically clearing out all particles entering the region (Backman *et al.* 1989).

Were the sun to have such a dust cloud, similar to those that have been observed in other systems, it would probably still be undetectable from the earth using present techniques. The present lack of firm evidence for such system does not, therefore, necessarily prove its absence, and searches to discover dust and larger bodies on the outskirts of our planetary system are continuing. Of course, the general idea that there might be a ring of cometary bodies surrounding the planetary system is not new, and dates back at least to Edgeworth (1949), Kuiper (1951a) and Whipple (1964a,b). Indeed, as we have already mentioned (see Section 13.3.4, p.296) such a ring has even been postulated by Fernández (1980a) and others as the most likely source of short-period comets. From this point of view, it would be particularly useful to know whether the particles in the circumstellar discs around other stars are icy, and detailed models of the formation and evolution of such discs are required.

14.1.5 IMPACT ON THEORY

Although it cannot be claimed that these new observations have yet provided crucial tests of theories of cometary origin, the potential is obviously there, and they clearly contain the seeds of many new arguments which might eventually confirm or rule out many of the 'traditional' ideas about cometary growth, including the possibility of coagulation in a quiescent protoplanetary disc, formation in dense inner rings and so on. As to how important a rôle comets play in the star formation process, however, this too is a matter for future work. In most theories of star formation, such as the core collapse picture described above, comets play almost no part at all; nevertheless, there are a number of indications that their rôle might, on the contrary, be crucial.

For example, the removal of angular momentum from a collapsing protostar represents one of the main difficulties for traditional collapse theories. Now if the Beta Pictoris ring has a mass similar to that of the earth, its angular momentum would be comparable to that of the central star. Were the ring much more massive, say in excess of the mass of Jupiter (as seems to be required by the replenishment timescales), the ring would have more than 99% of the angular momentum of the system, and allowing for the gas which must initially have been associated with the planetesimals, an original angular momentum comparable to that of the original cloud from which the star formed is involved. Likewise if there is, or ever was, a primordial comet cloud with, say, a mass comparable to that of the planetary system, then the rotation acquired by the comet cloud during the protostellar collapse phase would ensure that it carried an order of magnitude more angular momentum than that of the planets, comparable, perhaps, to that carried by the planets before their loss of volatiles (cf. Marochnik & Mukhin 1987, 1988; Section 13.1, p.275).

Considerations such as these suggest that the aggregation of discrete masses may in some manner not yet understood perhaps play an as important a rôle in star formation as that which seems to be required by fragmentation of the ordinary 'smooth' gas component (*cf.* McCrea 1960, 1961; Urey 1972). A further suggestion that this might be so lies in the depletion of the heavier elements observed in molecular clouds, carrying with it the possibility that interstellar space may contain not only gas and dust but also a population of kilometre-sized (and larger) 'dirty snowballs'. In that case, the process of star formation would involve not only the collapse of a mass of gas, but also the collapse of gas already seeded with planetesimals. Krat (1952), for example, argued along lines similar to these, suggesting that nebulae may contain large numbers of invisible subplanetary bodies with masses on the order of 10^{20} kg, collisions between which generated stars and star clusters.

The existence of such pre-grown comets in interstellar space could have profound implications for the mechanics of star and planet formation. For example, the slow homologous collapse of a molecular cloud core containing comets, from original dimensions of order 10^4 AU to a final size of around 1 AU, would cause the indigenous comets to spiral in, leading to a newly formed protostar of about a solar mass surrounded by $\approx 10^{14}$ comets orbiting within the inner $\simeq 5$ AU. For the most part these would be absorbed into the protostar or later destroyed, but some fraction of bodies at larger distances might survive and be retained. In a solar nebula with comets ready formed, problems such as the long growth times for comets in the Uranus-Neptune region, or indeed the problem of their growth at all, are avoided (though of course not necessarily solved!). Once again, the investigation and development of such ideas, and the incorporation of new observational data into them, is a task for the future.

In summary, therefore, recent progress towards understanding the formation of comets in the context of a primordial solar system hypothesis has led us along a number of quite promising lines of enquiry, such as those developed by Öpik, Safronov, Cameron and Hills; but in the end we seem to have been left with important new observations which as yet have no definite interpretation. Indeed, with preferences for a low-mass or high-mass protoplanetary disc still being frequently expressed, there is no sign yet of the desired convergence of opinion. This contrasts sharply with expectations expressed during the decade immediately following the introduction of Oort's original comet cloud model, and also with the progress actually made in the period since 1950 in understanding the basic 'physics' of comets: their detailed morphological structures, the mechanisms of gas and dust production from the nucleus, and the interaction of the emitted gas with the solar wind (see, for example, the books by Wilkening 1982, Brandt & Chapman 1982, and reviews by Hughes 1982b, Fernández & Jockers 1983, Butterworth 1985, Mendis *et al.* 1985, A'Hearn 1988, Mendis 1988). It is possible, therefore, that the present lack of agreement amongst cosmogonists may be symptomatic of a much deeper malaise: and raises the important question of whether the underlying assumption linking all these ideas so far discussed — the 'primordial solar system' hypothesis — should itself perhaps be re-examined.

14.2   Solar system discord

The question of the validity of the usual primordial solar system hypothesis for the origin of comets divides into two parts: first, on whether comets are genuinely 'primordial' material, solar system stuff somehow formed *coevally* with the sun and planets; and secondly, whether they are 'solar system' bodies at all. These alternative interpretations of the place of comets in our understanding of the solar system have generally been ignored by authors working within mainstream cometary theories, who almost without exception have adopted what by now has become a 'traditional' framework comprising a standard Oort cloud theory of cometary provenance together with one or another form of the planetesimal hypothesis for generating comets within a primordial solar nebula. Nevertheless, a significant number of astronomers (albeit a minority) have continued to entertain considerable reservations about the validity of this overall scheme, and to their credit have not been deterred by mere fashion or peer pressure from exploring what from a distance has sometimes seemed to be an almost kaleidoscopic array of alternative options.

Many of these ideas for cometary origin are (it must be said) subject to severe theoretical or observational difficulties of one sort or another, but their existence has nevertheless helped to convey to a wider audience, if not actually illuminate, a number of important points generally ignored by those working on more conventional theories. It is also worth noting that many of the new proposals, whether fundamentally of a solar system or interstellar complexion, have resonances that can often be traced back as far as the nineteenth century, or sometimes even earlier. This occasionally cloaks these apparently 'radical' theories with a degree of familiarity that can sometimes produce a quite unexpected degree of popular support for the idea.

For this reason, we may therefore describe these alternative theories somewhat loosely as 'new' variations on 'old' themes, and, by extending the influence of an otherwise long-dead theory beyond its natural span, they gain a rather more prominent rôle in the history of cometary astronomy than they might generally be thought to deserve. Moreover, by raising an old issue, perhaps long-forgotten (for example when they have echoed the Laplace vs. Lagrange debate of the nineteenth century), these 'new-for-old' theories often indirectly continue to influence the longer term development of the subject.

Having set the scene, we now divide our review of the principal alternatives into two main parts. First, we complete this chapter by describing those alternative views which retain the usual 'solar system' hypothesis for cometary origin, but which mostly drop the assumption that the material is 'primordial' in origin. Then, in the following Chapter 15, we describe a group of ideas which many consider to represent a more promising alternative: namely those theories which involve modifications in one form or another of Laplace's original interstellar hypothesis, several interesting new variants of which have also been proposed in the years since 1950.

14.2.1   SOMETHING OLD

Among these 'old and new' suggestions to explain the origin of comets within a broadly solar system viewpoint, perhaps the most frequently expressed idea is that represented by modifications of Lagrange's planetary explosion hypothesis (*cf.* Section 8.1.1, p.149) connecting the origin of comets to that of the asteroids. This general idea was first revived in recent years by Oort (1950) and Katasseff (1955), and has since been reconsidered in detail by Van Flandern (1975, 1976, 1977, 1978a,b).

This author drew on earlier work by Ovenden (*e.g.* 1972, 1973, 1975) who in turn was developing the suggestion (originally due to Olbers) that there might once have been a massive planet in the region of the asteroid belt, which had disintegrated, so yielding the asteroids. Ovenden proposed a principle of 'least interaction action', according to which a system of gravitating bodies — such as the planets orbiting the sun — would adjust their mutual distances in such a way as to minimise their net interactions. Applying this idea to the planetary system, he found that the observed distances of the planets from the sun showed slight departures from such a 'minimum perturbation' configuration. However, if a planet of mass $90 \, M_\oplus$ had once existed in the region now occupied by the main asteroid belt, and if that planet had disintegrated only 16 million years ago, then the observed relative distances of the planets could be explained in terms of relaxation from one optimum configuration towards another. The bulk of the débris, it was supposed, would have been swallowed up by Jupiter or ejected from the solar system.

Van Flandern followed this controversial suggestion with the proposal that not only the asteroids but also long-period comets themselves were fragments of the same great planetary explosion. He argued that a spherically symmetrical explosion would generate a strong asymmetry in the distribution of the perihelion directions of the long-period comets, and that such an asymmetry was in fact observed. From the observed distribution he concluded that the explosion should have occurred at an ecliptic longitude 222°, at a distance of 2.8 AU from the sun. The long-period comets were then interpreted as high energy fragments from the explosion, making their first return to the realm of the planets having originally had too little kinetic energy to escape from the sun. This argument allowed him to date the original catastrophe as occurring some 5.5 ± 0.6 million years ago. This makes the event rather more recent than Ovenden's estimate, but the latter was known to be imprecise and there was no real inconsistency. Van Flandern thought he could in this way also explain an unexpected correlation between the perihelion directions and the absolute magnitudes of comets, a fact which had previously been remarked upon by Tomanov (1973).

Van Flandern's theory thus implied a remarkably recent origin for comets, certainly within the timescale for development of human life on earth. However, an event as gigantic as the recent explosion of a massive planet could not have failed to leave prominent signatures, both on the earth and on the solar system more generally (cf. discussion following Van Flandern 1977), and astronomers have mostly tended to dismiss the idea out of hand. Nevertheless, some have given time to the suggestion, and Öpik (1978), for example, pointed out that one of these 'predictions' would be the removal of life on earth (!), due principally to three blasts of energy likely to be generated by such an event. First, a burst of radiation from the explosion itself, then a blast of débris from the arrival of ejecta falling directly on to the earth, and finally a second burst of radiation caused by material falling on to the sun, temporarily increasing the solar luminosity. The climatological effects of such a sequence of events can hardly be guessed at, and it almost goes without saying that there is no evidence for such a recent catastrophe in either the fossil or geological records. Moreover, Harrington (1985) has now questioned the existence of the perihelion asymmetry claimed to exist by Van Flandern, thereby removing any remaining rationale for a very recent event.

In general, however, it is interesting to explore the wider question of whether a disrupted planet might possibly have been the source of comets, or even the asteroid belt, perhaps at some remote epoch in the distant past. One difficulty with the idea — which immediately begs the question of a mechanism — is the huge energy required (Napier & Dodd 1973). To explode a planet of mass M and radius R requires a minimum energy on the order of the gravitational binding energy of the planet, i.e. $E \simeq GM^2/R$. For a planet with mass $M = 90\,M_\oplus$ and density equal to that of the earth, $R \simeq 4.5R_\oplus$ and $E \simeq 6.7 \times 10^{35}$ J. The energy per unit mass is then $E/M \simeq 1.3 \times 10^9$ J kg^{-1}, about 300 times the equivalent detonation energy of TNT: even were the planet to be made of pure dynamite it could not be dissipated on detonation! Any mechanism using a purely chemical source of energy is equally inadequate to destroy a large planet. Alternatively, it might be supposed that a slow accumulation of energy through radioactive heating could build up a high pressure core, constrained by an overlying mantle until bursting occurred. However, the crushing strength of rock is about 10^7 J kg^{-1}, and it does not seem likely that any such mechanism could thus be made to work: a rocky crust would fracture prematurely. These difficulties are of course a testimony to the strength of gravity, and it is doubtful whether a body much larger than Ceres could be made to disrupt by any internal process.

14.2.2   TIDAL LINKS

The question of an external process remains, however, and the suggestion that the smallest bodies in the solar system might have been generated by larger worlds in collision, possibly in the remote past, was raised by Woolfson (1978c). This author had for some time been concerned with reviving Jeans's tidal theory for the origin of the solar system. According to this idea (see Figure 14.2), the planets originated in an extremely close encounter of another star with the sun that tidally drew out a

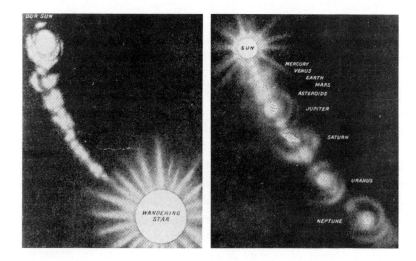

Figure 14.2: Early representation of Jeans's tidal theory of the origin of the solar system. Taken from Whipple (1964b).

filament of material from our sun, out of which the planets condensed. Such encounters are extremely rare in the general interstellar environment and for this reason the theory has long been regarded as obsolete. However, it is now known that the number density of newly formed stars in young clusters can range up to more than 10^4 times that in the ambient field, and since encounter rates vary quadratically with the number density, the possibility of a catastrophic stellar collision occurring in such an environment should perhaps be taken more seriously.

In particular, Woolfson (1978a,b,c) suggested that the newly formed sun might have passed close to a cool, collapsing protostar within its parent star cluster, and that a long filament of cold, self-gravitating material had been drawn out from the protostar by the sun's tidal action. This overcame some of the difficulties associated with Jeans's original hypothesis, for example that the tidal filament from the sun, being hot, would have simply dispersed into space. Woolfson has also argued that many features in the planetary system today can now be understood by assuming that a catastrophic collision had taken place between two planets formed in the filament. On this picture, then, the asteroids, comets and meteorites are débris resulting from such a collision (Woolfson 1978c), while the present Oort cloud was formed by the ejection of such fragments into long-period orbits, a suggestion which had also been made by Oort (1950) in his seminal paper.

Both the Woolfson and Van Flandern hypotheses involve an essentially catastrophic origin for comets, one in the remote past, the other very recently. The remote epoch of the Woolfson collision means that observational tests, at least those based on the observed orbital properties of comets, are relatively much more difficult to obtain. There are, however, other difficulties with the process, one being that the planets involved in the collision are supposed to have a total mass of only about 40 $M_{\oplus}$. Given that only a small proportion of the collisional débris would be expected to condense into comets, and that only a further small proportion of these comets would eventually find their way into stable orbits within the Oort cloud, it seems extremely unlikely that enough material to form a sufficiently massive primordial Oort cloud could be made in this way. While modifications of the hypothesis might be imagined which could in principle overcome some of these difficulties (e.g. the formation of comets in the outer parts of the tidal filament, or planetary collisions further out), no detailed attempt has yet been made to reconcile the picture with current interpretations of the overall structure and mass of a primordial Oort cloud.

A second possible difficulty with the tidal theory concerns the fact that the planetary system rotates in the same sense as the sun, with a pole of rotation located within 7° of the pole of rotation of the sun. This argues, albeit from the statistics of a single example (a recurring problem in solar system cosmogony), that an encounter with another star, approaching from a random direction in space, would not be likely to produce the observed planetary system.

14.2.3   BINARY THEORY

Of course, this problem need not arise if the young sun had originally been part of a binary system. Binary stars are extremely common, and Drobyshevski (1974a,b) proposed a novel idea in which the two principal components of the original solar nebula were the protosun and the proto-Jupiter, with proto-Jupiter containing most of the mass ($\simeq 1\,M_\odot$). When such binary components are very close, there is a propensity for an instability in which the larger star may lose mass. As it expands, material from the larger star's surface spills over on to the smaller companion star which, having thereby increased its mass, exerts a stronger tidal effect, pulling more material on to itself and so on. Of course, the conditions inside the proto-Jupiter at this time would not have resembled those inside ordinary stars; rather, they would have been similar in many ways to those postulated in the massive disc scenarios described by Cameron (1962, 1978). Drobyshevski (1978) thus argued that during an initial phase of rapid mass transfer, in which most of the material within the proto-Jupiter was transferred on to what is now the sun, a large number ($\approx 10^4$) of lunar-sized planetoids would have formed inside the proto-Jupiter.

As the transfer of mass from proto-Jupiter continued, the small planetoids would be expected to escape from its declining gravitational field, eventually to be placed in eccentric orbits beyond Neptune, forming a belt, or swarm of bodies lying between 50 and 300 AU from the sun. Drobyshevski predicted that the little planets would have rocky cores, liquid mantles and icy crusts. From time to time they would collide with one another, breaking up their icy crusts and throwing fragments, identified as comets, into space. It was also suggested that volcanic activity in their cores might have a similar effect. Some comets would diffuse inwards to populate the short and intermediate period systems, while others would be scattered outwards to form the conventional Oort cloud.

In this way, Drobyshevski replaced the idea of a single planetary explosion, or a single pair of worlds in collision, with that of a continuing sequence of disruptive collisions between small ice-covered planets beyond Neptune, and he was able to put this idea (originally attributed to Krat 1952) into the context of a modern astrophysical view of binary star evolution. He also made a number of specific predictions, particularly that large numbers of lunar-sized bodies should exist beyond the orbit of Neptune. Moreover, these ought to be detectable optically or, because of their low temperature, with present or planned infrared surveys such as those of the Infrared Astronomical Satellite (IRAS) and missions such as the Cosmic Background Explorer (COBE) and the Infrared Space Observatory (ISO).

The possibility that lunar-sized bodies might originally have played a significant rôle in the formation of the solar system seems first to have been put forward in recent years by Urey (1972), and it is an interesting coincidence that there are at least seven known bodies with diameters of this order: the Moon (3476 km), Io (3630 km), Europa (3138 km), Triton (3800 km), and the rocky cores of Ganymede (3700 ± 200 km), Callisto (3200 ± 200 km) and Pluto (3000 ± 500 km). That a large population of Moon-sized bodies might be orbiting beyond Neptune may thus be quite reasonable, and comets could in principle be produced by the collisions between such bodies or their icy fragments right up to the present day.

More recently, Drobyshevski (e.g. 1980, 1981, 1986) has introduced a second scheme for expelling comets from satellites, in which it is supposed that their motion through an external magnetic field (for example, that carried by the solar wind) induces a small internal electric current which electrolyses the dirty water ice found on a satellite surface. Hydrogen and oxygen build up in the ice to a point where there is enough energy stored in these gases to blow great chunks of ice into space whenever explosive combustion occurs from whatever cause.

Drobyshevski has suggested that this basic mechanism could account for the existence of such diverse phenomena as Saturn's rings, the Trojan asteroids and the grooves on Phobos, while he has also argued (Drobyshevski 1987, 1989) that the ejection velocity of the gas and dust emitted from the nucleus of Halley's comet during the spacecraft encounters was too high ($\simeq 1\,\mathrm{km\,s^{-1}}$) to be accounted for by solar heating alone, again suggesting an explosive ejection of material due to the release of stored chemical energy. However, there are a number of unanswered questions concerning the model, for example relating to whether detonation occurs prematurely (or even at all), whether large comets might actually be produced in this way, and whether the débris from such an explosion would actually reach the necessary escape velocity. These do not invalidate the theory, of course, but most astronomers are cautious folk, slow to follow up ideas which may at first sight appear rather radical, and Drobyshevski's theory has not yet been put to a proper test.

The general idea of a catastrophic origin of comets, whether from planetary or satellite eruptions or from the fragmentation of larger bodies, has therefore been a recurring theme amongst explorers of ideas about cometary origin, the present epoch included (e.g. Padevět 1987). However, despite occasional investigations by a relatively small number of authors (e.g. Radzievskii 1987), it has never attained a particularly high profile, and at the present time the idea continues to attract very little attention. This, of course, says nothing about its fundamental validity, though the extreme fragility of comets and the evidence (discussed in Chapter 18) that they probably formed in extremely low temperature environments, do argue against a very violent or explosive origin.

14.2.4   SOMETHING NEW

An entirely different proposal for the origin of comets was put forward at about the same time by Reeves (1974), who noted that there is a rough balance between the observed outflow of material in the solar wind, and the mass influx (corrected to solar abundances) in the form of comets. Reeves therefore speculated that the comet cloud might be in a dynamical steady state, with new comets continually forming out of the solar wind to replace those lost through decay and planetary perturbations. He thought that this might come about if comets were somehow produced in processes operating in a turbulent boundary layer dividing the solar wind from the surrounding interstellar medium. Reeves therefore argued that if comets did condense out of solar wind material they should have a deuterium-to-hydrogen ratio equal to that measured in the solar wind, *i.e.* $D/H \lesssim 3 \times 10^{-6}$, and this was presented as a crucial test of his ideas.

In 1974 also, Whipple & Lecar (1976) presented what was conceptually a rather similar model, in which comets were supposed to form in a shell of circumsolar material swept up by a powerful protosolar wind. They suggested that radiation pressure acting on dust grains in the shell might well concentrate the dust to such an extent that it became gravitationally unstable to collapse into kilometre sized comet-like nuclei. The D/H ratio expected on this model would then equal that of the primordial sun. However, deuterium is a fragile element, easily destroyed in the process of star formation, and it is likely that the primordial sun probably had a D/H ratio of order 2×10^{-5}, to within about a factor of two. The deuterium ratio therefore potentially provides a critical test of this hypothesis too, irrespective of any other physical difficulties (or otherwise) associated with the idea.

It first became possible to apply this test during the spacecraft encounters with Comet Halley in 1986. Measurements of the D/H ratio in this comet made by mass spectrometers on board the Giotto spacecraft (Eberhardt *et al.* 1986) indicated that the water ice in this comet had $D/H \simeq 2 \times 10^{-4}$ to within a factor of about three, higher even than that expected in the primordial sun. This indicates that deuterium in Comet Halley must have been enriched relative to the gas out of which most of the solar system formed, possibly in ion-molecule reactions on the icy mantles of interstellar dust predating the origin of the solar system (*e.g.* Owen *et al.* 1986). It seems, therefore, that both the Reeves and Whipple & Lecar models, in which comets originate by a process of condensation in the hydrogen atmosphere of the sun, whether past or present, can be ruled out.

We note, however, that the actual process by which dust particles might accumulate into comet-sized bodies at the boundary of the solar or protosolar wind was never worked out in detail, a defect which has now been partially remedied by Bailey (1987a). In particular, Bailey considered the effect of a powerful protostellar wind on the primordial gas and dust expected to surround a newly formed star, and presented a theory which bears a number of conceptual similarities to the original qualitative proposal of Whipple & Lecar.

On this picture, a strong protostellar wind drives a shock into the surrounding circumstellar envelope, causing the material in the envelope to be swept up into a thin, dense wind-driven shell. The parameters of the shell are such that for a wide range of plausible initial conditions the dust density is high enough that rapid aggregation of pre-existing interstellar dust grains can occur (*cf.* Elmegreen 1981). This leads both to 'giant' grains (*e.g.* Elsässer *et al.* 1982, Rouan & Léger 1984; Bailey 1987b, and references therein) and, possibly, to bodies large enough that their motions may become decoupled from the gas. When this occurs, the largest grains drift together by a process of sedimentation in the still decelerating shell, and may then produce bodies the size of observed comets by a process of gravitational collapse analogous to the formation of planetesimals in conventional protoplanetary disc theories.

This theory therefore predicts the existence of large numbers of interstellar comets in regions of recent star formation (*cf.* Bailey 1988b), and also implies that the sun's present comet family should have originally formed as a result of capture of comets from wind-driven shells expanding about neighbouring stars formed contemporaneously with the sun. Moreover, by assuming that comets form essentially through an aggregation of cold circumstellar dust grains, presumably with icy mantles, one is also able in principle to overcome the above-mentioned problem of the D/H ratio.

14.2.5   JET STREAMS

Another completely new approach to comet formation was also proposed during the nineteen-seventies by Alfvén and colleagues (e.g. Alfvén & Arrhenius 1970), arising from Alfvén's earlier work on the origin of the solar system in which he strongly emphasized the fundamental importance of unexpected plasma effects demonstrated in laboratory experiments. These authors argued that interstellar dust grains in the protosolar nebula might dynamically evolve to produce dense, narrow streams of co-orbiting particles which they called 'jet streams'.

Their basic idea was that collisions will take place in any system of dust particles revolving around the sun, and that such collisions, whether or not they result in fragmentation, will certainly result in dissipation of the relative velocities of the colliding masses. As collisions proceed, therefore, the orbits of the bodies in the system will tend to equalise. If initially the envelope of the orbits has a roughly toroidal shape, like a smoke ring, then the torus or ring will eventually narrow down until it finally becomes a Keplerian ellipse. A stage will then be reached when there is so little residual motion among the particles of the system that when they do collide they will tend to stick together rather than break up, the ultimate stage being the accumulation of the particles into a single body.

On this picture, long-period comets are supposed to have formed *in situ* at an early epoch, possibly in jet streams extending throughout the whole Oort cloud. (This is rather reminiscent of an idea independently proposed by Witkowski as a mechanism to slow down and capture interstellar comets; see p.336.) The short-period comets, on the other hand, are supposed to form continually right up to the present time, so overcoming the problem of their relatively large numbers as discussed for example by Vsekhsvyatski, van Woerkom and others.

The suggestion that planetesimals might aggregate out of co-orbiting streams of dust particles was later developed and extended by several other workers (*e.g.* Trulsen 1971, Mendis 1973, Mendis & Alfvén 1976, Alfvén & Arrhenius 1976 and references therein), and even applied to the present-day asteroid belt. Indeed, several asteroid families or groups have now been recognized, each containing typically 20–30 members (Carusi & Valsecchi 1982). However, whereas on the conventional view individual members of a family are seen as fragmentation products of a collision, on the jet stream concept they are regarded as bodies *en route* to coalescence, and the entire asteroid belt is reinterpreted as a system currently in the process of forming a single planet.

Although the jet stream concept has an appealing simplicity, it suffers from the fatal difficulty that such a stream would not in general be formed in isolation. In the asteroid belt, for example, a stream would be rapidly broken up through impacts with other bodies, which would feed energy into the system faster than it could be internally dispersed (Napier & Dodd 1974, Whipple 1972b,c). In a primordial system which was so quiescent that jet streams would not be destroyed by collisions, gravitational forces would in any case probably dominate and jet streams would then be irrelevant. There is indeed some evidence that comets have formed in regions of extreme quiescence; but the precise nature of such environments, and the rôle of jet streams within them, remains obscure.

14.2.6   FROSTED DUST

Despite this, the notion that co-orbiting streams of dust particles might aggregate into bodies resembling observed cometary nuclei did not die out entirely, and variations on the jet-stream concept have still occasionally been reintroduced from time to time. A recent example is provided by the work of O'Dell (1986), motivated, it seems, as much by the desire to provoke others into investigating alternative means of forming comets, as it was to present a plausible scenario for comet formation as a by-product of observed solar system processes in the present planetary system.

First, he noted that the steady 'grinding' action of collisions in the asteroid belt will tend to produce a large number of fine dust particles, some of which might have just the right size and density so that solar radiation pressure would drive them out of the planetary system into much more eccentric orbits of longer period. Such collisionally produced streams of dust were generally expected to disperse (even if radiation pressure allowed them to remain bound to the solar system), but O'Dell further proposed that gravitational perturbations and collisions in the asteroid belt might also cause much larger bodies — boulders and small asteroids — to be thrown into similar orbits, where they would subsequently act as nucleation centres for the dust.

While at large distances from the sun, the dust grains were then supposed to acquire a mantle, or 'frosting' of interstellar ices by simple accretion of interstellar gas. In this way, O'Dell argued that a cometary nucleus could be expected to comprise a central 'core' of boulders and small asteroidal fragments resembling a 'rubble pile' (*cf.* Weissman 1986c), stuck together and surrounded by small dust grains originally of asteroidal provenance but now covered by thin mantles of recently accreted interstellar ice. In particular, the theory predicted that the $^{12}C/^{13}C$ ratio in comets should be closer to the present interstellar value (roughly in the range 60–75) than the value ($\simeq 89$) usually associated with solar system bodies.

Interestingly, this prediction seems recently to have been borne out, at least according to one group of workers using ground-based observations of Comet Halley (Wyckoff *et al.* 1989): the reported determination of the ratio $^{12}C/^{13}C$ for Halley's comet is 65 ± 9. Nevertheless, although this observation is consistent with O'Dell's model (as indeed it is with the theories requiring a recent origin of comets in the interstellar medium), there are a large number of theoretical difficulties with the general idea as a viable mechanism by which to form comets.

In particular, because the dust grains are strongly affected by radiation pressure, the boulders or asteroids which are supposed to accrete the dust must drift through these streams at a substantial relative velocity, thereby leading to a much lower accretion rate than the more favourable case considered by O'Dell, in which the accreting bodies and dust were assumed to be comoving. A fundamental difficulty with the idea, therefore, is how to arrange for asteroids ejected from the solar system to accrete sufficient amounts of interplanetary dust (even if ice-coated) to explain observed comets. Moreover, a successful theory must also be able to account for the general statistical properties of observed comets, particularly their extremely long periods and the nearly isotropic distribution of orbits over the sky, as shown by the dominant long-period group. At the present time, therefore, O'Dell's recent modification of the jet-stream concept seems neither to have gained support nor yet given us much insight into the mystery of the origin of comets.

In summary, as we have already indicated, many of the ideas discussed in this section seem to have a distinctly *ad hoc* flavour, often appearing to the reader as an afterthought, or sometimes as a by-product arising out of some other postulated process, and frequently with little serious attempt being made to match the proposition to the known dynamics or chemistry of comets. In some cases an idea has been designed to meet only a specific aspect of the totality of knowledge about comets, and it is exaggerating only slightly to say that many (though not all) of these alternative solar system proposals amount to little more than speculative scenarios, having little predictive power and sometimes even less significance in relation to the overall body of knowledge that they attempt to explain. In general they have not greatly disturbed the broad consensus which has grown up favouring the standard Oort cloud hypothesis and a theory of comet formation firmly rooted in some way within the *primordial* solar nebula. However, the observational difficulties which these various theories were primarily set up to explain have proved remarkably hard to shift. Given these developments, it is important to ask whether perhaps *all* these 'solar system' suggestions might in some way be fundamentally flawed. Should one, therefore, give renewed consideration to the other alternative, namely the 'interstellar' hypothesis?

15

Interstellar angle

"We are all in the gutter, but some of us are looking at the stars."

Oscar Wilde.

15.1 Awkward facts

One reason for the continuing unease with the conventional primordial Oort cloud picture was emphasized quite early on by Tyror (1957) and Witkowski (1958). According to Oort's theory, the perihelion directions of new comets were expected to be randomly distributed on the sky. However, Witkowski and Tyror independently confirmed the early results of Eddington (1913), Natanson (1923), Oppenheim (1922, 1924), Bourgeois & Cox (1934), and others (see Section 7.1.2, p.130), that this was not the case. In particular, the perihelion directions seemed to align with the plane of the Galaxy, and Tyror and Witkowski interpreted this to mean that comets had an interstellar origin (*cf.* Russell 1935). Another tendency noted by these authors was for the directions of the perihelia to align also with the solar apex, which is a point in the constellation Hercules towards which the sun is moving when measured against the mean motion of the neighbouring stars.

Whereas Tyror interpreted these observations as supporting Lyttleton's accretion theory, Witkowski at first left the question open of the origin and capture of interstellar comets. However, he and his associates (*e.g.* Witkowski 1968, 1972; Piotrowski 1965, Piotrowski & Sitarski 1976) later argued for a capture mechanism involving a frictional resistance or drag due to the motion of the comets through a hypothetical cloud of gas and dust which was assumed to surround the solar system and extend far beyond the planets. These authors therefore recognized one of the crucial problems which any interstellar comet theory would have to face, namely the problem of capturing such comets into bound orbits about the sun.

Although the other major problem, that of growing kilometre-sized icy bodies in the tenuous interstellar medium, was not addressed by them, it was soon appreciated that the proposed capture mechanism required an impossibly large mass of gas and dust in the outer solar system if the dust cloud was assumed to be uniform (Witkowski 1972, Delsemme 1977). Witkowski (1968) therefore proposed that the dust cloud was, in effect, a highly non-uniform 'Oort cloud' of proto-comets which acted as targets for the genuine passing interstellar comets. However, calculations readily show that the capture probability for interstellar comets by this mechanism is extremely small, and it does not seem that even this provides a satisfactory quantitative basis for the theory. The galactic and solar apex alignments remained, however, as thorns in the flesh of the conventional primordial solar system paradigm.

15.1.1   ABUNDANCE PROBLEMS

That large numbers of comets might be present in interstellar space was also suggested at this time by Greenberg (1974) and Tinsley & Cameron (1974) from a completely different point of view. Greenberg drew attention to the fact that significant depletion of elements occurred in dense nebulae, in the sense that the metal-to-hydrogen ratio in the gas was less than that observed in young stars. (Note that in astronomical terminology, a 'metal' is loosely defined to be any element with atomic weight greater than that of helium.) This depletion seemed to be more than could be accounted for by the locking up of carbon, nitrogen and oxygen into small dust grains, at least those of a size which contributed significantly to the general interstellar extinction.

More recent studies have confirmed that the diffuse interstellar nebulae are indeed deficient in heavy elements relative to solar abundances, the deficiency in most cases increasing strongly with increasing nebular density (*e.g.* Cardelli & Böhm-Vitense 1982, Menteşe 1982, Phillips *et al.* 1982, Tarafdar *et al.* 1983, Jenkins 1987, Van Steenberg & Shull 1988). This deficiency applies not only to volatile elements such as sulphur, oxygen, nitrogen and argon, which would readily form ices, but also to the more refractory elements such as carbon, magnesium, iron and titanium. Moreover, the deficiency increases with the density of the nebula to such an extent that the densest nebulae are depleted by over ninety per cent in the proportion of 'metals' relative to the solar abundance.

Tinsley & Cameron also drew attention to the fact that the progressive enrichment of the Galaxy with heavier elements, as predicted by simple models of galactic chemical evolution, did not occur at the expected rate. They argued that this might be explained if the newly created elements were also being locked up in planetesimals, rather than being simply transferred back to the gas or into stars. Vanýsek (1987a), for example, has recently estimated that such effects on galactic chemical evolution will begin to be significant if, on the average, a star of about one solar mass is normally associated with about 10^{28} kg of cometary material (*cf.* Van den Bergh 1982).

Of course, if interstellar comets do exist then from time to time one should penetrate the solar system with a significantly hyperbolic velocity. The fact that none such has been observed since scientific observations began is therefore an important constraint on the numbers which might exist in interstellar space, at least in the solar neighbourhood. In this way Sekanina (1976), for example, was able to show that the ambient number density of interstellar comets was likely to be no more than about $10^{-4}\,\mathrm{AU}^{-3}$. However, this limit is also consistent with the proposition that a significant part of the observed heavy element depletion in the gas phase of the interstellar medium could be due to the presence of interstellar comets. In principle there might be as much as $10^{8}\,M_{\odot}$ of material in the Galaxy locked up in 10^{24} interstellar comets!

15.1.2 ANISOTROPIC APHELIA

Throughout the nineteen-seventies various authors (*e.g.* Joss 1973b, Oja 1975, Hasegawa 1976, Tomanov 1976, Bogart & Noerdlinger 1982) continued to draw attention to the anisotropy in the distributions of cometary perihelia and aphelia over the celestial sphere. Not only were the distributions patchy on the sky, with a definite tendency towards clustering (*cf.* Section 7.1.2, p.130), but there also seemed to be an excess of comets with aphelia in the general direction of the solar antapex, the direction from which the sun is moving. This result has recently been confirmed by Sharma & Khanna (1988), who report an especially pronounced correlation of the perihelion directions of the so-called 'new' comets with the direction of the solar apex.

However, there is also an observational bias in the number of astronomers able to discover comets in the northern and southern hemispheres, and the possibility has been raised from time to time that this observational selection effect might thereby introduce a spurious anisotropy in the observed distribution of comets. Moreover, several of the studies which had been made either did not discriminate between good and poor orbits, or the orbits of the long-period comets examined were not always the original ones, many having been altered by planetary perturbations. Evidently, a study of comets whose orbits had been disturbed as little as possible by the planets was called for, to determine whether any 'fossil trace' of past extraneous disturbances can be reliably inferred from the observed orbital characteristics.

More recent studies, using comets with well-determined orbits, have indeed clarified the situation. In a statistical analysis carried out by Yabushita (1985), for example, it was shown that the north-south selection effect, although present (Lüst 1984), was not by itself capable of yielding the observed clustering of the aphelia towards the solar antapex direction, while in another study, Delsemme (1986) has analyzed the orbits of 126 long-period comets which had not been subject to previous planetary influences. The comets in this sample gave the initially unexpected result that their aphelia appeared to 'avoid' three areas of the celestial sphere: the regions around the galactic equator and the north and south galactic poles.

The existence of such zones with relatively few cometary aphelia had been previously noted by Lüst (1984, 1985), who had argued that the deficiencies around the galactic poles were probably not statistically significant; so the recurrence of such effects in Delsemme's study was initially a surprise. However, the realization about this time of the crucially important effects of the galactic tide in driving new comets into the inner solar system gave a ready explanation of the new results: namely, in terms of the newly discovered 'galactic' effects on the Oort cloud.

As we have already seen (cf. equation 12.16, p.268), the rate of change in perihelion distance per revolution, Δq, influences the rate at which new comets are injected into the planetary system from the Oort cloud, and according to the theory of the galactic tide this quantity is proportional to the sine of twice the galactic latitude of the aphelion point, $\sin 2b$. Moreover, since the number of comets with aphelia in the directions of galactic latitude and longitude (b, l) is roughly proportional to $\cos b \, db \, dl$, for a spherically symmetrical comet cloud, the observed numbers of new comets vs. galactic latitude should vary roughly proportional to the product $\sin 2b \cos b$. This has a maximum at about 35°, much as observed, and the general anisotropy in the distribution of cometary aphelia is now regarded by many authors as confirming the overall importance of the galactic tide in controlling the flux of comets into the planetary system.

15.1.3   Time dependence

Closer inspection of these major underlying structures in the distribution of long-period comets on the sky has revealed a number of more detailed correlations (see Figure 15.1). For example, the apparent patchiness of the distribution of the aphelion directions on the sky has been confirmed, and an unexpectedly large number of comets has been found which do indeed have aphelia clustered within a few tens of degrees around the solar antapex. This excess was attributed by Biermann *et al.* (1983) to the effect of a single (chance) stellar perturbation on the Oort cloud, called a 'star track', though its coincidence with the direction of the solar antapex still amounts to a relatively rare event, and some therefore continue to argue that it is more reasonable to ascribe the clustering to a result of the solar motion through space, though still indicative of a recent disturbance of the Oort cloud.

Nevertheless, the degree of clustering of the cometary aphelia towards the solar antapex does not, on its own, appear to be statistically significant (Lüst 1984, 1985), unless one takes the view, on other grounds, that the apex-antapex line should receive a preferred status. The apparent significance of these statistical results thus depends on one's theoretical outlook. From a primordial solar system point of view, the present direction of the solar antapex in relation to the Oort cloud has no particular theoretical significance, and the degree of clustering of the cometary aphelia towards this particular point on the sky is then usually regarded as no more than a chance coincidence: given the observed number of comets a similar degree of clustering might generally be expected to occur *somewhere* on the sky for a completely random distribution. On the other hand, on those theories in which comets are captured from interstellar space (such as Lyttleton's accretion theory; see Section 8.3, p.170) the solar apex-antapex line often assumes much greater importance in the discussion. From this 'capture' perspective, therefore, it is possible that the observed degree of clustering of the aphelia towards the solar antapex is indeed rather more significant than usually calculated, though one would still have to explain, for example, why the aphelia rather than the perihelia were correlated with the antapex.

Moreover, in addition to the 'zones of avoidance' symmetrical about the galactic plane described by Delsemme, the long-period comets also seem to be affected by a second plane of symmetry,

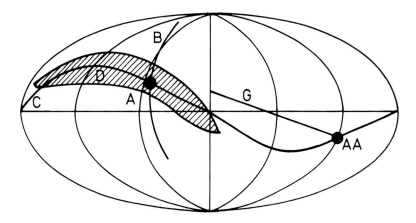

Figure 15.1: Patterns of perihelia in galactic coordinates. The
North Galactic Pole is to the top and the galactic centre is in
the middle. The diagram is coded as follows: (A) the solar apex;
(AA) the antapex; (B) the 'star-track' found by Biermann *et al.*;
(C) the great circle passing through the solar apex and the galactic
centre; (D) the strip of corotating comets discussed by Delsemme;
and (G) Gould's Belt. Adapted from Delsemme (1989).

corresponding to an enhancement in their numbers along a seg-
ment of a great circle about the sky approximately 90° long and
30° wide, orientated in a direction apparently unrelated to either
the galactic plane or the ecliptic. (The pole of this new plane
of symmetry has ecliptic coordinates $\lambda \simeq 181°$ and $\beta \simeq 3°$, with
uncertainties of about ±5°.) Of the 38 comets occupying this
strip, about two-thirds (25) have orbits in a retrograde sense,
while the remainder (13) move in a prograde direction relative
to the strip. Indeed, the mean specific orbital angular momentum of the retrograde comets was found to be more than 3 times
that of those with prograde orbits.

As we have mentioned, this newly found strip of symmetry
does not correlate with either the galactic plane or the ecliptic, but it may be significant that it includes, within the errors,
both the galactic centre and the current direction of the solar

motion. Since the solar apex moves across the sky at an angular speed of about 1.5 degrees per million years, this again hints at an unlikely coincidence in time, thereby again possibly providing evidence for a recent strong perturbation of the Oort cloud within the past few million years, by material sharing the mean motion of the sun's surrounding stars.

Additional arguments supporting this possibility are provided by direct observations of the sun's local interstellar environment. For example, several lines of evidence (such as the pattern of interstellar extinction along the lines of sight to OB stars; Urasin 1987), indicate that the sun is now close to the inner edge of a local spiral arm of the Galaxy. Blue stars, being young, act as spiral arm tracers, and it has been known — since at least the time of Ptolemy (c.150 AD) — that the brightest blue stars visible in the night sky form a belt, now called Gould's Belt (see Gould 1874). These stars are also associated with numerous dense nebulae in the solar neighbourhood, the whole region comprising a massive, expanding ring of material some 500 pc across (Olano 1982).

Indeed, it appears that the Gould Belt complex may be an old, disintegrating giant molecular cloud and that the sun could have passed through the rim of the belt some 5–10 Myr ago (Napier & Clube 1979, Olano 1982, Clube & Napier 1989a). Moreover, since the convergent point of the young stellar association in Scorpio-Centaurus is close to the direction of the solar antapex (Figure 15.2), it is possible that a close encounter with, or passage through, a star-forming molecular cloud of mass greater than $10^4 \, M_\odot$ might have taken place in the quite recent past. Since the infall time of a long-period comet into the inner solar system is on the order of 3 Myr, these observations raise the possibility that the Oort cloud might have recently experienced a quite major disturbance, or, on an interstellar hypothesis, might even have been captured (cf. Yabushita 1988, 1989a,b).

While these points were being raised, others (e.g. Yabushita & Hasegawa 1978, Yabushita 1979, 1983a) were also drawing attention to the essential arbitrariness in what had by this time be-

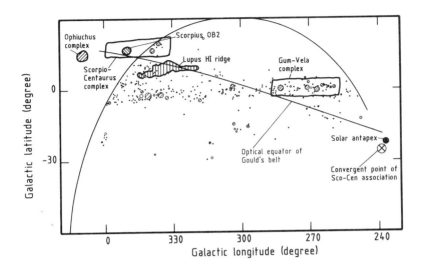

Figure 15.2: Diagram illustrating the position of Gould's belt and the solar antapex in relation to other star-forming regions and molecular clouds in the solar neighbourhood.

come the standard interpretation of the observed $1/a$ distribution of long-period comets. Whereas on the standard picture one appealed to a degree of cometary fading, of just the right amount to produce the observed $1/a$ distribution, Yabushita noted that the sharp peak in the $1/a$ distribution could also arise if the Oort cloud had been recently captured, provided that the capture event took place between 4 and 9 million years ago (cf. Bobrovnikoff 1929a).

These authors therefore suggested that instead of postulating an otherwise unexplained rapid fading for new comets, the observations might be better interpreted at face value, simply to mean that the Oort cloud is in a non-steady state (cf. Kresák 1977a). In fact, although comets are generally expected to fade significantly on their first close approach to the sun, there is still no strong theoretical explanation of the exact degree of fading, which must have a rather precise form if it is to reproduce the particular shape of the observed $1/a$ distribution (Bailey 1984a).

To sum up, the nineteen-seventies and early eighties saw the development of three principal arguments which suggested that an interstellar origin for comets ought to be reconsidered. First, the galactic and solar apex/antapex alignments of cometary orbits and their apparent groupings on the sky demonstrated that systematic effects of the galaxy (in the form of tides) and random effects (in the form of recent encounters with stars or massive nebulae) were both operative. Secondly, the sharpness of the peak in the $1/a$ distribution now had an alternative explanation in terms of a time-dependent Oort cloud, either recently strongly perturbed or recently captured; and thirdly, although less directly, the apparent anomalies in chemical abundances in different parts of the Galaxy, particularly in dense nebulae, suggested that the aggregation of non-volatile species into otherwise unobservable objects must have occurred. In order to be consistent with observations of the general interstellar extinction towards such clouds, these hidden particles had to correspond in size to large dust grains (at least), with an associated possibility that some might range in mass right up to the size of observed cometary nuclei.

To these arguments might also be added the implications of the inclination distribution and the total number of short-period comets (*cf.* Section 13.3.4, p.296). If short-period comets are not captured from an extended disc or inner Oort cloud structure but come instead from the 'observed' near-parabolic flux, the total number of short-period comets probably requires that the latter is time-dependent and, therefore, that the conventional Oort cloud may have been recently perturbed or replenished.

15.2   Capture models

15.2.1   THEORETICAL DIFFICULTIES

The burgeoning cosmogony was soon faced, however, with a major difficulty: the problem of cometary capture. This has been considered by numerous authors in the years since Laplace's original statement of the interstellar theory at the beginning of the nineteenth century, and the late nineteen-seventies now saw a further rash of papers dealing with the same general topic (e.g. Whipple 1975, Sekanina 1976, Hasegawa 1976, Noerdlinger 1977). Following van Woerkom (1948), for example, the general problem of capture may be divided into three main parts: first, that of determining the cometary velocity distribution in the (moving) frame of reference represented by the solar orbit; secondly, that of converting this to an observable flux of 'new' interstellar comets vs. both perihelion distance and the equivalent hyperbolic semi-major axis; and finally, that of calculating the proportion of such comets that are eventually captured to bound elliptical orbits as a result of planetary or other perturbations.

The first aspect of the problem may be readily solved by the method outlined by van Woerkom (1948). If $f(v)\,dv$ denotes the total number of interstellar comets per unit volume with speeds v in the range $(v, v+dv)$, measured in the 'interstellar' frame in which their mean velocity is zero, then the observed distribution of relative speeds, measured in a heliocentric reference frame moving with velocity $V_\odot$ through the cloud of comets, may be written as

$$\mu(V) = \int_0^\pi V^2 \frac{\sin A}{2} \frac{f(v)}{v^2}\, dA \qquad (15.1)$$

where $v^2 = V_\odot^2 + V^2 - 2VV_\odot \cos A$. This can be readily integrated for the special case in which the interstellar comets are assumed to have a random Maxwellian velocity distribution, i.e.

$$f(v) = n_0 \left(\frac{2}{\pi}\right)^{1/2} \frac{v^2}{c_s^3} \exp(-v^2/2c_s^2) \qquad (15.2)$$

where n_0 is the total number density of interstellar comets and c_s is the one-dimensional velocity dispersion. Eliminating A in favour of v^2 in equation (15.1) then gives

$$\mu(V) = n_0 \left(\frac{2}{\pi}\right)^{1/2} \frac{V}{V_\odot c_s} \exp[-(V^2 + V_\odot^2)/2c_s^2] \sinh(VV_\odot/c_s^2)$$
(15.3)

an equation also derived, for example, by Noerdlinger (1977).

Van Woerkom then went on to solve the second part of the problem (loc. cit., equation 4.16), but here it is more convenient to quote the result obtained more recently by Sekanina (1976, equation 12). That is, again assuming a Maxwellian distribution of velocities, the number of interstellar comets passing perihelion per unit time with perihelia in the range $(q, q+dq)$ and negative $1/a$-values in the range $(x, x+dx)$ is $\nu(x, q)\, dq dx$, where

$$\nu(x, q) = n_0 (2\pi)^{1/2} \frac{(GM_\odot)^{3/2}}{V_\odot c_s} \frac{(1 + qx)}{x^{1/2}} \exp\left(-\frac{(V_\odot^2 + GM_\odot x)}{2c_s^2}\right)$$
$$\times \sinh\left(\frac{V_\odot(GM_\odot x)^{1/2}}{c_s^2}\right)$$
(15.4)

This is a particularly useful result as it can now be integrated to give the total flux of interstellar comets with perihelia less than some value q and with x less than some particular value (cf. Hasegawa 1976), or alternatively the total interstellar flux without regard to x, i.e. irrespective of the asymptotic velocity $V = (GM_\odot x)^{1/2}$ of the comets far from the sun. Performing the latter integration, we find that the total interstellar flux within a sphere of radius q is

$$\dot{N}(\le q) = \frac{2\pi n_0 GM_\odot q}{V_\odot}\left\{\mathrm{erf}\left(\frac{V_\odot}{\sqrt{2}c_s}\right)\left[1 + \frac{q(V_\odot^2 + c_s^2)}{2GM_\odot}\right]\right.$$
$$\left. + \frac{qc_s V_\odot}{GM_\odot}\frac{1}{\sqrt{2\pi}}\exp\left(-\frac{V_\odot^2}{2c_s^2}\right)\right\}$$
(15.5)

a result also given by Sekanina (1976) and Noerdlinger (1977). For example, if $V_\odot = 15\,\mathrm{km\,s^{-1}}$ and $c_s = 5\,\mathrm{km\,s^{-1}}$, the total interstellar flux with perihelia less than the radius of Jupiter's orbit is on the order of 700 comets per year, assuming an ambient interstellar number density $n_0 = 1\,\text{AU}^{-3}$.

Such a large flux of interstellar comets, if real, would certainly have been noticed; and the inescapable conclusion is that the true local number density of such comets is much less than $1\,\text{AU}^{-3}$. For example, if we could detect 10% of all comets passing within Jupiter's orbit, the fact that no significantly hyperbolic orbit has been seen during the past two hundred years implies $n_0 \lesssim 10^{-4}\,\text{AU}^{-3}$. This is the same limit obtained by Sekanina (1976) by a rather more detailed argument, and is comparable with the number density of comets in the standard Oort cloud.

This shows that interstellar comets cannot now be entering the inner solar system in large numbers, but the question still remains whether the present Oort cloud might be due to a recently finished episode of past capture, possibly involving an encounter with the nebulae of Gould's Belt. However, because most comets arriving from interstellar space are expected to have orbits that are significantly hyperbolic in form, the presence of a third body, capable of slowing them down, is necessary if some proportion of them are to be captured into the solar system. The perturbing body might in principle lie outside the solar system (e.g. a passing star or molecular cloud; see below) or it could be part of the solar system itself, in which case the major planets, especially Jupiter, are the usually considered candidates (cf. Section 6.3.2, p.120). However, in order to reduce the initial hyperbolic velocities sufficiently for capture to occur, an unlikely close encounter with a planet has to be invoked, thus casting some doubt on the efficiency of this particular process as the dominant capture mechanism. Nevertheless, the general question of the proportion of interstellar comets which are captured hinges on the distribution of perturbations experienced by such comets; in other words, on an accurate determination of the capture cross-section, σ_{capt}, which must therefore be evaluated for each particular model of the sun's local galactic environment (e.g. whether isolated or containing nearby external bodies), and for each initial relative velocity V of the comets at large helio-centric distances.

15.2.2 CAPTURE BY JUPITER

The problem of capture by Jupiter was addressed by Valtonen & Innanen (1982) and Valtonen (1983), who expressed the total number of captured comets per unit time in the form

$$\dot{N}_{\text{capt}} = \int_0^\infty V\mu(V)\,\sigma_{\text{capt}}(V)\,dV \qquad (15.6)$$

and used numerical experiments to determine the variation of the overall capture cross-section as a function of the initial relative velocity V. Their results broadly confirmed those of earlier investigators (*e.g.* van Woerkom 1948), and demonstrate that capture of an Oort cloud could only occur if both the mean speed of the sun through the comet cloud and the internal velocity dispersion of the cloud are extremely small, typically less than $1\,\text{km}\,\text{s}^{-1}$.

In fact, of course, such a favourable situation is not at all likely to occur. For example, if the interstellar comets were formed a long time ago, one would expect the accumulation of stellar and other perturbations over their lifetimes to have randomized their velocities up to at least of order $20\,\text{km}\,\text{s}^{-1}$, comparable to the velocity dispersion of stars in the disc of the Galaxy. Alternatively, if the comets were still close to their original sites of formation, for example within a molecular cloud, then $V_\odot$ and c_s should be at least on the order of $(GM_c/R_c)^{1/2}$, where M_c and R_c denote the mass and radius of the cloud respectively. For typical values of the parameters one then expects $V_\odot$ and c_s to range upwards from at least $3\,\text{km}\,\text{s}^{-1}$, again making capture of an Oort cloud from such a system, at least by planetary perturbations, extremely unlikely.

Nevertheless, if the velocities were in fact suitable, capture might occur, and for sufficiently small $V_\odot$ and c_s the results of

Valtonen & Innanen indicated that capture might proceed at a rate up to $2000\,(n_0/1\mathrm{AU}^{-3})$ comets per year. Passage of the solar system through a small molecular cloud containing comets with a number density of order $1\,\mathrm{AU}^{-3}$ (10^4 times the maximum permitted ambient interstellar density), for a period of a million years, might therefore produce a temporary captured Oort cloud containing $\approx 10^9$ comets. Although this is less than 1% of the number of comets in the present Oort cloud, the orbits of the captured comets would have relatively small perihelion distances (contrary to the usual Oort cloud, in which all values occur), and it may thus be possible to explain the observed influx of long-period comets in the context of such a model.

We also mention the results of an earlier analytical study by Radzievskii & Tomanov (1977), this time based on a more qualitative 'sphere of influence' argument (cf. Section 15.2.3) rather than on direct numerical integrations. This study suggested that for realistic encounter speeds between the sun and field comets, between 50% and 80% of the captured comets would be thrown into orbits with periods less than 500 years. Passage through a metal-depleted nebula with molecular hydrogen density $n_{\mathrm{H}_2} \simeq 300\,\mathrm{cm}^{-3}$, typical for a giant molecular cloud, might then yield a few captured comets per century with short and intermediate period orbits, leading during the crossing time of a nebula to a total population of captured comets numbering a few times 10^4. If Uranus and Neptune were also able to contribute appreciably, one might then predict a short-lived population of about 10^5 comets of relatively short period (i.e. with periods less than about 500 yr), initially captured a few million years ago and therefore still showing some evidence of recent capture in their orbital distribution. It might therefore be that the present-day short-period comets derive from such a system, and if so, the long-period comets would then no longer be their primary source and there would be no reason to expect a balance of supply and demand between the two cometary systems. However, even accepting the validity of these analytic estimates, separate capture mechanisms for the long-period and short-period comets would thus be implied, an unattractive feature of the theory which suggests (*cf.* van Woerkom 1948) that the gravitational capture of observed comets by *planetary* action is not a particularly plausible way to resolve the overall problem of capture.

15.2.3   CAPTURE BY CLOUDS

Accepting, therefore, the realistic difficulty of using planetary perturbations to capture a large number of comets during a plausible encounter of the solar system with an interstellar comet cloud, Valtonen (1983) explored possible mechanisms involving bodies other than the major planets. In particular, he has emphasized that strong perturbations by passing stars which happen to be temporarily within the solar sphere of influence may increase the net efficiency of the capture process by a factor of about 10^3, while if the sun were assumed to be part of a wide binary system (as are many stars), the capture rate could be increased by a further factor of order 10^3.

The existence of such a companion star might then imply that an Oort cloud of comets could be sporadically captured, though it has to be emphasized (*cf.* Section 13.3.2, p.290) that the sun's putative companion star has still not been found! More recently, Zheng & Valtonen (1989) have emphasized (following a line of argument originally started by Donn; see p.281) that perturbations on interstellar comets formed together with stars in a dense star cluster might under some circumstances lead to capture of comets by the associated stars as the latter are eventually dispersed into the general interstellar field. The estimated efficiency of this process is around 0.05%, indicating that a large number of interstellar comets should exist in the interstellar medium, possibly concentrated close to the central mid-plane of the galactic disc.

An alternative suggestion is that the processes which tidally strip comets from the Oort cloud also lead to its replenishment (*e.g.* Clube & Napier 1982a, 1984a; Napier 1982). Because time can be reversed in the equations of motion (so that what was escape becomes capture), and because massive nebulae are demonstrably effective in dispersing the long-period comet system, it has been conjectured that in some circumstances passage of the solar system through a highly structured, comet-rich giant molecular cloud might result in the capture of a sufficient number of comets from the nebular field into bound orbits around the sun.

For example, suppose that the sun were to pass through a molecular cloud of mass $2 \times 10^4 \, M_\odot$ and radius $2\,\mathrm{pc}$, at the edge of which the solar sphere of influence would have a radius $R_s \simeq 1.5 \times 10^4 \, \mathrm{AU}$. If the observed strong metal depletion within such nebulae can indeed be ascribed to a concentration of heavy elements in comets, then for a mean cometary mass of order $10^{14}\,\mathrm{kg}$ say, one finds that the mean cometary number density in the cloud is $\approx 10\,\mathrm{AU}^{-3}$. The sun would then be passing through a cometary field with density almost a million times that of the present long-period system; the mean relative speed might typically be around $20\,\mathrm{km\,s}^{-1}$, the duration of encounter would be $\simeq 0.1\,\mathrm{Myr}$, and the molecular cloud system could indeed have a relatively small velocity dispersion. Such intense, short-lived encounters may have taken place several times during the age of the solar system, while passages through giant molecular clouds, expected to occur at a mean interval of order $5 \times 10^8\,\mathrm{yr}$, could involve more long-lasting interactions (lasting about $1\,\mathrm{Myr}$) with a rather lower field density of comets ($n_0 \simeq 0.1\,\mathrm{AU}^{-3}$; *cf.* Clube & Napier 1982a, 1984a).

Detailed computations have not yet been carried out to test this possibility, however, so the question of its overall efficiency and consistency with other data (such as the evidence or otherwise for strong 'showers' in the terrestrial cratering record) remains open. Nevertheless, we may describe some of the requirements of a model by outlining the results of a simple calculation. First, we assume that the sun is passing at speed $V_\odot$ through an interstellar field of comets with a random Maxwellian velocity distribution of velocity dispersion c_s in one dimension. As the sun moves away from the perturbing sources its sphere of influence will expand, thus overtaking a number of comets which would formerly have had orbits lying outside the original compressed sphere of influence in the neighbourhood of a massive cloud.

The suggested model, then, is one in which the perturbing effect of the cloud is removed, allowing the sphere of influence to expand to its usual value ($R_s \simeq 1\,\mathrm{pc}$), thereby resulting in the 'netting' of all those comets initially lying within the sphere of influence and moving with sufficiently small relative velocities V subsequently to remain bound to the sun. However, the expansion of the sphere of influence is not the only effect to consider, since as the sun climbs out of the potential well of the massive molecular cloud the relative velocities of the sun and its cometary neighbours will systematically decrease. It is necessary, therefore, also to include these effects in any calculation of the number of comets which might eventually be captured during such a molecular cloud encounter.

Two extreme situations can be considered, one in which the sphere of influence expands slowly, leading to a significant alteration of comet velocities relative to the sun, and one in which the solar sphere of influence expands so rapidly that comets find themselves instantaneously under solar control without having undergone much evolution of velocities in the transition zone. These extremes correspond respectively to the situations where the asymptotic approach speed of the sun to the molecular cloud is rather less than, and rather greater than, the escape velocity at the surface of the nebula.

Consider, first, the situation where the sun undergoes a relatively slow encounter with a nebula. A modified 'sphere of influence' concept may still be used (at least as a rough approximation), but now with the understanding that the molecular cloud exerts an effect on comets in a transition zone even within the sphere. At some fixed point relative to the sun, then, the number of comets per unit volume with relative speeds V in the range $(V, V + dV)$ may be written in the form $\mu(V)\, dV$, where $\mu(V)$ is given (see p.346) by equation (15.3). The rate at which comets with speeds less than V enter the sun's sphere of influence is then

$$\dot{N}(\leq V) = \pi R_{\rm s}^2 \int_0^V V\mu(V)\, dV \tag{15.7}$$

which can be readily cast into the same form as the corresponding expression derived by Hasegawa (1976, equation A5).

However, the integration limit is specifically that for captured interstellar comets which, having passed the sun, return to the surface of the sphere of influence with speed V less than the escape velocity $(GM_\odot/R_{\rm s})^{1/2}$. For capture as the sun climbs out of the gravitational potential well due to a molecular cloud or spiral arm, such as we are now considering, comets making their first return to the sphere of influence will generally have entered this sphere with a larger velocity. Those entering along the sun's line of motion, for example, will experience a tidal deceleration from the cometary source (whose mass and radius, corresponding to the impact parameter, we denote by M and R) during their first descent towards the sun, which is significantly greater than the acceleration experienced during the subsequent ascent. The corresponding integration limit is therefore larger than V, and may be written in the form

$$V' = \left[V^2 + \frac{GM}{R}\left(\frac{R_{\rm s}}{R}\right)^2\right]^{1/2} \tag{15.8}$$

In general, the second term on the right-hand side may be much greater than V^2, though in directions other than the one considered, where the solar and cometary motions are not approximately aligned, the second term is reduced by an appropriate geometrical factor. Thus, to obtain a rough estimate of the total number of comets captured under these circumstances, we need to set the integration limit to

$$V' = \left(\frac{GM}{R}\right)^{1/2} \frac{R_{\rm s}}{R} \frac{1}{f} \tag{15.9}$$

where f is a factor on the order of a few. This corresponds to retaining the usual integration limit in equation (15.7) and multiplying $\dot{N}(\leq V)$ by a factor $\kappa \approx (V'/V)^4$, so we finally obtain

$$\dot{N}(\leq V') = \kappa \, \pi R_s^2 \int_0^V V \mu(V) \, dV \qquad (15.10)$$

To obtain an accurate estimate of the factor κ, a more detailed calculation is evidently necessary, but values ranging up to 10^2–10^4 may be appropriate for typical molecular clouds.

In this way, for example following Clube & Napier (1984a) in assuming that $VV_\odot/c_s^2 \ll 1$ and $V/\sqrt{2}c_s \ll 1$ (corresponding to considering only comets moving with small velocities relative to the sun), the total number of comets 'captured' during a time t in which the sun passes through a length $L = V_\odot t$ of the nebula, may be written in the form

$$N_{\text{capt}} \simeq \kappa \left[\frac{4}{\sqrt{\pi}} x_\odot^3 \exp(-x_\odot^2) \right] \pi R_A^2 L \, n_0 \qquad (15.11)$$

Here, $x_\odot = V_\odot/\sqrt{2}c_s$, $R_A = GM_\odot/V_\odot^2$ represents the solar accretion radius for an initial velocity $V_\odot$, and the factor in square brackets is typically of order unity, provided c_s is not too small.

If one then assumes a slow solar drift velocity of order $V_\odot \simeq 5 \, \text{km s}^{-1}$ and an interstellar comet cloud of radius $R_c \simeq 2 \, \text{pc}$ with internal velocity dispersion $c_s \simeq 5 \, \text{km s}^{-1}$, then $x_\odot \simeq 0.71$ and the total number of captured comets for a typical passage with mean chord length $L = 4R_c/3$ is of order

$$N_{\text{capt}} \simeq 10^9 \, \kappa \left(n_0/1 \, \text{AU}^{-3} \right) \qquad (15.12)$$

This would yield, for a dense interstellar comet cloud with a cometary number density $n_0 \simeq 10 \, \text{AU}^{-3}$, a captured Oort cloud containing around $10^{10} \kappa$ comets, in agreement with that required to explain the observed long-period comet flux if $\kappa \gtrsim 10$. The comets so captured would initially be comoving with the

sun to within a speed of order $1\,\mathrm{km\,s^{-1}}$, say, and so would tend
to derive from the high-velocity tail of the cloud's velocity distribution, this tail comprising comets in the process of escaping
from their original star-forming region or giant molecular cloud.

In the alternative situation in which the sun moves through a
nebula at a speed greatly in excess of the latter's escape velocity,
the sphere of influence of the sun expands (say at about $1\,\mathrm{km\,s^{-1}}$)
at a speed greatly in excess of the escape velocity from the sun
(say $v_e \simeq 0.2\,\mathrm{km\,s^{-1}}$ at $r = 5 \times 10^4\,\mathrm{AU}$). In that situation, a
comet escaping from a nebula and roughly comoving with the
sun will find itself moving from the nebular to the solar sphere
of influence almost instantaneously: all comets within the final
sphere of influence which happened to be comoving with the
sun to within about $0.2\,\mathrm{km\,s^{-1}}$ are then permanently captured:
the sun simply 'nets' such comets, in its neighbourhood, from a
Maxwellian distribution of velocities (*cf.* Clube & Napier 1984a,
Napier 1985). Following these authors (*loc. cit.*, equation 9), one
readily finds a total number of captured comets on the order
of $2 \times 10^8\,(n_0/1\,\mathrm{AU^{-3}})$. Passage of the solar system through
a dense, disintegrating star-forming region within a molecular
cloud could therefore result in the capture of a comet population
to within an order of magnitude of that usually inferred for the
current Oort cloud; there have probably been on the order of
5–15 such encounters throughout solar system history.

The passage time through a star-forming region is a few
$\times 10^5\,\mathrm{yr}$, shorter than the disintegration time of an OB association, but comparable with the anticipated lifetime of a newly
formed T Tauri star and a number of proposed comet growth
mechanisms. Apart from placing pre-existing comets into bound
solar orbits, then, it is also possible that interstellar comets may
condense or otherwise be created *in situ* during passage of the
sun through a star-forming region. Indeed, it is even conceivable that the sun itself might be involved in their creation, although, leaving aside the specific mechanism proposed by Lyttleton (see p.170), such speculations have not yet been explored
in the present galactic context.

In concluding this section, it should be emphasized that while the theoretical problem of capturing comets from an interstellar field has attracted the attention of a good many astronomers, the problem has been successfully modelled only for relatively straightforward conditions: for example, a constant density cometary field through which the sun is moving at a constant speed. The rather more complicated question of capture in a field of varying cometary number density and changing gravitational potential has scarcely been touched upon. Thus, we cannot say with certainty whether the effects that arise will necessarily produce the roughly random distribution of cometary orbits that is expected, or whether the observed $1/a$ distribution and the relative number of long and short-period comets can be readily reproduced. Indeed, it has not even been shown whether the proposed capture scenarios (with the exception of Lyttleton's accretion theory, which has its own difficulties) will produce the observed correlation of the cometary aphelia with the solar antapex.

Nevertheless, as we have indicated, a number of approximate arguments do provide some justification for the belief that something like the original Oort cloud (*i.e. sans* inner core) may be captured during a typical molecular cloud passage, or even during passage of the solar system through spiral arms, provided that these galactic systems contain sufficient interstellar comets. Apparent difficulties associated with the evaluation of capture efficiencies in actual interactions between the solar system and either molecular clouds or spiral arms, may simply reflect the comparative lack of attention that has so far been given to models of a sufficiently realistic kind. We cannot exclude the possibility, therefore, that the current Oort cloud may be just as readily explained in terms of cometary reserves within molecular clouds and spiral arms, as it has more conventionally been explained in terms of the hidden 'inner core' reserves postulated in some primordial solar system models.

15.3   Growth mechanisms

15.3.1   JEANS INSTABILITY

The circumstances surrounding the capture of comets from the interstellar medium are thus rather more complicated than have formerly been supposed, and although the dynamical problems which arise in removing comets from the potential wells associated with star-forming regions are still far from being fully understood, the possibility has nevertheless led to growing interest — since at least the mid-nineteen-seventies — in the problem of growing comets under interstellar conditions. In particular, McCrea (1975a,b; see also Gribbin 1975) emphasized a curious coincidence concerning the masses of comets. A small mass of gas, left to itself in space, will generally disperse due to the individual random motions of its atoms. As the mass of gas is increased, however, there comes a point when the escape velocity from the initial volume of gas exceeds the mean random speed of the particles, and the gas is then able to hold itself together by self-gravity. Indeed, it will then probably begin to collapse under its own weight as it cools.

The critical mass, above which the gas cloud collapses, is known as the Jeans mass. This is clearly a function of temperature and density, and for typical interstellar conditions is found to be broadly in the range of observed stellar masses. The Jeans mass also varies as $m^{-3/2}$ where m is the mean mass per particle. McCrea had noted that if one replaced the mass of the hydrogen atom by the mean mass of an interstellar dust particle, the resulting Jeans mass falls to cometary values. It is thus tempting to associate the conventional 'gas' Jeans mass with stars, and the 'grain' Jeans mass with comets.

There is, however, a difficulty with this simple association, namely that dust grains tend to be swept along with the gas, so that any tendency for grains to undergo gravitational collapse would be obviated by the tendency for the dust to disperse. But McCrea also noted that were the size of the potentially collapsing region smaller than the mean free path of a gas molecule with respect to dust collisions, then the gas and dust would be uncoupled from each other and grain collapse might then proceed. The grains within larger masses of gas would still behave as a fluid, being swept along by the streams of gas, but grains within smaller elements of gas might then separate out.

McCrea thus identified two critical masses within a nebula, namely the 'dust' Jeans mass, M_D, above which collapse of dust particles might in principle occur (provided the gas and dust could be decoupled), and an 'evaporation mass', M_E, below which gas and dust are decoupled, and therefore below which collapse might actually occur. These are given respectively by

$$M_D \simeq \frac{1}{3} \left(\frac{kT}{G\rho_{\text{grain}}} \right)^{3/2} a_d^{-9/2} (\zeta\rho)^{-1/2} \qquad (15.13)$$

and

$$M_E \simeq 10 \, \rho_{\text{grain}}^3 a_d^3 (\zeta\rho)^{-2} \qquad (15.14)$$

where k and G are the usual Boltzmann and gravitational constants, ρ and T are the density and temperature of the gas in which the dust grains are immersed, and ρ_{grain}, $\zeta\rho$ and a_d are the grain material density, the smoothed-out grain density and the mean grain radius respectively. The dust-to-gas ratio by mass in the nebula is ζ. In the derivation of these equations, it is assumed that the random grain velocities are due solely to Brownian motion, and that there is equipartition of energy between the gas and dust components.

In this way it was considered that comets of mass M might in principle be directly formed by gravitational collapse of the dust component provided that $M_D < M < M_E$. Using this criterion it is easy to show that comets may form by Jeans collapse of dust provided that the nebular gas has a density less than a critical value ρ_c given to order of magnitude by

$$\rho_c \simeq 10 \, \zeta^{-1} \rho_{\text{grain}}^3 a_d^5 (G/kT) \qquad (15.15)$$

At this density, comets should form with a single mass

$$M_c \simeq 10^{-1} \rho_{\text{grain}}^{-3} a_d^{-7} (kT/G)^2 \qquad (15.16)$$

a result illustrated by McCrea (1975b, Fig. 2 and Table 1).

Adopting $\rho_{\text{grain}} = 10^3 \, \text{kg m}^{-3}$, $a_d = 0.1 \, \mu\text{m}$, $T = 10 \, \text{K}$ and $\zeta = 10^{-2}$, one finds $M_c \simeq 4 \times 10^{15} \, \text{kg}$ and $\rho_c \simeq 5 \times 10^{-12} \, \text{kg m}^{-3}$, corresponding to a gas number density $n \simeq 2 \times 10^9 \, \text{cm}^{-3}$. This is much higher than that directly observed in even the densest molecular clouds, for which $n \simeq 10^4 \text{–} 10^5 \, \text{cm}^{-3}$, though it is also much less than must occur at some time during the formation of a typical protostellar disc. The path from one régime to the other must therefore pass through the critical density, at which point the dust might segregate out. The characteristic collapse time is $t_{\text{coll}} \simeq 1/(G\zeta\rho_c)^{-1/2}$, which for the above figures is about 2×10^4 yr.

The likely kinematic state of a nebula at such high densities, and whether the dust grains might indeed have a chance to amalgamate in the presence of turbulence, are unknown, and it remains unclear whether this simple Jeans collapse of dust is a significant process either in the general interstellar medium or in molecular clouds as a natural concomitant of star formation. Nevertheless, McCrea's study was an important step in that it had identified a possible mechanism for growing comets under interstellar conditions. Given that there are two Jeans masses in the interstellar medium, one associated with the gas and comparable with stellar masses, the other associated with dust and comparable with cometary masses, what more natural than to suppose that comets, like stars, are simply formed as a result of gravitational collapse of their primordial material?

15.3.2   NOVEL SUGGESTIONS

We have already described (p.328) the work by Bailey (1987a), in which interstellar comets initially accumulate in wind-driven shells around protostars. In fact, this theory can be looked upon as a kind of half-way house between the protostellar and interstellar hypotheses, since while linking comet formation to 'primordial' processes associated with ordinary star formation it also predicts that the newly formed comets will initially be ejected into the interstellar environment. The total number of comets which might in principle be formed in such a process was predicted to range up to of order 10% the original mass of condensibles in the protostellar cloud, corresponding to around $10^3 M_\oplus$ of comets for a typical star of about a solar mass. Such a mass of comets could have important consequences for understanding both the gas dynamics and chemistry of such regions (Bailey 1988b). Other suggestions as to how interstellar comets might be made have not been so closely tied to star formation, however, and we particularly mention the recent investigations by Yabushita (1983b), Humphries (1982) and Napier & Humphries (1986).

Yabushita (1983b), following an earlier suggestion by Flannery & Krook (1978), returned to the problem of separating the dust from the gas in a general interstellar environment, and suggested that if conditions were sufficiently quiescent it might be possible for simple gravitational sedimentation of the dust to occur in a particular class of dense, cold clouds called globules. For representative conditions in such a cloud, a sedimentation time on the order of 10^7–10^8 yr was expected, which although rather on the long side might under some circumstances be short enough for the process to be physically realized. However, it is not certain whether conditions in interstellar space more generally would be suitable for this mechanism to dominate the production of large solid aggregates, and the original qualitative idea has not yet been followed up by detailed calculations.

The second suggestion, by Napier & Humphries (1986; cf. Humphries 1982), is that comets might form in interstellar gas clouds of very much lower density, corresponding to a number density $n_H \approx 10^3 \, \text{cm}^{-3}$. Their idea may be regarded as an extension of that described by Hills (1982); but whereas Hills employed differential radiation pressure to drive dust grains together (see Section 13.2, p.283; cf. Spitzer 1941, Whipple 1946),

Napier & Humphries used a kind of 'jet reaction' effect. This was produced by a process similar to the photoelectric effect, which in this case used the anticipated anisotropic ultraviolet radiation field to eject molecules from the icy mantles of dust grains, causing a back reaction on the grain due to the momentum imparted by the ejected molecule.

The importance of this process can be many times greater than the direct effect of an anisotropic radiation field, and the effective force acting on the grains is increased by a factor on the order of 10^2. This greatly extends the range of environments in which grains might be driven together. For example, assuming only the usual background radiation field predominates, collapse might take place in molecular clouds with a number density $n_H \approx 10^3 \, \text{cm}^{-3}$ and temperature $T \simeq 20 \, \text{K}$. The collapse time for such a situation, however, would be on the order of $10^6 \, \text{yr}$, still rather long for the mechanism to be widely applicable.

On the other hand, in a region of recent star formation containing massive early-type OB stars, the collapse times may be reduced to around $10^3 \, \text{yr}$. This can be much less than the corresponding time for the dust to be driven apart by turbulent processes, and, by thus ignoring turbulence and balancing the inward drift of the grains by photodesorption with their tendency to expand by Brownian motion, Napier & Humphries obtained a rough lower limit to the masses of comets formed by this process, namely $m_L \simeq 10^{11} - 10^{13} \, \text{kg}$. A somewhat different argument allowed them to set an upper limit to the masses of such comets, based this time on the expectation of thermal instability in very dense small-scale structures in molecular clouds (Gilden 1984). This gave $m_U \approx 10^{22} \, \text{kg}$, and showed that interstellar comets (if formed by this mechanism) should have diameters less than $10^3 \, \text{km}$. If it is assumed that the dust sheets or spheres break up randomly as they collapse, then the mass distribution of the collapsing fragments turns out to be a power law with an index roughly equal to that observed. This hypothesis therefore has a considerable advantage over a purely gravitational collapse picture, in that it may produce comets over the extremely wide mass range observed, whereas the more conventional Jeans collapse calculations tend to produce bodies having a characteristic mass.

15.3.3   INTERSTELLAR ALTERNATIVE

As we have seen, the problem of the survival of comets in the outer parts of the Oort cloud for the age of the solar system (*i.e.* the persistence of comets in the region from where long-period comets are primarily observed to come) has led astronomers along diverging paths: either to consider replenishment of the outer cloud from a hypothetical dense inner core, or towards investigation of alternative interstellar capture scenarios. The problem of capture from the interstellar medium is undoubtedly far from solved, but it has yet to be demonstrated that a realistic capture mechanism is unable to capture the desired number of comets ($\approx 10^{11}$) sufficiently often to explain observations of comets at the present epoch.

In particular, it is important to emphasize that the conventional statement of the capture problem, involving capture of comets from a uniform medium comprising a static gravitational potential, is certainly not realistic if one is considering capture from spiral arms or molecular clouds. Indeed, the heavy element depletions in molecular clouds (if these are attributable to interstellar comets) already tell us that the density distribution of interstellar comets *must* be highly non-uniform and concentrated around the regions of greatest density fluctuation. Taking these effects into consideration, the rough calculation that we have described indicates that something like the 'observed' Oort cloud may indeed be captured from typical star-forming regions, while such direct measurements as there are of the chemical composition of comets (*e.g.* the $^{12}C/^{13}C$ ratio in Halley's comet; *cf.* Section 18.2.4, p.449) may also suggest that an interstellar origin is not at all implausible.

Likewise, the disconcerting suggestions of perihelion alignments with the directions of the solar apex and the galactic equator are difficult to reconcile with a 'closed box' view of the Oort cloud. The solar apex moves about 1.5 degrees per million years over the celestial sphere, and an alignment of this point with the mean perihelion direction to within 8°, as claimed for example by Oja (1975), implies either an unlikely coincidence or an extremely rapid response of the Oort cloud to the changing solar trajectory. Nothing in the conventional solar system theory during the nineteen-seventies appeared able to account for this, although the correlations with the galactic plane may now be explained in terms of the influence of the galactic tide on the Oort cloud (Matese & Whitman 1989). Moreover, the simple demonstration by McCrea that the Jeans mass of dust capable of condensing out of the interstellar medium lay in the range of cometary masses was an equally disturbing coincidence.

Nevertheless, despite these arguments, it seems that most astronomers at the present time continue to subscribe to one or another version of the conventional primordial solar system hypothesis for comet formation (defects and all), and implicitly assume that the Oort cloud is an essentially closed system, relatively immune from external perturbations and secure from its surrounding galactic environment. However, the arguments for and against capture are not at all clear-cut, nor are there definitive reasons why cometary bodies should not be formed in the denser regions of interstellar space.

In this way, while many authors have considered these issues in detail and still conclude that on balance the conventional primordial solar system view is more likely to be correct, there is a growing suspicion that much of the strength of their detailed arguments may in the end boil down to a question of fashion; in other words to which fundamental assumptions one considers as being the most reasonable. Certainly the interstellar capture hypothesis has not yet been so thoroughly investigated that it can be ruled out, while the standard Oort cloud, having been with us for forty years, is extremely hard to shift!

16

Galactic signals

"It is the customary fate of new truths, to begin as heresies, and to end as superstitions."

Thomas Huxley.

16.1   Terrestrial record

16.1.1   MUNDANE ARGUMENTS

While the theories described in the previous two chapters have raised many important issues relating to cometary origin, they have not yet as a group significantly disturbed the prevailing opinion favouring an origin of comets in some way associated with a primordial Oort cloud. Nevertheless, this probing of alternative ideas served to remind astronomers and others throughout the period of the nineteen-seventies that the observational and theoretical situation concerning comets was considerably less secure than one would wish. The beginning of the nineteen-eighties, therefore, saw a clear need for some new input to the subject: different arguments; perhaps even a reassessment of the whole scheme.

One of the earliest indications that such considerations might provide new leads came, in fact, from geological arguments during the nineteen-twenties (Section 16.1.3, p.370). These, by once again raising the spectre of intermittent episodes of catastrophic change affecting the earth, provided unexpected evidence of galactic control somehow implicating comets with scenes of death and destruction. The idea that comets are in some way associated with both man-made and terrestrial disasters is, of course, very old, dating back at least to the earliest astronomers of Babylon four or five thousand years ago (Chapters 2–4). Subsequently, however, despite the generally baleful influence that comets seem to have exerted throughout much of recorded history, the ensuing 'fear' of comets eventually came to be seen by leading astronomers and intellectuals alike as a superstitious relic dating from a more primitive past. Thus, whilst it was definitely not right to view comets as mere atmospheric phenomena, it was certainly regarded as excusable to consider them as potentially harmless, no more able to damage the earth than a rainbow. This perception of the general insignificance of comets was finally consolidated during the Age of Enlightenment, and the idea subsequently became an established 'fact' of modern science.

The notion that comets, as celestial bodies, do not interact significantly with the earth was first put forward by Newton, originally on what were essentially metaphysical grounds (Section 5.2.2, p.101). It then became fashionable, at least in Britain, to regard comets as comprising something approaching the essence of life: the principal source of 'that Spirit, which though it constitutes the least, is yet the subtilist and best part of our Air, and necessary to the life of every thing' (Costard 1767). Later, when it was realized that short-period comets undergo rapid physical evolution compared to ordinary astronomical timescales, producing gas and dust-tails and what appear to be relatively harmless streams of sand-sized dust particles (*i.e.* meteor streams), Newton's thesis seemed to acquire a rather more secure observational foundation. Moreover, advances made about the same time in geological science complemented this non-catastrophic world-view, and led to a simultaneous rise of uniformitarianism inspired by the work of Hutton and Lyell (Sections 5.2, 6.1; see pp. 99, 105). In this way, during the middle decades of the nineteenth century and especially with the advent of the Darwin/Wallace theory of evolution, the gradualist world-view increasingly took precedence and became firmly established within theories of terrestrial evolution.

The uniformitarian viewpoint has thus dominated both evolutionist and geological thinking for at least the last hundred years — to such an extent that its original astronomical foundations seem to have become blurred and almost forgotten. Nevertheless, the question of whether or not celestial bodies, such as comets, do interact strongly with the earth is an important issue, no longer a mere hypothetical or metaphysical point. Indeed, the possibility now demands attention: astronomical advances made during the last twenty years have produced an almost explosive gain in our knowledge of the structure and dynamics of the solar system, and have led to a corresponding awareness that there are, in fact, many bodies of quite significant size circulating in potentially earth-colliding orbits. Given the progress which has also been made in understanding the influence of the galactic tide, and of stellar, molecular-cloud and spiral-arm perturbations of the Oort cloud, there is now a very strong case for reconsidering the possible effects of astronomical mechanisms on both geological and biological processes on earth. By the same token, the existence of such effects, mediated, for example, by comets and the effects of the Galaxy, could mean that one may now be able to use these seemingly 'mundane' arguments to provide new, albeit indirect, constraints on the question of the nature and origin of comets.

16.1.2 Fossil record

Despite the general acceptance of these gradualist assumptions by most geologists up to the present day, not every aspect of the palaeontological record automatically fits the uniformitarian mould. Often the fossil record has a discontinuous rather than smooth appearance, the larger discontinuities being diagnostic of major breaks in the development of life. In these so-called 'mass extinctions', large fractions of the prevailing terrestrial flora and fauna seem to have died out over quite short intervals of time, as if en masse.

Amongst the many minor marine extinctions, for example, there have been at least five major ones during the Phanerozoic, that is during the last approximately 600 Myr. Table 16.1 provides a brief summary of the principal geological strata that have been identified during this period, highlighting those times since the end of the Paleozoic which seem to be most strongly associated with periods of mass extinction and significant biological

Era	Period	Epoch	Age	Age of base (Myr)
Cenozoic	Quaternary (Q)	Holocene		0.01
		Pleistocene		2.00
	Tertiary (TT)	Pliocene		5.1
			Tortonian*	11.3*
		Miocene		24.6
		Oligocene	Rupelian*	38.0*
		Eocene		54.9
		Paleocene	Danain*	65.0*
Mezozoic	Cretaceous (K)		Turonian*	91.0*
		Late K_2		97.5
		Early K_1	Berriasian*	144.0*
	Jurassic (J)	J_3 Malm		163
		J_2 Dogger		188
			Toarcian*	194*
		J_1 Lias		213
	Triassic (Tr)		Rhaetian*	219*
		Late Tr_3		231
		Middle Tr_2		243
		Scythian Tr_1		248
Paleozoic	Permian (P)		Tatarian*	253*
		Late P_2		258
		Early P_1		286
	Carboniferous (C)			360
	Devonian (D)			408
	Silurian (S)			438
	Ordovician (O)			505
	Cambrian (C)			590

Table 16.1: The Phanerozoic timescale, after Walker (1988). An asterisk by the age indicates that this particular time corresponds to the base of the geological age coming immediately after a significant mass extinction at the familial level, as defined by Raup & Sepkoski (1986). The exact times of these ages and other stratigraphic features in the fossil record are not yet generally agreed.

upheaval on the earth (cf. Raup & Sepkoski 1986). These, it is argued, occur at a mean interval of about 26 Myr, although there is much debate as to whether the extinctions are all similar in kind to one another, and whether the data on which the roughly 30 Myr cyclicity is based are really adequate to allow a regular periodicity to be inferred at all (e.g. Hoffman 1985, Patterson & Smith 1987, Boucot 1988). One of the greatest of the marine extinctions, for example, occurred at the Permo-Triassic boundary about 250 Myr ago; life on earth, then, was all but removed, and the biosphere took about 30 Myr to recover. Moreover, the direction of evolution after a break is often quite different from that which preceded it. For example, after the extinction of the dinosaurs (about 65 Myr ago), who made up a complex and thriving community that lasted for almost 150 Myr, there was a sudden adaptive radiation of birds and mammals into the ensuing ecological gaps. A single event, it seems, can reset the biological clock!

These and other extinctions were indeed rapid, at least on the timescale of the resolving power of the stratigraphy, but whether they were truly instantaneous has long been a contentious issue amongst geologists (cf. Hallam 1979). A particular difficulty is the often incomplete and fragmentary nature of the fossil record, which is especially severe when large (and correspondingly rare) individuals, such as belonged to many species of dinosaur, are concerned. What is clear, however, is that these extinctions of life were not purely local affairs: they were global phenomena affecting life world-wide — although in many cases it is still difficult to understand why some life-forms died out, while others, living at the same time and apparently inhabiting a rather similar ecological niche, managed to survive (e.g. Whalley 1987). Many suggested mechanisms have been put forward to explain some of these events, sometimes based on observed correlations of extinctions with episodes of volcanism or with variations in the general level of the oceans (e.g. Hallam 1984b, 1987; Officer et al. 1987; cf. Whyte 1977); however, most of these notions have been based on the assumption that changes in the earth's astronomical environment can be ignored.

16.1.3 GALACTIC CYCLES

The first indication that something might be wrong with this 'closed box' view of earth history came with the discovery, some sixty years ago, of what seemed to be 'galactic' cycles in the terrestrial record. If real, these cycles demonstrated that some kind of interaction with the astronomical environment was probably taking place, although the mode of action remained obscure, involving not only mass extinctions of life but also deep-seated geological phenomena, including episodes of global volcanism. For example, Holmes (1927) considered that the level of the oceans, as well as world-wide volcanic and mountain-building activity, came and went on an approximately 30 Myr year cycle; the cycle of activity being superposed upon a more general variation which was episodic in character with intervals of activity lasting approximately 100 Myr whose peaks are separated by roughly 200 Myr (Figure 16.1). The 30 Myr timescale corresponds to the half-period of the sun's vertical oscillation about the galactic plane, whilst the episodic interval corresponds roughly to the period of the sun's orbit around the Galaxy (cf. Section 12.3.2, p.264, and Section 17.2, p.404).

At first, it was thought that dust in interstellar clouds might intermittently affect the earth, either by its effect on the solar luminosity, or by directly affecting the terrestrial climate by accretion or effects related to the opacity of the atmosphere (see Shapley 1921, Hoyle & Lyttleton 1939, McCrea 1975c, Begelman & Rees 1976, Yabushita & Allen 1985, 1989; cf. Dennison & Mansfield 1976). Later, it was suspected that supernovae in neighbouring star-forming regions might have been more influential (cf. discussions by McCrea 1975b, 1981; Hallam 1979, Russell 1979 and references therein). However, the development of these ideas remained mostly at a qualitative level, and since no agreed mechanism for galactic control had been established the claims for cycles and periodicities in the geological record

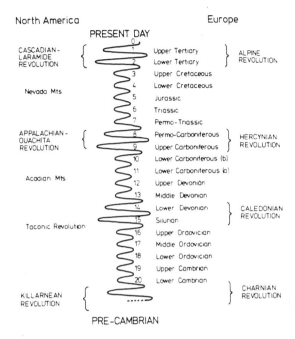

North America   Europe

PRESENT DAY

CASCADIAN-   {   Upper Tertiary   } ALPINE
LARAMIDE   REVOLUTION
REVOLUTION   Lower Tertiary

                                  Upper Cretaceous

Nevada Mts   Lower Cretaceous

                                  Jurassic

                                  Triassic

                                  Permo-Triassic

APPALACHIAN-   {   Permo-Carboniferous } HERCYNIAN
OUACHITA   REVOLUTION
REVOLUTION   Upper Carboniferous

                                  Lower Carboniferous (b)

                                  Lower Carboniferous (a)

Acadian Mts   Upper Devonian

                                  Middle Devonian

                                  Lower Devonian   } CALEDONIAN
                                                       REVOLUTION
                                  Silurian

Taconic Revolution   Upper Ordovician

                                  Middle Ordovician

                                  Lower Ordovician

                                  Upper Cambrian

                                  Lower Cambrian

KILLARNEAN   {   } CHARNIAN
REVOLUTION   REVOLUTION

PRE-CAMBRIAN

Figure 16.1: Early evidence for geological rhythms in the terrestrial record. After Holmes (1927).

were eventually little noticed. Indeed, with the plate tectonic revolution of the nineteen-sixties, building on earlier evidence for continental drift (*e.g.* Hallam 1973), it seemed likely that the episodic interval was only coincidentally galactic and that a purely 'internal' mechanism might eventually explain the forces which shaped the earth's surface, taking the form of a gently sustained or gradually weakening 'motor' in the earth's core.

Admittedly, the nature of this motor, for example whether due to a lunar torque, the earth's gravitational contraction or the earth simply cooling, was not known; but at least it seemed clear that plate tectonics had no need of any astronomical help that was not already known. In any case, even if the Galaxy were involved, one still had to explain how the sun's slowly varying position in its galactic orbit could cause a million cubic kilometres of lava to well up from the interior of the earth, for example as happened 65 Myr ago, creating the mountains of Greenland, the highlands of Scotland and the Deccan traps of Western India — whilst also precipitating the death of the dinosaurs! This lack of an obvious physical mechanism involving the Galaxy meant that until recently there was no serious challenge to uniformitarianism.

16.2   Cometary link

16.2.1   ASTEROIDAL COMETS

Nevertheless, whilst the plate tectonic revolution was making its mark in geology and geophysics, important developments were also occurring in astronomy, changes which ultimately were to undermine the logic that had originally led to the gradualist viewpoint. One such discovery, in particular, provided the clue that a galactic mechanism might after all exist: namely, the existence of 'earth-crossing' asteroids (*i.e.* asteroids in potentially earth-colliding orbits, loosely described as Apollo asteroids), in sufficient numbers to be the main cause of catastrophic cratering on the planetary and satellite surfaces.

Earth-crossing asteroids are either swept up by the inner planets or dynamically ejected from the inner solar system on a timescale of a few tens of millions of years, short compared to the age of the solar system. It is clear, therefore, that some replenishing source is required, although at this time it did not seem likely that perturbations in the main asteroid belt could be sufficiently strong to deflect bodies from the main belt at a fast enough rate to maintain the observed number of earth-crossers. Öpik (1963) thus became the first to propose that these asteroids might largely originate through the break-up and decay of short-period comets.

This could happen, for example, if comets had non-volatile interiors, or if outgassing due to the sublimation of ices was choked off by the formation of a non-volatile crust (*cf.* Section 17.1.3, p.394, and Section 18.1.1, p.429). Another possibility was that an occasional very large comet might break up to produce both short-period comets and earth-crossing asteroids (cf. Alexander 1850, 1851; Bredichin 1889, Bobrovnikoff 1931), simultaneously creating large amounts of meteoric dust which could seriously affect the terrestrial climate (Hoyle & Wickramasinghe 1978). Either way, this meant that observed comets and Apollo asteroids might represent different evolutionary phases of an underlying non-steady population, implying that the solar system, even now, could be in the midst of an upheaval.

In this way, it became possible to envisage that the intermittent ice-epochs now affecting the earth (lasting typically 10^4–10^5 years) were triggered by cometary rather than interstellar dust. Moreover, enhancements of the short-period comet and Apollo asteroid populations, if also associated with an assumed disturbed state of the long-period cometary system, might then be linked to recent disturbances or replenishments of the outer Oort cloud by massive structures in the Galaxy: molecular clouds or Gould's Belt, for example, or some other part of the Galaxy's spiral arm system (cf. Bobrovnikoff 1929a, 1951; Clube 1978, Napier & Clube 1979).

16.2.2   TIME DEPENDENCE

The question of long-term variations in the rates of deposition of meteoric dust and the generation of craters is an important one, therefore, both for galactic and solar system reasons, and one that is potentially amenable to test by examining the lunar and terrestrial records. For example, the cratering record on the moon and inner planets shows that the flux of earth-crossing bodies initially underwent a steep decline for the first 800 Myr of the solar system's existence, and then attained an approximately constant mean value for the remaining 3800 Myr (e.g. Baldwin 1985; cf. Figure 16.2).

Superposed on this underlying trend, however, are apparent

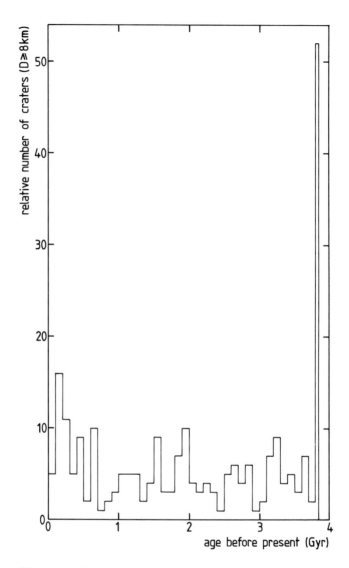

Figure 16.2: Time dependence of the lunar cratering rate over the age of the solar system, after Baldwin (1985). The strong peak for the interval 3.80–3.85×10^9 years ago is probably a residue of the late heavy lunar bombardment.

episodes of enhanced and reduced bombardment, each lasting some 100 Myr and separated by intervals of comparable duration. The time-resolution of the cratering record is not adequate to tell whether this bombardment pattern is actually a sequence of 'showers' of much shorter duration (i.e. lasting a few Myr; cf. Section 13.3.1, p.287), and it is possible that the various uncertainties may even make a secure identification of the approximately 100 Myr fluctuations questionable. Nevertheless, the general trend and the relative magnitude of the long-term variations certainly do appear to be such as to preclude an absolutely steady flux.

A similar variability, also consistent with a characteristic time-scale for fluctuations of order 100 Myr, is evident in the deposition rate of meteoric dust and small meteorites on the lunar soil (Lindsay & Srnka 1975, Goswami & Lal 1978; cf. Figure 16.2). In this case, whereas siderophile trace element studies on deep-sea sediments (e.g. Barker & Anders 1968, Kyte & Wasson 1986), the lunar regolith (Anders et al. 1973), and in antarctic ice cores (Ganapathy 1983) suggest the presence of a sustained background flux of material producing typically on the order of 10^8 kg yr^{-1} on the earth, they do not exclude the possibility that during extended periods lasting about 100 Myr the flux may have increased by up to two orders of magnitude for intervals of much shorter duration of order 0.1–1 Myr (Clube 1987b).

Taken together, therefore, the cratering and meteoric deposition records are consistent with the idea of a fundamentally episodic source, variable on timescales of order 100 Myr, but with considerable fine structure extending down to timescales of 1 Myr or less. Although this may or may not be indicative of 'showers' lasting several million years, it should be mentioned that the terrestrial iridium record for the period 33–67 Myr ago, whilst showing (like the cratering record) no evidence for major fluctuations about the mean level apart from the single 'K-T' event at the Cretaceous-Tertiary boundary (Kyte & Wasson 1986), is consistent with a gentle secular trend surmounted by minor fluctuations. Limited observations of more recently exposed lunar surfaces (Morrison & Zinner 1977) also suggest that the flux of micrometeorites has been roughly constant, at least on average, over the past 10^4–10^6 years. However, the *present* infall rate of extraterrestrial material on to the earth may be slightly higher than these average values would indicate, suggesting the possibility of a recently increased rate of bombardment of the earth within the past 10^4 years or so.

Despite this somewhat inconclusive evidence for significant variations in the meteoroidal fluxes on *short* timescales, therefore, episodicity on the longer 100 Myr timescale, possibly no different from the approximately 200 Myr cyclicity first detected by Holmes in the terrestrial record, does appear to be a highly significant feature of both the cratering and meteoroidal fluxes. Its existence, if confirmed, would seem virtually to eliminate any simple solar system mechanism, since no known solar system process has yet been shown capable of yielding an episodic variation in the flux of asteroids from the main belt with a period as long as 100 Myr. On the other hand, the detected period is consistent with the time for the solar system to pass between spiral arm features in the Galaxy, assuming a relative velocity less than about $50\,\mathrm{km\,s^{-1}}$. It is conceivable, therefore, that the observed time dependence in terrestrial evolution and in the cratering and meteoric deposition records, which are otherwise unexplained, may fundamentally be due to the capture of long-period comets into the solar system during spiral arm passages, or to an enhanced Oort cloud disturbance during such passages.

16.2.3 MAJOR CRISES

That some asteroids may approach the neighbourhood of the earth had in fact been known as early as 1898, with the independent discovery by Charlois and Witt of minor planet 433 Eros, which can approach within about 22 million kilometres. However, the first asteroid to be found in an actual earth-crossing orbit — and therefore a potential collision hazard — was 1862

Data base	Interval (Myr)	Cratering rate ($D \geq 20\,\mathrm{km}$)	
		Per unit area ($\mathrm{km}^{-2}\,\mathrm{yr}^{-1}$)	Whole earth (per Myr)
Missippi lowlands	200–360	$(5.5 \pm 2.7) \times 10^{-15}$	2.8 ± 1.4
North American and European cratons	0–485	$(3.5 \pm 1.3) \times 10^{-15}$	1.8 ± 0.7
Apollo 12, 15 landing sites	0–3200	$(2.0 \pm 0.8) \times 10^{-15}$	1.0 ± 0.4
Craters younger than 120 Myr	0–120	$(5.4 \pm 2.7) \times 10^{-15}$	2.8 ± 1.4

Table 16.2: Observed production rate of large craters on the earth, with diameters $D \geq 20\,\mathrm{km}$. The data for each row come respectively from Shoemaker (1977), Grieve & Dence (1979), BVSP (1981), and Grieve (1984). The crater production rate for other diameters scales roughly as D^{-2}. After Grieve (1984).

Apollo, after which the 'Apollo' asteroids are named, discovered by Reinmuth in 1932.

In 1963, Öpik found that the population of such bodies larger than 1 km in diameter in the inner planetary system was about 40; and as recently as the early nineteen-seventies Whipple (1973) had thought that the total number was only of order 100. However, systematic searches around this time, largely by Shoemaker and collaborators (e.g. Shoemaker 1977, Shoemaker et al. 1979) were rapidly transforming the situation, and by the end of this period it was estimated that there were more than 1000 earth-approaching asteroids moving within the orbit of Mars. Thus, within little more than a decade, the estimated number of such asteroids had increased by a factor of about 20, making collisions with the earth a relatively common occurrence on geological timescales, and bringing the frequency of collisions more or less into line with the independently estimated rate of production of large craters on the earth and the moon.

It should be emphasized, of course, that these latest population estimates, although much improved, are not yet final, as they rely on an extrapolation from 50–100 observed bodies. Depending on observational factors such as the completeness of sky coverage, rediscovery rates and so on, they are clearly still subject to revision. The largest of the known Apollos, Hephaistos and Sisyphus (minor planets 2212 and 1866 respectively), are only 10 km across; but despite this, such a body striking the earth at a typical relative velocity of order $20 \, \mathrm{km \, s^{-1}}$ is bound to release an enormous amount of kinetic energy, equal to around 10^8 Mt, where 1 Mt represents the explosive yield of one million tons of TNT, corresponding to 10^{15} calories or 4.2×10^{15} J.

As McCrea (1981) has pointed out, an impact of this magnitude is equivalent in energy to about ten atomic bombs of Hiroshima size exploding on every square kilometre of the earth's surface. It is, of course, unrealistic to suppose that the energy released in so vast an explosion would be uniformly distributed over the earth's surface, but such calculations clearly indicate the scale of destruction involved. Impacts of earth-crossing asteroids, occurring at a rate equivalent to the production of one 20 km diameter crater every 300,000 years (see Table 16.2), can clearly have dramatic terrestrial consequences. It is this — the huge energies involved and the apparent inevitability of the process, results implicit in both the observed numbers and sizes of the asteroids and in their predicted rate of arrival on the earth (Table 16.3; cf. Öpik 1958, Grieve & Dence 1979, Weissman 1989) — which leads most naturally to the suggestion that mass extinctions of species, climatic and other geophysical phenomena, may be catastrophically caused (Napier & Clube 1979).

It follows, of course, that the most recent of the prominent mass extinctions, that responsible for the demise of the dinosaurs about 65 Myr ago, required one of the largest Apollo asteroids, around 10 km in diameter. But if a significant number of Apollo asteroids come from comets it also follows that these impact events, and other effects possibly associated with the disinte-

Body	v_{impact} (km s^{-1})	d_{20} (km)	$\dot{N}_c(\geq 20\,\mathrm{km})$ (per Myr)
Long-period comets	55	0.8	0.003–0.18
Short-period comets	26	1.3	0.004–0.04
Earth-crossing asteroids	20	1.5	0.55–28.5

Table 16.3: Estimates of the collision rates of comets and asteroids with the earth. v_{impact} denotes the most probable impact velocity, d_{20} is the estimated diameter of the body required to produce a 20 km diameter crater, and $\dot{N}_c(\geq 20\,\mathrm{km})$ denotes the expected production rate of craters larger than 20 km across from each kind of body. Results from Bailey & Stagg (1988).

gration of large comets, should be bunched in time, occurring stochastically yet revealing an underlying galactic modulation as well. At the same time, we should not be blind to the possibility of other equally dramatic catastrophic agencies whose effects need to be explored: comet showers from the Oort cloud, and meteoroid swarms associated with the break-up of giant comets.

16.3   Galactic connexion

16.3.1   SPIRAL IMPRINT

We have already given a brief description of the structure and dynamics of our Galaxy as usually understood (Section 12.3, p.259, and Appendix B and references therein). Implicit also in this understanding is the widely held view that spiral arms are relatively weak features arising through the action of spiral density waves which circulate more or less continuously through the gas-and-star discs of galaxies, these being presumed to be in a state of virtually pure rotation. It should be said, however, that this standard picture of galactic dynamics is not universally held, and a minority opinion has also been expressed for some time that the observational evidence instead favours a picture in which the long-term evolution of the Galaxy is dominated by a succession of violent events occurring within the galactic nucleus, culminating in the intermittent ejection of short-lived material spiral arms from the galactic centre into the surrounding disc (Clube 1978; cf. Bailey & Clube 1978).

Such a picture has also been described by Ambartsumian (1958, 1960, 1965), who developed a unified, if pragmatic, theory in which stars and galaxy formation are part of the same process, matter at high density in the nuclei of galaxies being ejected to form globular clusters, spiral arms and even companion galaxies (see also Hoyle & Narlikar 1966). Each of these nuclear ejection events is expected to take place at intervals comparable to the wind-up and dissipation time of individual spiral arm systems (2–3 turns, 100–200 Myr), so that it is possible for some galaxies to contain more than one spiral arm system at any one time, as observed. It should be emphasized that this picture of galactic dynamics and evolution is not generally favoured at present, probably because of the requirement for 'new physics'. Nevertheless, it is possible to incorporate within it a number of conspicuously anomalous motions displayed by the stellar and gaseous components of the Galaxy, thereby providing additional arguments in its support (Appendix C). Clearly, if comet and star formation are to be understood in the context of such a theory, the properties of comets, and indeed the terrestrial record, might bear evidence of this alternative cosmogony.

An important implication of this particular picture (e.g. Clube 1977, 1980, 1983) is that the nucleus of a galaxy may intermittently enter a 'hypermassive' or highly inflationary phase, somehow connected with the gravitational collapse and associated highly energetic phenomena that arise in successive supermassive stars formed in the galactic centre. These short-lived, highly inflationary phases in the evolution of supermassive stars, limited possibly by the ultimate incompressibility of matter, lead each time to the rapid contraction and subsequent re-expansion (as spiral arms) of the whole of the inner galactic disc, together with similar though less serious perturbations of the outer parts of the galaxy as well.

This stage in the evolution of a supermassive star or galaxy is not predicted by conventional theories of stellar or galactic evolution, the new theory's principal point of departure being the rejection of standard general relativistic principles (cf. Atkinson 1963, 1965a,b) and the introduction of a new gravitational physics based on the Lorentzian theory of matter (Dicke 1962). Conventional theories of stellar evolution usually predict the complete disruption of collapsing supermassive stars $(M \lesssim 10^5$–$10^7 \, M_\odot)$, following a giant nuclear explosion analogous to a massive supernova. Such events are associated with the onset of nuclear burning in the collapsing stellar material (e.g. Hoyle & Fowler 1963, Fricke 1973, 1974; Von Hoerner & Saslaw 1976; cf. Lynden-Bell 1969, Ozernoy & Usov 1971, 1973, 1977; Rees 1978a,b), well before any stage of relativistic collapse occurs. More massive stars $(M \gtrsim 10^8 \, M_\odot)$, however, although very much harder to form in a galactic nucleus, are expected to collapse to form a massive black hole.

On the other hand, the Lorentz-Dicke theory implies that there will be a significant increase in the strength of the gravitational binding as the supermassive stars evolve, with an associated tendency for explosions (when they occur) to take place at the termination of the collapse in a relativistic régime. The new gravitational theory predicts, in fact, that the overall gravitational attraction of any such highly energetic, collapsing body should increase in proportion to the fourth power of the special relativistic Lorentz factor γ, which in turn is an exponential function of the Newtonian gravitational potential of the material involved (Clube 1977, 1980, 1989a). This leads to the generation of a temporary 'hypermassive' body at the galactic centre.

As far as the theory of comets is concerned, it is obviously not possible for such a loosely bound configuration as the conventional Oort cloud to survive this sort of galactic upheaval. The proposed galactic collapse and re-expansion involves briefly accelerating the solar system in towards the galactic centre and out again, and necessarily implies an impulsive disturbance (augmented by close encounters with massive molecular clouds, stars and spiral arms near the point of maximum contraction) of the sun's weakly bound comets, causing most of them to be released into the interstellar environment. So — assuming this galactic theory to be correct — comets have to be considered as interstellar in origin and recently acquired. Moreover, the theory makes certain predictions about the nature of spiral arms, viewing them essentially as initially hot material associated with the ejection of dense plasma from the contracted inner disc at the end of the central star's assumed 'hypermassive' nuclear state. Thus, on this hypothesis, it seems natural to regard each Oort cloud as short-lived and comets as the final result of the formation and accumulation of dust grains, originally formed via the gravitational condensation and cooling of initially hot material in an otherwise expanding state (*cf.* Clube 1988b).

16.3.2   HOT BEGINNINGS

This alternative hot origin for comets, based on a radical reinterpretation of galactic dynamics, is evidently so different from the more usually favoured 'cold' formation scenario that it would seem that the validity of one or the other theory might in the end be settled simply by examining the detailed physical and chemical properties of cometary dust and ices. For example, the condensations which are formed in hot spiral arms might be expected to resemble those envisaged as arising in the aftermath of the hot 'Big Bang' cosmology (Palla 1988) or in the cooling flows of hot X-ray emitting gas observed in clusters of galaxies (*e.g.* Fabian *et al.* 1987); namely, a rapidly produced sequence of Jeans condensations ranging in mass from that of stellar superclusters and globular clusters ($\gtrsim 10^6 \, M_\odot$), down to substellar bodies which could be completely dark ($\approx 10^{-9}$–$10^{-2} \, M_\odot$; *cf.*

Table 16.4).

This evolutionary sequence leads to a physical régime at the stellar mass or solar system level in which the rapidly cooling subcondensations, in which core-mantle grains may eventually form, can be expected to undergo differentiation, causing the refractory and more volatile components to segregate in a natural manner (cf. Section 15.3.1, p.357). Such bodies, in which the dust and gas partially separate, are thought to be initially rather similar to the floccules introduced by McCrea (1960, 1961, 1978), for example, in order to provide an explanation of the observed mass and angular momentum distribution in the solar system. A more detailed discussion of some of these ideas has also been given by Clube (1988b; cf. Appendix C).

The smallest substellar bodies formed in spiral arms could then be highly differentiated 'parent bodies', with overall dimensions on the order of 10^2–10^3 km, of the sort originally conceived (mostly for chemical reasons) as necessary to explain the general properties of meteorites (Anders 1963, 1964). Such bodies can therefore be expected to combine, in a single mass, properties corresponding to asteroidal cores (expected to be meteoritic if large enough), meteoroidal mantles (possibly of a devolatilized, fluffy nature), and cometary surfaces (possibly dust-impregnated volatiles), and may be very liable to fragment.

An important feature of this proposed hot origin of comets is the expected very short pre-cometary lifetime of the constituent cometary dust particles, no more than the dynamical timescale associated with the expansion of spiral arms from the galactic nucleus ($\lesssim 50\,\mathrm{Myr}$). This may be compared with the standard picture, in which the expected lifetime of refractory interstellar grains which could survive undegraded and become incorporated within meteorites is currently calculated to be at least $500\,\mathrm{Myr}$ (e.g. Barlow 1978, Seab 1987, 1988). A test of this general proposal, therefore, is to identify and date the small refractory inclusions of presumed interstellar origin that are sometimes observed as grains within meteorites.

For example, well preserved particles apparently of interstel-

System	R (m)	T (K)	μ	Jeans mass (kg)
Star/planet system	$\approx 10^{12}$	2000	2	10^{30}
Parent body	$\approx 10^{5.5}$	> 20	> 20	$\gtrsim 10^{21}$

Table 16.4: Representative low-mass condensation cells in spiral arms. μ denotes the mean molecular weight of the bodies in question, while the Jeans mass is given approximately by $m_{\rm J} \approx 10^{-9} (T^3/\mu^3\rho)^{1/2} M_\odot$, where ρ is the density. After Clube (1988b).

lar origin have now been identified in a number of carbonaceous chondrites (Ming & Anders 1988). In particular, grains of silicon carbide (SiC) have been found with trace-element signatures characteristic of an origin in red-giant stars (Xe, Kr) or novae (^{22}Ne, ^{15}N), while carbon and silicon isotope heterogeneity in the formative medium on the scale of individual stars seems to be consistent with that expected from a nuclear disc. It turns out that the pre-solar exposure age of SiC, based on the production of ^{21}Ne by the cosmic-ray spallation of Si, is between 21 and 61 Myr, this relatively very young age (ten times smaller than that expected on current understanding of the evolution of interstellar dust grains) also being strongly supported by the log-normal size distribution of the crystals and by their fresh, uneroded appearance (*e.g.* Zinner *et al.* 1988, Ming & Anders 1988). This result is consistent, therefore, with the proposed shorter timescale for the pre-solar evolution of dust grains, and hence possibly with a hot origin for small primitive bodies in star-forming regions and the solar system. In this way, one important prediction of the expanding galaxy picture — that comets originate through the accumulation of highly refractory dust grains with a relatively short pre-cometary existence — seems already to be confirmed, increasing, albeit indirectly, observational support for both the galactic theory and the associated 'hot potato' theory of comet formation!

16.3.3 GALACTIC ALTERNATIVES

The validity or otherwise of the Lorentz-Dicke gravitational theory is an important problem for future research. In particular, since it provides a very different perspective from which to view possible galactic effects on the earth (e.g. Clube 1978), the existence of 'episodes' and 'cycles' in the terrestrial record, apparently of galactic origin, and of giant bodies in spiral arms which are as meteoroidal and friable as they are cometary, may become crucial tests of the proposed galactic theory.

On the other hand, we must also emphasize that none of these arguments is currently regarded as completely watertight, and it remains to be seen whether the 'galactic' periodicities claimed for many terrestrial phenomena may, in the end have some other explanation. For example, it is conceivable that what may now *appear* to be galactic-driven cyclicities in the terrestrial record could be caused by a still undiscovered 'internal' process on earth (perhaps related to volcanism or the underlying mechanism of plate tectonics). This would not, of course, explain the episodic cratering and meteoric deposition records on the moon. Alternatively, assuming a greater understanding of either solar system or galactic evolution, it is possible to imagine a variety of other mechanisms which might also be consistent with the same data, perhaps more closely related to conventional views of solar system or galactic dynamics.

For example, the apparently chaotic nature of the outer planetary orbits over very long timescales (e.g. Sussman & Wisdom 1988, Laskar 1989) may eventually lead to a suitable generalization of the Milankovitch mechanism (e.g. Weertman 1976) to explain long-term climatic changes; while other ideas, perhaps more firmly rooted in other known terrestrial, solar system or galactic processes almost certainly also have a rôle to play (cf. Williams 1975, Alvarez 1986, Courtillot & Cisowski

1987, Rampino 1987, 1989; Rampino *et al.* 1988, Rampino & Stothers 1986a,b; 1988). The very wide range of topics covered by these several papers and references therein gives some insight into the probable complexity of effects which might be expected to accompany any realistic theory of terrestrial catastrophism, whether or not based on a time-varying astronomical environment and whether or not directly related to the impact of comets and their disintegration products on the earth.

Nevertheless, whatever the detailed difficulty in generating a unique 'predictive' model of the earth's long-term evolution, it is important to emphasize some principal achievements of the 'catastrophist' debate since the nineteen-seventies. In particular, it has at last concentrated the attention of geologists on the possible reality of very long period 'cyclic' phenomena on the earth; whilst astronomers' attention, too, has become sharply focused on the same question, and on possibly the only kinds of astronomical body likely to interact at all strongly with the earth: namely, comets and earth-crossing asteroids. Furthermore, the discussion has highlighted the importance of episodicity on timescales in the range 100–200 Myr, characteristic of the earth's passage through spiral arms. This feature is no longer a uniquely terrestrial phenomenon, since similar periodicities are also found on the moon in both the cratering and meteoric deposition records. If these episodicities *are* physically related, the range of theoretical options could in fact become very restricted, and there would then seem to be a good prospect for finally arriving at a rather precise understanding of the proposed galacto-terrestrial relationship.

These general lines of argument suggested, during the nineteen-seventies, that the impactors which seem so significantly to affect the earth might arise from comets originating in a transient Oort cloud, episodically enhanced by comet capture from molecular clouds or spiral arms. Although such a model was clearly at odds with the conventional solar system picture of comet formation, it was in principle consistent with an interstellar capture scenario involving the occasional disruption of

the Oort cloud by external perturbations and its subsequent replenishment by the capture of interstellar comets from without.
A clear basis was thus available for the development of a physical theory of terrestrial catastrophism, mediated not through
supernovae or the effects of interstellar dust, but through the
agency of significantly processed comets captured from interstellar space (Napier & Clube 1979, Clube & Napier 1989a,b
and references therein).

However, it is not clear to what extent the detailed physical
picture necessarily depends on the unconventional 'expanding
galaxy' viewpoint described in Section 16.3.1 (see p.379). Oort
cloud disruption and capture might be understood in terms of interactions with molecular clouds without the intervention of violent galactic convulsions (cf. Sections 12.2 and 15.2, pp.254 344);
while 'hot' signatures observed in cold comets and in meteorite
inclusions, albeit with apparently the 'wrong' age, might arise
from interstellar dust generated in stellar atmospheres. In this
way, the apparently galactic timescales found in the terrestrial
record might also be understandable in terms of passages of
the solar system through molecular clouds or spiral arms in the
context of a 'quiescent' rather than a 'violent' galaxy. Discrimination between these alternatives remains a task for the future.

17

Catastrophic impact

*"That the asteroid hit, and that the impact triggered the extinction
of much of the life in the sea are no longer debatable points.
Nearly everybody now believes them."*

Luis W. Alvarez.

17.1 Giant comets

17.1.1 CRETACEOUS-TERTIARY BOUNDARY

The suggestion of a significant galacto-terrestrial relationship
mediated by the effects of what were essentially 'giant' comets
was not at first well received by most astronomers. The comet
community, it seems, was repelled by the idea of Oort cloud disruption, and by the notion that earth-crossing asteroids might
fundamentally be of cometary provenance, comets themselves
being of interstellar origin: none of these views was generally
acceptable during the late nineteen-seventies. Nevertheless, recognizing that a complete theory of terrestrial catastrophism was
now for the first time in prospect, several earth-scientists began seriously to consider the proposed rôle of 10 km diameter
asteroids, comets or cometary fragments in major extinctions
(*e.g.* Alvarez *et al.* 1980, Emiliani 1980, Emiliani *et al.* 1981;
Ganapathy 1980, Hsü 1980, Kyte *et al.* 1980; *cf.* McLaren 1970,
Urey 1973). The group led by Alvarez at Berkeley created the
greatest impression, however, with its announcement of the discovery (*cf.* Smit & Hertogen 1980) of an intense concentration
of noble elements, exemplified by iridium, in the clay layer at
the Cretaceous-Tertiary 'K-T' boundary.

The interpretation of this observation had at first presented
great difficulties, since the Berkeley group in particular began its
investigations under the impression that terrestrial rather than

cosmic factors were responsible. For example, they initially set out to explain the enhanced concentrations of iridium by local variations in the rate of deposition of material leading to the clay layer, and were later forced to consider a nearby supernova event to escape the difficulties that then arose (*e.g.* Alvarez *et al.* 1979, Alvarez 1983). However, such were the obvious strengths of the 'catastrophic' thesis, with its basis in the impact explosion produced by large bodies from space, that the authors immediately abandoned these earlier ideas when the potential importance of earth-crossing asteroids was recognized during the course of their research.

Iridium occurs in a few parts per billion in meteorites but has been leached out of the earth's crust into the mantle. An iridium-bearing stratum was therefore regarded as a secure indicator of material of cosmic origin. In this way, the observed iridium excess could be seen as greatly improving the 'credibility rating' of the proposed galacto-terrestrial relationship, although it was still possible to treat the Cretaceous-Tertiary extinction in isolation and regard the event as a one-off occurrence, due to an isolated asteroidal impact or a kind of 'super-Tunguska' phenomenon (Kyte *et al.* 1980).

In fact, it is now known that iridium may be ejected by particular types of volcanic eruption, and it is interesting to speculate whether, had this fact been known in 1980, the impact hypothesis would have received quite so much attention by geologists. Nevertheless, other probable cosmic signatures have now also been identified, while an unusually high iridium abundance is similarly associated with at least one other mass extinction event showing impact signatures (Ganapathy 1982, Alvarez *et al.* 1982). This suggests that the extra-terrestrial link — the impact of large bodies — connecting these events cannot be entirely coincidental.

Nevertheless, despite broad agreement as to the general importance of collisions between the earth and other interplanetary bodies, the various theories of terrestrial catastrophism during the early nineteen-eighties can be seen as gradually diverging from one another. In particular, one can identify at least three separate strands of opinion on which the various proposals differed. First, there was the question whether the effects of even the very largest impacts were likely to be detected in the terrestrial record (this question was critical for many earth-scientists — some of whom even seemed to doubt that earth-crossing asteroids existed!); secondly, whether a shower of comets, rather than the effects of a single comet or asteroid, was crucial to the whole story; thirdly, whether the apparent cyclicities in the terrestrial record were a real phenomenon to be explained in terms of the behaviour of either comets or asteroids (or both), and if so, which underlying galactic or solar system theory explained them. During the nineteen-eighties there has been an almost explosive growth of the scientific literature in this subject, which would take us well beyond the scope of the present discussion to review. An introduction to the range of possibilities considered and subsequently investigated may be found, for example, in the papers by Clube (1978), Napier & Clube (1979), Clube & Napier (1982a,b; 1984b, 1986b, 1989a); Alvarez et al. (1980), Alvarez (1983), Alvarez (1986), Bailey (1984b), Bailey et al. (1987), Bohor et al. (1984), Hut et al. (1987), and many references therein.

Strictly speaking, of course, the existence of interstellar comets (assumed in the galactic theory) was opposed as well, depending as it did on the unknown physical nature and material content of spiral arms. Although the Galaxy is known to contain both dust and stars, there is a surprising reluctance amongst astronomers (cf. Fogg 1989) to countenance the possibility of anything in between! Moreover, in this respect the galactic theory was still open-ended, since the explanation of episodicity was not settled and the presumed speed of the sun's motion through spiral arms did not automatically distinguish between the suggested alternatives of spiral density waves (with a relative speed in the range 15–125 $\mathrm{km\,s^{-1}}$) and spiral-arm streaming ($\lesssim 50\,\mathrm{km\,s^{-1}}$, say), both of which seemed viable theoretical possibilities. In the former case, one could expect comets to be formed as part of the cold, molecular-cloud complex in the interstellar medium; while in the latter, a hot origin seemed more likely.

17.1.2   MASS DISTRIBUTION

Regardless of the way in which comet-sized bodies are formed in the Galaxy (see Sections 14.1, 14.2, 15.3.1, 15.3.2, 16.3.2), the galactic 'episodes' and 'cycles', apparently present in the terrestrial record, together with indications of fine structure suggestive of 'showers' extending down to timescales of order 1 Myr and less, force one to consider possible mechanisms by which the Galaxy might exert its control over the earth. If comets are the clue, an obvious possibility is the rôle played by the largest comets — giant comets — especially those with diameters ranging beyond 100 km or so. For example, the observed brightness distribution of long-period comets (*e.g.* Hughes & Daniels 1980, Donnison 1986) is well known to extend upwards to very large masses. The results of these authors indicate that the number of comets, $N(m)\, dm$, with masses m in the range $(m, m + dm)$, can be fitted closely by a power law $N(m) = km^{-s}$, where k is an arbitrary normalizing constant and the population index s is given, albeit with some uncertainty, as $s \simeq 1.75 \pm 0.2$. This suggests that most of the mass in a random sample of, say, a hundred comets will probably be contained in the largest one or two.

It should be emphasized, however, that the degree to which the observed power law can be extrapolated to both large and small cometary masses is not certain, due to the scarcity, on the one hand, of observed large comets to fix the high mass end; and on the other, to the difficulty of reliably allowing for the effects of observational selection, which greatly reduce the probability of discovering both faint and intermediately bright comets. For example, following the detailed discussion by Everhart (1967), both Weissman (1983b) and Bailey & Stagg (1988) have argued that, if the observed numbers of comets are corrected for these effects, then the intrinsic mass distribution of comets towards high masses decreases rather more steeply than that indicated simply by a power-law of constant slope $s = 1.75$. They find an effective mass-distribution index at the bright end corresponding to $s \simeq 2.1$–2.5. By the same token, it also appears (after correction) that the low-mass comets are rather less numerous than the simple law would suggest (possibly very much so; cf. Kresák 1978b, Sekanina & Yeomans 1984), having an effective population index $s \simeq 1.6$–1.8 or even less. The transition between the two laws occurs at about an absolute magnitude $H \simeq 7$–5, corresponding to masses in the approximate range $10^{13.5}$–$10^{14.5}$ kg. This suggests that a substantial part of the influx of cometary mass into the solar system may be dominated by the flux of comets with masses only in the range 10^{14}–10^{17} kg, although terrestrial disturbances would still be dominated by the contribution of the occasional rare, 'giant' comet to the instantaneous mass flux.

However, neither the effects of observational selection on the observed brightness distribution of comets, nor the detailed problem of reliably determining cometary masses from their absolute magnitudes, are yet settled. It is possible, therefore, that a more appropriate treatment may indeed be to take the brightness distribution data more or less at face value, as indicating an underlying mass distribution with a constant slope of order $s \simeq 1.8$ at the bright end (cf. Hughes 1987a,c). In this case, the net influx of cometary mass into the solar system would certainly be dominated by the few largest comets.

The question of the upper limit of cometary masses, therefore, remains an important problem. Whatever its solution, however, the answer seems almost bound to be larger than the 10^{18} kg associated with the presumed progenitor of the Kreutz sun-grazing comets. Indeed, if as originally seemed likely from orbital considerations (e.g. Oikawa & Everhart 1979) and now more recently from the presence of a coma (see p.427), minor planet Chiron is a comet, masses ranging up to $\approx 10^{20}$ kg may be implied; while it has even been suggested, not entirely flip-pantly, that Pluto — with a mass on the order of 10^{22} kg — may itself have originated as a planetesimal in the inner core of the Oort cloud (Olsson-Steel 1988c, McKinnon & Mueller 1988)!

For these reasons, it seems reasonable to assume that the detailed distribution of cometary masses extends upwards to very large values; while the disintegration products associated with the break-up of these occasional 'giant' comets moving tem-porarily in short-period earth-crossing orbits must certainly have dramatic terrestrial consequences. For example, even a body only as large as the progenitor of the observed sun-grazer group (with an estimated mass of order 10^{18} kg) would be equivalent in mass to more than a thousand comets the size of Comet Hal-ley; and, as we have seen, the collision of the earth with even quite a small cometary fragment would have quite a devastating local effect. The injection of Chiron into the inner planetary system, as will happen with about 80% probability within the next 10^5 yr, will almost certainly also produce major biological and climatic trauma on earth.

Nevertheless, despite the importance of these larger members of the cometary mass distribution, it should also be emphasized that while the total mass in comets is dominated by the largest bodies, in terms of surface area the effects of cometary *disin-tegration* are probably dominated by the very smallest parts of comets, possibly even the submicron sized dust particles (*e.g.* Mukai 1985). Whatever the detailed cometary mass distrib-ution, therefore, the overall effect of giant comets inevitably in-volves the whole process of cometary disintegration, and the var-ious interactions with each type of disintegration product (*e.g.* dust, boulders, asteroids) must be considered at each stage.

17.1.3 ASTEROIDAL LINK

A question of special interest is whether short-period comets can evolve into asteroids (*cf.* Section 16.2.1, p.372). If they can, then were the short-period comet population to undergo significant variations, so too would the population of earth-crossing asteroids. As we have seen, Öpik (1963) suggested that comets are probably the main source of asteroids in earth-crossing orbits (*cf.* Herschel 1802; Bobrovnikoff 1931, and references therein), although a substantial body of opinion (*e.g.* Kresák 1977b, Rickman & Froeschlé 1980, Levin & Simonenko 1981, Nakamura 1983, Simonenko & Levin 1983) continues to maintain that they are at most a relatively minor contributor. Nevertheless, Öpik's conjecture was based on a very robust argument, namely that given the estimated lifetime of the earth-crossers against ejection or collision (approximately 3×10^7 yr; even less if physical decay is significant), there simply did not seem to be a sufficiently strong source in the main asteroid belt to replace them.

Recent work related to this question has tended to confirm Öpik's original conclusion, although the dynamical argument is now by no means clear-cut. It is known, for example, that a significant number of asteroids can indeed be scattered from the main belt into earth-crossing orbits, by way of a complex route based on the underlying 'chaotic' behaviour of orbits lying near the 3/1 resonance with Jupiter (Wisdom 1983, 1985a,b). In this way, Wetherill (1985) estimated that some 10–20% of the observed Apollo-Amor asteroids could be derived in this way; while in later work (Wetherill 1988), he has revised this figure upwards to around 40%. Despite this, at least half the earth-crossing asteroids still seem to be unaccounted for, and it seems probable that many of them are in fact ultimately derived from comets.

Indeed, while the dynamical argument about the origin of the earth-crossing asteroids is not completely settled, the case based on physical arguments that at least some comets eventually decay into asteroids (and some bodies originally classified as asteroids may become comets) has become quite convincing. For example, the evidence has been strengthened by a number of discoveries in recent years: the existence of asteroids in comet-like orbits (*e.g.* 2060 Chiron, 944 Hidalgo, and the still unnamed minor planets 3552 [1983 SA], 4015 [1979 VA], and 1983 XF);

comets with nearly asteroidal appearance that emit gas from only very small areas of their surfaces (*e.g.* Tempel-Tuttle, Neujmin 1, and Arend-Rigaux); observations of fireballs of apparently cometary constitution whose orbits suggest they are probably derived from Apollo asteroids (Drummond 1982); and the recently discovered Apollo asteroid 3200 Phaethon (1983 TB), which appears to be the source of the Geminid meteor stream (Whipple 1983, Fox *et al.* 1984). Olsson-Steel (1988b) has also found that a substantial fraction of the known Apollo asteroids appear to have meteor streams associated with them. The probable connexion between comets and asteroids has also been reviewed by Marsden (1970), Degewij & Tedesco (1982), Rickman (1985), and Weissman *et al.* (1989), while the particular evidence that a comet of mass $\approx 10^{18}$ kg may have entered the inner solar system on an Apollo orbit some few times 10^4 years ago and subsequently experienced a hierarchy of disintegrations has been discussed by Clube & Napier (1984b, 1986b) and Olsson-Steel (1986).

The zodiacal cloud, of course, is the ultimate comminution product of disintegrating comets and asteroids, and the general difficulties that arise in accounting for the observed mass of the zodiacal cloud in terms of the currently observed comets and asteroids have long suggested that it might best be attributed to a single large comet which arrived in the fairly recent past (*e.g.* Whipple 1967, Sekanina 1972, Delsemme 1976b, Kresák 1980) whose invisible meteoroidal débris are still in the process of disintegrating (Clube & Napier 1984b, 1989b). The suggestion that quite substantial fragments of friable cometary material may be ejected from cometary nuclei and then continue to sublimate and break up through a series of subsequent disintegrations has recently been strengthened, for example, by radio observations of Comet Wilson and spacecraft observations of the dust in Halley's comet (de Pater *et al.* 1989, Boehnhardt 1989). Indeed, whatever its ultimate source, the zodiacal cloud is probably best modelled at present in terms of a family of disintegrating meteoroids (Grün *et al.* 1986; *cf.* Clube 1987b).

17.1.4 Taurid débris

If a single 'giant' comet is indeed the fount of much of the transient meteoroidal débris observed at any one time in the inner solar system, the most likely candidate for any related meteoroid complex seems at present to be the massive Taurid-Arietid meteor stream. The suspected cometary fragments and meteor showers associated with this complex are shown in Table 17.1. Of these, Encke's comet is currently the most active, though there are also signs of weak activity from 2201 Oljato (McFadden et al. 1984, Russell et al. 1984), a body thought on quite different grounds to have probably been an 'ordinary' comet about 3×10^4 years ago (Babadžhanov & Obrubov 1983). The largest known asteroid in this list of earth-crossing bodies, Hephaistos, which may have separated from Encke's comet some 2×10^4 years ago (Napier 1983; cf. Clube & Napier 1982c), is more than 10 km across!

Making a rough estimate based on the number of known asteroids in this complex, allowing for one or two possible chance coincidences (cf. Porubčan & Štohl 1989, Ziołkowski 1989) and multiplying by a factor based on the probable incompleteness of the discovered earth-crossing asteroid population as a whole ($\approx$ 5–10% found so far), it would appear that there are something like 50–100 asteroid-size bodies circulating within the broad confines of the Taurid meteor streams. Moreover, in addition to these large bodies, ranging in size up to 10 km in diameter, there are also more widely dispersed streams of meteoroidal material together with denser clumps, or swarms, of somewhat larger boulder-size bodies, with diameters in the approximate range 1–100 m.

The recognized meteor showers are in fact encompassed by a much broader system described by Štohl (1983), the meteoroids of which appear to account for a significant fraction of the 'sporadic' meteor population. Indeed, the earth-moon system appears to have run through a cluster of relatively large

Object	a (AU)	e	i (deg)	ϖ (deg)	Notes
Meteor streams					
S Taurids	1.93	0.806	5.2	153.2	
N Taurids	2.59	0.861	2.4	162.3	
β Taurids	2.2	0.85	6	162.4	
ξ Perseids	1.6	0.79	0	137	
S Piscids	2.33	0.82	2	104	
N Piscids	2.06	0.80	3	130	
S χ Orionids	2.18	0.78	7	180	
N χ Orionids	2.22	0.79	2	179	
Active comets					
Encke	2.2	0.85	11.9	160	
Rudnicki	—	1.00	9.1	154.7	
Asteroids					
2201 Oljato	2.2	0.71	2.5	172	
1982 TA	2.2	0.76	11.8	128	
1984 KB	2.2	0.76	4.6	146	
5025 P-L	4.20	0.895	6.2	145.8	
2212 Hephaistos	2.1	0.83	11.9	258	
1987 SB	2.16	0.650	2.9	167.4	
Unseen companion	2.4	0.86	—	160	(1)
Impactors on the earth or moon					
Boulder flux					(2)
Boulder swarm					(2)
Tunguska object					(3)
Bruno object					(4)
Larger complexes					
Štohl stream					(5)
Zodiacal cloud					(5)
β Taurid 'trail'					(6)

Table 17.1: Probable débris from the most recent giant short-period comet, as discussed in the text. The source code is as follows: (1) Whipple & Hamid (1952); (2) Dorman *et al.* (1978); (3) Kresák (1978); (4) Brecher (1984); (5) See text; (6) Sykes *et al.* (1986).

bodies, having masses as great as a ton, in a five-day period around June 30th 1975 coincident with the maximum of the β-Taurid stream (Dorman et al. 1978). The much larger Tunguska object, possibly weighing more than a million tons (cf. Ganapathy 1983), which fell on June 30th 1908, is also a probable member of this stream (Kresák 1978a; cf. Sekanina 1983, Clube & Napier 1984b), whilst an extended concentration or 'trail' of dust about 1 AU in length has now also been detected by IRAS in the orbit of Encke's comet (e.g. Sykes 1988), the most likely source of the β Taurid stream.

These facts together with the historical evidence discussed in Chapters 2–4 suggest that the zodiacal cloud may have been significantly enhanced when the presumed giant comet first arrived in an earth-crossing orbit several times 10^4 years ago, while subsequent enhancements could have followed a major fragmentation event thought to have occurred some 5000 years ago (Whipple & Hamid 1952). Ziołkowski (1989), for example, has recently collected evidence suggesting that the separation of 1982 TA and Comet Encke occurred about 6000 years ago, while the Farmington meteorite (with an exceptionally low cosmic-ray exposure age on the order of 10^4 yr) may also be a member of the Taurid stream (Oberst & Nakamura 1989). Both these bodies, therefore, may be linked with the formerly proposed fragmentation events. Taken together, these observations suggest that the mode of break-up of a very large comet is disintegration of its nucleus into asteroids, boulders and dust (cf. Bobrovnikoff 1931). The observation of dust and meteoroidal bodies on a wide range of scales in the solar system therefore provides the basis of a physical mechanism by which the fine structure of cometary arrivals into the inner solar system may be inferred, while the fact of cometary break-up provides information on the physical nature of the nucleus. Indirectly, therefore, these considerations provide clues as to the origin of comets.

The observations thus indicate that, at intervals of order 10^5–10^6 years (the mean time between successive arrivals of giant comets in the inner solar system), the inner planetary system will be dominated by the disintegration products of such comets that have arrived, typically depositing up to 10^{18} kg of material in the form of dust, boulders and short-lived Apollo asteroids. Later, while the rate of disintegration diminishes, the earth will run through the ensuing streams of material at intervals of order 10^3–10^4 years, leading perhaps to between 100 and 10 encounters respectively with bodies of mass 10^8 to 10^{11} kg. Such bodies will usually explode in the atmosphere with locally devastating effect (Clube & Napier 1986a, Clube 1987b, 1989a,b), whilst less frequent larger bodies or asteroids may penetrate the protection of our atmosphere to produce impact craters.

An important implication of this picture is that the smaller 'Tunguska-like' fragments of comets will be concentrated in clusters or swarms, rather than being randomly distributed through interplanetary space (*cf.* Section 2.2.3, p.18). Encounters of the earth with these swarms will produce bursts of bombardment at roughly millennial intervals, with associated armageddon-like effects on the ground, analogous to nuclear war followed by nuclear winter (*cf.* Clube & Napier 1989b). This, of course, seems to be in general accord with otherwise unexplained aspects of the historical record reviewed in Chapters 2–4 (*cf.* Clube 1989a,b), while the psychological effects of such trauma (hinted at by contemporary investigations into the effects of modern natural disasters) would be expected to influence the outlook of the societies so affected for generations after the event. During the early stages of such disintegrations there will be an annual influx of $\approx 5 \times 10^9$ kg of micron-sized dust particles, with a stratospheric settling time in polar regions of 1–3 years, generating an atmospheric dust veil of optical depth in the range $\simeq 0.1$–1, whose adverse climatic effects may last for a time on the order of $\approx 10^3$–10^4 yr.

Indeed, although the dust by itself might generally appear to be relatively harmless, it is important to note that the total mass of dust released by a large comet may be an order of magnitude or more greater than that now present in the zodiacal cloud. Any one of these stratospheric 'dustings', coming from an enhanced zodiacal cloud or due to the earth running through an especially dense meteor stream, might in principle be capable of providing the trigger for major perturbations of the earth's climatic system such as that leading to the most recent ice age (*e.g.* Clube & Napier 1982a,b; 1986b; *cf.* Kominz & Pisias 1979, and papers in Silver & Schultz 1982). Moreover, the various phenomena we have described, not all of which may be present simultaneously, are nevertheless predicted to be correlated in time.

17.1.5   TERRESTRIAL RESPONSE

These comet-induced catastrophes, arising primarily through climatic effects, are of course in addition to the ordinary 'thermal' perturbations of the terrestrial system associated with the so-called Milankovitch mechanism (Milankovitch 1920; *cf.* Ball 1891, Pearson 1978). In this latter mechanism, fluctuations in the mean climate are attributed to quasi-periodic and long-term changes of the average heat input from the sun, arising from perturbations of the earth's orbit by the other planets. Discussions of these and other 'astronomical' theories of climatic change have been given, for example, by Öpik (1965) and Kopal (1980); while a more detailed description of the general effects of cometary bombardment, and their possibly episodic geophysical, climatic and biological trauma, has recently been presented by Clube & Napier (1989b).

In general, therefore, during periods of heightened cometary flux, when the interval between the arrival of giant comets may be less than 10^5 yr, the environmental deterioration caused by the series of sharp climatic coolings following intermittent stratospheric dustings may compete with or even dominate the locally more adverse effects of large impacts. The latter could complicate the issue in a number of ways, for example leading to mass extinctions of certain species through the effects of 'global fire' (*e.g.* Wolbach *et al.* 1988) or even through a longer period of atmospheric heating caused by a greatly enhanced 'greenhouse effect' associated with the effects of the impact (*e.g.* Emiliani *et al.* 1981, O'Keefe & Ahrens 1989; *cf.* Cowles 1939).

It is to be expected, therefore, that extinction mechanisms and their associated geophysical and biological signatures will be complex. Moreover, apart from the arrival of the rarest, most massive impactors, there is no reason to suppose that the particular catastrophic effects attributable to the proposed galacto-terrestrial relationship should generally be either short-lived or instantaneous. Terrestrial catastrophism, on this picture, is by its nature continuous, almost uniformitarian! Only on timescales less than a thousand years or so, during periods of sustained low-mass cometary influx from the Oort cloud, is it likely that the dominant long-term effects of large comets might fail to be recognized. Indeed, it is possible that we are now living through one such period, and have only just recognized the principal rôle played by giant comets!

To conclude this section, we note that although biological evolution on the earth may now be implicitly understood in terms of the response of a primordial gene pool to occasional comet-induced changes in the earth's astronomical environment, giant comets may also have other significant rôles to play in the development and evolution of life on earth. The possibly catastrophic effect of cometary dust on the biosphere was recognized, for example, very early on by Hoyle & Wickramasinghe (1978) and Butler & Hoyle (1979, 1980); and in subsequent work Hoyle and colleagues (*e.g.* Hoyle 1980, 1984, 1987; Hoyle & Wickramasinghe 1981, 1985; and references therein) have emphasized not only the importance of climatic trauma, but also the apparent necessity for subsequent external additions to the gene pool in order to maintain episodic speciation.

In particular, they have suggested that cometary dust may be biologically active, and that the intense 'rain' of this potentially pathogenic 'biotic' material on the earth's upper atmosphere during comet showers or the occasional break-up of a large comet may itself be the primary cause of mass extinctions of species (Hoyle & Wickramasinghe 1985). In this case, although climatic change and the effects of large-body impacts would undoubtedly also play a rôle, the principal cause of extinctions and speciation may be the devastating effect of new viruses and other pathogens acting on an otherwise unprepared terrestrial ecosystem. The viruses themselves are assumed to have multiplied in the complex primordial organic 'soup' supposed to have existed in comet nuclei from the time of their formation, while the authors further suggest that, subject to certain limitations, the only way to pass in quantity from inorganic materials to organic materials *anywhere at all* is through the action of biologically active organisms. If this important conjecture should prove correct, then life itself must presumably have originated far beyond the earth, either in comets or possibly elsewhere in the depths of interstellar space.

It is not clear where this recently started line of enquiry will eventually lead, based as it is on what may prove to be an interstellar origin of both comets and life, and on cosmological concepts that themselves depart significantly from the norm (*e.g.* Hoyle 1982). Nevertheless, from an experimental point of view the assumed biological compounds do seem to be remarkably resilient under anticipated interstellar conditions (*e.g.* Weber & Greenberg 1985), while observations of Halley's comet may also be explicable in terms of an assumed biotic composition for cometary dust (Wallis *et al.* 1989, Wickramasinghe & Hoyle 1989). The studies completed so far do not, therefore, exclude the possibility that differentiated giant comets may be significant sources of biogenic material. Although the idea is still regarded by most astronomers as lying impossibly beyond the pale (especially bearing in mind cosmochemical constraints based on certain elemental abundances, for example that of phosphorus; *cf.* Duley 1984, Whittet 1984; Hoyle & Wickramasinghe 1985, Appendix), they do once again re-open the important question (*cf.* Newton and Herschel), still largely unexplored, whether comets might possibly play *the* fundamental rôle in the origin and subsequent development of life on earth.

17.2   Galactic modulation

17.2.1   TEMPORAL PATTERNS

Since the Oort cloud is undeniably disturbed by galactic effects (for example, through perturbations by the galactic tide, stars and massive molecular clouds, or because it originates by cometary capture from molecular clouds or the underlying spiral arm medium), it follows that the pattern of terrestrial bombardment by the disintegration products of giant comets will not be entirely random.   Temporal structures may arise, for example, from the effect of giant molecular clouds tending to concentrate in spiral arms and towards the mid-plane of the galactic disc or the galactic centre; and from the quasi-periodic radial and out-of-plane motions of the solar system in its orbit about the Galaxy.

From a theoretical point of view, the population of earth-crossing bodies, given that some are comets and others are cometary disintegration products, is therefore expected to undergo relatively large stochastic fluctuations with an underlying galactic modulation. The strengths of these variations is a crucial issue to be resolved, and — if cyclicity is present — it should certainly be detectable both in the terrestrial record and in samples of lunar soil (e.g. Goswami & Lal 1978).

Table 17.2 summarizes some of the principal periodicities, both short-term and long-term, which have apparently been observed in the terrestrial record. In particular, cycles of order 30 Myr and episodes of order 200–300 Myr seem to be especially prominent. These periods should be compared, for example, with the theoretically predicted variations of order 30 Myr and 100–200 Myr, corresponding respectively to the more regular out-of-plane component of the solar motion and the more episodic interval between successive spiral arm penetrations (or the displacements in the galactic radial direction arising as a result of the solar motion). Distinguishing between these principal periodicities, and identifying their terrestrial analogues,

Phenomenon	'Period' (Myr)	Source
Climatic and sea-level changes	≃ 30	Dorman (1968)
	≃ 32	Leggett *et al.* (1981)
	≃ 30	Fischer & Arthur (1977)
	≃ 30	Shackleton (1989)
Tectonic cycles	≃ 30	Holmes (1927)
Mass extinctions	≃ 32	Fischer & Arthur (1977)
	≃ 26	Raup & Sepkoski (1984)
Geomagnetic reversal frequency	32–34	Negi & Tiwari (1983)
	≃ 30	Pal & Creer (1986)
	≃ 15	Mazaud *et al.* (1983)
	≃ 15	Creer & Pal (1989)
Ages of craters	≃ 27	Seyfert & Sirkin (1979)
	31 ± 1	Rampino & Stothers (1984b)
	≃ 28	Alvarez & Muller (1984)
Ice ages	≃ 250	Holmes (1927)
	≃ 200	Steiner & Grillmair (1973)
Major tectonic events	≃ 200	Holmes (1927)
	≃ 230	Macintyre (1971)
Climatic cycle	≃ 300	Fischer & Arthur (1977)
Mixed magnetic intervals	≃ 285	Negi & Tiwari (1983)

Table 17.2: Short and long-term periodicities that have been claimed in the geophysical record.

is clearly no easy task, and it is therefore important to assess the most significant galactic effects. In this section we briefly look at some of the questions which arise, and summarize the still controversial debate concerning the existence or otherwise of possible periodicities in various facets of the terrestrial record.

17.2.2   INTERSTELLAR CLOUDS

As we have already seen (Section 13.3.2, p.290), the years following Raup & Sepkoski's (1984) suggestion of a regular 26 Myr periodicity in the record of mass extinctions, correlating with similar evidence for a roughly 30 Myr periodicity in the observed cratering record (*e.g.* Alvarez & Muller 1984, Rampino & Stothers 1984b, Shoemaker & Wolfe 1984b), led almost immediately to a flurry of papers advocating various sorts of astronomical explanation for the effect (*e.g.* Rampino & Stothers 1984a, Whitmire & Jackson 1984, Davis *et al.* 1984, Schwartz & James 1984). Among these, the idea proposed by Rampino & Stothers (see also Rampino & Stothers 1986a), highlighting the importance of molecular cloud perturbations on the Oort cloud, seemed to many to be the most astrophysically plausible, and a number of investigators subsequently considered the detailed predictions of such a scheme, which inevitably depend largely on the properties (*e.g.* their numbers and typical masses) assumed for the molecular clouds.

Observationally, as we have described earlier (Section 12.1.1, p.250), the distribution of molecular gas in the Galaxy is dominated by a relatively small number of extremely large clouds of material, with radii typically on the order of 20 pc and masses in the range 10^5–10^6 $M_\odot$ (see Figure 17.1). The total number of such 'giant' molecular clouds in the inner part of the Galaxy is on the order of 6000 (*e.g.* Sanders *et al.* 1985), being mostly concentrated within a disc of remarkably small thickness about the galactic plane; the number density of clouds normal to the plane is roughly proportional to $\exp(-Z^2/2h^2)$, where the scale height h is of order $60 \pm 10\,\text{pc}$ in the solar neighbourhood (e.g. Gordon & Burton 1979, Sanders et al. 1984, Dame & Thaddeus 1985, Dame et al. 1987). This figure should be reduced by a further 15% or so (Stothers 1985) if the sun's distance from the galactic centre is taken instead to be $R_0 = 8.5\,\text{kpc}$ rather than the usually assumed value of $10\,\text{kpc}$.

It is suspected that these molecular clouds probably also trace the spiral arms of the Galaxy (see Cohen et al. 1980, Thaddeus & Dame 1984, Sanders et al. 1984, 1985). Whilst warm clouds, which also seem to be amongst the largest observed, appear to delineate a pattern of two arms and a $4\,\text{kpc}$ ring, there is also a large amount of molecular material between the arms and in generally smaller clouds. Averaging the observed surface brightness of molecular gas in concentric annuli about the galactic centre shows the presence of a prominent peak in the distribution vs. galactocentric distance, indicating the presence of a massive 'molecular ring' of material lying between distances 5 and $7\,\text{kpc}$ from the galactic centre, with the surface density falling off particularly steeply at larger radii. In the solar neighbourhood, for example, at a nominal distance $R_0 = 10\,\text{kpc}$, the surface density is rather less than 1/3 that at the peak of the ring (Sanders et al. 1985). Although the relative strength of the molecular ring has been questioned by Bhat et al. (1985), its existence is not really in doubt; it is also seen, for example, in the IRAS data for the radial variation of the temperature of interstellar dust, this too almost certainly tracing the distribution of the warmer gas associated with molecular cloud cores (e.g. Burton et al. 1986).

Following the discussion in Bailey (1986a), the mean mass of giant molecular clouds may be estimated with some uncertainty as about $3 \times 10^5\,M_\odot$, while the observed number of clouds per unit area of the galactic disc in the solar neighbourhood is on the order of $(8 \pm 1) \times 10^{-6}\,\text{pc}^{-2}$. The corresponding mid-plane number density of such clouds is then around $5 \times 10^{-8}\,\text{pc}^{-3}$ in the solar neighbourhood, with an uncertainty of about 30% either

Figure 17.1: The Rho Ophiuchi molecular cloud and the region of Antares. This dense molecular cloud complex is believed to be part of Gould's Belt. Photograph courtesy of the Royal Observatory, Edinburgh.

way, leading to a mean mid-plane local molecular gas density of order 0.01–0.02 $M_\odot$ pc^{-3}. This may be compared, for example, with the values 0.007 $M_\odot$ pc^{-3} and 0.033 $M_\odot$ pc^{-3} independently obtained by Dame et $al.$ (1987) and Sanders et $al.$ (1984).

An important consequence of this extremely thin layer of molecular material in the Galaxy is that the sun is expected to encounter molecular clouds with a heightened probability at those times in its orbit when it passes close to the galactic plane. Since the sun crosses the galactic plane about once every 30 million years, it is possible to imagine, as outlined by Rampino & Stothers (1984a), that this changing probability of molecular cloud encounters ultimately leads to a variable cometary influx whose effects are apparently shown in the terrestrial record and cited as evidence for comet showers.

If perturbations by molecular clouds are indeed an important way by which dynamically 'new' long-period comets are scattered into the inner solar system, then one would expect a roughly 30 Myr signature also to be present in the new-comet flux from the Oort cloud, and hence — possibly — in the terrestrial cratering and mass extinction records too. However, although $some$ effect of this general type must be present, the suggestion seems to founder on three important points. First, the number of molecular clouds in the galactic plane is too small for the occurrence of sufficiently close molecular cloud encounters on a timescale as short as 30 Myr ($e.g.$ Morris & Muller 1986) — a typical closest approach to a cloud is about 70 pc rather than the 20 pc necessary for an effective perturbation. Secondly, the amplitude of the solar motion normal to the plane may be too small compared to the width of the molecular cloud layer in the galactic disc, leading to a severe 'signal-to-noise' problem for the theory (Thaddeus & Chanan 1985; $cf.$ Stothers 1985); and thirdly, even if one drops the requirement that the perturbations are approximately periodic, the total mass density of molecular gas is still too small to account for clouds being significant perturbers of the Oort cloud on timescales much less than about 200 Myr (Bailey et $al.$ 1987).

In view of these difficulties, Rampino & Stothers (1984a) argued that disturbances due to the more numerous 'small' molecular clouds (with masses on the order of $10^4 \, M_\odot$) were probably the principal perturbers of the Oort cloud (*cf.* Stothers 1988). Stothers (1984) also suggested that perturbations by hitherto unidentified 'dark matter' in the galactic disc might be important too, provided that its scale height perpendicular to the galactic plane was at least as small as that of the observed molecular gas (*cf.* Section 17.3.1, p.415).

However, even assuming that the perturbers — whatever they are — are sufficiently numerous to affect the Oort cloud at every galactic plane crossing, one still has to show that they can impose a significant 30 Myr signal in the otherwise random rate of arrival of new comets. This is the 'signal-to-noise' problem, originally highlighted by Thaddeus & Chanan (1985) and Thaddeus (1986), and its resolution depends on the relative amplitude of the solar motion compared to the scale height of the assumed perturbers of the Oort cloud. In particular, the current amplitude of the sun's motion normal to the galactic plane is less than two scale heights of the molecular cloud layer, implying that any periodic signal in the arrival rate of new comets, if assumed to be simply proportional to the rate of close encounters with molecular clouds, is probably too weak to be detected against the 'noise' introduced by encounters with the still randomly distributed 'background' stars and clouds.

On the other hand, the sun now lies close to the inner edge of the Orion spiral arm, and it appears that only a few million years ago it passed through the extended region of molecular clouds and newly formed stars which makes up part of the local system close to the sun known as Gould's Belt (see Figure 15.2, p.343). This is an expanding, rotating ring of nebulae and young stars which may be the remains of a highly evolved, disintegrating giant molecular cloud. It seemed possible, therefore, that the solar motion might have been disturbed quite recently (*e.g.* Clube & Napier 1986b, Bailey *et al.* 1986), allowing one to assume that the mean out-of-plane solar velocity during the Phanerozoic (the last approximately 600 Myr) was closer to that expected for stars of the sun's age than indicated by its present rather low value of $8\,\mathrm{km\,s^{-1}}$. In principle, this suggestion might overcome the problem of the signal-to-noise ratio; while if the perturbers were also allowed to be hypothetical dark matter with a sufficient mean mass density (*cf.* Stothers 1984), then the same suggestion might also resolve the 'signal' problem too.

Nevertheless, before this proposal can be considered as valid one still has to show that a greater amplitude of the solar motion during the past 250 Myr is indeed a reasonable proposition. Moreover, one should also check that the revised solar orbit would indeed reproduce the required 30 Myr interval between galactic plane crossings. Later work, in fact, has cast doubt on both these aspects: first, because no readily identified perturbers now in the solar neighbourhood actually have sufficient mass to disturb the solar velocity by the required amount ($\gtrsim 5\,\mathrm{km\,s^{-1}}$); and secondly, because increasing the amplitude of the solar motion inevitably leads to an orbit with a *longer* period about the galactic plane (Wolfendale & Wilkinson 1989). If the sun soars high enough to overcome the signal-to-noise problem identified by Thaddeus & Chanan (assuming the perturbers are distributed in the same way as the observed molecular clouds), then it becomes difficult to arrange also for the mean interval between successive galactic plane crossings to be as short as 30 million years or less, as required by the terrestrial record.

These difficulties with the comet shower model of the 30 Myr periodicity in the terrestrial record, even if rather loosely interpreted as referring only to the average interval between the arrival of random comet showers, and allowed to be caused by bodies other than identified stars and molecular clouds (*i.e.* hypothetical dark matter), have been discussed in detail by Bailey *et al.* (1987) and Wolfendale & Wilkinson (1989). These authors also point out, for example, that even if the long-period comet flux is found to vary in a cyclic manner, the majority of terrestrial craters might still come from earth-crossing asteroids originating through the break-up of short-period comets or in the asteroid belt, thereby further diluting any predicted 'signal'. It is concluded, therefore, that there is no plausible justification of the 30 Myr cyclicity on the basis of terrestrial effects arising from exceptionally strong individual perturbations of the Oort cloud, whether by single molecular clouds, stars or dark matter.

17.2.3   GALACTIC TIDE

An alternative proposal to explain the apparently periodic variations in the terrestrial record, this time based on the effects of the galactic tide on the Oort cloud (*e.g.* Scalo & Smoluchowski 1984), has been studied in some detail by Clube & Napier (1989a). On this theory, the forces acting on the Oort cloud are assumed to be both stochastic and regular; the former arising from encounters with discrete local masses such as stars and molecular clouds; the latter from the cumulative action of similar but more distant perturbers through their organization into larger structures such as spiral arms and the galactic disc. On the largest scale, the most important perturber is the vertical galactic tide, which is usually expressed (according to the plane parallel assumption; *cf.* Section 12.3, p.259; and Appendix B, equations B.11 and B.14) in the approximate form

$$F_{\text{tide},z} = -4\pi G \rho(Z_0) z \qquad (17.1)$$

In this expression, z is the instantaneous difference between the heights of the comet and the sun above the galactic plane (this is simply the z-component of the comet's heliocentric distance $\mathbf{r}(t)$), while $\rho(Z_0)$ denotes the local density of galactic matter at the height $Z_0(t)$ of the sun above the galactic plane, the latter varying cyclically in an approximately simple harmonic way according to equation (12.15) of Chapter 12 (see p.266).

The varying position of the sun in the Galaxy thus yields, mainly through changes in the orbital angular momenta of long-period comets, a temporal flux of nearly parabolic comets into the inner solar system which, to first order at least, is proportional to $\rho(Z_0)$ (e.g. Clube & Napier 1989a). It follows, therefore, that the vertical galactic tide will impose a regular approximately 30 Myr periodicity on the cometary influx, whose amplitude is roughly proportional to $(1 - \rho(Z_{max})/\rho(0))$ and thus possibly detectable, depending on the amplitude of the sun's excursions normal to the plane and the relative importance of random perturbations by passing stars and interstellar clouds.

In addition to the tide from the galactic disc, however, there is also that exerted by spiral arms. In ordinary density wave theory, spiral arms are assumed to have a typical stellar density enhancement of order 5–10% above that of the surrounding galactic disc; and under these circumstances the assumption of a plane parallel approximation to the galactic potential may generally be valid. However, much larger density enhancements may occur in real galaxies. For example, a recent study of 34 non-barred spiral galaxies (Elmegreen & Elmegreen 1984) has shown the presence of visible contrasts frequently in excess of around 60%, which may even extend to include not only a population of red stars (Zwicky 1955) but also invisible substellar objects as well. The latest observations indicate that our Galaxy may well contain a substantial young population of very low-mass objects (Hawkins & Bessel 1988), and it is therefore possible that both visible and dark matter contained within spiral arms significantly distort the disc's gravitational field close to the galactic plane $Z = 0$. Taking account also of the strong gas density enhancements in spiral arms, overall arm-to-interarm density contrasts of order 5:1 are probably to be found in our Galaxy and others (Elmegreen 1987). In that situation, the tidal force in the neighbourhood of a spiral arm (as is the sun), may not be even remotely plane parallel.

The A stars (Woolley 1957, 1965) and the youngest F stars (e.g. Kuijken & Gilmore 1989a,b; cf. Hill et al. 1979) in the solar neighbourhood have often been used to trace the local disc gravitational potential. These stars, lying at relatively low levels in the disc, do indeed indicate the presence of such a distortion in the gravitational field, the vertical acceleration taking on its usual axisymmetric plane-parallel character in the region about the sun, for example, only at heights above the plane of order $Z \gtrsim 150$ pc. In general, of course, at such heights the plane-parallel approximation itself becomes suspect, as significant radial variations in the galactic potential then become increasingly important (*cf.* equation B.6, p.497). However, it is possible that the axisymmetrical approximation may begin to break down quite close to the galactic plane, and it has been suggested (Woolley 1957) that the gravitational field in the solar neighbourhood is in fact largely determined by the effects of a single spiral arm, albeit one with an appreciable overdensity (*i.e.* $\rho \simeq 0.2 \, M_{\odot} \, \mathrm{pc}^{-3}$).

In order to model the effects of what must therefore be assumed to be massive spiral arms, Clube & Napier (1989a) have approximated the gravitational field of such an arm by an infinitely long homogeneous elliptic cylinder, with an average density contrast upward of unity and cross-sectional semi-major axes of order 100 pc in the galactic plane and 60 pc normal to the plane. Such strings of gravitating matter act so as to counteract the normally compressive effects of the galactic tide whenever the sun happens to pass close to the vicinity of one of the spiral arm upper or lower faces; *i.e.* at those times when the sun's distance above or below the galactic plane is of order 60 pc or so.

In this way, as the sun moves in its orbit both in and out of these rather flat spiral arms four times during each complete 60 Myr cycle of the vertical solar oscillation about the galactic plane, the galactic tide is significantly diminished, leading to a temporarily reduced influx of long-period comets. Conversely, strong 30 Myr surges in the tide acting on the Oort cloud occur as the sun crosses the galactic plane, while it is also found that for arm-to-interarm density contrasts in the approximate range 2:1 to 4:1, which are quite modest by the standards observed in other galaxies, a weak secondary enhancement of the tide takes place when the sun is at its greatest vertical distance from the arm. In other words, this theory indicates that an approximately 15 Myr cycle may be imposed on the underlying cometary influx during spiral arm passages, with strong (in-plane) and weak (out-of-plane) signals interspersing (*cf.* Figure 17.2, p.421). Moreover, if the capture of a classical Oort cloud should be a frequent occurrence during spiral arm passages (*e.g.* Section 15.2.3, p.350), the new-comet flux through the inner planetary system may disappear altogether in the interarm region, leading to episodicity in the rate of comet arrivals also consistent with the 100–200 Myr variations seen in the terrestrial record.

17.3   Outstanding issues

17.3.1   DARK MATTER

There are currently two principal alternatives on which to explain possible fluctuations in the rate of cometary material entering the solar system and affecting the terrestrial record. On the one hand, it may be assumed that these variations are predominantly stochastic in nature and occur in the form of short-lived, but intense, comet showers (Section 17.2.2). On the other, it may be assumed that they are predominantly regular in nature and that the fluctuations take the form of an *episodically* variable cometary flux (Section 17.2.3). It seems, however, that difficulties arise with the molecular cloud (*i.e.* stochastic) scenario, in that there is too little observed material to impose a significant modulation on the cometary flux from the Oort cloud.

One possible outcome of these calculations, then, is that significant galactic periodicities cannot be produced by comets in the terrestrial record, at least in the context of those theories which assume the Oort cloud is randomly perturbed by individual massive bodies in the galactic disc, whether by stars, molecular clouds or hypothetical dark matter. There is a tendency therefore for some authors to be unimpressed by the evidence for cycles (*e.g.* Heisler & Tremaine 1989, Stothers 1989, and references therein) and to suppose that the dark matter in the galactic disc, the so-called 'missing mass', even if present, is unimportant (*e.g.* Bailey *et al.* 1987). It is possible, however, that dark matter or even visible matter in the galactic disc may be preferentially concentrated within spiral arms and molecular clouds, making the relative gravitational effect of such systems very much more significant. This suggestion has been explored by Clube & Napier (1989a), although the nature of the dark matter may then seem to have become rather specific. In particular, as the probable precursor of stars, it is likely to exist in largely substellar form in pre-stellar aggregates, and is not expected to remain confined for long either in molecular clouds or spiral arms.

The largest giant molecular clouds delineating spiral arms have masses of order 10^5–10^6 $M_\odot$, based on dynamical arguments. These assume that the virial theorem is valid (Sanders *et al.* 1984, Scoville *et al.* 1987, Solomon *et al.* 1987); that the clouds themselves should not be tidally disrupted by the Galaxy (Stark & Blitz 1978); and that the observed velocity dispersion of disc stars arises due to encounters with clouds (*e.g.* Wielen 1977, Icke 1982, Lacey 1984). Taken together, these arguments indicate a total dynamical mass for the giant molecular cloud system of order 2×10^9 $M_\odot$, with the clouds more or less confined to a thin disc of radius $\simeq 10\,\mathrm{kpc}$ and full width of order $150\,\mathrm{pc}$ normal to the plane. Hence the mean mass density in the galactic plane of material associated with molecular clouds is on the order of $\rho_{\mathrm{GMC}}(0) \simeq 0.04\,M_\odot\,\mathrm{pc}^{-3}$ (*cf.* Section 17.2.2, p.406).

On the other hand, alternative total mass estimates of the same molecular clouds, based on CO intensity measurements and determinations of γ-ray emissivity (*e.g.* Bhat *et al.* 1985, 1986) and on infrared modelling (Broadbent *et al.* 1988, 1989), are much smaller ($\simeq 6 \times 10^8$ $M_\odot$), giving values for $\rho_{\mathrm{H_2}}(0)$ on the order of $0.01\,M_\odot\,\mathrm{pc}^{-3}$, even as low as $0.007\,M_\odot\,\mathrm{pc}^{-3}$ in the solar neighbourhood (*e.g.* Dame *et al.* 1987). Observations thus indicate a ratio of dynamically determined mass within molecular clouds to the apparent mass of molecular hydrogen on the order of 3 or less; and since the current mass density limit (*e.g.* Bahcall 1984) based on observed stellar motions in the galactic disc implies a smoothed-out dark-matter density in the solar neighbourhood of around $0.1\,M_\odot\,\mathrm{pc}^{-3}$, unevolved dark matter with a significantly higher mass density (consistent with observations of the youngest stars nearby; Section 17.2.3) may be present in spiral arms where the largest giant molecular clouds reside, and may not be present to any significant degree elsewhere in the disc.

The dynamical and photometric evidence based on molecular clouds alone is consistent, therefore, with the suggestion that spiral arms contain a significant mass of very small bodies (*i.e.* pre-stellar aggregates, or substellar condensates such as brown or black dwarfs, 'Jupiters', and 'giant' comets) from which the Oort cloud may be captured during spiral arm crossings. This dark matter is likely to be additional to that implied by the heavy element depletions in dense clouds (Tarafdar *et al.* 1983), and it must therefore be assumed to exist amongst the various higher temperature components of the galactic disc which are now known to be present (*e.g.* Savage 1987, Kulkarni & Heiles 1987). Moreover, the assumption that dark matter is concentrated in spiral arms is consistent, at least, with a hot origin for molecular clouds (see Section 16.3.1, p.379).

17.3.2   15 MYR CYCLE

As we have seen, one of the principal objections raised against a galactic modulation of the terrestrial impact rate is that the scale height of the molecular cloud system is too great for a 30 Myr cycle to become evident. This statement has been disputed (Stothers 1985), but the question at issue in any case refers only to the stochastic component of the galactic potential field, that is to encounters with individual nebulae. However, following the discovery of the importance of galactic tides, it appears now that a strongly driven 15 Myr cycle, probably resolved as a 30 Myr cycle in a very incomplete geological record, is anticipated from the systemic large-scale structure of the galactic spiral arms and disc. These cycles will persist for as long as the solar system is in the neighbourhood of a spiral arm; *i.e.* it should persist for about 100 million years during spiral arm crossings and may well disappear altogether in the interarm regions for periods of similar duration. The fluctuations are also expected to show a characteristic 'strong-weak-strong-weak' signature over the full 60 Myr period of the sun's vertical oscillation about the galactic plane. The existence or otherwise of a pattern of this complexity in the terrestrial record, although very hard to settle, evidently constitutes an important test of the idea that terrestrial evolution is dominated by cometary processes that are themselves modulated by an underlying galactic mechanism.

Overall, the inferred relationship between comets, the earth and the Galaxy implies that the incidence of giant comets (arriving at random times with a mean interval of order 0.1–1 Myr) should be modulated by the processes which periodically disturb and episodically replenish the Oort cloud, and that galactic periodicities should probably appear in the terrestrial record primarily through the effect of giant comets on climate. For example, it has been known for more than sixty years that an approximately 30 Myr cycle seems to affect a variety of terrestrial indicators (Holmes 1927; *cf.* Table 17.2, p.405), while similar variability in the incidence of impact cratering has also been claimed more recently by Seyfert & Sirkin (1979) and others (Alvarez & Muller 1984, Rampino & Stothers 1984b, Shoemaker & Wolfe 1984b), consistent with apparent clusterings in the ages of meteorites (Perlmutter & Muller 1988). If this evidence for correlated cycles of activity is substantiated (*cf.* Grieve 1989), it would presumably imply exogenous forcing.

Whether these periodicities imply a significant difference from the roughly 26 Myr cycle in the fossil record (*e.g.* Raup & Sepkoski 1984, 1986) is not at present clear. If real, the peaks in the cratering record and the times of global mass extinctions would be expected generally to be in phase, but it has been persuasively argued by Stigler & Wagner (1987) that the 26 Myr cycle may be an artefact of the particular data used. Moreover, because of the inevitable stochastic component in the arrival rate of large bodies (including meteorites), a strong periodicity in impact cratering is probably not to be expected (cf. Bailey & Stagg 1988).

It may be, therefore, that the most accurate periodicities will ultimately be traced to geophysical and biological phenomena more sensitive to the dust input from giant comets (e.g. climate, sea-level, mass extinctions, speciation etc.), where the random component on timescales greater than a few million years may be relatively small. On the other hand, hiatuses do exist in the terrestrial record, and although glacio-eustasy and tectonic-eustasy, for example, may reflect the incidence of climatic variations due to meteoroidal débris (Clube & Napier 1984b) and may generally be well correlated with other events such as extinctions in the biosphere (e.g. Hallam 1984b), the suggested 15 Myr cycle may still be below the current level of resolution in most terrestrial data (cf. Shackleton 1989). Nevertheless, the record of recent reversals of the earth's magnetic field is relatively complete, and may reflect disturbances of the core-mantle boundary consequent upon both climatic and impact trauma (Clube & Napier 1982b, 1989a; cf. Pal & Creer 1986, Creer & Pal 1989). An intermittent 15 Myr cycle in geomagnetic reversal frequency should therefore not only be detectable, but could also become a crucial test of the proposed galacto-terrestrial relationship.

17.3.3   MAGNETIC RECORD

The nature of the geomagnetic reversal frequency during the last 150 Myr is shown in Figure 17.2. Significant periodicities of 30 and 32–34 Myr (Raup 1985a, Negi & Tiwari 1983) and 15 Myr (Lowrie & Kent 1983, Mazaud et al. 1983) have been claimed, though the status of the longer cycle is somewhat less clear and it was subsequently withdrawn (Raup 1985b). It has also been argued that the 15 Myr cycle is due to the 30 Myr cycle being fortuitously enhanced by noise (*cf.* McFadden 1984, Stothers 1986), or that the 30 Myr cycle itself may be an artefact of the data arising from finite record lengths and non-stationarity of the record (Lutz 1985, Lutz & Watson 1988).

On the other hand, the 15 Myr cycle is regarded by Mazaud *et al.* as both *the* fundamental and most prominent terrestrial cycle ever found (see also Creer & Pal 1989), whilst a recent reassessment of the 15 Myr period confidence level suggests that, along with the 100 Myr episodicity, it is clearly present (Clube & Napier 1989a), in good agreement with the galactic theory. Remembering also that magnetic reversals have been associated with three of the five tektite age groups (Glass & Heezen 1967, Durrani & Kahn 1971) and that a relationship between reversals and climatic events seems to be well established at least for the upper Pleistocene (Doake 1978; *cf.* Burek & Wänke 1988), and furthermore that no acceptable alternative explanation for the cycle has yet been given (Creer & Pal 1989), there is *prima facie* evidence, at least, in the hypothesis that field reversals are forced or modulated by a galactic process (Clube & Napier 1982b, *cf.* Muller & Morris 1986).

In summary, we should emphasize that whilst there are now strong indications of a physical connexion between processes in the Galaxy and evolution on the earth, with giant comets and the terrestrial climate appearing as the principal intermediaries, the conjectured rôle of dark matter in the Galaxy requires further study. Moreover, the length of the geomagnetic record that is reasonably complete is still very short, less than 165 Myr and probably less than 90 Myr. There is perhaps no immediate prospect of rapidly improving the observational situation in these respects, and this unfortunately means that rather extreme attitudes are likely to be taken over the critical issue of cyclicity. Under these circumstances, it does not seem likely that cyclicity alone will settle the issue, and one must then turn to such evidence as may be available in the historical record (Chapters 2–4), or in the long-term cratering records on both

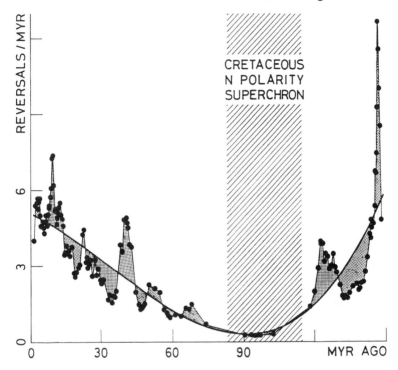

Figure 17.2: Geomagnetic reversal frequency during the past 150 Myr, from Creer & Pal (1989). Superimposed on the long-term trend are fluctuations which, it has been claimed, have a 15 Myr periodicity.

the earth-moon system and on other bodies in the solar system.

17.3.4 Cratering record

As we have seen, Figure 16.2 (see p.374) indicates a roughly constant average cratering flux in the inner solar system for the last 3800 Myr (Baldwin 1985), and hence — if comets contribute significantly to the cratering projectiles — a similarly constant, time-averaged Oort cloud. However, the perturbation lifetime of the standard 'outer' Oort cloud is on the order of 10^9 years, depending on semi-major axis (*cf.* Section 12.2.2, p.256), substantially less than the age of the solar system and consistent, for example, with the absence of wide binary systems of solar age in the galactic disc (*cf.* Saarinen & Gilmore 1989, Abt 1986, 1988). This overall constancy in the cratering record has to be understood, therefore, either in terms of intermittent replenishment from an inner core or by episodic capture from other star-forming regions.

In the former case, it is assumed that any departures from a constant cratering flux may generally be understood in terms of occasional intense comet showers from the inner core of the Oort cloud (*e.g.* Hills 1981, Shoemaker & Wolfe 1984b, Weissman 1985c, Bailey *et al.* 1987, Fernández & Ip 1987, Heisler *et al.* 1987, Hut *et al.* 1987). This line of argument may lead to difficulties, however, in reconciling the precise degree of concentration of the inner core with the initial mass necessary in order to sustain the outer Oort cloud for the age of the solar system. On the other hand, if comets are captured from interstellar space, whilst not denying the possibility of comet showers, the same departures from a strictly constant cratering rate may also be regarded as intrinsically episodic in nature, and therefore as indirect evidence supporting the cometary capture hypothesis described above (*cf.* Clube & Napier 1989a).

We should not overlook the possibility, of course, even though the process is not thought to be efficient, that the majority of crater-producing projectiles come instead from the asteroid belt, and that it is the number of these bodies in the asteroid belt which is being steadily replenished. This could occur, for example, either as a result of the injection of inert earth-crossing asteroids (originally short-period comets) into the main belt by non-gravitational forces, or through a time-reversed analogue of the route by which such bodies are normally assumed to arrive at the earth; or even by continuing collisional evolution of the largest bodies in the main belt, producing a gradually increasing population of smaller crater-producing asteroids which may then evolve so as to strike the earth.

The questions raised by all these studies, including those of interactions between the earth and short-period comets, between comets and asteroids, and between cometary débris on all scales and terrestrial climate and evolution, together with connecting links to human history and biological evolution, therefore have important implications for understanding the origin of comets. We close this chapter, as we began, by emphasizing once again the importance of clarifying the precise nature of the terrestrial cratering and fossil records, the origin and evolution of short-period comets, and the evolutionary history of the small bodies in the solar system. Clearly, there is much to be learned: the scientific study of the lunar surface is not yet at an end, while similarly detailed studies of the other terrestrial planets and the satellites of the outer planets, which may themselves yield crucial information, are still in their infancy.

18

New vistas

"Observation, not old age, brings wisdom."

Publilius Syrus.

18.1   Comet nucleus

18.1.1   SIZE AND SHAPE

It might be hoped that the physical structure of comets, or their chemistry, would provide evidence of their ultimate origin, or at least of the state of the medium out of which they were formed. In this respect the interception of Halley's comet in March 1986 by a small armada of spacecraft (Giotto from Europe, Vega 1 and Vega 2 from the Soviet Union, Suisei and Sakigake from Japan, and the International Cometary Explorer from the United States) marked another watershed in the study of the problem. Nevertheless in dividing the subject into pre-Halley and post-Halley eras the considerable achievements of comet observers in the years up to 1986 should be recognized. For example, ground-based observations using new infrared and other techniques had already given valuable new insights into the nature of cometary nuclei even before Halley's encounter with the space probes. In this way, although observations of Halley's comet during its recent apparition provided a number of surprises, they also confirmed observational trends which were already under way.

Early attempts to determine the sizes of comet nuclei (*e.g.* Vorontsov-Velyaminov 1946) were generally based on methods which combined the measured visual magnitude of a nucleus with estimates of the reflectivity, or albedo, of its surface. In particular, the apparent magnitude of a cometary nucleus of radius R_c at a heliocentric distance r, geocentric distance Δ, and phase angle α (defined to be the angle sun-comet-earth)

425

may be written in the form

$$m = m_\odot - 2.5 \log\left[\frac{r_\oplus^2}{r^2} \frac{R_c^2}{\Delta^2} p\, \Phi_p(\alpha)\right] \qquad (18.1)$$

where $m_\odot$ is the apparent magnitude of the sun ($m_\odot = -26.71$ for the visual waveband; Labs & Neckel 1968), $r_\oplus = 1\,\mathrm{AU}$, p is the geometric albedo, and $\Phi_p(\alpha)$ is the phase variation, which describes how the comet's brightness changes for different values of α. The phase variation is normalized to unity at $\alpha = 0$, *i.e.* when the sun, earth and comet are in a straight line. In this way, given the observed values of m, r, Δ and α, equation (18.1) can be solved to yield the product pR_c^2, and hence the nuclear radius R_c, once the albedo is known.

In discussions of the reflected radiation from an asteroid or cometary nucleus, it is important to distinguish two types of albedo: the geometric albedo, p, and the so-called 'Bond' albedo, A, first introduced by Bond (1861). The geometric albedo of a comet is defined as the ratio of the observed flux at zero phase angle to that of an ideal Lambert disc orientated perpendicular to the sun's rays and subtending the same angular diameter as the comet. The Bond albedo, on the other hand, is a measure of the *total* reflectivity of the surface, and equals the fraction of the total incident light which is reflected in all directions by the body. That is, a body with Bond albedo A absorbs a fraction $1 - A$ of the total light incident upon it.

These two measures of the albedo of a body are connected to one another and to the detailed surface structure by the relation $A = p\,q$, where q denotes the phase integral

$$q = 2\int_0^\pi \Phi_p(\alpha)\sin\alpha\,d\alpha \qquad (18.2)$$

originally defined by Russell (1916). For example, an idealized Lambert sphere has $q = 1.5$, while a body with surface properties similar to that of the moon has $q \simeq 0.6$ (*e.g.* Kopal 1969).

Using this approach, based on equation (18.1) and assuming values for the geometric albedos of cometary nuclei, Roemer (1966) deduced average diameters for nineteen short-period comets which had been observed from Flagstaff, Arizona. For example, adopting a visual geometric albedo of $p = 0.7$, roughly corresponding to that of the clouds of Venus or freshly fallen snow, she found a mean radius of about 1 km, while ten long-period comets for the same assumption yielded a slightly larger mean radius of 3 km.

One problem with such estimates is that even at large distances much of the light apparently scattered from the nucleus may come from a somewhat larger halo of dust grains, or from dust jets emitted by the nucleus, with the result that the measured brightness will not in general refer to the bare nucleus. Although cometary activity usually declines rapidly beyond distances of a few AU from the sun, there are many instances of observed activity much further out. For example, as we have already seen (see Section 10.2.2, p.218), activity was detected in the case of Comet Bowell out to about 13.6 AU from the sun, while object Chiron was seen to approximately double in brightness early in 1988 while still at the relatively large distance of around 12 AU (Tholen 1988). Further evidence that Chiron is almost certainly cometary, and now shows a detectable coma, was recently reported by Meech & Belton (1989). Moreover, Comet Schwassmann-Wachmann 1, with a perihelion distance of 5.5 AU, undergoes sporadic increases in brightness by typically 5–8 magnitudes, corresponding to factors of order 10^2–10^3. Even Halley's comet was seen to emit gas and dust on its most recent approach when it was more than 6 AU from the sun (Wyckoff *et al.* 1985), while intermittent activity had already begun when it was first detected in October 1982, while still at a distance of order 11 AU (Festou *et al.* 1986).

Radar signals can also be used to obtain a radius for the nucleus, but only if the radio reflectivity of the surface and its rotational characteristics are both known; the latter affects the strength of the reflected signal through the rotational Doppler effect (see review by Ostro 1987). Kamoun *et al.* (1982) deduced that Encke's comet has a nuclear radius in the approximate range 1–4 km, while that of the long-period comet Iras-Araki-

Alcock (possibly the first comet to have its nucleus visually resolved; Larson & Johnson 1983) was found by Goldstein *et al.* (1984) to be around 3 km. Much of the radar return from this comet, however, appeared to come from a cloud of metre-sized boulders around the nucleus.

Any sunlight incident on a distant nucleus which is neither reflected nor scattered must be absorbed, being ultimately reradiated as heat in the infrared. Observations have been made in recent years to determine the proportion of radiation emitted in the waveband $\simeq$ 10–20 microns from a comet nucleus. Coupled with the visual brightness this too yields the albedo and dimensions of the comet nucleus, assuming that the optical radiation reflected by the nucleus can be separated from that scattered by a halo or jets of dust (*cf.* Morrison & Lebofsky 1979). In this way Cruikshank & Brown (1983) found Comet Schwassmann-Wachmann 1 to have a diameter of about 40 km and an albedo of around 0.13. Two periodic comets of nearly asteroidal appearance, Neujmin 1 and Arend-Rigaux, have likewise been found to have very low albedos (around 0.03), and diameters around 20 km and 10 km respectively (A'Hearn 1986, Campins *et al.* 1987, Millis *et al.* 1988).

Such values for the albedo are remarkably small: they imply that these periodic comets are amongst the darkest bodies in the solar system; black paper, for example, has a reflection coefficient typically around 0.05–0.06. A similarly low albedo was also found to apply to Halley's comet, though 'red', rather than 'black', probably provides a more accurate description of the colour of its nucleus (*e.g.* Tholen *et al.* 1986, Thomas & Keller 1989). Detailed analysis of the Vega and Giotto images revealed a body of dimensions approximately 16 × 8 × 7.5 km, with a geometric albedo of a few percent (see discussions, for example, by A'Hearn 1988, Mendis 1988, Keller & Thomas 1989).

Infrared radiation from this comet was measured by a spectrometer on board Vega 1; the surface was surprisingly warm (*e.g.* Combes *et al.* 1986, Emerich *et al.* 1986): ranging from around 300 K up to more than 400 K, rather than the approxi-

mately 200 K expected were sublimation of water ice the dominant factor. This implies not only that the surface of the nucleus
is very dark, absorbing a large fraction of the incident solar radiation, but also that it is porous and insulating, thermally decoupled from the sublimating ices below. This insulating 'blanket'
may be centimetres or many metres thick. Its existence is consistent with a dust-choking model for the nucleus (e.g. Shul'man
1972, Mendis & Brin 1977, Brin & Mendis 1979) in which dust
particles ejected by the sublimating ices settle back on to the
nucleus, eventually choking off the cometary activity. Alternatively, it may arise because a 'friable sponge' model (Horanyi
et al. 1984) is more appropriate, in which case ices sublimate
from the base of a porous matrix, and gases escape through the
overlying pores.

Periodic variations in the light curves of comets may in principle be used to obtain their rotation periods and shapes. However, in practice, the procedure is not straightforward nor does it
readily discriminate between different models. From such data,
however, it appears that the nuclei of many comets are roughly
prolate in shape (A'Hearn 1988). This shape, rather like a rugby
ball or American football, was seen to apply directly in the
case of Halley's comet, though in this case the more often used
'potato-shape' image probably provides a better description of
the generally asymmetric appearance of the nucleus. The most
unusual shape found for a nucleus is that of the periodic comet
Giacobini-Zinner, which according to Sekanina (1985) is virtually disk-shaped, with a diameter of about 2.5 km and thickness
$\simeq 0.3$ km. With a rotation period estimated at about 1.66 hours,
it must be on the verge of rotational disintegration, suggesting
(Sekanina 1985) that the comet may be the spun-up fragment
of a once much larger object.

If this extraordinary variety of shapes — flywheels, 'pota-
toes' and boulder clouds — is primordial in origin, then it must
be explained by any truly comprehensive theory of the origin of
comets. It should be remembered, however, that none of these
comets are pristine; most will have lost many metres, if not

kilometres, of their original surfaces, and the presently observed shapes may simply be the result of splitting and irregular out-gassing from the nucleus. The probes to Halley's comet revealed that the ejected gas and dust mostly came from a relatively small number of 'active' regions, each having a total area of a few square kilometres and apparently lying along ridges or fissures which seem to have persisted at least since the 1910 apparition (*e.g.* Sekanina & Larson 1986a). One of these active areas had a diameter of about 5 km, comparable in size to the dimensions of the whole nucleus and giving information, perhaps, on the size of the basic building blocks making up the body (Möhlman *et al.* 1987).

The rotation periods have also been obtained for a few com-ets, and are found mostly to lie in the range of several hours to a few days (*e.g.* Whipple 1982, Wallis 1984, Jewitt & Meech 1988). However, it is likely that the effects of jets is to force considerable changes in the rotational properties of the nucleus, even during just one or only a few apparitions (Samarasinha *et al.* 1986), though the effects of these non-gravitational forces are generally found to decline with increasing time spent in the inner solar system (Rickman *et al.* 1987). Nevertheless, those acting on Halley's comet seem to have remained remarkably con-stant both in intensity and direction for many hundreds of years (Yeomans & Kiang 1981, Yeomans 1986).

In the case of Halley's comet, for example, a retrograde ro-tation with a period of 2.2 days has been inferred both from ob-servations in space and from the ground (*e.g.* Sekanina & Larson 1986b; Sekanina 1986). On the other hand Millis & Schleicher (1986) found a periodicity of 7.4 days in the observed outgassing from the comet, a signal which is also seen in older photometric data (Festou *et al.* 1987) and in the morphology of the CN jets (Hoban *et al.* 1988). This has been interpreted as evidence either for a basic 2.2 day rotational period around an axis orthogonal to its long axis, together with a longer period superimposed pre-cessional or 'nodding' motion (*e.g.* Smith *et al.* 1987, Wilhelm 1987, Sagdeev *et al.* 1989), or for a basic 14.6 day rotational

Comet	Diameter (km)	Geometric albedo	Rotational period (h)	Source
P/Encke	1–10	0.04	15.1/22.4	(1)
IRAS-Araki-Alcock 1983 VII	16 × 7 × 7	0.03	51.4	(2)
P/Schwassmann-Wachmann 1	40	0.13	120.0	(3)
P/Neujmin 1	20	0.03	12.6/25.2	(4)
P/Arend-Rigaux	13 × 8 × 8	0.03	13.5	(5)
P/Halley	16 × 8 × 7.5	0.03	52.1	(6)
P/Giacobini-Zinner	2.5 × 2.5 × 0.3		1.66	(7)
P/Tempel 2	15.8 × 8.2 × 8.2	0.02	8.95	(8)
Bennett 1970 II	7.5	0.66	33–36	(9)
P/d'Arrest	6.6	0.02	5.2	(10)
Wirtanen 1957 VI	60–100	0.02		(11)
Chiron	180–300	0.04–0.1	5.92	(12)

Table 18.1: Physical properties of some representative cometary nuclei. The source code is as follows: (1) Kamoun et al. (1982), Jewitt & Meech (1987), Luu & Jewitt (1989); (2) Sekanina (1988); (3) Cruikshank & Brown (1983), Whipple (1982); (4) Campins et al. (1987); (5) Millis et al. (1988); (6) See text; (7) Sekanina (1985); (8) Jewitt & Luu (1989); (9) Larson & Minton (1972), Delsemme & Rud (1973); (10) Roemer (1966), Fay & Wisniewski (1978); (11) Roemer (1966), Mendis et al. (1985); (12) Lebofsky et al. (1984), Hartmann et al. (1987), Bus et al. (1989).

period with a superimposed 2.1 day precession (Festou et al. 1987). A detailed review of some of these apparently contradictory results on the rotation of Halley's comet has been given by Sekanina (1987), while the picture has recently been further complicated by the suggestion (Belton 1989) that the discrepancies might be reconciled by postulating a complex motion of the nucleus involving a 3.7 day rotation period about one axis combined with a 2.5 day 'spin' about another. However, despite the importance of understanding the individual rotational properties of particular comets (in order properly to interpret other observations, for example), because of the net accelerating effects of the gas and dust jets which escape from the nuclei of active comets, acting something like rocket exhausts, it does not seem that much information about cometary origin can be easily extracted from these data (*e.g.* Burns 1989). The known physical properties of some representative cometary nuclei are summarized in Table 18.1.

18.1.2   REVISED MASSES

The remarkably low albedo of the surface of Halley's comet confirmed a trend which was already under way both from earlier infrared observations and theoretical expectations (*e.g.* Fraundorf *et al.* 1982, Cruikshank *et al.* 1985, Fernández 1985b, Hughes 1985, Tokunaga & Hanner 1985, Greenberg 1986a). The low mean reflectivities of cometary nuclei do, however, have important implications for their cosmogony, in that the dimensions and masses of comets, and so the mass of the Oort cloud, may have to be substantially revised (*e.g.* Weissman 1985c, 1986b; Mendis & Marconi 1986, Marochnik & Mukhin 1987, 1988; Marochnik *et al.* 1988).

Before the Vega and Giotto missions, the mass of the outer, 'dynamically active' Oort cloud had been estimated by Weissman (1983b) from the brightness distribution of comets newly arrived from the cloud together with an assumed albedo $A = 0.6$. This value came originally from determinations of cometary albedos made by Delsemme & Rud (1973), the first authors to attempt to separate the twin effects of albedo and cross-sectional area on the apparent brightness of a cometary nucleus, adopting a 'pristine snow' concept for nuclei. A figure of $1.9\,M_\oplus$ was then obtained, though later estimates, assuming a revised numerical scaling factor based upon more recent Monte Carlo studies and a slightly lower albedo of 0.3 (Weissman 1985c, *cf.* Weissman & Keiffer 1981), gave a total mass for the outer Oort cloud on the order of 7–8 $M_\oplus$. This was subsequently increased to around 25 $M_\oplus$ in later models incorporating a much lower 'observed' albedo for Halley's comet, and a variety of other effects (Weissman 1986b).

The general trend of these results can be explained as coming primarily from the assumption of a much lower mean albedo for cometary nuclei. For example, since the estimated diameter of a distant comet varies roughly as $A^{-1/2}$, and the mass therefore as $A^{-3/2}$, then if the albedos of the comets Neujmin 1, Arend-Rigaux and Halley are indeed typical, one might imagine simply multiplying all former estimates of the mass of the Oort cloud ($\approx 1 M_\oplus$; *e.g.* Safronov 1972, Weissman 1983b) by factors of order $(0.6/0.03)^{3/2} \simeq 90$, giving a total mass for the outer Oort cloud of more than 100 $M_\oplus$! Indeed, this is essentially what has been done by a number of authors (*e.g.* Mendis & Marconi 1986, Marochnik *et al.* 1988).

However, a much lower determination of the total mass of the outer Oort cloud population (comprising comets with semi-major axes greater than 2×10^4 AU) has also recently been given by Bailey & Stagg (1988), using an average mass-magnitude relationship based on the independent determinations of a number of other authors, including those founded on recent observations of Halley's comet. The adopted mean relationship, *i.e.* $\log(m^*) = 16.9 - 0.5H$, where m^* is the comet's mass in units of 1 kg and H is the 'absolute' magnitude of the comet plus coma (*i.e.* a measure of its brightness normalized to a heliocentric and geocentric distance both equal to 1 AU), together with the observed brightness distribution of cometary magnitudes (*e.g.* Everhart 1967, Donnison 1986, Hughes 1987a,b), leads to a value of order 4.3 $M_\oplus$ for the mass of the outer cloud, only about twice that formerly generally accepted. Moreover, extrapolating this result to include what the authors consider to be a reasonably realistic model of the hypothetical dense inner core, the total mass of the Oort cloud is found to be around 14 $M_\oplus$ overall, quite compatible with the predictions of the planetesimal hypothesis.

This result may be compared with Weissman's (1986b) estimate of 250 $M_\oplus$ and with those of Mendis & Marconi (1986) and Marochnik *et al.* (1988), which range up to $10^4\,M_\oplus$. Accepting such high estimates for the total mass of the Oort cloud, however, even a value as low as 25 $M_\oplus$ for the outer Oort cloud, places the standard planetesimal hypothesis in severe difficulty. For example, if the Oort cloud does indeed have a current mass of order 100 $M_\oplus$, its original mass (assuming evolutionary losses by a factor only of order two; *cf.* Section 12.2.2, p.256, and Appendix A.1) would have been about 200 $M_\oplus$. The calculation presented on page 243 then yields $f \simeq 20$, and an original total planetesimal mass of order 2000 $M_\oplus$!

Such a huge mass of comets in the protoplanetary disc is not consistent with the standard planetesimal picture of comet formation. The total mass of comets would then have far outweighed not only the total planetary mass, but even the solar mass itself when abundance considerations are included, requiring considerable changes to be made in the detailed physical picture. This argument does not, of course, show that the recently adopted 'high' estimates of the mass of the Oort cloud are necessarily incorrect, since other theories of comet formation in the solar nebula may be preferred (*e.g.* Marochnik & Mukhin 1988; *cf.* Chapter 13), but the difficulty does suggest that the arguments leading to such values for the total mass of the Oort cloud should be carefully scrutinized. In a similar way, it is possible that the arguments leading to the concept of a massive inner extension of the Oort cloud may also have to be reassessed (*cf.* Section 13.3, p.286; Bailey & Stagg 1989), even to the extent that a 'capture scenario' for the Oort cloud might then seem to be a more attractive alternative (*cf.* Section 15.2, p.344).

Despite the caution thus expressed by Bailey & Stagg (1988) against too ready acceptance of a very great mass for the Oort cloud (see also arguments by Napier 1987, Stothers 1988), the mostly low albedos that have been determined for a few cometary nuclei — if these are indeed typical — certainly do imply a general upward revision of the masses of individual comets. For example, before the Vega and Giotto encounters, the mass of Halley's comet was estimated by various authors to range from about 5×10^{12} kg (Hughes 1983) up to around 7×10^{13} kg (Belton 1985), the latter assuming a radius of about 2.5 km and a visual albedo close to 0.3. More recent estimates, as inferred from the non-gravitational acceleration of the nucleus produced by jet-reaction forces due to outgassing (*e.g.* Rickman 1986, Sagdeev *et al.* 1988), range between 5×10^{13} kg and 7×10^{14} kg, with a mean value of order 2×10^{14} kg, about three times larger than the previously accepted upper limit (although with similar uncertainty). The corresponding average density is thought to be somewhat less than 0.5 g cm^{-3}, with an uncertainty of about a factor of four, indicating the likelihood of an extremely porous structure.

The increase in the mass may also apply to the estimates of the masses of great comets of the past. For example, one of the largest comets to appear in recent centuries was the great comet of 1729, Comet Sarabat (Vsekhsvyatski 1964). Its orbit was parabolic (with inclination $i = 77°$ and perihelion distance 4.05 AU, *e.g.* Hind 1884), and it was discovered soon after perihelion with an apparent magnitude of about 4; it was subsequently observed for several months thereafter. The mass of this comet has been estimated to be in excess of 10^{18} kg (Whipple 1975), nearly four orders of magnitude larger than Halley's comet, and the nucleus has a corresponding diameter somewhat greater than 100 km (*cf.* Section 17.1.2, p.392). Similar adjustment of its mass might then mean that this comet was as large as 300 km across, essentially equivalent to Chiron, though this is very uncertain. If a comet such as this, or the probably equally massive parent of the sun-grazer family (Öpik 1966b), were thrown into an orbit like that of Comet Encke, as must certainly have happened throughout the earth's history, the climatic and other effects would be considerable. Adopting a generally increased mass and porosity for comets merely strengthens this conclusion.

The importance of these more massive members of the cometary flux can thus hardly be overestimated. Indeed, given the usually assumed mass distribution of comets (*e.g.* Hughes & Daniels 1980, Donnison 1986), the bulk of the mass of a random sample of say 100 comets would almost certainly reside in the few most massive bodies (*cf.* Section 17.1.2, p.392). This raises the important question of whether the relatively small, fragile and undifferentiated bodies that we generally call 'comets' are in fact representative of the bulk of material which lies in 'cometary' bodies as a whole. Indeed, it seems very likely, for example, that the intermittently active object Chiron (*e.g.* Kowal 1979, Hartmann *et al.* 1987) provides an illustration of one of these larger members of the cometary population; this body has a typically low albedo and a diameter estimated to range between about 180 and 300 km (Hartmann *et al.* 1987, Lebofsky *et al.* 1984). Although the derived masses of individual comets therefore remain extremely uncertain, it is nevertheless still worth emphasizing that so far no secure 'sublunar' upper limit to the size of comets has yet been firmly established!

18.2   Detailed chemistry

18.2.1   BULK COMPOSITION

The Giotto probe flew past Halley's comet at $68.4\,\mathrm{km\,s^{-1}}$; Vega 1 and Vega 2 at about $78\,\mathrm{km\,s^{-1}}$ (Reinhard 1986, Sagdeev *et al.* 1986). All these spacecraft carried time-of-flight mass spectrometers, and dust particles, striking metal targets within these instruments, were instantly vaporized allowing their masses and elemental compositions to be measured (*e.g.* Krueger & Kissel 1987, Kissel & Krueger 1987). Several thousand particles of dust were so studied, lying in the broad mass range 10^{-5}–$10^{-19}\,\mathrm{kg}$ (Green *et al.* 1987, McDonnell *et al.* 1986, 1987), the least of these corresponding in size to particles almost as small as individual interstellar grains.

A great variety of grain types, with various chemical compositions, was detected by the mass spectrometers. The average composition of these grains, with regard to the major rock-forming elements, was within a factor of order two of that for class C I carbonaceous chondrites (*e.g.* Jessberger *et al.* 1986, 1988). These are primitive meteorites of a kind believed to represent the most unprocessed protoplanetary material, the carbonaceous chondrites themselves representing only a minor fraction ($\simeq 4\%$) of all meteorites, whilst most meteorite falls are classified as 'ordinary chondrites'.

However, unlike meteoritic material generally, the cometary dust was found to be richer in volatiles, an appreciable fraction being composed of the light elements carbon, hydrogen, oxygen and nitrogen (*e.g.* Clark *et al.* 1986, Krueger & Kissel 1987). These so-called 'CHON' particles are enriched in carbon by about an order of magnitude compared to the most primitive, carbonaceous chondrites. Their existence implies that organic matter is relatively abundant within the nucleus of the comet, although there is no immediate implication that the detailed physical and chemical composition of the dust should therefore be linked to that of living 'biological' organisms (*cf.* Wickramasinghe *et al.* 1988, Kissel & Krueger 1987). There are also silicate grains, some apparently of crystalline form (Campins & Ryan 1989), composite grains, pure carbon grains and a number of other types.

Of the many ices detected in Halley's comet, water is by far the most abundant, comprising around 80% of the volatiles. Also present as ices were carbon monoxide (5–15%), carbon dioxide ($\simeq 3\%$), and a number of minor constituents, although ammonia and methane were not directly detected by the spacecraft experiments (Krankowsky *et al.* 1986, Balsiger *et al.* 1986; *cf.* Wegmann *et al.* 1987, Drapatz *et al.* 1987). For example, an upper limit to the methane abundance, estimated from these observations and from the CH_3^+ ion detected by Giotto (Allen *et al.* 1987) seems to be around 2%, in agreement with recently reported observations which suggest that methane may indeed have been detected at about the 1% level in both Comet Halley (Kawara *et al.* 1988) and Comet Wilson. Ground-based observations have now also indicated the presence of ammonia in Comet Halley, though only at the very low relative abundance of around 0.2% the total volatile fraction (Wyckoff *et al.* 1988). The proportions of these molecules are, of course, quite unlike those of the outer planets, their relatively low abundances suggestive of an origin of comets in some way far removed from that of the giant planets (*e.g.* Drake *et al.* 1987).

Combining these observations, the average composition of Halley's comet can thus be determined if the gas-to-dust ratio is known; this is usually taken to be on the order of 2, with an uncertainty which is usually estimated to be less than a factor of about 2, though we note that McDonnell *et al.* (1989) have recently presented evidence indicating that the gas-to-dust ratio might be as low as 0.5. From these considerations it turns out that the detailed bulk composition of Halley's comet is rather uncertain, although, apart from the expected deficiency of hydrogen and helium, it can nevertheless be generally described as broadly similar to that of the sun (Geiss 1987). In particular, the overall trend of the Comet Halley compositional data fits in well with the underlying relationship found for most other solar system bodies: namely, that the smaller the hydrogen content the greater is the relative deficiency of other volatiles, such as carbon, nitrogen and oxygen.

For example, the C I carbonaceous chondrites are found to be relatively deficient in carbon by about an order of magnitude compared to solar abundances, and in nitrogen by a factor of about 100. Halley's comet, however, reveals no such strong deficiency in carbon, and although nitrogen was still significantly underabundant, this was only by about one order of magnitude. This suggests that whatever the processing which affects primitive meteoritic material (*e.g.* differentiation, subsequent reheating *etc.*), it is somehow avoided by cometary material. Indeed, if meteorites and comets are assumed to be derived from chemically similar pools of material, it might be possible to understand these results by assuming that much of the processing which goes on in the formation of meteorites simply involves a substantial loss of the 'CHON' material more easily retained by comets.

The presence of a substantial fraction of simple organic molecules and compounds in cometary ices and dust (the latter appearing also to be a significant source of volatile molecules such as CO, H_2CO and CN, for example), suggests that the environment in which comets are formed must have been very conducive to the formation and survival of such organic material, analogous perhaps to the complex molecules often seen in the ices associated with interstellar grains or in the cold gas towards dark clouds (e.g. Encrenaz et al. 1987, 1988; cf. Allamandola & Sandford 1988a, Whittet 1988 and references therein). For example, Greenberg (e.g. 1982, 1984, 1986b,c; 1988) has long argued that these sorts of consideration imply that comet nuclei can be regarded as essentially pristine aggregates of ice-covered interstellar grains, brought together on the outskirts of the pre-solar nebula, or in its parent molecular cloud. On the other hand, one could equally argue that the most primitive condensations themselves initially possess near 'solar system' abundances, and that as a result of differentiation whilst cooling down from an initially hot state (cf. Section 16.3.1, p.379), such condensations release refractory-depleted molecular gas whilst forming bodies with meteoritic cores and 'CHON' enriched mantles. In general, however, because broadly 'solar system' abundances are characteristic of the interstellar medium as a whole, the bulk composition of Halley's comet is rather non-specific as to its precise origin, and a recent 'interstellar' source for comets may be no more nor less plausible than a 'solar system' source.

18.2.2 FORMATION ENVIRONMENT

Freezing of some of the detected molecules at low pressures requires temperatures typically within a few tens of degrees of

Molecule	T_{subl}	Molecule	T_{subl}
H_2O	152	CH_3C_2H	65
HCOOH	112	H_2CO	64
CH_3OH	99	C_2H_2	57
HCN	95	H_2S	57
CH_3CN	91	C_2H_4	42
SO_2	83	CH_4	31
NH_3	78	CO	25
CS_2	78	O_2	24
HC_3N	74	N_2	22
CO_2	72	H_2	5

Table 18.2: Sublimation temperatures of various ices, assuming a gas density $n = 10^{13}\,\mathrm{cm}^{-3}$. Taken from Yamamoto (1985a).

absolute zero. Table 18.2 illustrates this result by showing the critical 'sublimation' temperatures of various ices calculated by Yamamoto (1985a). This is the temperature above which the rate of mass loss of a particle by sublimation exceeds the rate of mass gain by accretion from the gas phase, assuming a nebular density of order $10^{13}\,\mathrm{cm}^{-3}$ and typical 'cosmic' abundances of the elements.

At densities and pressures characteristic of the outer regions of the protoplanetary disc, therefore, the existence of carbon monoxide on interstellar grains — and hence its presence within any final aggregated comet — requires that the grains should have aggregated at temperatures less than about 25 K, whilst the presence of methane requires $T \lesssim 31$ K. These results are somewhat model-dependent, however, since it is possible that volatile molecules such as carbon monoxide might become trapped within the dominant water-ice component of the cometary material, to such an extent that the effective sublimation temperatures of the more volatile species might approach the corresponding temperature evaluated for pure water ice. For example, laboratory experiments (*e.g.* Lacy *et al.* 1984, Schmitt *et al.* 1988) suggest that some carbon monoxide can remain trapped in water ice for long periods even at temperatures ranging up to around 100 K. Despite this, the presence of volatile material within typical cometary ices does provide some evidence, albeit indirect, that comets accumulated by the accretion of cold ice-covered interstellar grains which have remained cold ever since.

Further support for this conclusion has also come from detailed infrared observations of the spectra of water vapour in comets Halley and Wilson (Larson *et al.* 1989 and Mumma *et al.* 1989; *cf.* Mumma *et al.* 1986, 1987), which provide enough spectral resolution to determine the so-called ortho/para ratio of the sublimating water ice in these comets. The intensity ratio of the two sets of molecular lines is thought to give information on the temperature of the ice deep within the nucleus, and in the case of Halley's comet led to a derived temperature for the nucleus of around 25 K. On the other hand, the water ice in Comet Wilson (a dynamically new comet from the Oort cloud) seems somewhat surprisingly to have come from a rather hotter régime ($\gtrsim 50$ K), indicating either a fundamentally different source for this comet or the effects of cosmic-ray heating on the outer layers of this nucleus due to a presumed longer sojourn in the Oort cloud. These observations provide a potentially powerful way to constrain theories of cometary origin, but their correct interpretation obviously involves detailed considerations of infrared spectroscopy (such as how correctly to determine the appropriate line ratios) and also more general theoretical questions concerning the physical evolution of the cometary nucleus, including the possibility of surface modification whilst in the Oort cloud (or elsewhere) and the precise heating history of individual comets during the often long timescales associated with the subsequent dynamical transfer into any given short-period orbit.

Perhaps the most impressive evidence for a very cold environment for the formation of comets is provided by the sulphur S_2 molecule. This extremely fragile molecule was discovered in 1983 in the coma of Comet IRAS-Araki-Alcock (A'Hearn et al. 1983), and used as a 'fossil thermometer' by A'Hearn & Feldman (1985) to infer a formation temperature for this comet of less than a few tens of degrees Kelvin. Grim & Greenberg (1987) emphasized that before these arguments can reliably be made account must also be taken of both the physical nature of the ice (e.g. whether dominated by the ordinary water-ice component as discussed above) and the timescale of aggregation. Nevertheless, they found experimentally that if comets are able to aggregate from smaller grains in interstellar conditions whilst preserving their primordial S_2, formation temperatures much less than $100\,\mathrm{K}$ — perhaps as low as 30 to $40\,\mathrm{K}$ — are probably required. The S_2 molecule has now also been provisionally identified in Halley's comet and a number of others (e.g. Krishna Swamy & Wallis 1986, 1987; Wallis & Krishna Swamy 1986), though it should be noted that these proposed detections are not widely accepted and are regarded by many as being extremely controversial (e.g. Feldman 1989).

This particular molecule has the additional advantage that there seems to be no efficient mechanism whereby it can be produced in situ within a comet, and it may therefore be interpreted as evidence of pre-processing of the cometary ices by energetic particles or high-energy photons (A'Hearn & Feldman 1985) while still in the 'interstellar dust' phase. Laboratory experiments by Grim & Greenberg (1987) have revealed that S_2 is formed when ices of interstellar composition are exposed to ultraviolet radiation, and they propose that the cometary grains have been irradiated whilst in interstellar or circumstellar space prior to their final aggregation into cometary nuclei.

However, although the final accretion temperature of cometary material seems to be very low, the detailed chemistry of the volatile component does not generally resemble that expected for a gas condensing in equilibrium from a hotter phase (*e.g.* Anders 1986, Geiss 1988). For example, a gas of solar composition at a pressure of 10^{-4} atmospheres, cooling under equilibrium conditions, would yield molecules predominantly in the form of methane (CH_4) rather than carbon monoxide (CO). The particular molecular abundances imply, therefore, not only a very low formation temperature for comets, but also an origin associated in some way with a non-equilibrium process such as might occur in a turbulent protoplanetary disc (Lewis & Prinn 1980) or in material accumulating within a cold system such as a molecular cloud. These explanations may also account for the deficiency of nitrogen observed in Halley's comet, particularly molecular nitrogen N_2, although it should be emphasized that even quite detailed non-equilibrium solar nebula models still fail to produce the appropriate ratio of N_2/NH_3, for example, as compared to the proportions observed in Comet Halley (Engel *et al.* 1989).

On the other hand, it may nevertheless be possible to maintain that equilibrium chemical conditions might prevail for the more refractory component in comets (but see Anders 1986), as is often still assumed in theoretical models of the collapsing protosolar nebula during the earliest stages of evolution. It may then only be the later stages of a generally cooling régime which might then require non-equilibrium conditions or an environment of high dust-to-gas ratio, for example. While the largest (planetary) bodies might therefore have segregated from their environment at a relatively high temperature and experienced relatively little change in overall composition, the observed tendency towards differentiation would then be more closely associated with the formation of the smallest (cometary) bodies, or planetesimals. The evidence is therefore consistent with a formation scenario in which bodies of ever decreasing mass are produced as the temperature falls, and in which the smallest condensations are eventually formed only when the medium achieves molecular cloud temperatures.

The other possibility, of course, is that despite the evident continuity of properties amongst meteorites and comets, there might really be no direct connexion between the cooling régime associated with the formation of meteorites and the apparently very cold régime associated with the formation of comets. One might then simply assume that the aggregation of cometary material always occurs in the low-density, cold environments characteristic of observed molecular clouds or the outskirts of the solar nebula. Depending on the circumstances pertaining to differentiation or aggregation, as the case may be, it could then be that the deficiency of nitrogen observed in Halley's comet may also be explained. One suggested explanation, for example, is that the N_2 component, like the molecular hydrogen, would be expected to remain as uncondensed gas when comets form. Carbon monoxide, although also very volatile, is chemically less inert and may attach itself to other compounds, thereby becoming incorporated within the body of the grains themselves (e.g. Geiss 1988). The nitrogen abundance in Comet Kohoutek was also found to be very low, only about 0.1% that of water (cf. Yamamoto et al. 1983), suggesting that a low nitrogen abundance may indeed be a general feature of cometary ices, and therefore a valuable diagnostic of the state of the medium from which comets formed.

If comets originate by the accretion of ice-covered interstellar grains, sufficiently low temperatures to explain the survival of many of the observed molecules would generally have occurred only towards the outskirts of the protoplanetary disc, probably at distances greater than about 15 AU outwards (e.g. Yamamoto 1985b), i.e. beyond the likely formation zone of the proto-Saturn. However, depending on the degree of shielding of any direct solar radiation by small dust grains in the pre-planetary nebula (e.g. Weidenschilling 1988), it is possible that comets might also have aggregated somewhat closer in (cf. Öpik 1973). This is because, in the absence of direct solar heating the only significant heat source for the grains would then be the relatively inefficient process of gas-dust collisions, the gas temperature being maintained by viscous processes or infall associated with the dynamical evolution of the disc.

Another alternative is that growth of cold ice-covered 'interstellar grains' might occur in the non-equilibrium *mantles* of primitive cometary bodies. Such primitive bodies might have condensed within the molecular cloud component of a spiral arm prior to the formation of the sun or other parent stars. The precise way in which the molecular cloud medium is formed is not, of course, known. However, if spiral arms form through the action of density waves, as commonly supposed, then it is reasonable to assume that the earlier state of the icy grains was itself very cold. On the other hand, if spiral arms are the result of some kind of ejection process from the galactic centre (Section 16.3.1, p.379, and Appendix C), it is also possible that the icy grains may have cooled very rapidly prior to the condensation of primitive bodies and that their previous state was extremely hot. These possibilities are distinguished, in principle, by measurements of the pre-cometary lifetimes of individual crystal grains within meteorites and comets, and although such measurements are not yet definitive, preliminary evidence (*e.g.* Zinner *et al.* 1987) does seem to be consistent with a relatively short timescale and hence a hot origin (*cf.* Section 16.3.2, p.382).

It is theoretically plausible, therefore, to assume that icy grains might have survived and accumulated into comets almost anywhere in the protoplanetary disc from about the present distance of Saturn outwards (*e.g.* Izakov 1988), though whether conditions were in fact sufficiently quiescent for this to occur, especially closer to the sun, is still not known (*cf.* Section 14.1.3, p.308). In a less dusty protoplanetary nebula, however, for which shielding was less effective, corresponding perhaps to a later phase of evolution in which most of the original dust had settled towards mid-plane and aggregated into larger particles, sufficiently low temperatures (*e.g.* below about 20 K) would probably only be maintained beyond $\simeq$ 100 AU (Nakagawa *et al.* 1986). The requirement of a very low formation temperature for comets is, of course, also perfectly consistent with an origin of comets within dense molecular clouds, including the alternative possibility that rapidly cooling non-equilibrium chemical conditions might occur in the smallest primitive bodies before their final incorporation into planets and stars can take place.

18.2.3   ISOTOPIC RATIOS

An equally sensitive discriminant for the origin of comets, at least in principle, is provided by the isotopic ratios of the various elements. The isotopes of a given element are chemically virtually identical and therefore not easily separated; their observed ratio is thus expected to reflect the original relative abundances in which they were produced. As the Galaxy is progressively enriched with heavy elements, due to their production in stars and subsequent mixing throughout the interstellar medium by stellar winds and supernova explosions, it is possible to envisage that the isotopic ratios of certain elements will vary with time. If, then, a comet is found to have a significantly different isotopic composition from that of other bodies in the solar system, a recent interstellar origin might therefore be indicated.

In Table 18.3 are listed some of the common isotopic ratios of various elements, as measured in representative solar system bodies, in various localities beyond the solar system, and in the dust of Halley's comet by the accurate mass spectrometer on board Vega 1 (Šolc et al. 1987a,b). The galactic magnesium isotope ratios were obtained from metal-rich stars (Barbuy et al. 1987), the silicon ratios from the cool red giant star IRC + 10216 (Cernicharo et al. 1986), the iron isotope ratio from high-energy cosmic rays (Mewaldt et al. 1980), and the sulphur and oxygen ratios from interstellar nebulae (e.g. Penzias 1980). Departures from solar system ratios occur in various sources, but can usually be attributed to isotopic fractionation or other local effects (Smith 1981). A particularly important diagnostic in this respect would be the secure identification of $^{16}O/^{17}O$ and $^{16}O/^{18}O$ ratios in comets (cf. Drake et al. 1987), providing the possibility of discriminating between the source regions of a variety of dif-

Isotopic ratio	Comet Halley	Galaxy	Solar system
$^{12}C/^{13}C$	65±8 (gas)	62±7 (Models)	89±4
	175^{+132}_{-87} (dust)	43±4 (Stars)	
		67 (Gas)	
$^{16}O/^{18}O$	480^{+100}_{-33}	500	500±25
$^{24}Mg/^{25}Mg$	27±9.8	7.9±0.8	7.8
$^{24}Mg/^{26}Mg$	14±3.9	7.2±0.7	7.0
$^{28}Si/^{29}Si$		19.0±1.5	19.6
$^{28}Si/^{30}Si$		30.7±2.3	29.8
$^{32}S/^{34}S$	22±2	20	22.6
$^{56}Fe/^{54}Fe$	15.2 ± 3.2	9^{+6}_{-5}	15.8

Table 18.3: Comparison of common isotopic ratios in Halley's comet (mostly based on Giotto mass spectrometer measurements), various sources within the Galaxy and bodies in the solar system, as discussed in the text.

ferent bodies in the solar system. This might offer direct proof or otherwise that much of the earth's water came from comets. In general, however, a striking feature of the ratios tabulated is that, with the exception of the carbon isotope ratio, the solar system and galactic values are identical within the errors. It appears that the average values of these particular isotopes have not varied significantly over the age of the solar system $(4.6 \times 10^9$ years), and they cannot therefore be readily used as chronometers to determine the birth-dates of cometary material.

At first sight it also appears that both the magnesium and carbon isotope ratios in the dust grains of Comet Halley are distinctly anomalous. However, it is usually believed that this can be explained by contamination effects associated with the presence of other ions having similar charge-to-mass ratios. For example, measurements made by the neutral mass spectrometer on board the Giotto spacecraft showed the presence of significant numbers of $^{12}CH^+$ ions in Halley's coma within about 50,000 km of the nucleus (Krankowsky *et al.* 1986), indicating that the derived $^{12}C/^{13}C$ isotope ratio may well be subject to this kind of contamination (*e.g.* Šolc *et al.* 1987a,b).

Nevertheless, it should be noted that measurements of individual dust grains also showed a very wide range in the relative abundance of particles having masses 12 and 13 atomic mass units (1 a.m.u. $= 1.66 \times 10^{-27}$ kg, about the mass of a hydrogen atom), and if the observations do genuinely reflect the intrinsic carbon isotope ratio, then the full range of galactic values, covering $^{12}C/^{13}C$ ratios less than 50 to greater than the solar system value of 89, may well be present in the comet. This would be consistent with recent determinations of carbon isotope ratios in certain interstellar dust inclusions within meteorites (Ming *et al.* 1989). Since it seems unlikely that contamination effects alone will explain the entire range of these measurements, the data indicate the presence of an extremely heterogeneous assembly of particles, which must therefore have come from a diverse range of environments.

If the Halley measurements are interpreted in this way, the evidence would be consistent with the comet comprising a relatively unhomogenized assemblage of interstellar grains — whose carbon isotope ratio may therefore reflect the evolution of galactic chemistry over the several billion years of its history, and may possibly have nothing to do with the solar system value! On the other hand, if the process of condensation generally takes place in a molecular cloud environment prior to the formation of the sun (assuming comets are primordial) or parent stars (assuming comets are captured), it is possible that chemical fractionation might occur preferentially amongst the low atomic weight species during the later stages of collapse associated with the onset of energetic T Tauri activity. At the present time, however, such conclusions are speculative, and all that can be said with any certainty is that the isotopic ratios of the more refractory elements accessible to measurement are broadly consistent with both the solar system and the average interstellar values.

18.2.4 CARBON

Nevertheless, the value of the carbon isotope ratio $^{12}C/^{13}C$ in particular remains a quantity of considerable interest for theories of cometary origin, and it has long been a proposed candidate for ground-based study. Several authors (e.g. Vanýsek 1977, Clube & Napier 1982a) have suggested that the isotopic ratios of this particular element might turn out to be a crucial diagnostic of cometary cosmogony, although in cometary ices it was well known to be subject to severe chemical and fractionation effects under interstellar conditions at very low temperatures. Theoretical values for the $^{12}C/^{13}C$ isotope ratio in the solar neighbourhood, based on a number of models of the Galaxy's assumed chemical evolution (e.g. Tosi 1988) lie typically in the approximate range 40–80, a middle of the range determination being 62 ± 7 (Dimitrov 1981).

Observations of this ratio in the current interstellar medium about the sun are consistent with these figures, and, with few exceptions, suggest that the local gas is homogeneous to within about 10%. If the interstellar gas $^{12}C/^{13}C$ ratio is representative of the Galaxy as a whole, the latter does indeed appear to have evolved since the sun formed, a value of 43 ± 4 being found from optical observations along the lines of sight to several stars (Hawkins & Jura 1987), while a mean value of 67 is obtained from radio observations of the molecular cloud system (Frerking et al. 1980). This value seems to be more or less uniform over the galactic disc, and significantly lower than the standard value for solar system bodies of order 89 ± 4.

Early attempts to determine this isotopic ratio in comets spectroscopically had previously been made by a number of

authors, but were generally too uncertain to be really useful
(*e.g.* Vanýsek 1987b). The first accurate determination of the
$^{12}C/^{13}C$ abundance ratio, this time using high-resolution ground-
based observations of Halley's comet, was made by Wyckoff *et
al.* (1989). The parent molecule in which the carbon was observed was cyanogen (CN), probably deriving mainly from the
disintegration of hydrogen cyanide (HCN) found predominantly
in the form of ice in the nucleus of the comet. A relatively
small amount of cyanogen ($\approx$ 10–15%) is known also to come
from an additional source, associated with the spiral or jet-like
CN features observed in the inner coma, and is probably associated with the outgassing of volatiles from the 'CHON' particles
(A'Hearn *et al.* 1986). A final value for the $^{12}C/^{13}C$ ratio of
65 ± 8 was thus obtained by Wyckoff *et al.*, consistent with the
spread of ratios both expected and observed in the current interstellar medium, and apparently significantly different from
the usual solar system value. Interestingly, values of 50 ± 15
and 60 ± 15 had been derived somewhat earlier in Comet West
(1976 VI), but the authors, Lambert & Danks (1983), had been
reluctant to claim these measurements as representing a definite
departure from the usual solar system value. They are, however,
quite consistent with the value now found in the gas of Halley's
comet, itself derived from parent ices.

The ice component of cometary nuclei, then, seems not to
have originated in the region of the major planets; in particular the carbon isotope ratio is inconsistent with that measured
in the Jupiter-Saturn region (*e.g.* Encrenaz 1984, 1985), suggesting a formation zone for comets much further out (*cf.* Cosmovici & Ortolani 1985). A recent capture of Halley's comet
from interstellar space might also explain this ratio, although
departures from the average values of the $^{12}C/^{13}C$ ratio in both
solar system and galactic material (*cf.* Table 18.3) might be understood equally well if pre-cometary grains are subject to significant chemical fractionation. This could occur, for example,
if the parent molecule (*e.g.* HCN, condensed as ice on the pre-
cometary interstellar grain) had been exposed to a sufficiently

intense flux of ionizing particles or ultraviolet radiation. Nevertheless, whatever the merits of these suggestions, until it has been shown that a primordial solar system model of comet formation can indeed be constructed consistent with the observed values of the $^{12}C/^{13}C$ ratio, the interstellar hypothesis would appear to have been significantly advanced (Wyckoff et al. 1989).

18.2.5   HYDROGEN

A second important isotopic ratio is that associated with molecules containing various combinations of hydrogen and deuterium; the latter having been detected in the water ice of Halley's comet (e.g. Eberhardt et al. 1986). There is some evidence that the observed deuterium in the solar system has come from two distinct reservoirs (e.g. Owen et al. 1986, and Figure 18.1). If one measures the D/H ratio in various parts of the solar system relative to that in the solar wind, for example, one finds values for methane in the atmospheres of Jupiter and Saturn in the range 1–2, while the equivalent ratios for Titan and the earth are about 10. Recent observations reported by Smith et al. (1989) suggest that the D/H ratios in Jupiter and Saturn may even be slightly *lower* than that in the sun. The presence of a roughly common ratio in objects as disparate as the earth and Titan may at first seem rather strange, but it is consistent with the view that the water in the earth's oceans, along with other volatiles, has been largely brought in from cometary impacts in the remote past, say during the late heavy lunar bombardment which ended some 3.8 Gyr ago (cf. Section 11.2.2, p.246). Nevertheless, it remains to be seen whether the oxygen isotope ratio data, when they are obtained, will support this conclusion, while it has yet to be shown that the relative abundances of noble gases in the earth, such as xenon, are consistent with this picture.

The measured value of the D/H ratio in Halley's comet is still uncertain (Eberhardt et al. 1986), but probably lies in the range 3–24 times that in the solar wind. These figures suggest that significant enrichment relative to the protosolar value has

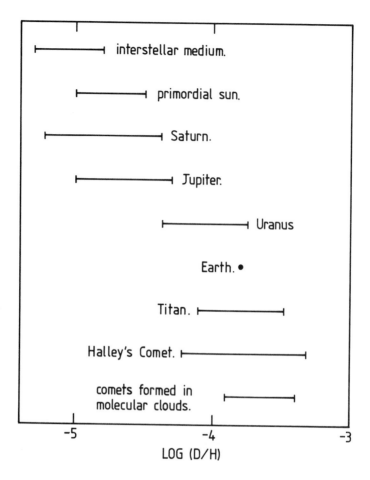

Figure 18.1: Comparison of the deuterium abundance in different sources. See text for discussion.

occurred, probably even compared to that in Jupiter or Saturn, indicating that the origin of comets is most likely to have occurred beyond the formation zones of these planets. Moreover, the observed cometary D/H ratio corresponds quite well to the solar system values in the second reservoir, from which the deuterium of the earth and Titan may derive. This would again be consistent with the hypothesis of a cometary origin for much of the earth's water, although the argument does not very tightly constrain the formation zone of comets, except that it must presumably lie somewhat beyond Saturn.

In the interstellar medium, however, the deuterium abundance covers an enormous range. Values for interstellar hydrogen are usually about half the solar wind value, but interstellar molecules containing hydrogen can sometimes be enriched in deuterium by factors up to more than 10^3. This arises because at temperatures less than a few hundred degrees, deuterium first preferentially attaches itself to hydrogen, and then tends to escape from the resulting HD molecules to become part of other hydrogen-bearing species including water (e.g. Geiss & Reeves 1981, Vanýsek 1983, 1984).

In this way Encrenaz et al. (1984) calculated, for example, that if comets formed in a molecular cloud environment, their D/H ratio should lie in the range 8–20 times that in the solar wind. This calculation was carried out prior to measurement of the deuterium ratio in Halley's comet, and it is interesting to note the very good agreement between the predicted and observed ratios. However, deuterated material, showing a significant excess of the D/H ratio relative to the usual solar system value, is also found in meteorites (e.g. Wood et al. 1986, Allamandola & Sandford 1988b, Zinner 1988 and references therein), the latter of unquestionably solar system origin.

The overall situation concerning the measurement of isotopic ratios is therefore still obscure (cf. Section 18.3.3, p.458). On the one hand, observations of the $^{12}C/^{13}C$ ratio may perhaps be best interpreted as evidence of a predominantly galactic evolutionary effect (however, see Section 18.2.4, p.449); while, on the other, those of the D/H ratio seem to be most simply understood in terms of extreme chemical fractionation effects. It is possible, of course, that both arguments contain a grain of truth, and that the effects of galactic chemical evolution and processes of isotopic fractionation are equally important in determining the chemistry of cometary material. These arguments thus touch on complex and very fundamental questions of physics, chem-

istry, and galactic chemical evolution, and until progress is more
secure in each of these fields it seems advisable to reserve judgement on the origin of comets, at least in this instance, and await
the results of other investigations.

18.3   Comet dust

18.3.1   DIRECT SAMPLES

The disintegration products of comets enter the earth's atmosphere as visible meteors and fireballs, or as the highly commin-
uted products of largely invisible, extremely friable dustballs
(cf. Öpik 1955a,b; Fechtig 1982). A study of the spectra and
flight paths of the fiery streaks produced by meteors and fireballs yields information about their compositions and densities,
while recovery of the associated particles means that cometary
material is also available for direct study in the laboratory.

There are a number of ways in which this cosmic material
can be collected (see reviews, for example, by Brownlee 1985,
Sandford 1987); in particular, although stratospheric particles
of demonstrably extraterrestrial provenance were first collected
by balloon experiments in 1970 (Brownlee et al. 1973), high-
flying U-2 aircraft are now routinely used to gather such particles directly from the stratosphere at altitudes of around 20 km.
Whilst the bulk of the collected samples is found usually to be
man-made or volcanic in origin, a large number of fine-grained
or fluffy extraterrestrial particles are also found, with sizes ranging from about 2 to 50 microns across. These tiny particles can
hardly be seen except under a microscope; the study of their
structure usually involves electron microscopy, the major elemental abundances being determined by firing narrow beams of
high-energy electrons at the particle, and analyzing the resulting
distributions of X-rays. More recently, precise isotopic ratios of

a few common elements have also become available through the use of ion probes.

The cosmic origin of these little particles can be deduced from a number of considerations. These include the detection of high abundances of rare gases (implanted by the present solar wind, or possibly much earlier by a T Tauri wind), the detection of radiation damage attributable to high-energy particles emanating from solar flares, and the presence in a few particles of a distinctly non-terrestrial D/H ratio (*e.g.* Zinner *et al.* 1983, Brownlee 1985). It is likely that there is on the order of a million such particles per cubic kilometre in the stratosphere, and that one such particle falls per day on each square metre of the earth's surface.

Somewhat larger particles, ranging in size up to about a millimetre in diameter have also been collected from the ocean floor for over a century, starting with the HMS Challenger Expedition during the eighteen-seventies (*e.g.* Murray 1876, Murray & Renard 1884, Parkin & Tilles 1968, Murrell *et al.* 1980). More recently, similar particles have also been collected from the blue ice lakes of Greenland (Maurette *et al.* 1986). Their cosmic provenance can be inferred from their chemical compositions, which are remarkably uniform and similar to those of rare, primitive meteorites. At least some of these large particles may be meteorite ablation products: experimental and theoretical studies have shown that dense stony meteorites, entering the atmosphere at many kilometres per second, lose much of their mass through the splitting off of particles with diameters of order $100\,\mu$m (Bronshten 1983). For example, at the site of the Sikhote-Alin stony meteorite fall (*e.g.* Fessenkov 1955, Krinov 1963; *cf.* Figure 3.4, p.49) the most numerous small particles found had sizes in the range 30–$100\,\mu$m. The samples collected from deep-sea sediments and from Greenland sites may also contain mineral inclusions; but they have usually been significantly altered by atmospheric heating, as the larger interplanetary particles are often melted during passage through the earth's atmosphere.

18.3.2　ORIGIN

Submicron dust particles exist in space either as individual grains or as components of larger friable bodies (Fechtig 1982), whilst these and stratospheric dust particles are usually thought to be cometary in origin (*e.g.* Millman 1972, Delsemme 1976a,b, Bradley & Brownlee 1986). For example, the presence of ionization tracks due to solar flares in many of the so-called Brownlee particles suggests a separate existence in the zodiacal cloud for periods of order 10^3–10^5 yr, consistent with a cometary source, while many of the particles seem also to have experienced remarkably low levels of heating on entering the earth's atmosphere. This indicates a relatively small impact velocity with the earth, consistent with a population of particles having a residence time in the zodiacal cloud similar to the ages indicated by the solar flare tracks. Indeed, in view of the probable dominance of Encke's comet (or its progenitor) in the interplanetary environment during the last 10^4 years or so (*e.g.* Clube & Napier 1984b, Štohl 1986, Gustafson *et al.* 1987; *cf.* Section 17.1.4, p.397) it seems plausible to assume that many Brownlee particles in fact derive from a single comet of exceptional dimensions (Clube 1987b). This suggestion is supported, for example, by the porous structure of many of the observed particles (which also argues in favour of a cometary origin, though not necessarily one involving a quiescent assemblage of ordinary ice-covered interstellar grains; *e.g.* McDonnell 1988); while if a single large comet is involved, the detailed particle properties may be expected additionally to reflect an origin and subsequent processing within the rather hotter régime which might then have prevailed.

On the other hand, there must be some asteroidal contamination amongst the Brownlee particles, the extent of which may eventually be determined by detailed chemical and isotopic analyses of the grains, which in principle provide information on the actual number of 'parent' bodies or source reservoirs necessary to explain the whole range of particle properties. Meteorites, for example, appear to come from at least seventy such bodies (e.g. Dodd 1986), while recent research has shown that a significant proportion of meteors originate within bodies which may be identified with the asteroid belt (e.g. Olsson-Steel 1988b). Indeed, infrared observations of bands, belts and dust-trails superposed on the more uniform background zodiacal light have indicated that collisions among asteroids may be a significant source of small dust particles in the solar system (cf. Dermott et al. 1988, Sykes 1988), while the evidence that Brownlee particles have mostly entered the earth's atmosphere at low relative velocities has also been interpreted as a signature of an asteroidal source (Flynn 1989). Nevertheless, the *submicron* particle flux at the earth is probably not yet fully sampled, while the zodiacal dust bands could also be cometary in origin, being associated with the major fragmentation event in the Taurid stream thought to have occurred some 5000 years ago (Section 17.1.4, p.397; cf. Clube & Asher 1989). This fragmentation may simultaneously have produced a population of very friable interplanetary boulders. Indeed, it is possible that some of the interplanetary dust particles might even originate from a *primordial* population of interplanetary 'boulders', themselves having a very primitive, friable structure analogous to the surfaces of evolved cometary nuclei (e.g. Whipple 1968).

In this way, although these arguments show that the assumption that Brownlee particles are primarily cometary in origin is plausible, we cannot exclude the possibility that a significant proportion of the collected particles in fact come from asteroids, for example via collisions in the asteroid belt and subsequently trapped by the earth as they spiral sunwards under the influence of the Poynting-Robertson effect. This is currently an active field of research, and it is clear that any firmly expressed opinion one way or the other may soon be overtaken by events. Nevertheless, it does seem that on balance the evidence still favours a cometary source for most of the interplanetary dust. In what follows, therefore, we *assume* that the collected stratospheric particles are mostly cometary in origin, and leave open the wider question whether earth-crossing asteroids and larger meteoroids, which may also supply a proportion of the dust, might themselves eventually be traced to a similar cometary source.

18.3.3   IMPLICATIONS

The exceedingly small size of the stratospheric particles means that their initially high entry velocities into the earth's atmosphere are mostly dissipated at very high altitudes, where the atmospheric density remains extremely low. This, together with their very large surface areas compared to their mass, means that the particles may only be heated to temperatures no more than 500–1000 K, the thermal 'pulse' lasting typically only a few seconds or so. Furthermore, if many of these particles initially enter the atmosphere as a component of larger but friable bodies (e.g. Fechtig 1982), the heating that the majority experience on entry may not even reach 500 K. Many of the tiny stratospheric particles indeed seem not to have melted upon entry (Fraundorf 1981), and their properties may thus give rather direct insights into the cosmogony of their parent bodies.

A proportion of Brownlee particles, the chondritic porous (CP) fraction, are often described as having a 'bunch of grapes' morphology (Fraundorf et al. 1982), the 'grapes' in this description being grains typically about 0.03 μm in diameter. These are either rounded or plate-like in shape, and divide into two main mineralogical groupings: namely, minerals with, and those without, water or hydroxyl bondings, the anhydrous form being the most common. These individual grains occur in clusters to form a composite particle with 'fluffy' structure. Often imbedded in the bunch of grapes are crystals, sometimes no more than one in a Brownlee particle. These also come in two main types: whiskers with lengths up to about 6 μm; and smaller (up to $\simeq$ 1 μm) hexagonal grains which may be made of the minerals olivine, enstatite or iron sulphide. Such crystals seem to indicate the presence of components that have condensed in a reducing environment at temperatures somewhat higher than those likely to arise during ablation or expected to occur during formation. Thus, there is in general a great diversity of particle properties, even within the very smallest structures seen, and any broad understanding of the origin of comets must now include an explanation of these complexities as well.

Some general conclusions may be drawn from the known properties of these particles. The diversity of grain properties implies that they have probably been formed in a wide range of environments or have been processed through a wide range of physical conditions prior to assembly into a comet (Fraundorf 1981). There also seem to have been two stages of aggregation, the first involving the creation of the 'grapes', that is the basic crystals and amorphous materials of sizes $\simeq 0.01$–$1\,\mu$m and with elements having roughly cosmic abundances; and the second involving the assembly of these individual units. It is possible that the fluffiness of the Brownlee particles arises during differentiation or from the evaporation of ice which originally coated the small submicron particles. This structure is consistent, for example, with the low densities that have been deduced for some cometary meteors from their rate of deceleration on entering the atmosphere. Thus, a mean density of $0.01\,\mathrm{gm\ cm^{-3}}$ has been derived for the October Draconid meteors, associated with Comet Giacobini-Zinner, though it should be mentioned that most comet-associated meteors seem to have rather larger mean densities, lying typically in the range 0.1–$0.6\,\mathrm{gm\ cm^{-3}}$ (Verniani 1969, cf. Hughes 1986).

On the other hand, the creation of some of the observed crystals within Brownlee particles seems to require initial temperatures much higher than those normally deduced from the presence of cometary ices. In particular the 'whiskers', composed of enstatite ($MgSiO_3$), have a structure characteristic of crystals grown by condensation from a vapour (Donn & Sears 1963, Bradley et al. 1983). Thus, even if the bulk of cometary material is formed during a process of differentiation in parent bodies, these crystals must themselves presumably have condensed during an earlier stage from a hot, hydrogen-rich gas phase prior to their aggregation into the parent bodies (*cf.* Tomeoka & Buseck 1986).

Carbon isotope ratios have also been measured in a few stratospheric dust particles (*e.g.* McKeegan *et al.* 1985), and only modest departures from the standard solar system value have been found. For example, a particle named Skywalker has $^{12}C/^{13}C \simeq 85$, rather than the usual value of 89; much lower values than this, presumably due to interstellar or significantly fractionated inclusions, have also been obtained for a few carbonaceous components within primitive meteorites, themselves undoubtedly of solar system origin. Magnesium isotope ratios have also been reported for a few Brownlee particles and generally accord with solar system values to within about 1%. These measurements would seem to indicate that the stratospheric dust particles, and hence the comets from which they presumably derived, originated with the sun and planets 4.5 Gyr ago. Alternatively, assuming an interstellar origin, one would have to contrive that galactic abundances have not significantly changed during the age of the solar system, although there may be differing degrees of fractionation within 'CHON' material due to the longer time taken for these organic compounds to condense.

Whilst anomalous ^{13}C abundances have been detected in primitive meteorites of undoubtedly solar system origin, it is interesting that in one carbon-carrying component of the meteorites examined, there was no evidence of the expected heavy carbon enrichment, in spite of clear indications that the component itself derived from unprocessed interstellar grains (the indications taking the form of isotopic anomalies: for example $^{14}N/^{15}N$ ratios ranging up to 400 against the terrestrial value of about 270; Pillinger 1987). Moreover, the anomalies in the magnesium isotope ratios, although small (at the level of only a few parts in a thousand), are nevertheless significant (Esat *et al.* 1979, Esat & Taylor 1987), and are in the sense that the particles contain slight excesses of ^{26}Mg. This might be taken to indicate that at least some of the dust originates in a source beyond the solar system, for example in comets recently formed in interstellar space. However, magnesium isotope ratios as measured in the atmospheres of a number of nearby stars (e.g. Boesgaard 1968, Bell & Branch 1970, Tomkin & Lambert 1976, 1980) generally show no clear indication of non-terrestrial values, while theoretically the element is produced by the transmutation of carbon and neon in massive stars which later become supernovae. Woosley & Weaver (1986), for example, have shown that nucleosynthesis in massive Population I stars, which eventually explode as supernovae, will produce ^{24}Mg, ^{25}Mg and ^{26}Mg in nearly solar proportions.

Although observations of the ejecta from the supernova which exploded in the Large Magellanic Cloud in 1987 will presumably test these theoretical models in the near future, the necessity (on an interstellar hypothesis for comet formation) to produce these isotopes in the current Galaxy in proportions equalling that of the solar system to better than one percent, would seem to require an exceptionally well-mixed Galaxy, with virtually no secular evolution of this isotope ratio over the age of the solar system. On this evidence, therefore, the stratospheric dust particles seem rather more likely to have derived from primitive solar system bodies than from recently formed interstellar ones. However, it should be emphasized that the chemical evolution of galaxies is not well understood, and it may well be that the evidence from comets and Brownlee particles can also be understood in terms of galactic material that changes very little with time overall, whilst cometary material in particular is likely to have experienced significant fractionation effects especially amongst elements of low atomic weight.

18.3.4   Dusty dilemma

These new results bring us right up to the frontiers of research on the cometary enigma, and they raise many problems, the answers to which are not yet clear. In particular, we seem to have arrived at two paradoxes. First, there is a temperature paradox. The ices of Halley's comet, and others, seem to imply that comets were formed in an extremely cold environment, the outer regions of the protosolar nebula or within pre-stellar molecular clouds. Why, then, do the crystals embedded in the stratospheric dust particles seem to have come from a higher temperature régime such as one might associate with stellar winds or the inner few astronomical units of the primordial solar nebula? Secondly, there is an isotopic ratio paradox. The carbon isotope ratio in the ice of Halley's comet has a distinctly interstellar flavour. Why, then, is this not reflected in the isotopic ratios seen in stratospheric dust particles, which seem to indicate a strong solar system connexion?

One might suppose that the dust within the central few astronomical units of the primordial solar system, perhaps condensing from the hot gas close to the sun, was somehow transported to the Uranus-Neptune zone or beyond, there to be incorporated into growing, icy planetesimals. Recent models of the primordial solar nebula (e.g. Morfill & Völk 1984) do indicate that strong turbulence might have occurred which could lead to substantial radial mixing. On the other hand, a radial circulation sufficiently large to incorporate significant amounts of 'inner' solar system material into bodies formed further out might also transport material from the comet-forming regions back to the inner solar system, thereby probably destroying the fragile S_2 component (for example) of the original interstellar grains. Since this could not be rebuilt in less than the circulation time of the material, the potential cost of transporting grains from the hot inner regions to the outskirts of the nebula could be the loss of many of the cold signatures actually observed.

There are several possible resolutions of this difficulty. For example, there might be more than one type of comet. The process of accumulation of larger bodies might vary continuously throughout the solar nebula, producing rocky or metallic planetesimals in the hot inner regions, and bodies more akin to icebergs in the cold outer zones (e.g. Vanýsek 1987b). In this case, whereas the Brownlee particles might be samples of asteroids or of a relatively 'hot' comet, such as Comet Encke perhaps; the Iras-Araki-Alcock comet, Halley's comet and other comets apparently showing 'cold' signatures (as indicated by observations of the S_2 molecule and the ortho/para ratio of H_2O emission) might represent material originally located in the outer regions of the solar nebula or in the interstellar medium. However, even on this hypothesis it is difficult to reconcile the existence of enstatite whiskers (condensed from a vapour with $T \gtrsim 10^3$ K) in some Brownlee particles with the presence of enriched deuterium in others, such enrichments approaching those measured in molecular clouds and again indicating formation and subsequent processing in an extremely low temperature environment (McKeegan *et al.* 1985). In any case S_2 has now also been reported in the spectrum of Encke's comet (Krishna Swamy & Wallis 1987), belonging to the broad meteor stream which is the probable source of most such particles (*cf.* Section 17.1.4, p.397), though as we have mentioned the detection of S_2 in any comet other than IRAS-Araki-Alcock (and then probably only during an outburst) is still regarded as questionable.

Alternatively, the crystals may simply be interstellar grains formed by condensation processes in the atmospheres of cool stars (*e.g.* Wickramasinghe 1967) and subsequently accreted into comets in a molecular cloud or circumstellar environment. In that case one would expect a great diversity of particle types to exist within a given comet, covering a range of isotopic ratios reflecting the characteristics of the specific environments in which the individual grains condensed. The wide variation in the abundance of species with atomic weights 12 and 13 detected within individual grains in Halley's comet supports this point of view, but one might then expect a similar range in the measured carbon isotope ratios of Brownlee particles, which has not been observed.

These observations might be compatible with one another and with a cometary origin for Brownlee particles if the discordant $^{12}C/^{13}C$ ratios were specifically associated with the 'CHON' particles first observed in Halley's comet. These are not present to any significant degree amongst the collected interplanetary dust particles, presumably due to the effects of heating and ablation on entry into the earth's atmosphere, or because they are removed in the interplanetary environment or even as a result of devolatilization during their formation or initial ejection from the comet. Under these circumstances, it might be supposed that the earliest condensates in a very hot environment may correspond to fairly standard cosmic proportions, whilst later condensations at lower temperatures could be contaminated by irradiation or by contributions from evolved stars in the vicinity of the original condensation. For this picture to be valid, however, there would have to be very little secular evolution in the fundamental galactic $^{12}C/^{13}C$ ratio over 4.5 Gyr, an issue on which it is not yet possible to pronounce with any confidence.

On the other hand, of course, Brownlee particles might be more asteroidal than cometary, making the cometary connexion much harder to elucidate, and, quite possibly, much of the above discussion redundant! To some extent, by appealing to a model in which the bulk of cometary material occurs in relatively large bodies or evolves from a hot environment, an asteroidal component will inevitably be present in comets as well. But under these circumstances, the evidence might then be committing us to the view that the majority of asteroids are evolutionary products of (admittedly large) comets, a view that despite the not unfavourable physical and dynamical evidence is still not unanimously held.

To conclude this section, therefore, it seems clear that very important questions are now being raised by the detailed chemical and isotopic properties of the collected interplanetary dust particles and the comparisons with observations of the dust and gas from Comet Halley. It may be that these questions will remain unresolved until one or another planned space mission to land on a comet nucleus has been successful. In the meantime, it is clear that the conventional picture of comet formation in a solar nebula may now have as much, if not more, difficulty in explaining the microscopic properties of cometary dust as the still less conventional pictures involving the recent capture of comets from a molecular cloud or from the current spiral arm environment.

18.4   Puzzling trends

In spite of the great observational advances of the last few years, their implications for the origin of comets remains unclear. Nevertheless, these advances give a definite sense of progress. The extremely dark surfaces of at least the periodic comets have led to a significant upwards revision of the dimensions, and hence probably of the masses, of comets and the Oort cloud. This, in turn, has led to severe constraints being placed on models which predict the existence of a dense inner core, at least insofar as the core is produced as a dynamical consequence of the formation of comets originally orbiting within the protoplanetary disc, as in the standard planetesimal picture.

The dust in Halley's comet seems also to have come from an environment which has not had the processing one sees in even the most primitive meteorites. Apart from the possibility of a certain amount of surface alteration (e.g. Reitmeijer & MacKinnon 1987), the nucleus is indeed a relatively pristine object. Although it is not clear what this means for theoretical models of the protosolar nebula, the pristine, relatively unprocessed state of cometary dust does mean that further detailed studies of the physical and chemical make-up of individual grains should eventually provide new insight into the history and evolution of the 'pre-cometary' particle. Such studies should not only link models of comets directly to other areas of astrophysics but will also provide interesting new connexions to theoretical models of both galactic and solar system chemical evolution (e.g. Clayton 1982, 1988; Clube 1988b, Greenberg 1988, McDonnell 1988).

The deuterium abundance in Halley's comet, and the presence of certain very fragile molecules such as S_2, also suggest an origin for comets in an extremely low-temperature environment resembling conditions within a molecular cloud. The presence of S_2 also seems to require, plausibly, a grain environment infused with a flux of high energy particles, probably ultraviolet photons (Greenberg & Grim 1986). Especially intriguing, of course, is the anomalous carbon isotope ratio, which is most simply interpreted in terms of the signature of a current molecular cloud, rather than one of a primordial protoplanetary nebula still condensing after the sun has formed.

These detailed chemical and isotopic arguments, including indirect dynamical constraints, while still being consistent with a solar system origin for comets, therefore increasingly seem to suggest that comet formation may instead be more easily understood as a process of condensation occurring in a molecular cloud environment *prior to* the formation of either the sun (if primordial) or other parent stars (if captured). The isotopic evidence for fractionation, especially amongst low atomic weight species like carbon, and the chemical evidence for irradiation in a cold, formative environment are also consistent with the later stages of condensation taking place in the presence of T Tauri star activity as the parent star evolves on to the main sequence. These unexpected results, coming as they do from detailed observations of several comets seen during the last ten years or so, have a key rôle to play in the question of cometary and stellar origins. It is important that their detailed implications should be carefully assessed and properly incorporated into future theoretical models, allowing the full strength of chemical arguments to be used in discriminating 'solar system' from 'interstellar' hypotheses for cometary origin.

Thus, although we have not yet observed comets being born, whether in a solar nebula or beyond, the new inputs to the subject in recent years have served greatly to restrict the range of acceptable possibilities. When these new developments have taken their place alongside such new findings as may come from current studies of interplanetary and interstellar dust, together with the developing science of cosmic chemical memory (*e.g.*

Clayton 1982), it is likely that we shall have a much clearer idea not only of whence comets came, but also what this means for star formation, solar system cosmogony and astrophysics generally. In this way, as Halley's Comet has given yet another once-in-a-lifetime boost to astronomy, the study of the origin of comets is now once again poised on the brink of an exciting new period of rapid change and development.

19

Epilogue

"History is about people and their ideas; and that, when you come down to it, is what science is about as well."

M.W. Ovenden

19.1 New constraints

19.1.1 INNER CORE

There can be little doubt that an appreciation of the possible rôle of comet-induced catastrophism in the history and evolution of the earth has now revolutionized our understanding of the status of comets and opened up new and previously unsuspected lines of research relating to cometary cosmogony. Thus, the dominating rôle of giant comets in evolution causes one to question the origin of these comets above others, whilst ideas about populating the Oort cloud must also be reviewed in the knowledge that it is a fairly rapidly dissipating system which requires steady or intermittent replenishment. Moreover, new information about the past behaviour of the Oort cloud may become available using the earth as a kind of test particle, with such phenomena as geochemical anomalies, the distribution of crater ages, and the mass-extinction record becoming increasingly useful diagnostic tools. The implications of these results are still largely unexplored, but a few straightforward deductions may be made.

First, let us look at the group of hypotheses which have comets populating an inner cloud with a radius of order 10^3–10^4 AU. Evidently, no matter how effective is the disruption of the conventional Oort (1950) cloud, by passing stars and molecular clouds, one can always postulate a sufficiently massive 'inner core' to replenish the dynamically unstable long-period orbits through unbinding. Such models, however, must satisfy an additional constraint based on the cratering record, namely the lack

469

of evidence for a secular decline in the lunar cratering rate over the last 3.8×10^9 yr. Instead, there is a tendency for the impact rate to increase over this interval, and this is especially marked during the last 300 Myr. Superposed on this trend appear to be large oscillations with duration typically of order 100 Myr (Baldwin 1985). Thus, if comets ultimately supply the population of earth-crossing asteroids, which themselves dominate the terrestrial cratering rate, the reservoir supplying the long-period comets must be maintained without sensible decline for the age of the solar system. Alternatively, it is possible that most earth-impactors come more or less directly from the asteroid belt and it is the number of *these* bodies which is secularly increasing. This could happen either as a result of collisions amongst the largest asteroids, or by a constant resupply of 'dead' comets from the inner core of the Oort cloud, either during comet showers or by the break-up of the largest active short-period comets and their subsequent dynamical transfer into the main belt.

Nevertheless, if comets are indeed the major contributors to the terrestrial cratering process (*cf.* Hut *et al.* 1987), whether directly or indirectly (*e.g.* through the asteroids they produce), the observed nearly steady cratering rate must be maintained despite losses from the outer Oort cloud which may be an order of magnitude larger than those expected if stars (*e.g.* Weissman 1982) were the only significant perturbers. Because the mass distribution of molecular clouds is steep (*e.g.* Sanders *et al.* 1985), a few large discrete inputs of energy are expected for any hypothetical inner cloud having a radius greater than a few thousand AU. But then, when a comet does begin to move outwards, it is more likely to be ejected than to attain the near-zero energy necessary for successful placement in the outer cloud.

The problem is analogous to that of producing the conventional Oort (1950) comet cloud from Cameron's satellite nebulae or through a massive disc hypothesis. A placement efficiency of order 10% may not be unreasonable for such a process, indicating that to explain the present outer cloud, containing around 10^{11} average-sized comets, one must unbind on the order of

10^{12} comets from the hypothetical inner core. If there were ten such replenishments during the age of the solar system (corresponding, for example, to the number of close encounters of the sun with giant molecular clouds), then approximately 10^{13} comets must have been lost from the inner reservoir. To achieve this without sensible decline in the cratering rate probably requires that the core should have a mass an order of magnitude greater still, say 10^{14} comets. For a mean cometary mass of order 10^{14} kg, this would imply a total cometary mass ranging up to $10^3 M_\oplus$. Although this is a very loose argument (*cf.* Bailey 1986a), observations of the terrestrial cratering record combined with evolutionary estimates for the Oort cloud population may in principle tightly constrain those theories of the Oort cloud which predict the existence of a massive inner core (*e.g.* Napier 1987, Stothers 1988).

On the solar system hypothesis, therefore, it seems that one is almost inevitably driven to conclude that comets are the next most important bodies in terms of mass to the sun itself, a result which has important implications for many current ideas about the structure and evolution of the protosolar nebula and of the processes leading to planet formation. On the other hand, it should be mentioned that there is still no *direct* evidence for the existence of such a large mass of comets in the solar system (*cf.* Bailey 1983b,c,d; Bailey *et al.* 1984), and such evidence as exists for comets around other stars (*e.g.* Weissman 1984, Harper *et al.* 1984) indicates much lower masses, for example of order $15 M_\oplus$ for the comet cloud of radius 85 AU which is thought to surround Vega. Indeed, recent work on the capture of short-period comets by planetary perturbations (Stagg & Bailey 1989) has suggested that very tight constraints can now be placed on any viable, spherically symmetrical model of the inner core, provided it has an isotropic velocity distribution, by the requirement that it should not produce *too many* observable short-period comets (*e.g.* Bailey 1989, Bailey & Stagg 1989).

Thus, while it is astrophysically quite plausible to postulate the existence of a massive inner core of comets to replenish the dynamically unstable outer cloud (*e.g.* Fernández 1985a, Weissman 1985b, and references therein), it remains uncertain firstly whether such a cloud exists, and secondly (if it exists) whether the available mass is large enough to provide for sufficient replenishment. This 'survival problem' for the inner cloud is still an active field of research. We note in particular that an important problem to be addressed in future work is the question of perturbations by bodies in the sun's immediate neighbourhood at the time of its formation (*cf.* Donn 1973, 1976; Clube & Napier 1986b, Appendix). Strong perturbations by stars or clouds in the immediate solar neighbourhood at this time might also have exerted a significantly disruptive influence on any massive inner core.

19.1.2   CAPTURE

Although the required mass of any inner core to the Oort cloud may lead to difficulties for the solar system hypothesis, it might seem that the alternative hypothesis of capturing comets from the interstellar medium is subject to even more severe difficulties, as it involves retarding the motion of hyperbolic comets by around $20\,\mathrm{km\,s^{-1}}$ or capturing them from an equivalently small volume of phase space. A number of possible capture mechanisms have been proposed, however, using various kinds of third body to extract the excess kinetic energy involved. These include Jupiter (*e.g.* Radzievskii & Tomanov 1977); an unseen solar companion (*e.g.* Valtonen 1983); and the molecular cloud itself (*e.g.* Clube & Napier 1984a). All involve capture from a dense, localized comet cloud (*cf.* Bobrovnikoff 1929a) rather than from the general interstellar field.

Capture by Jupiter is inadequate by a factor of order 10^8, assuming a typical relative velocity of $20\,\mathrm{km\,s^{-1}}$ and a density of interstellar comets of order $10^{-1}\,\mathrm{AU^{-3}}$ (Valtonen & Innanen 1982), and in any case would lead to a surfeit of prograde long-period comets in the ecliptic plane, contrary to observations (*e.g.* Fernández & Jockers 1983; but see Delsemme 1985). On the other hand, capture by an unseen solar companion star involves passage through a field of interstellar comets with a number density only of order 10^{-1} AU^{-3}, which may not be astrophysically unreasonable. Symmetry of the distribution of aphelion axes about the orbital plane might then be expected, with an excess of prograde or retrograde comets in this particular plane.

It is notable that there is indeed such a plane of symmetry, about which Delsemme (1986) has found the proportion of such retrograde long-period comets is about 54%, the ratio of retrograde-to-prograde comets ranging up to 2:1 on a strip of sky 24° wide. This sort of effect has subsequently been interpreted as due to a galactic influence on the Oort cloud (e.g. Delsemme & Patmiou 1986), though because the solar antapex lies at the centre of this strip, it could more plausibly be assumed that the asymmetry is associated in some way with the solar motion or a recent strong perturbation of the Oort cloud. Such a perturbation could have been induced during penetration of the sun through a molecular cloud containing substructure.

In fact, there are now several indications that the Oort cloud did indeed suffer a major disturbance a few million years ago. Apart from Delsemme's strip of comets, there are asymmetries in the inclination distribution of long-period comets which are inconsistent with an equilibrium response to a steady-state galactic tide (Yabushita 1989a), in addition to their apparently unrelaxed energy distribution. Direct evidence also lies in the fact that the trajectory of the sun, projected backwards, reveals that it passed through Gould's Belt a few million years ago.

The influence of molecular clouds and the Galaxy on the Oort cloud has been reviewed for example by Torbett (1986a), while a third capture mechanism, using a molecular cloud as the third body, has been described by Clube & Napier (1984a, 1985; cf. Section 15.2.3, p.350). It is particularly emphasized that the sun's sphere of influence is not constant during a close encounter with a giant molecular cloud, and that this together with other non-stationary effects may lead to a higher efficiency of cometary capture in such a complex dynamical situation. In this way, the capture of $\approx 10^{11}$ comets into long-period orbits around the sun may be possible if the sun passes through a molecular cloud containing locally on the order of 10^2 comets AU^{-3}. This density might be consistent with Sekanina's limit on the mean cometary space density in the local solar neighbourhood (*i.e.* about 10^{-4} comets AU^{-3}; Sekanina 1976), and also with the observed elemental depletions in dense nebulae (*e.g.* Tarafdar *et al.* 1984). However, all these capture mechanisms involve uncertain assumptions of one sort or another, and it cannot yet be said that the general problem of capturing comets from a dense nebula has been satisfactorily solved.

The discovery that the outskirts of the Oort cloud are probably unstable has therefore raised a number of unresolved problems. Empirically, it might seem that the lack of ecliptic alignments in the aphelion distribution of comets, and the preference for galactic ones, might be indicative of recent capture or a major galactic disturbance of the Oort cloud; while additional indirect evidence supporting this view may be obtained by examining the inferred density distribution of comets in the outer cloud. Although uncertain, this density distribution seems to be closer in form to Oort's original model than to alternatives based on the assumption of a hypothetical massive inner core (*cf.* Delsemme 1977, Bailey 1983a, 1986a). However, the available arguments remain indirect, and a safer conclusion at the present time is that the question of cometary provenance remains open.

19.1.3   FORMATION

Nevertheless, whatever the ultimate site of the comet factory, the subject of our review is intimately bound up with wider issues concerning star formation and evolution generally. Traditionally, there has been a tendency for solar system scientists to overlook this broader perspective and to treat the solar system as somehow isolated from the Galaxy at large. To some extent this perspective was inevitable, given the lack of secure data on other star-forming regions, but this situation has now ended forever, as instrumental and observational techniques of various kinds give us new and exciting insights into the process of star formation elsewhere in the Galaxy. For example, as we have described in Chapter 14, energetic bipolar flows are now known to be prevalent amongst new star systems, even to the extent of being a fundamental and universal phenomenon, yet the flows are so far from being understood that they usually gain little more than a passing reference in most current models of solar system formation, let alone theories of comet formation! Whether such processes should figure prominently in the final story about comets is still unknown; but if we are to progress to a complete theory of the origin of comets it is clearly important to make some attempt to place both their dynamics and cosmogony into the wider galactic context.

We have noted that there has recently been a tendency to place comet formation further from the sun, and have indicated several possibilities in which comet growth might occur on the outskirts of a star-forming region (*e.g.* Bailey 1987a) or in the general interstellar medium (*e.g.* Yabushita 1983b, Napier & Humphries 1986). These mechanisms imply that comets are essentially formed by the cold ($T \simeq 20\,\mathrm{K}$) coagulation of ordinary ice-covered interstellar grains (*cf.* Greenberg 1983), leading to the suggestion that a pristine comet might therefore comprise a heterogeneous mixture of organic molecules and frozen radicals within which are embedded submicron sized interstellar particles (*e.g.* Greenberg *et al.* 1985). Cold aggregation of icy grains also yields a roughly chondritic composition (*e.g.* Greenberg 1982), which is consistent, for example, with the spectra of cometary meteors (Millman 1977) and with the generally 'interstellar' abundances of the parent molecules inferred from chemical models of the cometary coma (*e.g.* Mitchell *et al.* 1981). The framework for all these models is, of course, the standard one in which star formation occurs through the gravitational collapse of cold, dense regions.

It is interesting, however, to consider whether the observations might equally be fitted by an entirely different set of initial conditions (*e.g.* Clube 1985, 1988b; *cf.* Section 16.3.2, p.382). This possibility is suggested by the likely presence of high-temperature condensates in cometary material. For example, Brownlee particles of presumed cometary origin contain large ($\simeq 1\,\mu$m) crystalline particles, formed in a hot hydrogen-rich atmosphere (Fraundorf 1981), while crystalline silicates have also been identified in infrared spectra of the dust observed in Halley's comet (Campins & Ryan 1989). Likewise, chondritic meteorites at the most primitive end of the meteorite sequence have bulk compositions not unlike those of comets, but contain chondrules and even smaller crystalline high-temperature condensates ($\simeq 1500\,$K) immersed in an ultra-fine-grained matrix corresponding to lower temperatures of condensation ($\simeq 500\,$K). The existence of Apollo asteroids circulating in similar orbits to Encke's comet is also consistent with the idea that the largest comets (which, though rare, may still dominate the total mass of the cometary system) have a differentiated primitive structure.

Comets, then, may have grown through a non-equilibrium chemical condensation sequence from a high-density, high-temperature régime, or they may have accreted cold. The difference has important implications for the whole question of star formation, and may in principle be resolved through measuring the ages of interstellar inclusions in meteorites and comets (*e.g.* Ming & Anders 1988) or by examining the chemistry of cometary dust and ices. So far as the latter is concerned, for example, the occurrence of amorphous water ice in comets (*e.g.* Patashnick *et al.* 1974, Klinger 1981, 1983; Smoluchowski 1981) argues strongly against the proposition that comets have condensed directly from a *hot* equilibrated state, though it does not necessarily exclude non-equilibrium processes occurring at lower temperatures, such as may arise in differentiated bodies. It is clear, however, from the presence of water ice in comets that they cannot have accumulated at temperatures much above $\simeq 200\,$K. Otherwise, unless the process occurred in a gravitationally bound condensation, the ice would have sublimated and been rapidly lost from the system.

Yamamoto (1985b) has extended this general line of argument to encompass other common ices, and finds that in the solar nebula context comet formation must have taken place below about 60 K (*cf.* Whipple 1978b). An even more severe constraint is set by the discovery, with the IUE satellite, of the molecule S_2 close to the nucleus of Comet IRAS-Araki-Alcock (A'Hearn & Feldman 1985). The free lifetime of this sulphur dimer is so short, and its production time in the interstellar medium so long, that it seems that it must have originated *in situ* when the comet was first formed (Greenberg *et al.* 1985). Greenberg and colleagues infer that the nucleus must therefore have been formed and maintained at temperatures less than 15 K, and that on aggregation the grain speeds were no higher than 40 m s^{-1}. These requirements would seem to rule out comet formation anywhere within about 10^2 AU of the protosun, and additionally place tight constraints on any environment involving collisions between free particles orbiting the sun within its sphere of influence. If subsequent processing is disallowed, comet formation in conditions of extreme cold and quiescence seems to be indicated. The current trends, then, are towards the extreme periphery of the supposed solar nebula, to dense clouds within interstellar space, or to the atmosphere of a rapidly cooled parent body. These alternatives are so remarkably different that, even though the issue is not yet settled, the prospects for doing so would seem to be very much at hand.

19.2   Synopsis

In this monograph we have traced developments in understanding the origin of comets from the earliest days right up to the present, highlighting the important links with other branches of astronomy and the contemporary cosmology of the day. For example, the first reliable source of information about the origin of comets dates from the founding of early Greek science, though there are hints of similar ideas reaching right into prehistory and exciting links with the possibility that the current interplanetary complex may be an example of a rapidly decaying system evolving on a timescale on the order of 10^4 years.

Thus, Aristotle's account of the Milky Way as an accumulation of the disintegration products of many comets leaps sharply into focus, when, as we have argued, the term 'Milky Way' is replaced by 'zodiacal light'. The prominence given to discussions of meteoric phenomena by the early Greek philosophers, and the curious insistence that the 'stars' lie below either the sun or moon and that the Milky Way is in the earth's shadow, combine to give the impression of a rather more active celestial environment than we now have. In the light of present knowledge, it now seems reasonable to attribute this to a relatively recent change in the local short-period comet population. Indeed, if this hypothesis should prove correct, the earliest Greek accounts of creation, in which the currently observed world is said to have been built out of elements deriving from a cosmic egg (e.g. West 1971), might now be interpreted as having been founded on earlier observations of the evolution and decay of an exceptionally large periodic comet whose disintegration may have been witnessed by a possibly fearful populace in protohistoric times.

With regard to cometary origins, however, despite the attention given to the subject by the early Greek philosophers and the many suggestions at this time that comets were definitely celestial bodies (cf. Apollonius Myndus and Seneca), the Aristotelian view — that comets were merely a kind of insubstantial atmospheric fire — eventually led the field. To a considerable degree, as we have shown, the Aristotelian view owed its survival to its attractiveness as part of a general theoretical package supporting a distinctly moral outlook on the world, incorporated first into Roman, then Islamic, and later European thinking, each time apparently following some major upheaval in the sky. As a consequence, despite the survival also in Europe of a generally 'protestant' view of the world, harking back to the much earlier Babylonian view of the cosmos, the Aristotelian view remained pre-eminent, especially in political circles, for nearly two thousand years. The rôle of comets in human affairs was inevitably perceived as being of little importance.

Indeed, it was not until 1577, following the careful observations by Tycho Brahe which proved the comet of that year lay beyond the moon, that Aristotelian dogma (as it had become) is seen now as having been finally overthrown. But, as we have also shown, the presumption that Aristotelian dogma was completely overturned at this stage has itself become something of a dogma, the new view of comets that arrived not being entirely unconstrained by former ideas.

In this way, by the beginning of the seventeenth century the celestial nature of comets became firmly established, and the question 'atmospheric or celestial' changed quickly into a debate 'solar system vs. interstellar'. One of the first to present a solar system model seems to have been Hevelius, whilst somewhat earlier, Kepler had suggested that comets arrived from interstellar space and that they travelled in straight lines. It was Halley, however, who seems first to have insisted that comets ought to be subject to Newton's universal law of gravity, whereupon their vast sizes (and presumed masses) once again raised serious concern over the human significance of comets.

In particular, Halley and Whiston believed that comets could cause terrestrial catastrophes; but Newton argued instead that comets were the means by which stars and planets could replenish their resources and sustain life. Although these ideas each had supporters and detractors, when it was finally appreciated a century or so later that cometary masses were relatively small and that they decayed into ineffectual streams of dust, the suggestion that comets might continue to exert a major influence on the earth eventually became unfashionable and was quietly forgotten. Again there was a regression in the perceived significance of comets, and geologists and biologists began to develop new theories of evolution based entirely on terrestrial processes.

These years up to about 1800 were ones in which the study of cometary origins made slow progress. Kant (1755) was probably the first to present a 'scientific' theory of comet formation based on a solar nebula hypothesis; but during the nineteenth century most astronomers tended to follow Laplace (1805), who argued that comets could not easily be incorporated into this kind of theory. In fact, Laplace argued that comets could be captured from interstellar space by the action of Jupiter, and his theory appeared to explain not only the observed excess of nearly parabolic orbits but also the existence of short-period comets. However, he had neglected the finite velocity of the sun with respect to the comets, and, as Schiaparelli (*c.*1860) seems first to have pointed out, this completely reversed Laplace's conclusions, suggesting instead the existence of a solar system comet cloud (*cf.* Peirce 1849).

Another defect with the capture theory was that it did not quantitatively predict the observed number of short-period comets. This problem led Proctor (*c.*1880) to revive the planetary explosion theory for these comets, which had earlier been proposed by Lagrange (1814) and independently by Brewster about the same time. However, despite these severe difficulties for the interstellar theory, it was not until nearly the end of the nineteenth century that most astronomers seriously began to reconsider the solar system hypothesis.

The early years of the present century, therefore, saw comets being reintroduced into the nebular hypothesis on a more or less *ad hoc* basis, and the proportion of long-period *vs.* short-period comets was at first explained essentially on a Darwinian 'survival of the fittest' approach (Crommelin 1910). When, however, as a result of progress in the field of nuclear physics, a vastly increased age for the solar system was accepted by astronomers, measured now in thousands of millions of years, the Darwinian argument was reversed, and in fact shown to lead to a *reductio ad absurdum* for the solar system model. This led to a temporary revival in the interstellar theory, strengthened also by the apparent solar apex and galactic equator alignments which by then were beginning to be found (*e.g.* Eddington 1913) in the distribution and orientation of long-period cometary orbits on the sky.

This line of argument finally culminated in the suggestion by Bobrovnikoff (1929a) that perhaps the sun's present family of comets had been recently captured from a dense interstellar cloud of comets, about 10^6 years ago. This was the first suggestion that we might now be living at a rather special epoch so far as long-period comets are concerned, the idea conflicting with the generally uniformitarian view of nature that had already become well established by this time. Needless to say, the notion was not particularly well received, especially because somewhat unusual circumstances were considered necessary in order to justify possible fluctuations in the size of the earth's family of comets. Within a few years, an alternative 'steady-state' primordial solar system solution to the problem was presented by Öpik (1932), which in some ways anticipated many of the concepts used later so successfully by Oort (1950). Russell (1935), however, considered that both suggestions to explain long-period comets involved so many uncertain and ad hoc assumptions that neither could be believed.

The period immediately following publication of Oort's paper in 1950, however, was dominated by discussions both of this important work and of the new theory of cometary origin proposed by Lyttleton two years earlier. For reasons we have described, Oort's solar system hypothesis was rapidly accepted by virtually the whole astronomical community, and for almost thirty years theories of cometary origin came to rest on the foundation of a 'standard' Oort cloud. On this hypothesis, comets were supposed to be formed somehow in the primordial solar nebula, and subsequently placed into orbits extending nearly half-way to the nearest stars from whence observed long-period comets are seen to come.

During the last two decades, however, the situation has once more begun to change, stimulated again by new inputs from other sciences and branches of astronomy. First and foremost, there has been the evidence space-age astronomy, of cratering and meteoroidal débris in the inner solar system, leading to a growth in our understanding of the potentially important rôle played by earth-crossing asteroids and meteor streams in terrestrial affairs. In addition, there has been the evidence of galactic astronomy: the discovery of giant molecular clouds and the effects of the galactic tide have likewise had a profound effect on our understanding of the comet cloud, primordial or otherwise, raising the interrelated issues of comet showers, Oort cloud disruption and its possible replenishment.

These studies suggest that a whole variety of galactic obstacles may take a hand in controlling the flux of comets into the inner planetary system — with potentially catastrophic consequences. Moreover, if a few large short-period comets are the major source of the Apollo earth-crossing asteroid and meteoroid populations, this conclusion becomes even stronger, and the whole question of the importance of comets to the evolution of the earth needs once again to be examined. Indeed, the earth now appears to be under the influence of an episodically varying astronomical environment, and there are significant strands of evidence pointing towards new and unexpected historical and biological connexions. These considerations suggest that we are now beginning, only at this surprisingly late stage, to shed from science the last vestiges of a wholly fantastic cometary dogma devised by Aristotle, whose principles first became rooted in European thought some seven or eight hundred years ago.

We still do not know where comets are born, whether in a solar nebula or beyond. However, these and other astrophysical inputs to the subject in recent years have served both to heighten interest in comets and to tighten severely the range of acceptable possibilities. We live in an exciting period: long-established notions are being overthrown, new ideas and unexpected interrelations are frequently being advanced. Undoubtedly, the subject will continue to surprise its practitioners, and others, for years to come. The origin of comets, with implications for a host of other fields, is now high on the human and scientific agenda.

A

Appendix A:
Oort cloud evolution

A.1 Half-life estimates

The simplest way of dealing with the problem of determining the half-life of the Oort cloud is to consider the evolution of the cometary energy spectrum $N(E,t)$, where $N(E,t)\,dE$ represents the total number of comets in the cloud at time t with orbital energies per unit mass E in the range $(E, E + dE)$, and $E = -GM_\odot/2a$. In fact, for example under Oort's assumptions of spherical symmetry and isotropy of the cometary velocity distribution at each point in the cloud (*i.e.* the orbital velocities at each point are directed randomly), there is a straightforward connexion between the energy spectrum $N(E,t)$ and the cometary number density $n_c(r,t)$ at heliocentric distance r. Thus, the evolution of the energy spectrum gives direct information on the slowly varying density distribution of comets in the cloud and on the inevitable losses to interstellar space. For example, if the energy spectrum is a strict power law, *i.e.* $N(E) \propto |E|^{-\gamma}$, then it can be shown (Bailey 1983a) that the density distribution in the cloud is approximately a power law in radius, with $n_c(r) \propto r^{\gamma-4}$. Indeed, Oort's 1950 model of the comet cloud is a power-law model of just this type, with $\gamma = 5/2$; and hence on this model $n_c(r) \propto r^{-3/2}$ (*cf.* equation 9.3).

Following Bailey (1983a, 1986a), the general expression for the evolution of the energy spectrum can be written in the form

$$\frac{\partial N}{\partial t} = \frac{\partial}{\partial x}\left\{\frac{N\langle\Delta\dot{E}\rangle}{(GM_\odot/2)}\right\} + \frac{1}{2}\frac{\partial^2}{\partial x^2}\left\{\frac{N\langle(\Delta\dot{E})^2\rangle}{(GM_\odot/2)^2}\right\} \qquad (A.1)$$

where $x = 1/a$, and $\langle\Delta\dot{E}\rangle$ is the mean rate of change of orbital energy (*i.e.* $\langle\Delta\dot{E}\rangle \equiv \dot{\varepsilon}$) and $\langle(\Delta\dot{E})^2\rangle$ is the mean-square change of the same quantity. This rather formidable expression is, in fact, only slightly different from the diffusion equation described in Section 8.2.4, which occurs in the discussion of the evolution of the $1/a$ distribution under the influence of planetary perturbations. For example, if we make the usual assumption that planetary perturbations are likely to change E equally in either a positive or negative sense, then $\langle \Delta \dot{E} \rangle = 0$ and $\langle (\Delta \dot{E})^2 \rangle = (GM_\odot/2)^2 \sigma_E^2/P(x)$, where σ_E is the r.m.s. change in $1/a$ per revolution and P is the orbital period. Hence, since $N(x,t) = \nu(x,t)\,P(x)$, equation (A.1) reduces to the identical diffusion equation solved by van Woerkom more than forty years ago.

In the present case, of course, the mean energy transfer rate is not zero, so a given comet not only experiences a diffusive 'random walk' in energy (as in the case of planetary perturbations), but it also steadily gains energy according to the magnitude of the mean energy transfer rate occurring in the first term on the right-hand side of equation (A.1). The solution of this equation is simplified, however, by the fact that it can be shown that $\langle (\Delta \dot{E})^2 \rangle \simeq -4k\,E\langle \Delta \dot{E} \rangle$, where k is a numerical factor of order unity. The particular value of k depends on the relative size of the individual changes in a comet's velocity (due to perturbations) compared with its r.m.s. orbital speed: for stellar perturbations (in which this ratio is small) $k = 1/3$, while for molecular cloud perturbations (for which typical velocity perturbations may be larger and for which one should also check that the whole diffusion approximation does not begin to break down; cf. Weinberg et al. 1986) values of k may range up to $\gtrsim 1$. Thus, apart from the parameter k, both the unknown quantities on the right-hand side of equation (A.1) are in principle known once the mean energy transfer rate has been calculated, and one can then solve the equation using standard numerical or analytical techniques. In fact, this kind of equation turns out to be extremely common in many branches of physics and astrophysics, occurring for example in fields such as the study of stellar accretion discs, protostellar discs and protoplanetary discs, and even in the dense 'nuclear' discs found in galactic centres (e.g. Lynden-Bell & Pringle 1974, Bath & Pringle 1981, Lissauer 1984, Bailey 1982, 1985b, 1986a).

In particular, if one assumes that the mean energy transfer rate varies as a constant power of the semi-major axis (e.g. $\dot{\varepsilon}(a)$ = constant or $\dot{\varepsilon} \propto a^2$; cf. equation 12.6), one can obtain an analytic solution of equation (A.1) and hence determine the evolution of the cometary energy spectrum in terms of the assumed slope of the power law and the value of the parameter $k = \langle (\Delta \dot{E})^2 \rangle / 4|E|\langle \Delta \dot{E} \rangle$. Although the validity of such solutions should not be pressed too far, this analytic approach provides a useful complement to the more complicated Monte Carlo simulations of the same problem that have been completed, and it allows the numerical results of different authors (whose calculations often use slightly different initial conditions and assumptions) to be more easily interrelated and compared with one another.

The principal underlying objective of these studies is to determine the number of primordial comets that might survive in the Oort cloud until the present day, in particular as a function of semi-major axis. Since the comets with the largest semi-major axes are those with the least stable orbits, there appears a 'critical' semi-major axis, a_{crit}, beyond which at least half the primordial comets with $a \geq a_{\mathrm{crit}}$ will have been lost from the solar system during its lifetime. In the same way one can define a 'half-life', $t_{1/2}(a)$, as the time necessary for precisely half the comets with some initial semi-major axis to be removed. Setting $t_{1/2}(a) = T$ (the age of the solar system), allows a_{crit} to be determined.

The precise expression for $t_{1/2}(a)$ will naturally depend on the detailed form of the expression for the mean energy transfer rate (for example, on whether the orbits are such that stellar or molecular cloud perturbations are dominant), and also on the choice of the coefficient k which determines the relative importance of the diffusive and secular terms in the energy evolution equation. For the relevant cases $\dot{\varepsilon} = A_* = $ constant and $\dot{\varepsilon}(a) = A_c a^2$, appropriate to stellar and molecular cloud perturbations respectively, the results of Bailey (1986a) can be summarized by the following relatively simple expression:

$$
t_{1/2} = \begin{cases} GM_\odot/(4k_{1/2}A_*a) & \dot{\varepsilon} = A_* = \text{const.} \\[2mm] GM_\odot/(36k'_{1/2}A_c a^3) & \dot{\varepsilon} = A_c a^2 \end{cases} \qquad (A.2)
$$

where $(k_{1/2}, k'_{1/2}) = (0.725, 0.178)$ and $(1.183, 0.227)$ for $k = 1/3$ and $k = 1$ respectively. In this way, substituting the approximate values $A_* \simeq 10^{-13}\,\text{m}^2\,\text{s}^{-3}$ and $A_c \simeq 10^{-44}\,\text{s}^{-3}$ for stars and clouds respectively, we obtain $t_{1/2,*} \simeq 6\text{--}10 \times 10^9 a_4^{-1}\,\text{yr}$ and $t_{1/2,c} \simeq 1.5\text{--}2.0 \times 10^9 a_4^{-3}\,\text{yr}$, where $a_4 = a/10^4\,\text{AU}$. These results again confirm the overall significance of molecular cloud perturbations for the long-term evolution of comets with $a \gtrsim 1\text{--}2 \times 10^4\,\text{AU}$, and show that the critical semi-major axis for which the half-life equals the age of the solar system, taking both kinds of perturbation into account, is on the order of $10^4\,\text{AU}$ (cf. Hut & Tremaine 1985, Bailey 1986a, Shoemaker & Wolfe 1986, Torbett 1986, Weinberg et al. 1986, 1987; Wasserman 1988).

A.2   Results of Monte-Carlo studies

The problem of numerically determining the evolution of cometary orbits is conceptually quite straightforward: one defines an initial orbit, and integrates it forwards in time under the combined influences of the sun, planets, passing stars, molecular clouds and the galactic tide, until it is eventually captured (ultimately to decay) or ejected from the solar system. The process is then repeated as often as necessary, until a sufficient number of comets have been evolved to give a statistically significant result for the evolution of the Oort cloud as a whole. Unfortunately, however, such an approach would be prohibitively expensive in computer time, let alone astronomers' time, and all the calculations that have been completed so far have had to rely upon one or another set of approximations in order to obtain results within a reasonable length of time.

The sorts of approximations that have been made are legion; and it is this which makes the task of comparing the results of different authors and of different Monte Carlo simulations so difficult: they all use slightly different assumptions and initial conditions, and, in some cases, even approximations that strictly speaking are not really appropriate to the problem in hand. It is nevertheless still useful to summarize the main conclusions from these studies, and in this section we highlight the most important common results. This is a necessarily brief survey of a complex field, and we refer the interested reader to the reviews by Fernández (1985a), Weissman (1982, 1985a,b, 1986a) and Froeschlé & Rickman (1988), and to individual papers by Fernández (1980b, 1982a,b), Mignard & Remy (1985), Remy & Mignard (1985), Duncan *et al.* (1987) and Lopatnikov *et al.* (1989).

The most frequently used approximation is to represent the perturbations of a planet, star or molecular cloud by a simple impulse, having a certain magnitude and direction, which is applied to the cometary orbit at a particular (or sometimes random) part of its orbit. In the case of planetary perturbations, the net result is to effect a certain change in the energy of the cometary orbit, with a magnitude governed by a particular probability distribution of energy changes with dispersion σ_E. The probability distribution of energy changes is usually taken to be Gaussian, though as we have seen (Everhart 1968, Stagg & Bailey 1989) a more realistic description is one in which the energy changes are largely determined by a component that falls off with increasing energy roughly proportional to $|E|^{-3}$ and in which the extended wings of the distribution may contain substantial asymmetric terms (Oikawa & Everhart 1979).

In the case of stellar perturbations the problem is intrinsically more complicated, as the distribution of $\Delta \mathbf{v}$ values is certainly non-Gaussian, and includes a significant stochastic element due to the unpredictable values of the stellar mass, encounter velocity and impact parameter, if these are allowed to vary in the model. Similar problems also arise in the case of molecular cloud perturbations.

An important point to bear in mind is that although comets spend most of their time near aphelion (the point in their orbit furthest from the sun, where they are moving most slowly), the actual value of the energy change per encounter also depends on the orbital velocity at the time of the perturbation. Simulations such as those of Weissman (1977, 1979, 1982, 1985b,c), which apply the impulse $\Delta\mathbf{v}$ at aphelion, have thus tended to underestimate the random 'diffusive' element of the energy change (cf. Remy & Mignard 1985, and equation 9.4), and hence have underestimated the degree of diffusive loss from the Oort cloud to interstellar space. In a similar way, if one assumes that the distribution of velocity changes is Gaussian, when in fact it is not (cf. Everhart 1968, Mignard & Remy 1985), one will again underestimate the losses of comets both from the planetary region and the Oort cloud.

A second frequently used approximation is to start the calculation with orbits that in some sense are already in the Oort cloud. This has the advantage that the initial complicated phase of construction of the Oort cloud can be ignored, but it has the great disadvantage that it is then often difficult to relate the calculated results unambiguously to particular models of cometary origin, such as the planetesimal picture.

The third, and perhaps the most understandable approximation, is simply to leave out a whole class of perturber entirely, for example the effects of the galactic tide (see Appendix B) or of molecular clouds. Although this may be justified for orbits with relatively small semi-major axes (e.g. $a \lesssim 10^4$ AU), in order to understand the dynamics of the outer *observed* part of the Oort cloud (corresponding to comets with $a \gtrsim 2 \times 10^4$ AU) the inclusion of such effects is an absolute necessity. This is particularly important, of course, if one subsequently attempts to use the calculated results in conjunction with observations to infer the actual number of comets with semi-major axes less than 10^4 AU.

A summary of results from a selected sample of such calculations is presented in Tables A.1 and A.2. The first of these presents the initial conditions and injection timescale assumed for the comets, while the second gives the proportion of comets that finish up (after 4.5×10^9 years) in each of the defined end-states. Although there is considerable overlap among the models that have been investigated, usually one or another version of the planetesimal picture or a model in which comets are somehow formed *in situ* in the Oort cloud, there are many detailed differences in the computational methods and assumptions used, and the results are often quite strikingly different. Thus, while the general features of the evolution of cometary orbits from the planetary system into the Oort cloud are now beginning to be reasonably well understood, a complete understanding of their precise long-term evolution is still lacking.

A detailed discussion of the models presented in these tables and of the principal reasons for the various discrepancies is beyond the scope of the present review, and in what follows we merely attempt to indicate what are probably the most important limitations or assumptions underlying each result. The interested reader should read these tables with care, and consult the original sources for further details on the computational procedures and/or references to other work.

First, in models W1–W6 (Weissman 1982, Table I), the results primarily indicate how increasing the initial perihelion distance of the original orbits leads to a steady reduction in the number of comets lost to the 'planetary ejection' end-state. This covers comets which either finished up under the gravitational influence of the major planets or were ejected hyperbolically by planetary perturbations. The effect is seen in the increasing proportion of survivors with initial perihelion distance, the other orbital parameters being kept constant, and is also present in the results of models D1–D7 (Duncan *et al.* 1987, Table I). Weissman (1982) also quotes results for different values of the aphelion distance and for cases in which the overall effect of stellar perturbations is greater than that assumed for models W1–W6, which are based on a total r.m.s. velocity perturbation over the age of

Model	Initial conditions			
	q (AU)	a (AU)	i (deg)	Injection interval (10^9 yr)
W1	20	2.0×10^4	Random	$t_0 = 0$
W2	100	2.0×10^4	Random	$t_0 = 0$
W3	200	2.0×10^4	Random	$t_0 = 0$
W4	1000	2.0×10^4	Random	$t_0 = 0$
W5	2000	2.1×10^4	Random	$t_0 = 0$
W6	10000	2.5×10^4	Random	$t_0 = 0$
F1	20–30	$> 10^4$	0–10	0.0–4.5
F2	20–30	$> 10^4$	0–10	0.5–1.5
F3	4–6	$> 10^4$	0–10	0.0–1.0
F4	1.0×10^4	1.0×10^4	0–10	$t_0 = 0$
F5	2.5×10^4	2.5×10^4	0–10	$t_0 = 0$
F6	5.0×10^4	5.0×10^4	0–10	$t_0 = 0$
R1	200–300	2.0–2.5×10^4	Random	$t_0 = 0$
R2	1.5–3×10^4	3–4×10^4	Random	$t_0 = 0$
R3	$\lesssim 10^5$	$\lesssim 10^5$	Random	$t_0 = 0$
R4	$\lesssim 2 \times 10^4$	$\lesssim 3 \times 10^4$	Random	$t_0 = 0$
R5	2–9×10^3	5–10×10^3	Random	$t_0 = 0$
D1	5	2000	18	$t_0 = 0$
D2	10	2000	18	$t_0 = 0$
D3	15	2000	18	$t_0 = 0$
D4	20	2000	18	$t_0 = 0$
D5	25	2000	18	$t_0 = 0$
D6	30	2000	18	$t_0 = 0$
D7	35	2000	18	$t_0 = 0$

Table A.1: Initial conditions for a selected sample of Monte Carlo studies of Oort cloud evolution. See text for discussion.

Model	Proportion of comets in each end-state				
	Planetary ejection	Stellar ejection	Diffusion $(r > 1\,\mathrm{pc})$	Diffusion (small a)	Survivors
W1	0.834	0.00	0.009	0.00	0.157
W2	0.609	0.00	0.024	0.00	0.367
W3	0.520	0.00	0.033	0.00	0.447
W4	0.313	0.00	0.051	0.00	0.636
W5	0.222	0.00	0.073	0.00	0.705
W6	0.075	0.00	0.212	0.00	0.713
F1	0.320		0.35	0.08	0.25
F2	0.330		0.51	0.08	0.08
F3	0.540		0.27	0.18	0.01
F4	0.000		0.08	0.00	0.92
F5	0.004		0.60	0.00	0.40
F6	0.004		0.94	0.00	0.06
R1	0.350	0.08	0.43	0.00	0.14
R2	0.040	0.10	0.80	0.00	0.06
R3	0.040	0.06	0.79	0.00	0.11
R4	0.050	0.09	0.26	0.00	0.60
R5	0.005	0.005	0.01	0.00	0.98
D1	0.840	0.02	0.04	0.09	0.02
D2	0.730	0.01	0.15	0.06	0.06
D3	0.450	0.05	0.21	0.05	0.24
D4	0.460	0.02	0.17	0.06	0.29
D5	0.440	0.01	0.16	0.05	0.34
D6	0.410	0.01	0.15	0.04	0.40
D7	0.350	0.03	0.13	0.04	0.41

Table A.2: Results from a selected sample of Monte Carlo studies of Oort cloud evolution. See text for discussion.

the solar system of magnitude $\Delta V_{\text{rms}} \equiv (2\dot{\varepsilon}_* T)^{1/2} = 120\,\text{m\,s}^{-1}$ (*cf.* equation 12.2). The principal limitations of these results are (i) the assumption that stars are the dominant perturbers in the outer solar system (*i.e.* the effects of molecular clouds and the galactic tide have been neglected), and (ii) the approximation that stellar perturbations can be modelled by a random impulse, applied at the aphelion position of the cometary orbit with a magnitude drawn from a Gaussian distribution with dispersion appropriate to ΔV_{rms}. As we have already mentioned, this approximation leads to an underestimate of the rate at which very eccentric orbits diffuse in energy, and hence to a systematic underestimate of the diffusive losses from the Oort cloud, both inwards and outwards.

Secondly, in models F1–F6, Fernández (1982a, Tables II and III) has investigated models that represent both the planetesimal picture (a Uranus-Neptune zone origin, F1 and F2; a Jupiter-zone origin, F3) and the *in situ* variety (models F4–F6). In these simulations the diffusive losses by stellar perturbations to $r \gtrsim 1\,\text{pc}$ and direct stellar ejection (stellar loss by a single close encounter) were counted as one, and although greater care was taken in the treatment of stellar and planetary perturbations than in Weissman's models, the effects of molecular clouds and the galactic tide were again ignored. Among the many detailed results to be obtained from this study, perhaps the most important were the demonstrably low survival probability for comets formed with initially long-period orbits in Jupiter's zone (*cf.* model D1), and (not shown here) the relatively large initial mass of comets necessary in the *in situ* models (F4–F6) in order to explain the currently observed flux of comets with small perihelia.

The study by Remy & Mignard, models R1–R5 (see Remy 1984, and Remy & Mignard 1985, Table II), once again considered only stellar perturbations, but this time gave an improved treatment of the non-Gaussian form of the distribution of impulses and included allowance for perturbations at random positions of the orbit. The principal result shown here is the extreme sensitivity of the diffusive losses from the Oort cloud to large distances as semi-major axes $a \gtrsim 3 \times 10^4$ AU and $a \lesssim 10^4$ AU are considered. This may be approximately understood in terms of our previous discussion of the half-life of the Oort cloud, which when stellar perturbations alone are considered equals the age of the solar system for a semi-major axis on the order of 2×10^4 AU. The sharp increase in the diffusive losses indicated by Weissman's models W5 to W6 may also be partly due to this effect, though the losses in models W5 and earlier (which correspond to only slightly smaller semi-major axes) have been somewhat depressed by application of the stellar impulse at aphelion.

Finally, among the most comprehensive Monte Carlo studies yet reported is the investigation by Duncan *et al.* (1987, Table I), shown here as models D1–D7. This calculation again ignored molecular cloud perturbations, but it did include the effects of stellar and planetary perturbations and made an approximate allowance for the galactic tide. The initial conditions were chosen to resemble a stage in the evolution of planetesimals originally formed in the Uranus-Neptune zone of the solar nebula. Although quite a high proportion of survivors is indicated for such comets, it should be remembered that this figure should be multiplied by a further efficiency factor to represent the probability for an initially nearly circular orbit with $q \simeq 30$ AU to evolve into the adopted starting orbit with $a = 2000$ AU. (On the basis of the argument leading to Table 11.1 we estimate that this factor should be on the order of $\approx 30\%$.) Among the conclusions drawn by Duncan *et al.* from their numerical investigation was that the combination of stellar, galactic and planetary perturbations would lead, after 4.5×10^9 years' evolution, to a density distribution described by $n_c(r) \propto r^{-3.5}$ (for $3000 \lesssim r \lesssim 5 \times 10^4$ AU).

This important result indicates that, at least on the planetesimal picture of comet formation, the observed near-parabolic flux may imply the existence of a dense inner core to the Oort cloud (*cf.* Section 13.3, p.286). One should remember, however, that despite this intriguing and potentially significant result, it cannot yet be claimed that the presence of an inner core has been firmly established — since the same observations might be equally consistent with the hypothesis of recent capture of comets from a molecular cloud or spiral arm! This alternative explanation (Section 15.2, p.344) has not yet been examined numerically in similar detail to the planetesimal picture; indeed, it is difficult to see how it could have been, since there is much less agreement on this model in specifying the appropriate initial conditions. In the end, therefore, it may finally turn out that factors other than purely dynamical ones (such as the age of comets or episodicity in the terrestrial record) will eventually prove more conclusive.

B

Appendix B:
Tidal detail

In the same way that perturbations from passing stars and molecular clouds sometimes deflect comets in their orbits about the sun, so too it appears that the overall distribution of matter in the Galaxy may introduce a slight 'tidal' disturbance of the sun-comet system, causing small, but significant long-term changes in the normally elliptical cometary orbits about the sun. Here, we briefly show how the general expression for the galactic tidal force can be derived, under the assumption of axisymmetry of the galactic potential, and then illustrate, slightly expanding upon the treatments given by Byl (1983, 1986) and Heisler & Tremaine (1986), how this may be used to derive the perturbed equations of motion for comets moving about the sun in the presence of galactic tidal field.

B.1 Tidal force

As before, we specify the position of a star or comet in the Galaxy by the vector $\mathbf{R} = (R, \Theta, Z)$, where R denotes the distance from the galactic centre projected on to the galactic plane, Θ is the angular variable measured in the direction of galactic rotation, and Z determines the height above the plane. Since the galactic potential ϕ_{gal} cannot depend on the angular variable Θ (by symmetry), we may write the gravitational acceleration of the Galaxy, $\mathbf{F}_{gal}$, in the general form $\mathbf{F}_{gal}(\mathbf{R}) = \mathbf{F}_{gal}(R, Z) = -\nabla \phi_{gal}(R, Z)$.

Thus, if we now define $\mathbf{R}_0 = (R_0, \Theta_0, Z_0)$ to be the galactic coordinates of the sun at some instant and let $\mathbf{R} = \mathbf{R}_0 + \mathbf{r}$ denote the coordinates of a comet with heliocentric position $\mathbf{r}$, the differential force between the comet and the sun is given by

$$\mathbf{F}_{tide}(\mathbf{r}, \mathbf{R}_0) = \mathbf{F}_{gal}(\mathbf{R}_0 + \mathbf{r}) - \mathbf{F}_{gal}(\mathbf{R}_0) \simeq (\mathbf{r}.\nabla)\mathbf{F}_{gal} \qquad (B.1)$$

We now expand this expression into its three independent components by introducing a rotating rectangular heliocentric coordinate system to describe the three orthogonal contributions to the tidal force. Thus, we let $\mathbf{r} = (x, y, z)$ and define a set of coordinates with x-axis towards the galactic centre, y-axis in the tangential direction parallel to galactic rotation and z-axis perpendicular to the galactic plane. Then, since the scale of typical cometary orbits is very much less than that associated with variations of the galactic force (this is measured in hundreds or thousands of parsecs), we may expand equation (B.1) in powers of the small quantities x/r etc. and retain only the dominant terms. (Alternatively, one could simply look up the components of $(\mathbf{r}.\nabla)\mathbf{F}_{\text{gal}}$ in any standard astronomical text which gives a comprehensive summary of the most useful vectorial relations; e.g. Binney & Tremaine 1987.)

In this way, we finally obtain under the assumption of axisymmetry:

$$F_{\text{tide},x} \;=\; -x\,\left.\frac{\partial^2 \phi_{\text{gal}}}{\partial R^2}\right|_0 + z\,\left.\frac{\partial^2 \phi_{\text{gal}}}{\partial R \partial Z}\right|_0 \tag{B.2}$$

$$F_{\text{tide},y} \;=\; -y\,\left.\frac{1}{R}\frac{\partial \phi_{\text{gal}}}{\partial R}\right|_0 \tag{B.3}$$

$$F_{\text{tide},z} \;=\; +x\,\left.\frac{\partial^2 \phi_{\text{gal}}}{\partial R \partial Z}\right|_0 - z\,\left.\frac{\partial^2 \phi_{\text{gal}}}{\partial Z^2}\right|_0 \tag{B.4}$$

B.2   Perturbed equations of motion

We use the same rotating rectangular heliocentric coordinate system, defined so that the x-axis is directed towards the galactic axis of rotation. We also neglect any small variations in angular velocity due to the sun's epicyclic motions, and assume for simplicity that the coordinate system is rotating with constant angular velocity $\Omega_c = \Omega_c \hat{\mathbf{z}}$, where $\hat{\mathbf{z}}$ is the unit vector in the z-direction and $\Omega_c = V_c/R_c \simeq 26\,\text{km s}^{-1}\,\text{kpc}^{-1}$.

The forces acting on a comet at heliocentric position $\mathbf{r}$ may be divided in general into three categories: the gravitational forces due to the sun and the Galaxy; the inertial force due to the acceleration of the coordinate system (by virtue of the sun's nearly circular motion about the Galaxy); and the inertial forces introduced by the constant rotation of the frame of reference. The equations of motion of the comet can therefore be written in the form:

$$\ddot{\mathbf{r}} = -\frac{GM_\odot \mathbf{r}}{r^3} + \mathbf{F}_{gal}(\mathbf{R})$$
$$-\mathbf{F}_{gal}(\mathbf{R}_0) - \{2\mathbf{\Omega}_c \wedge \dot{\mathbf{r}} + \mathbf{\Omega}_c \wedge (\mathbf{\Omega}_c \wedge \mathbf{r})\} \qquad (B.5)$$

The combination $\mathbf{F}_{gal}(\mathbf{R}) - \mathbf{F}_{gal}(\mathbf{R}_0)$, where $\mathbf{R}$ and $\mathbf{R}_0$ as before denote the galactocentric coordinates of the comet and sun respectively, is just the galactic tide, while the terms due to rotation of the frame of reference (representing the Coriolis and centrifugal terms respectively) may easily be resolved into their respective x and y components. In this way we obtain

$$\ddot{x} = -\frac{GM_\odot x}{r^3} - x \left.\frac{\partial^2 \phi_{gal}}{\partial R^2}\right|_0 + z \left.\frac{\partial^2 \phi_{gal}}{\partial R \partial Z}\right|_0 + 2\Omega_c \dot{y} + \Omega_c^2 x$$

$$\ddot{y} = -\frac{GM_\odot y}{r^3} - y \frac{1}{R}\left.\frac{\partial \phi_{gal}}{\partial R}\right|_0 - 2\Omega_c \dot{x} + \Omega_c^2 y$$

$$\ddot{z} = -\frac{GM_\odot z}{r^3} + x \left.\frac{\partial^2 \phi_{gal}}{\partial R \partial Z}\right|_0 - z \left.\frac{\partial^2 \phi_{gal}}{\partial Z^2}\right|_0 \qquad (B.6)$$

(cf. Heisler & Tremaine 1986, Byl 1986).

The appearance in these equations of all three second derivatives of the galactic potential shows that a complete description of the galactic effects on the Oort cloud, including the vertical epicyclic oscillation of the solar system, requires a full three-dimensional model of the Galaxy in the solar neighbourhood. This could be provided, for example, by the modified Kuzmin (1956) galaxy model described by Miyamoto & Nagai (1975), cf. Binney & Tremaine (1987), from which one can show that the usually neglected terms (e.g. $\partial^2 \phi_{gal}/\partial R \partial Z$) typically come in at about the 5–20% level depending on the height Z_0 of the sun above the galactic plane. Indeed, one might even question the implicit assumption of axisymmetry in these models, especially were the sun to lie close to a massive spiral arm or group of molecular clouds. However, a detailed investigation of these effects is beyond the scope of the present discussion, though we do emphasize that they might introduce significant modifications to the simple results described in Chapter 12, including potentially important periodic effects on both the evolution and injection rate of long-period comets.

The relative size of the various terms entering the expression for the galactic tide can now be estimated by assuming $Z_0 \simeq 0$ and making use of the definitions of Oort's constants A and B. This gives

$$\left.\frac{\partial^2 \phi_{\text{gal}}}{\partial R^2}\right|_{Z_0=0} = B^2 - 3A^2 + 2AB$$

$$\simeq -(28.7 \ \text{km}\,\text{s}^{-1}\ \text{kpc}^{-1})^2 \qquad \text{(B.7)}$$

$$\left.\frac{1}{R}\frac{\partial \phi_{\text{gal}}}{\partial R}\right|_{Z_0=0} = \Omega_{\text{c}}^2$$

$$\simeq +(26.0 \ \text{km}\,\text{s}^{-1}\ \text{kpc}^{-1})^2 \qquad \text{(B.8)}$$

$$\left.\frac{\partial^2 \phi_{\text{gal}}}{\partial R \partial Z}\right|_{Z_0=0} = 0 \qquad \text{(B.9)}$$

$$\left.\frac{\partial^2 \phi_{\text{gal}}}{\partial Z^2}\right|_{Z_0=0} = 4\pi G \rho_0 - 2(B^2 - A^2) \qquad \text{(B.10)}$$

where the latter equation reduces to

$$\left.\frac{\partial^2 \phi_{\text{gal}}}{\partial Z^2}\right|_{Z_0=0} = C^2 \simeq (100 \ \text{km}\,\text{s}^{-1}\ \text{kpc}^{-1})^2 \qquad \text{(B.11)}$$

and the quoted value of C^2 corresponds to an observed mid-plane total mass density in the solar neighbourhood on the order of $\rho_0 \simeq 0.2 \, M_\odot \text{pc}^{-3}$.

These expressions thus show that the galactic tide is dominated by the compressive effect of gravitating matter in the galactic disc. This exceeds the radial component of the tide (which acts in the usual 'stretching' sense) by about an order of magnitude, and most authors have therefore tended only to include the z component of the perturbation (cf. Morris & Muller 1986, Heisler & Tremaine 1986, Byl 1986, Torbett 1986b). With this approximation, the equations of motion reduce to

$$\ddot{x} = -\frac{GM_{\odot}x}{r^3} + 2\Omega_c\dot{y} + \Omega_c^2 x \qquad (\mathrm{B.12})$$

$$\ddot{y} = -\frac{GM_{\odot}y}{r^3} - 2\Omega_c\dot{x} \qquad (\mathrm{B.13})$$

$$\ddot{z} = -\frac{GM_{\odot}z}{r^3} - C^2 z \qquad (\mathrm{B.14})$$

the effects of which are described in Chapter 12.

C

Appendix C:
Violent galaxy

The large-scale distribution of material in galaxies is believed to be consistent with its generally being dynamically relaxed; in other words, that at almost any location within a galaxy, there is as much material on ingoing as on outgoing orbits. The nearest galaxy in which it is possible to test this assumption is obviously our own, but our Galaxy has never provided unequivocal support for this hypothesis. Early this century, for example, it seemed certain that the nearby stars divided into several distinct streams (Eddington 1914), but eventually the view was taken that only two streams existed and that these were equally represented by all stellar types. This interpretation of the evidence was considered to be indistinguishable from a single ellipsoidal distribution (Oort 1927a), albeit one whose velocity dispersion steadily increased with age due to the presumed influence of massive perturbers in the galactic plane on the motions of stars (Spitzer & Schwarzschild 1951, 1953).

The physical picture underlying this scheme was the expected existence in the plane of a galaxy of a relaxed gaseous disc in Keplerian rotation, in which star formation is periodically triggered by the passage of a spiral density wave. The first opportunity to test this hypothesis arose with the discovery by radio astronomers of neutral hydrogen gas in our Galaxy and with the measurement of its relative motion, using the 21 cm line, throughout the disc. As it turned out, however, unexpectedly large radial motions were found in the gas (Rougoor & Oort 1960), especially in spiral features lying close to the galactic centre (within $R \simeq 4\,\mathrm{kpc}$), raising the possibility that spiral arms (and galaxies) are in a dynamically unrelaxed state after all. Alternatively, of course, the spiral features could be temporary perturbations of the gas in the disc due to some unforeseen gravitational or non-gravitational effect (for example, the effect of a massive bar in the galactic centre), and it is this assumption that is usually accepted at present.

The empirical evidence against this hypothesis, *i.e.* that our Galaxy has a violent, non-steady dynamical history, has been reviewed by Clube (1978). In particular, there is evidence that the local standard of rest corresponding to the nearest spiral arms has a very large outward motion in our Galaxy, and there have been further indications of a more general expansion, similar to that of the neutral hydrogen gas, in both the globular cluster system (Clube & Watson 1979, Clube & Waddington 1989b) and the motions of gas clouds lying very close to the galactic centre (Clube & Pan 1985, Gatley *et al.* 1986, Clube & Waddington 1989a). We now briefly review some of the background observations leading to the theory of galactic structure described in Section 16.3.1 (see p.379), and to the associated theory of comet formation based on the production of dust and ices in rapidly cooling condensations within an expanding, initially hot spiral arm system.

C.1   Star streams

The period immediately following the consolidation of the Oort cloud theory of cometary origin was notable also in seeing significant advances in understanding the motions of nearby bright stars (*e.g.* Eggen 1963, 1965). The volume by Blaauw & Schmidt (1965), for example, presents many useful reviews with associated references. In particular, careful measurements of the positions and movements of all the most massive stars no older than about 5×10^8 years (mostly corresponding to spectral types A and F) within about 100 pc of the sun indicated that nearly all these stars belonged to one or other of a few distinct 'common motion' groupings of differing age which pervaded more or less the whole of this region of space. The coherence in velocity space of the stars in these spatially intermingled groups is consistent with the presence of separate 'superclusters' of mass $\approx 10^7 \, M_\odot$

(Eggen 1987), each formed at discrete times in successive spiral arms. Such superclusters are not obviously consistent with the density wave theory, however, since their motions differ by as much as $50\,\mathrm{km\,s^{-1}}$ and seem (for their age) to be considerably in excess of those that are expected to be produced by subsequent massive perturbers in the galactic plane.

There seem to be three principal superclusters in the solar neighbourhood: (i) the Hyades stream; (ii) the Gould Belt stream; and (iii) the Sirius stream, each named (rather confusingly) after a different kind of object: an ordinary star cluster, a stellar supercluster, and a single star. These streams have mean motions (u, v) in the galactic plane of order $(-40, -10)$, $(-10, -15)$ and $(+15, +5)$ $\mathrm{km\,s^{-1}}$ respectively, where u denotes the speed in the radial direction towards the galactic centre and v is the speed in the transverse direction parallel to that of galactic rotation.

The second of these, the Gould Belt stream, represents the strongest concentration in local velocity space, its kinematic structure also displaying a general expansion which extends over a region of about $500\,\mathrm{pc}$ within the plane, centred on the $\alpha\,\mathrm{Per}$ stellar association approximately $150\,\mathrm{pc}$ from the sun. Within this broad region, the Gould Belt comprises many individual concentrations, such as the Pleiades cluster and the Scorpio-Centaurus association, the general rate of separation being about $3\,\mathrm{km\,s^{-1}}$per $100\,\mathrm{pc}$, consistent with an age for the system which is in agreement with that of its member stars. Broadly speaking, the overall pattern of motions within the Gould Belt is similar to that found for the various gaseous complexes in the the solar neighbourhood, which include both extremely cold material (molecular clouds) and extremely hot material (ionized gas), and which appear also to be moving as a whole with the reflex of the standard solar motion: $(u, v) \simeq (-10, -15)\,\mathrm{km\,s^{-1}}$. In fact, the whole of the Gould Belt complex seems to move in unison with the Galaxy's large-scale spiral structure, so that its particular A and F stars are indeed the youngest in the solar neighbourhood (i.e. with ages less than about 5×10^7 years), being associated with the large-scale comoving population of O and B-type stars. Such stars are not present in either the Hyades or the Sirius superclusters, consistent with these older populations having been created by the immediately preceding generations of spiral arms.

At the beginning of this century, Gould's Belt was already recognized as stream O (Halm 1911, Eddington 1914), while the remaining nearby stars were placed into either of two other streams: namely Stream I or Stream II. At a casual glance, these might be mistaken for the Hyades and Sirius superclusters, since their in-plane (u, v) velocities are about $(-24, -18)\,\mathrm{km\,s^{-1}}$ and $(+11, -9)\,\mathrm{km\,s^{-1}}$ respectively (Allen 1963, p.243). However, detailed differences in the velocity distributions of the stars belonging to each stream and those identified with stellar superclusters preclude such an intimate association, and instead suggest that Stream II, for example, which is virtually devoid of stars earlier than spectral type G, largely comprises an old galactic disc population having kinematic characteristics quite distinct from each of the three principal superclusters, including the current spiral arm system. Stream I, on the other hand, includes parts of Stream O and the Hyades stream, and is evidently a younger population overall.

Later this century, when it became necessary to consider a rotational model of the Galaxy (*e.g.* Oort 1927b), in which substantial streaming was assumed not to be present, Stream II was disposed of in such a way that the stars of later spectral type in Streams O and I, *unlike their comoving counterparts of early spectral type,* were merged with those of later spectral type in Stream II. This had the effect of combining late-type disc stars, regardless of their initial stream membership and age, into a single population with a mean velocity close to that of the standard solar motion reflex. The arbitrary reconstitution of Stream II did not immediately have universal support (*e.g.* Smart 1938) but nevertheless came to be generally accepted by most astronomers. The result of this development, now, is that the spiral arm system and the old disc population are generally perceived to be more or less comoving systems. This, of course, is in accord with the usual idea that spiral arms are simply density waves originating in an underlying stellar disc, itself containing negligible non-circular motions. However, if the original Stream II is accepted still as real, and we reject the arbitrary split between stars of early and late spectral type in Stream I, then the same evidence suggests spiral arms with an outward motion in the Galaxy, relative to the old disc (Stream II), of at least $20\,\mathrm{km\,s^{-1}}$.

C.2   Radial motion

That the model of the Galaxy as a system rotating in approximately centrifugal balance might be seriously in error first emerged with the large-scale radio surveys in H I and CO (Rougoor & Oort 1960, Kerr 1962, Sanders *et al.* 1984), and with the results of new proper-motion surveys of very faint stars (Vasilevskis & Klemola 1971). Both these surveys could be interpreted as indicating similar, but very large, outward motions that increase towards the galactic centre (Clube 1973, *cf.* Kerr 1962); whilst the expected outward motion of the Gould Belt supercluster relative to the Galaxy (about $40\,\mathrm{km\,s^{-1}}$) was also clearly present if, as seemed likely, the overall velocity field within $4\,\mathrm{kpc}$ of the centre was axially symmetric. Thus, major features at a distance of $3\,\mathrm{kpc}$ from the centre, in front of and beyond, which were in the form of atomic hydrogen arms, have an apparent outward motion of $95\,\mathrm{km\,s^{-1}}$. A cloud of molecular material around the radio source at the centre, Sagittarius A West, on the other hand, appears to be expanding only slightly, if at all, with the result that it shows an absorption feature at $40\,\mathrm{km\,s^{-1}}$ against Sagittarius A West due to the presumed outward motion of the local standard of rest.

The molecular cloud material at the centre has in fact the general characteristics of a rotating ring or doughnut, but a very clearly defined circumnuclear 'disc' has now also been discovered rather closer to the galactic centre, which likewise shows a systematic velocity of order $40\,km\,s^{-1}$ with respect to the local standard of rest (Gatley *et al.* 1986, Clube & Waddington 1989a). It is entirely possible, therefore, that the rejection of streaming motions in the Galaxy during the nineteen-twenties was a serious error, and it may well turn out that the spiral arms in the main galactic disc, as in the galactic centre (*e.g.* Sanders & Wrixon 1972, Cohen & Davies 1976), have a very strong radial motion in addition to their rotation around the centre.

The significance of this unexpected finding lies in its implications for the nature and origin of spiral arms. Spiral arms are where stars and comets are formed, and the greatly differing radial motions now inferred for the local arms of our Galaxy have greatly differing things to say about their origin, and hence about the possible origin of comets! In particular, whereas it is commonly held at present that comets and stars are formed via the gravitational collapse of cold gas and dust moving in nearly circular orbits in the disc of our Galaxy, the very strong radial outward motion of the arms, increasing rapidly towards the galactic centre, suggests that another process may be involved. Thus, as Jeans once suggested, such evidence may be pointing rather insistently to the galactic nucleus as the primary source of spiral structure: 'Each failure to explain the spiral arms makes it more and more difficult to resist a suspicion that the spiral nebulae are the seat of types of forces entirely unknown to us, forces which may possibly express novel and unsuspected metric properties of space' (Jeans 1928, p.352).

Indeed, recurrent activity in galactic nuclei (*e.g.* Bailey & Clube 1978, Sanders 1981) is now an accepted feature of galactic evolution, although its detailed manifestation naturally depends on the assumptions made as to the evolution of the massive central object (*cf.* Bailey 1982, 1985b). In the present context it is assumed that still unaccepted 'new' laws of physics may be involved. In this case, the active Seyfert and quasar phase of galactic evolution may be viewed as a general precursor of spiral structure, the observed spiral arms being produced by the collapse and subsequent release of ordinary material within the central kiloparsec or so of galaxies.   This is assumed to come about first through the formation of ordinary supermassive stars ($M \approx 10^6 \, M_\odot$) evolving under 'normal' physical laws, and then — as these stars eventually experience gravitational collapse — under the effects of the postulated 'new physics' (the Lorentz-Dicke theory described in Section 16.3.1, p.379) which implies the existence of a temporary highly inflated state ($M \approx 10^{14} \, M_\odot$) for such stars at the ends of their lives.   The very high redshifts of quasars are no longer cosmological under these circumstances, but are largely gravitational in origin, and are simply due to the temporary very large masses that are now implied.

There is nothing particularly strange in the suggested 'new physics', since supposedly novel 'metric properties of space' were generally regarded as quite plausible until about 1930 (cf. Ellis 1988), when the cosmological redshift could still be thought of as a purely gravitational redshift in a supposedly stationary universe (de Sitter 1917).   Theory in this instance could be interpreted as giving redshifts in the form (North 1965, p.137):

$$\frac{\lambda - \lambda_0}{\lambda_0} = \sum (1 + \frac{u}{c})(1 - \frac{u^2}{c^2})^{-1/2} - 1 \qquad (C.1)$$

where u is the relative motion of successive gravitating systems transmitting observed radiation; and it followed that, for a large enough path in a stationary, uniform (constant $\overline{u^2}$) universe, a linear redshift-distance relationship of the form of Hubble's law applied; i.e.

$$\frac{\lambda - \lambda_0}{\lambda_0} = \sum \frac{u^2}{c^2} \propto \frac{H}{c} r \qquad (C.2)$$

For gravitating systems as large as the typical separation of galaxies, the observed cosmological redshift gives a mean relative velocity $\bar{u} \simeq 10^3 \, \mathrm{km \, s^{-1}}$, but at a time when H was still considered to be an order of magnitude larger than its true value, and large-scale streaming in the universe along with cosmological dark matter had not been discovered (i.e. $|\bar{u}|$ was thought to be a few hundred $\mathrm{km \, s^{-1}}$ at most), this formulation did not seem particularly relevant. More recently, with the cosmological distance scale reduced and with the discovery of large-scale streaming in the universe, the shortcomings of equation (C.2) are not so evident. Nevertheless, although Jeans envisaged the possibility of occasional galactic nuclei with extreme metric properties (*i.e.* a highly inflated mass) and Milne (1948) continued to develop a purely kinematic cosmology in which the spiral galaxies of the universe were considered to be continuously forming and dissolving under the influence of extreme fields in galactic nuclei (*i.e.* ones in which atomic oscillations ran slow), this mode of spiral arm formation was given no further consideration, and indeed was largely forgotten once the expanding universe became accepted.

Nevertheless, if this is the way that spiral arms originate (*e.g.* Clube 1977, 1978, 1980), then the intermittent ejection of hot, dense plasma in the form of bound spiral arms from active galactic nuclei does not seem such a strange idea, and has obviously far-reaching implications beyond any ability to explain the origin of comets. Indeed, to set the 'violent galaxy' in its proper perspective, it is clear that the very foundations of physics and astrophysics may be at stake in arriving at an understanding of cometary origins: these connexions are thus at the heart of the discussion leading to what we have dubbed the 'hot potato' theory of comet formation described in Section 16.3.2.

References

Abetti, G., 1954. *The History of Astronomy.* Sidgwick & Jackson, London.

Abt, H.A., 1986. *The ages and dimensions of Trapezium systems,* Astrophys. J., **304**, 688–694.

Abt, H.A., 1988. *Maximum separations among cataloged binaries,* Astrophys. J., **331**, 922–931.

Adachi, I., Hayashi, C. & Nakazawa, K., 1976. *The gas drag effect on the elliptic motion of a solid body in the primordial solar nebula,* Prog. Theor. Phys., **56**, 1756–1771.

A'Hearn, M.F., 1986. *Are cometary nuclei like asteroids?* Asteroids Comets Meteors II, eds, Lagerkvist, C.-I., Lindblad, B.A., Lundstedt, H. & Rickman, H., 187–190. Uppsala University, Uppsala, Sweden.

A'Hearn, M.F., 1988. *Observations of cometary nuclei,* Annu. Rev. Earth Planet. Sci., **16**, 273–293.

A'Hearn, M.F. & Feldman, P.D., 1985. S_2: *a clue to the origin of cometary ice?* Ices in the Solar System, eds. Klinger, J., Benest, D., Dollfus, A. & Smoluchowski, R., 463–471. Kluwer Acad. Publ., Dordrecht, Holland.

A'Hearn, M.F., Feldman, P.D. & Schleicher, D.G., 1983. *The discovery of S_2 in Comet IRAS-Araki-Alcock 1983d,* Astrophys. J. Lett., **274**, L99–L103.

A'Hearn, M.F., Hoban, S., Birch, P.V., Bowers, C., Martin, R. & Klinglesmith III, D.A., 1986. *Cyanogen jets in comet Halley,* Nature, **324**, 649–651.

Alexander, S., 1850. *On the classification and special points of resemblance of certain of the periodic comets; and the probability of a common origin in the case of some of them,* Astron. J., **1**, 147–150.

Alexander, S., 1851. *On the similarity of arrangement of the asteroids and the comets of short period, and the possibility of their common origin,* Astron. J., **1**, 181–184.

Alfvén, H. & Arrhenius, G., 1970. *Structure and evolutionary history of the Solar System. I,* Astrophys. Space Sci., **8**, 338–421.

Alfvén, H. & Arrhenius, G., 1976. *Evolution of the Solar System,* NASA-SP-345, Washington D.C.

Allamandola, L.J. & Sandford, S.A., 1988a. *Laboratory simulation of dust spectra,* Dust in the Universe, eds. Bailey, M.E. & Williams, D.A., 229–263. Cambridge University Press.

Allamandola, L.J. & Sandford, S.A., 1988b. *The presence of aromatic moieties in interplanetary dust particles,* Dust in the Universe, eds. Bailey, M.E. & Williams, D.A., 543–547. Cambridge University Press.

Allen, C.W., 1963. *Astrophysical Quantities.* (2nd Edition.) The Athlone Press, University of London.

Allen, M., Delitsky, M., Huntress, W., Yung, Y., Ip, W.-H., Schwenn, R., Rosenbauer, H., Shelley, E., Balsiger, H. & Geiss, J., 1987. *Evidence for methane and ammonia in the coma of comet P/Halley,* Astron. Astrophys., **187**, 502–512.

Alvarez, L.W., 1983. *Experimental evidence that an asteroid led to the extinction of many species 65 million years ago,* Proc. Natl. Acad. Sci. (USA), **80**, 627–642.

Alvarez, L.W., Alvarez, W., Asaro, F. & Mitchel, H.V., 1980. *Extraterrestrial cause for the Cretaceous-Tertiary extinction,* Science, **208**, 1095–1108.

Alvarez, W., 1986. *Toward a theory of impact crises,* Eos, **67**, (No. 35), pp.649, 653–655, 658.

Alvarez, W., Alvarez, L.W., Asaro, F. & Michel, H.V., 1979. *Experimental evidence in support of an extra-terrestrial trigger for the Cretaceous-Tertiary extinctions,* Eos, **60**, (No. 42), p.734.

Alvarez, W., Asaro, F., Michel, H.V. & Alvarez, L.W., 1982. *Iridium anomaly approximately synchronous with terminal Eocene extinction,* Science, **216**, 886–888.

Alvarez, W. & Muller, R.A., 1984. *Evidence from crater ages for periodic impacts on the Earth,* Nature, **308**, 718–720.

Ambartsumian, V.A., 1958. *On the evolution of galaxies*, La Structure et L'Évolution de L'Univers, 11th Solvay Conference on Physics, University of Brussels, ed. Stoops, R., 241–274.

Ambartsumian, V.A., 1960. *On the evolution of stellar systems*, Q. Jl. R. Astron. Soc., **1**, 152–163.

Ambartsumian, V.A., 1965. *On the nuclei of galaxies and their activity*, Structure and Evolution of Galaxies, 13th Solvay Conference on Physics, University of Brussels, 1–12. Wiley Interscience, New York.

Anders, E., 1963. *Meteorites and the early history of the Solar System*, Origin of the Solar System, eds. Jastrow, R. & Cameron, A.G.W., 95–142. Academic Press, New York.

Anders, E., 1964. *Origin, age and composition of meteorites*, Space Sci. Rev., **3**, 583–714.

Anders, E., 1986. *What can meteorites tell us about comets?* The Comet Nucleus Sample Return Mission, ed. Melita, O., ESA SP-249, 31–39. ESA Publications, ESTEC, Noordwijk, The Netherlands.

Anders, E. Ganapathy, R., Krähenbühl, U. & Morgan, J.W., 1973. *Meteoritic material on the moon*, The Moon, **8**, 3–24.

Anderson, J.D. & Standish Jr. E.M., 1986. *Dynamical evidence for Planet X*, The Galaxy and the Solar System, eds. Smoluchowski, R., Bahcall, J.N. & Matthews, M.S., 286–296. University of Arizona Press, Tucson.

Antonov, V.A. & Latyshev, I.N., 1972. *Determination of the form of the Oort cometary cloud as the Hill surface in the Galactic field*, The Motion, Evolution of Orbits, and Origin of Comets, eds. Chebotarev, G.A., Kazimirchak-Polonskaya, E.I. & Marsden, B.G., IAU Symp. No. 45, 341–345. Reidel, Dordrecht, The Netherlands.

Apian, P., 1531. *Cosmographie*. Anvers.

Arago, F., 1855. *Popular Astronomy, Volume 1*. Longman, Brown, Green & Longmans, London.

Arago, F., 1858. *Popular Astronomy, Volume 2*. Longman, Brown, Green, Longmans & Roberts, London.

Aristotle c.330 BC. *Meteorologica*. (See Lee 1952, Ross 1968, Barnes 1984.)

Armellini, G., 1922. *The secular comets and the movement of the sun through space*, Popular Astron., **30**, 280–286. (Translated from *Scientia*, September 1921.)

Armitage, A., 1966. *Edmond Halley*. Thomas Nelson & Sons, London.

Arnold, J.R., 1977. *Condensation and agglomeration of grains*, Comets Asteroids Meteorites: Interrelations, Evolution and Origins, ed. Delsemme, A.H., IAU Coll. No. 39, 519–524. University of Toledo, Toledo, Ohio.

Artymowicz, P., Burrows, C. & Paresce, F., 1989. *The structure of the Beta Pictoris circumstellar disk from combined IRAS and coronographic observations*, Astrophys. J., **337**, 494–513.

Astapovič, I.S. & Terenteva, A.K., 1968. *Fireball radiants of the 1st–15th centuries*, Physics and Dynamics of Meteors, eds. Kresák, Ľ. & Millman, P.M., IAU Symp. No. 33, 308–319. Reidel, Dordrecht, The Netherlands.

Atkinson, R. d'E., 1963. *General relativity in Euclidean terms*, Proc. R. Soc. London, Ser. A, **272**, 60–78.

Atkinson, R. d'E., 1965a. *Two general integrals of $G^\nu_\mu = 0$* Astron. J., **70**, 513–516.

Atkinson, R. d'E., 1965b. *On light tracks near a very massive star*, Astron. J., **70**, 517–523.

Aumann, H.H., 1985. *IRAS observations of matter around nearby stars*, Publ. Astron. Soc. Pac., **97**, 885–891.

Aumann, H.H., 1988. *Spectral class distribution of circumstellar material in main-sequence stars*, Astron. J., **96**, 1415–1419.

Aumann, H.H., Gillett, F.C., Beichman, C.A., de Jong, T., Houck, J.R., Low, F.J., Neugebauer, G., Walker, R.G. & Wesselius, P.R., 1984. *Discovery of a shell around*

Alpha Lyrae, Astrophys. J. Lett., **278**, L23–L27.

Aust, C. & Woolfson, M.M., 1973. *On the accretion mechanism for the formation of a protoplanetary disc*, Mon. Not. R. Astron. Soc., **161**, 7–13.

Babadžanov, P.B. & Kramer, E.N., 1968. *Some results of investigations of instantaneous meteor photographs*, Physics and Dynamics of Meteors, eds. Kresák, Ĺ. & Millman, P.M., IAU Symp. No. 33, 128–142. Reidel, Dordrecht, The Netherlands.

Babadžanov, P.B. & Obrubov, Yu. V., 1983. *Secular perturbations of Apollo, Amor and Aten asteroid orbits and theoretical radiants of meteor showers, probably associated with them*, Asteroids Comets Meteors, eds. Lagerkvist, C.-I. & Rickman, H., 411–417. Uppsala Observatory, Uppsala, Sweden.

Babinet, J., 1861. *Note sur un point de la cosmogonie de Laplace*, Comptes Rendus, **52**, 481–484.

Backman, D.E., Gillett, F.C. & Witteborn, F.C., 1989. *The particles in the β Pictoris disk: ground-based infrared photometry*, preprint.

Bahcall, J.N., 1984. *Self-consistent determinations of the total amount of matter near the sun*, Astrophys. J., **276**, 169–181.

Bahcall, J.N. & Soneira, R.M., 1980. *The Universe at faint magnitudes. I. Models for the Galaxy and the predicted star counts*, Astrophys. J. Suppl. Ser., **44**, 73–110.

Bailey, M.E., 1976. *Can 'invisible' bodies be observed in the solar system?* Nature, **259**, 290–291.

Bailey, M.E., 1977. *Some comments on the Oort Cloud*, Astrophys. Space Sci., **50**, 3–22.

Bailey, M.E., 1982. *The structure and evolution of nuclear discs*, Mon. Not. R. Astron. Soc., **200**, 247–262.

Bailey, M.E., 1983a. *The structure and evolution of the Solar System comet cloud*, Mon. Not. R. Astron. Soc., **204**, 603–633.

Bailey, M.E., 1983b. *Is there a dense primordial cloud of comets just beyond Pluto?* Asteroids Comets Meteors, eds. Lagerkvist, C.-I. & Rickman, H., 383–386. Uppsala Observatory, Uppsala, Sweden.

Bailey, M.E., 1983c. *Theories of cometary origin and the brightness of the infrared sky*, Mon. Not. R. Astron. Soc., **205**, 47P–52P.

Bailey, M.E., 1983d. *Comets, Planet X, and the orbit of Neptune*, Nature, **302**, 399–400.

Bailey, M.E., 1984a. *The steady-state 1/a-distribution and the problem of cometary fading*, Mon. Not. R. Astron. Soc., **211**, 347–368.

Bailey, M.E., 1984b. *Nemesis for Nemesis?* Nature, **311**, 602–603.

Bailey, M.E., 1985a. *The problem of the 1/a-distribution and cometary fading*, Dynamics of Comets: Their Origin and Evolution, eds. Carusi, A. & Valsecchi, G.B., IAU Coll. No. 83, 311–317. (Astrophys. Space Sci. Lib. **115.**) Reidel, Dordrecht, The Netherlands.

Bailey, M.E., 1985b. *Gas in galactic centres*, Cosmical Gas Dynamics, ed. Kahn, F., 49–62. VNU Science Press, Utrecht, The Netherlands.

Bailey, M.E., 1986a. *The mean energy transfer rate to comets in the Oort Cloud and implications for cometary origins*, Mon. Not. R. Astron. Soc., **218**, 1–30.

Bailey, M.E., 1986b. *A note on the mean energy transfer rate by point-mass perturbers*, Asteroids Comets Meteors II, eds, Lagerkvist, C.-I., Lindblad, B.A., Lundstedt, H. & Rickman, H., 207–210. Uppsala University, Uppsala, Sweden.

Bailey, M.E., 1986c. *The near-parabolic flux and the origin of short-period comets*, Nature, **324**, 350–352.

Bailey, M.E., 1987a. *The formation of comets in wind-driven shells around protostars*, Icarus, **69**, 70–82.

Bailey, M.E., 1987b. *Giant grains around protostars*, Q. Jl. R. Astron. Soc., **28**, 242–247.

Bailey, M.E., 1988a. *Periodicity of cometary impacts*, Observatory, **108**, 34–36.

Bailey, M.E., 1988b. *Comets in star-forming regions*, Dust in the Universe, eds. Bailey, M.E. & Williams, D.A., 113–120. Cambridge University Press.

Bailey, M.E., 1989. *Cometary dynamics — the inner core of the Oort cloud*, Catastrophes and Evolution: Astronomical Foundation, ed. Clube, S.V.M., in press. Cambridge University Press.

Bailey, M.E. & Clube, S.V.M., 1978. *Recurrent activity in galactic nuclei*, Nature, **275**, 278–282.

Bailey, M.E., Clube, S.V.M. & Napier, W.M., 1986. *The origin of comets*, Vistas Astron., **29**, 53–112.

Bailey, M.E., Cooke, J.A., Few, R.W., Morgan, J.G. & Ruggles, C.L.N., 1975. *Survey of three megalithic sites in Argyllshire*, Nature, **253**, 431–433.

Bailey, M.E., McBreen, B. & Ray, T.P., 1984. *Constraints on cometary origin from the isotropy of the microwave background and other measurements*, Mon. Not. R. Astron. Soc., **209**, 881–890. *Corrigendum:* **211**, 255.

Bailey, M.E. & Stagg, C.R., 1988. *Cratering constraints on the inner Oort cloud: steady-state models*, Mon. Not. R. Astron. Soc., **235**, 1–32.

Bailey, M.E. & Stagg, C.R., 1989. *The origin of short-period comets*, preprint. Presented at IAU Coll. No. 116 *Comets in the Post-Halley Era*, Bamberg (April 1989), submitted to *Icarus*.

Bailey, M.E., Wilkinson, D.A. & Wolfendale, A.W., 1987. *Can episodic comet showers explain the 30-Myr cyclicity in the terrestrial record?* Mon. Not. R. Astron. Soc., **227**, 863–885.

Baines, M.J., Williams, I.P. & Asebiomo, A.S., 1965. *Resistance to the motion of a small sphere moving through a gas*, Mon. Not. R. Astron. Soc., **130**, 63–74.

Baldwin, R.B., 1985. *Relative and absolute ages of individual craters and the rate of infalls on the Moon in the post-Imbrium period*, Icarus, **61**, 63–91.

Ball, R.S., 1891. *The Cause of an Ice Age*. Kegan, Paul, Trench, Trübner & Co. Ltd., London.

Ball, R.S., 1893. *Star-Land*. Cassell & Co. Ltd., London.

Balsiger, H., Altwegg, K., Bühler, F., Geiss, J., Ghielmetti, A.G., Goldstein, B.E., Goldstein, R., Huntress, W.T., Ip. W.-H., Lazarus, A.J., Meier, A., Neugebauer, M., Retttenmund, U., Rosenbauer, H., Schwenn, R., Sharp, R.D., Shelley, E.G., Ungstrup, E. & Young, D.T., 1986. *Ion composition and dynamics at comet Halley*, Nature, **321**, 330–334.

Barbuy, B., Spite, F. & Spite, M., 1987. *Magnesium isotopes in metal-poor and metal-rich stars*, Astron. Astrophys., **178**, 199–202.

Barker Jr., J.L. & Anders, E., 1968. *Accretion rate of cosmic matter from iridium and osmium contents of deep-sea sediments*, Geochim. Cosmochim. Acta, **32**, 627–645.

Barker, T., 1767. *An Account of Discoveries Concerning Comets*. London.

Barlow, M.J., 1978. *The destruction and growth of dust grains in interstellar space — I. Destruction by sputtering*, Mon. Not. R. Astron. Soc., **183**, 367–395.

Barnard, E.E., 1913. *Milky Way and Comets*, Publ. Lick. Obs., **11**, Plates 102 and 103.

Barnes, J., 1982. *Aristotle*. Oxford University Press.

Barnes, J., 1984. *The Complete Works of Aristotle*. (2 Volumes.) Princeton University Press.

Bath, G.T. & Pringle, J.E., 1981. *The evolution of viscous discs — I. Mass transfer variations*, Mon. Not. R. Astron. Soc., **194**, 967–986.

Begelman, M.C. & Rees, M.J., 1976. *Can cosmic clouds cause climatic catastrophe?* Nature, **261**, 298–299.

Bell, R.A. & Branch, D., 1970. *Relative abundances of magnesium isotopes in Arcturus*, Astrophys. Lett., **5**, 203–206.

Belton, M.J.S., 1985. *P/Halley: the quintessential comet*, Science, **230**, 1229–1236.

Belton, M.J.S., 1989. *Rationalization of Halley's periods: evidence for an inhomogeneous nucleus*, preprint. Presented at IAU Coll. No. 116 *Comets in the Post-Halley Era*,

Bamberg (April 1989), intended for publication in *Icarus*, or the main conference proceedings (eds. Newburn, R., Neugebauer, M. & Rahe, J., publisher Kluwer).

Belyaev, N.A., Kresák, Ĺ., Pittich, E.M. & Pushkarov, A.N., 1986. *Catalogue of Short-Period Orbits.* Astron. Inst. Slovak Acad. Sci., Bratislava.

Beust, H., Lagrange-Henri, A.M., Vidal-Madjar, A. & Ferlet, R., 1989. *The β Pictoris circumstellar disk IX. Theoretical results on the infall velocities of Ca II, Al III, Mg II,* Astron. Astrophys., in press.

Bhat, C.L., Issa, M.R., Houston, B.P., Mayer, C.J. & Wolfendale, A.W., 1985. *Cosmic γ-rays and the mass of gas in the Galaxy,* Nature, **314**, 511–515.

Bhat, C.L., Mayer, C.J. & Wolfendale, A.W., 1986. *A new estimate of the mass of molecular gas in the Galaxy and its implications,* Philos. Trans. R. Soc. London, Ser. A, **319**, 249–289.

Biermann, L., 1978. *Dense interstellar clouds and comets,* Astronomical Papers Dedicated to Bengt Strömgren, eds. Reiz, A. & Anderson, T., 327–336. Copenhagen University Press.

Biermann, L., 1981. *The smaller bodies of the solar system,* Philos. Trans. R. Soc. London, Ser. A, **303**, 351–352.

Biermann, L., Huebner, W.F. & Lüst, Rh., 1983. *Aphelion clustering of "new" comets: star tracks through Oort's cloud,* Proc. Natl. Acad. Sci. (USA), **80**, 5151–5155.

Biermann, L. & Michel, K.W., 1978. *The origin of cometary nuclei in the presolar nebula,* Moon & Planets, **18**, 447–464.

Binney, J. & Tremaine, S.D., 1987. *Galactic Dynamics.* Princeton University Press.

Biot, É., 1843. *Sur la direction de las queue des comètes,* Comptes Rendus, **16**, 751–752.

Biot, É., 1848. *Catalogue general des étoiles filantes et des autres meteores observes en Chine,* Mem. de l'Acad. des Sci. de l'Inst. National de France, **10**, 129–352.

Biot, J.-B., 1807. *Relation d'un voyage fait dans le Département de l'Orne, pour constater la réalité d'un météore observé á l'Aigle le floréal an 11,* Mémoires de la classes des sciences, mathematique et physique, L'Institut National de France, 224–266; 17 July 1803. (Cited by Burke 1986.)

Bischoff, M., 1986. *The Signs of Heaven.* (Verlegt bei Franz Greno, Nordlingen.)

Bjorkman, J.K., 1973. *Meteors and meteorites in the ancient Near East,* Meteoritics, **8**, 91–132.

Blaauw, A. & Schmidt, M., 1965. *Galactic Structure.* (Stars and Stellar Systems, Volume V, eds. Kuiper, G.P. & Middlehurst, B.M.) University of Chicago Press.

Boardman, J., Griffin, J. & Murray, O., 1986. *The Oxford History of the Classical World.* Oxford University Press.

Bobrovnikoff, N.T., 1929a. *On the disintegration of comets,* Lick Obs. Bull., **14**, 28–37.

Bobrovnikoff, N.T., 1929b. *The cosmological significance of comets,* Publ. Astron. Soc. Pac., **41**, 98–104.

Bobrovnikoff, N.T., 1931. *The origin of asteroids,* Publ. Astron. Soc. Pac., **43**, 324–333.

Bobrovnikoff, N.T., 1951. *Comets,* Astrophysics, ed. Hynek, J.A., 302–356. McGraw-Hill, New York.

Bode, J.E., 1812. *Ueber die Vertheilung der Perihelion, von 98 bisher beobachteter und berechneter Kometen,* Berliner Astron. Jahrbuch, 158–162.

Bode, M.F., 1985. *High view of Halley,* Manchester Evening News, 21 November.

Boehnhardt, H., 1989. *Clusters and packets of grains and the fragmentation of dust,* preprint. Presented at IAU Coll. No. 116 *Comets in the Post-Halley Era,* Bamberg (April 1989), submitted to *Icarus.*

Boesgaard, A.M., 1968. *Isotopes of magnesium in stellar atmospheres,* Astrophys. J., **154**, 185–190.

Bogart, R.S. & Noerdlinger, P.D., 1982. *On the distribution of orbits among long-period comets,* Astron. J., **87**, 911–917.

Bohor, B.F., Foord, E.E., Modreski, P.J. & Triplehorn, D.M., 1984. *Mineralogic evidence for an impact event at the Cretaceous-Tertiary boundary,* Science, **224**, 867–869.

Bond, G.P., 1861. *On the light of the moon and the planet Jupiter*, Mem. Amer. Acad. Arts & Sci., **8**, 221–286.

Bondi, C. & Bondi, H., 1950. *Models for red giant stars. II. Models with a chemical inhomogeneity and opacity due to photoelectric effect*, Mon. Not. R. Astron. Soc., **110**, 287–304.

Bondi, H., 1953. *Accretion and the origin of comets*, La Physique des Comètes, 332–336. Proc. 4th Int. Coll. Astrophys., Liège.

Bondi, H. & Hoyle, R., 1944. *On the mechanism of accretion by stars*, Mon. Not. R. Astron. Soc., **104**, 273–282.

Bonser, W., 1963. *The Medical Background of Anglo-Saxon England: A Study in History, Psychology, and Folklore*. Wellcome Historical Medical Library, London.

Bortle, J.E., 1989. *Sungrazing comets: big and small*, Sky & Telescope, **77**, No. 5 (May), 564–566.

Boucot, A.J., 1988. *Periodic extinctions within the Cenozoic*, Nature, **331**, 395–396.

Bourgeois, P. & Cox, J.-F, 1934. *Calcul de l'ellipsoide de dispersion des périhélies des comètes connues*, Bull. Astron., **8**, 271–304.

Bradley, J.P. & Brownlee, D.E., 1986. *Cometary particles: thin sectioning and electron beam analysis*, Science, **231**, 1542–1544.

Bradley, J.P., Brownlee, D.E. & Veblen, D.R., 1983. *Pyroxene whiskers and platelets in interplanetary dust: evidence of vapour phase growth*, Nature, **301**, 473–477.

Brandt, J.C. & Chapman, R.D., 1982. *Introduction to Comets*. Cambridge University Press.

Brecher, K., 1984. *The Canterbury swarm*, Bull. Amer. Astron. Soc., **16**, 476.

Bredichin, T., 1889. *Sur l'origine de comètes periodiques*, Annales de l'observatoire de Moscou (Ser. 2), **2**, 1–17.

Brewster, D., 1821. Supplementary chapters to Ferguson (1841, volume 2).

Brin, G.D. & Mendis, D.A., 1979. *Dust release and mantle development in comets*, Astrophys. J., **229**, 402–408.

Broadbent, A., MacLaren, I. & Wolfendale, A.W., 1988. *Dust and the mass of gas in the Galaxy*, Dust in the Universe, eds. Bailey, M.E. & Williams, D.A., 435–439. Cambridge University Press.

Broadbent, A., MacLaren, I. & Wolfendale, A.W., 1989. *Far-infrared estimates of the mass of gas in the Galaxy*, Mon. Not. R. Astron. Soc., **237**, 1075–1084.

Bronshten, V.A., 1983. *Physics of Meteoric Phenomena*. Reidel, Dordrecht, The Netherlands.

Brorsen, Th., 1852. *Ueber die Vertheilung der grossen Axen der Cometenbahnen*, Astron. Nachr., **34**, (No. 813) 337–338.

Brouwer, D. & Clemence, G.M., 1961. *Methods of Celestial Mechanics*. Academic Press, New York and London.

Brownlee, D.E., 1985. *Cosmic dust: collection and research*, Annu. Rev. Earth Planet. Sci., **13**, 147–173.

Brownlee, D.E., Hodge, P.W. & Bucher, W., 1973. *The physical nature of interplanetary dust as inferred by particles collected at 35 km*, Evolutionary and Physical Properties of Meteoroids, eds. Hemenway, C.L., Millman, P.M. & Cook, A.F., IAU Coll. No. 13, 291–295. NASA SP-319, Washington, D.C.

Brydon, H.B., 1945. *A possible origin of comets*, J. R. Astron. Soc. Canada, **39**, 392–393.

Buffon, G.L.L., 1745. *De la Formation des Planètes*. Paris.

Burke, J.C., 1986. *Cosmic Debris: Meteorites in History*. University of California Press, Berkeley.

Burns, J.A., 1989. *Are comet spins primordial?* Nature, **338**, 303.

Burton, W.B., Deul, E.R., Walker, H.J. & Jongeneelen, A.A.W., 1986. *The galactic morphology of the interstellar dust detected by IRAS*, Light on Dark Matter, ed.

Israel, F.P., 357–372. (Proceedings of the First IRAS Conference; Astrophys. Space Sci. Lib., **124.**) Reidel, Dordrecht, The Netherlands.

Burek, P.J. & Wänke, H., 1988. *Impacts and glacio-eustasy, plate-tectonic episodes, geomagnetic reversals: a concept to facilitate detection of impact craters*, Phys. Earth Planet. Inter., **50**, 183–194.

Bus, S.J., Bowell, E., Harris, A.W. & Hewitt, A.V., 1989. *2060 Chiron: CCD and electronographic photometry*, Icarus, **77**, 223–238.

Butler, E.J. & Hoyle, F., 1979. *On the effects of a sudden change in the albedo of the Earth*, Astrophys. Space Sci., **60**, 505–511.

Butler, E.J. & Hoyle, F., 1980. *The extinction of the mammoths*, Moon & Planets, **22**, 517–519.

Butterfield, H., 1981. *The Origins of History*. Methuen & Co., London.

Butterworth, P.S., 1985. *Physical properties of comets*, Vistas Astron., **27**, 361–419.

BVSP (Basaltic volcanism study project), 1981. *Basaltic Volcanism on the Terrestrial Planets*, Pergamon Press, New York. (Cited by Grieve 1984.)

Byl, J., 1983. *Galactic perturbations of nearly-parabolic cometary orbits*, Moon & Planets, **29**, 121–137.

Byl, J., 1986. *The effect of the Galaxy on cometary orbits*, Earth, Moon, Planets, **36**, 263–273.

Cameron, A.G.W., 1962. *The formation of the sun and planets*, Icarus, **1**, 13–69.

Cameron, A.G.W., 1973. *Accumulation processes in the primitive solar nebula*, Icarus, **18**, 407–450.

Cameron, A.G.W., 1978. *Physics of the primitive solar accretion disk*, Moon & Planets, **18**, 5–40.

Cameron, A.G.W., 1985. *Formation and evolution of the primitive solar nebula*, Protostars & Planets II, eds. Black, D.C. & Matthews, M.S., 1073–1099. University of Arizona Press, Tucson.

Cameron, A.G.W., 1988. *Origin of the solar system*, Annu. Rev. Astron. Astrophys., **26**, 441–472

Cameron, A.G.W. & Pine, M.R., 1973. *Numerical models of the primitive solar nebula*, Icarus, **18**, 377–406.

Campins, H., A'Hearn, M.F. & McFadden, L.-A., 1987. *The bare nucleus of Comet Neujmin 1*, Astrophys. J., **316**, 847–857.

Campins, H. & Ryan, E.V., 1989. *The identification of crystalline olivine in cometary silicates*, Astrophys. J., **341**, 1059–1066.

Cardelli, J. & Böhm-Vitense, E., 1982. *The interstellar absorption-line spectrum of μ Ophiuchi*, Astrophys. J., **262**, 213–223.

Carrington, R.C., 1860a. *On the distribution of the perihelia of the parabolic and hyperbolic comets in relation to the motion of the solar system in space*, Memoirs R. Astron. Soc., **29**, 355–367.

Carrington, R.C., 1860b. *On the distribution of the perihelia of the parabolic orbits in relation to the motion of the solar system in space*, Mon. Not. R. Astron. Soc., **21**, 42–43.

Carrington, R.C., 1863. *On the motion of the solar system in space*, Mon. Not. R. Astron. Soc., **23**, 203–204.

Carusi, A., Kresák, Ľ., Perozzi, E. & Valsecchi, G.B., 1986. *Long-Term Evolution of Short-Period Comets*. Adam Hilger, Bristol.

Carusi, A., Kresák, Ľ., Perozzi, E. & Valsecchi, G.B., 1987. *High-order librations of Halley-type comets*, Astron. Astrophys., **187**, 899–905.

Carusi, A. & Valsecchi, G.B., 1982. *On asteroid classification in families*, Astron. Astrophys., **115**, 327–335.

Carusi, A. & Valsecchi, G.B., 1985. *Statistical and numerical studies of the orbital evolution of short-period comets*, Dynamics of Comets: Their Origin and Evolution, eds. Carusi, A. & Valsecchi, G.B., IAU Coll. No. 83, 261–278. (Astrophys. Space Sci. Lib. **115.**) Reidel, Dordrecht, The Netherlands.

Carusi, A. & Valsecchi, G.B., 1987. *Dynamical evolution of short-period comets*, Interplanetary Matter, eds. Ceplecha, Z. & Pecina, P., 21–28. (Proc. Tenth European Regional Meeting in Astronomy, Vol. 2, Prague).

Caspar, M., 1959. *Kepler*. Translated and edited by C. Doris Hellman. Abelard-Schuman, London & New York.

Cassini, J.D., 1680. *Abrégé des observations sur la comete de 1680*, p.xxxi. (Cited by Lalande 1792.)

Cernicharo, J., Kahane, C., Gómez-Gonzá, J. & Guélin, M., 1986. *Detection of $^{29}SiC_2$ and $^{30}SiC_2$ toward IRC+ 10216*, Astron. Astrophys., **167**, L9–L12.

Chamberlin, T.C., 1901. *On a possible function of disruptive approach in the formation of meteorites, comets and nebulae*, Astrophys. J., **14**, 17–40.

Chamberlin, T.C., 1928. *The Two Solar Families: The Sun's Children.*, p.251 et seq. University of Chicago Press.

Chambers, G.F., 1909. *The Story of Comets.* Clarendon Press, Oxford.

Chambers, W. & Chambers, R., 1889. *Comet*, Chambers's Encyclopaedia **III**, 375–378.

Chebotarev, G.A., 1964. *Gravitational spheres of the major planets, moon and sun*, Sov. Astron., **7**, 618–622. Translated from Astron. Zh., **40**, 812–818, 1963.

Chebotarev, G.A., 1965. *On the dynamical limits of the solar system*, Sov. Astron., **8**, 787–792. Translated from Astron. Zh., **41**, 983–989, 1964.

Chebotarev, G.A., 1966. *Cometary motions in the outer solar system*, Sov. Astron., **10**, 341–344. Translated from Astron. Zh., **43**, 435–440, 1966.

Chladni, E.F.F., 1798. *Observations on a mass of iron found in Siberia by Professor Pallas, and on other masses of the same kind, with some conjectures respecting their connection with certain natural phenomena*, Philos. Mag. and Journ. of Sci. (1st series), **2**, 1–8.

Clark, B., Mason, L.W. & Kissel, J., 1986. *Systematics of the "CHON" and other light-element particle populations in Comet Halley*, 20th ESLAB Symposium on the Exploration of Halley's Comet, eds. Battrick, B., Rolfe, E.J. & Reinhard, R., ESA SP-250, Vol. III, 353–358. ESA Publications, ESTEC, Noordwijk, The Netherlands.

Clarke, J. & Geikie, A., 1910. *Physical Science in the Time of Nero*. Macmillan & Co., London.

Clayton, D.D., 1982. *Cosmic chemical memory: a new astronomy*, Q. Jl. R. Astron. Soc., **23**, 174–212.

Clayton, D.D., 1988. *The relationship between interstellar dust and the isotopic anomalies in meteorites*, Dust in the Universe, eds. Bailey, M.E. & Williams, D.A., 145–152. Cambridge University Press.

Clerke, A.M., 1908. *A Popular History of Astronomy During the Nineteenth Century.* (Fourth edition.) Adam & Charles Black, London.

Clube, S.V.M., 1973. *Another look at the absolute proper motions obtained from the Lick pilot programme*, Mon. Not. R. Astron. Soc., **161**, 445–463.

Clube, S.V.M., 1977. *The origin of gravity*, Astrophys. Space Sci., **50**, 425–443.

Clube, S.V.M., 1978. *Does our Galaxy have a violent history?* Vistas Astron., **22**, 77–118.

Clube, S.V.M., 1980. *The material vacuum*, Mon. Not. R. Astron. Soc., **193**, 385–397.

Clube, S.V.M., 1983. *An ejection theory of quasars*, 24th Astrophys. Coll. Liège, 393–396.

Clube, S.V.M., 1985. *Molecular clouds: comet factories?* Dynamics of Comets: Their Origin and Evolution, eds. Carusi, A. & Valsecchi, G.B., IAU Coll. No. 83, 19–30. (Astrophys. Space Sci. Lib. **115.**) Reidel, Dordrecht, The Netherlands.

Clube, S.V.M., 1986a. *Giant comets or ordinary comets; parent bodies or planetesimals*, 20th ESLAB Symposium on the Exploration of Halley's Comet, eds. Battrick,

B., Rolfe, E.J. & Reinhard, R., ESA SP-250, Vol. II, 403–408. ESA Publications, ESTEC, Noordwijk, The Netherlands.

Clube, S.V.M., 1987a. *The comet flux and the 15 Myr galactic cycle*, Symposium on the Diversity and Similarity of Comets, ESA SP-278, 49–53. ESA Publications, ESTEC, Noordwijk, The Netherlands.

Clube, S.V.M., 1987b. *The origin of dust in the solar system*, Philos. Trans. R. Soc. London, Ser. A, **323**, 421–436.

Clube, S.V.M., 1988a. *Giant comets and their relevance to the origin of the solar system*, The Physics of the Planets: Their Origin Evolution and Structure (Proc. NATO Adv. Study Inst., University of Newcastle-upon-Tyne, April 1985), ed. Runcorn, S.K., 411–420. John Wiley & Sons, Chichester.

Clube, S.V.M., 1988b. *Dust and star formation in a hot differentiating medium*, Dust in the Universe, eds. Bailey, M.E. & Williams, D.A., 331–339. Cambridge University Press.

Clube, S.V.M., 1989a. *The physical basis of terrestrial catastrophism*, Contemp. Phys., in press.

Clube, S.V.M., 1989b. *The catastrophic rôle of giant comets*, Catastrophes and Evolution: Astronomical Foundation, ed. Clube, S.V.M., in press. Cambridge University Press.

Clube, S.V.M., 1989c. *The dynamics of armaggedon*, Spec. Sci. Tech., **11**, 255–264.

Clube, S.V.M. & Asher, D.J., 1989. *The proposed giant comet fragmentation ca. 2700 BC and its relationship with the α, β, γ zodiacal bands*. Paper presented at Asteroids Comets Meteors III, Uppsala 1989.

Clube, S.V.M. & Napier, W.M., 1982a. *Spiral arms, comets and terrestrial catastrophism*, Q. Jl. R. Astron. Soc., **23**, 45–66.

Clube, S.V.M. & Napier, W.M., 1982b. *The rôle of episodic bombardment in geophysics*, Earth Planet. Sci. Lett., **57**, 251–262.

Clube, S.V.M. & Napier, W.M., 1982c. *The Cosmic Serpent: A Catastrophist View of Earth History*. Faber & Faber, London.

Clube, S.V.M. & Napier, W.M., 1983. *Some considerations relating to an interstellar origin of comets*, Highlights in Astronomy, ed. West, R., **6**, 355–362. Reidel, Dordrecht, The Netherlands.

Clube, S.V.M. & Napier, W.M., 1984a. *Comet capture from molecular clouds: a dynamical constraint on star and planet formation*, Mon. Not. R. Astron. Soc., **208**, 575–588.

Clube, S.V.M. & Napier, W.M., 1984b. *The microstructure of terrestrial catastrophism*, Mon. Not. R. Astron. Soc., **211**, 953–968.

Clube, S.V.M. & Napier, W.M., 1984c. *Terrestrial catastrophism — Nemesis or Galaxy?* Nature, **311**, 635–636.

Clube, S.V.M. & Napier, W.M., 1985a. *Comet formation in molecular clouds*, Icarus, **62**, 384–388.

Clube, S.V.M. & Napier, W.M., 1985b. *Reply to Davis, Hut & Muller (1985)*, Nature, **313**, 503.

Clube, S.V.M. & Napier, W.M., 1986a. *Mankind's future: an astronomical view. Comets, ice ages and catastrophes*, Interdisciplinary Science Reviews, **11**, (No. 3) 236–247. J.W. Arrowsmith.

Clube, S.V.M. & Napier, W.M., 1986b. *Giant comets and the Galaxy: implications of the terrestrial record*, The Galaxy and the Solar System, eds. Smoluchowski, R., Bahcall, J.N. & Matthews, M.S., 260–285. University of Arizona Press, Tucson.

Clube, S.V.M. & Napier, W.M., 1989a. *An episodic-cum-periodic galacto-terrestrial relationship*, Mon. Not. R. Astron. Soc., submitted.

Clube, S.V.M. & Napier, W.M., 1989b. *Cosmic Winter*. Basil Blackwell Ltd., Oxford.

Clube, S.V.M. & Pan, R., 1985. *The kinematic centre of the Galaxy*, Mon. Not. R. Astron. Soc., **216**, 511–519.

Clube, S.V.M. & Waddington, W.G., 1989a. *Velocities and the line-of-sight distribution of molecular clouds close to the Galactic Centre*, Mon. Not. R. Astron. Soc., **237**, 7P–13P.

Clube, S.V.M. & Waddington, W.G., 1989b. *An unrelaxed feature of the globular cluster system*, in preparation.

Clube, S.V.M. & Watson, F.G., 1979. *Radial motion in the galactic system of globular clusters*, Mon. Not. R. Astron. Soc., **187**, 863–870.

Cohen, M., 1983. *HL Tauri and its circumstellar disk*, Astrophys. J. Lett., **270**, L69–L71.

Cohen, R.J. & Davies, R.D., 1976. *Neutral hydrogen in the Galactic Centre region — II. Location of the emission features*, Mon. Not. R. Astron. Soc., **175**, 1–24.

Cohen, R.S., Cong, H., Dame, T.M. & Thaddeus, P., 1980. *Molecular clouds and galactic spiral structure*, Astrophys. J. Lett., **239**, L53–L56.

Cohn, N., 1957. *The Pursuit of the Millennium*. Secker & Warburg.

Cole, W., 1823. *On the Theory of Comets*. Holdsworth, London.

Colgrave, B. & Mynors, R.A.B., 1969. *Bede's Ecclesiastical History of the English People*. Clarendon Press, Oxford.

Combes, M., Moroz, V.I., Crifo, J.F., Lamarre, J.M., Charra, J., Sanko, N.F., Soufflot, A., Bibring, J.P., Cazes, S., Coron, N., Crovisier, J., Emerich, C., Encrenaz, T., Gispert, R., Grigoryev, A.V., Guyot, G., Krasnopolsky, V.A., Nikolsky, Yu.V. & Rocard, F., 1986. *Infrared sounding of comet Halley from Vega 1*, Nature, **321**, 266–268.

Coradini, A., Federico, C. & Magni, G., 1981. *Formation of planetesimals in an evolving protoplanetary disk*, Astron. Astrophys., **98**, 173–185.

Coradini, A., Magni, G. & Federico, C., 1977. *Grain accretion processes in a proto-planetary nebula*, Astrophys. Space Sci., **48**, 575–588.

Corlin, A., 1938. *How larger bodies may be built up out of small particles in interstellar space*, Zeitschrift für Astrophysik, **15**, 239–262.

Cornford, F.M., 1971. *Principium Sapientiae*. Peter Smith, Mass.

Cosmovici, C.B. & Ortolini, S., 1985. *Formaldehyde in comet IRAS-Araki-Alcock (1983d). Cosmogonical implications*, Ices in the Solar System, eds. Klinger, J., Benest, D., Dollfus, A. & Smoluchowski, R., 473–485. (NATO ASI series **C 156**.) Reidel, Dordrecht, The Netherlands.

Costard, G., 1767. *The History of Astronomy*. See p.288. James Lister, London.

Courtillot, V.E. & Cisowski, S., 1987. *The Cretaceous-Tertiary boundary events: external or internal causes?* Eos, **68**, (No. 14), pp. 193, 200.

Cowles, R.B., 1939. *Possible implications of reptilian thermal tolerance*, Science, **90**, 465–466.

Crawford, S.J., 1929. *Byrhtferth's Manual* AD 1011. Early English Text Society, No. 177. Humphrey Milford, Oxford University Press, London.

Creer, K.M. & Pal, P.C., 1989. *On the frequencies of reversals of the geomagnetic dipole*, Catastrophes and Evolution: Astronomical Foundation, ed. Clube, S.V.M., in press. Cambridge University Press.

Cristofani, M., 1979. *The Etruscans: a New Investigation*. Orbis Publishing Ltd., London.

Crommelin, A.C.D., 1907. *Lecture on Halley's comet*, Journ. Br. Astron. Assoc., **17**, 211–220.

Crommelin, A.C.D., 1910. *The origin and nature of comets*. Scientia; Revista di Scienza, **7**, 241 et seq. See also Proctor & Crommelin 1937, 177–198.

Crommelin, A.C.D., 1929. *Comets*. Encyclopaedia Britannica (14th edition) **6**, 100–104.

Crommelin, A.C.D., 1935. *Do comets belong to the solar system?* Observatory, **58**, 87–89.

Cronin, V., 1981. *The View From Planet Earth*. Collins, London.

Cruikshank, D.P., 1988. *Infrared studies of solar system bodies*, Comets to Cosmology, ed. Lawrence, A., 73–77. (Proceedings of Third IRAS Conference; Lecture Notes in Physics, **297**.) Springer-Verlag, Berlin.

Cruikshank, D.P. & Brown, R.H., 1983. *The nucleus of Comet Schwassmann-Wachmann 1*, Icarus, **56**, 377–380.

Cruikshank, D.P., Hartmann, W.K. & Tholen, D.J., 1985. *Colour, albedo and nucleus size of Halley's comet*, Nature, **315**, 122–124. *Corrigendum*, **315**, 690.

Daghlian, G.K., 1937. *A note on the origin of comets*, Popular Astron., **45**, 399–400.

Dall'Olmo, U., 1978. *Meteors, meteor showers and meteorites in the Middle Ages: from European medieval sources*, J. Hist. Astron., **9**, 123–134.

Dalton, O.M., 1927. *The History of the Franks by Gregory of Tours*. Volume 2. Clarendon Press, Oxford.

Dame, T.M. & Thaddeus, P., 1985. *A wide-latitude CO survey of molecular clouds in the Northern Milky Way*, Astrophys. J., **297**, 751–765.

Dame, T.M., Ungerechts, H., Cohen, R.S., de Geus, E.J., Grenier, I.A., May, J., Murphy, D.C., Nyman, L.-Å. & Thaddeus, P., 1987. *A composite CO survey of the entire Milky Way*, Astrophys. J., **322**, 706–720.

Dauvillier, A., 1964. *Cosmic Dust*. Philosophical Library, New York.

Davies, J.K., Green, S.F., Stewart, B.C., Meadows, A.J. & Aumann, H.H., 1984. *The IRAS fast-moving object search*, Nature, **309**, 315–319.

Davis, M., Hut, P. & Muller, R.A., 1984. *Extinction of species by periodic comet showers*, Nature, **308**, 715–717.

Davis, M., Hut, P. & Muller, R.A., 1985. *Terrestrial catastrophism — Nemesis or galaxy?* Nature, **313**, 503.

Degewij, J. & Tedesco, E.F., 1982. *Do comets evolve into asteroids? Evidence from physical studies*, Comets, ed. Wilkening, L., IAU Coll. No. 61, 665–695. University of Arizona Press, Tucson.

Delsemme, A.H., 1973. *Origin of the short-period comets*, Astron. Astrophys., **29**, 377–381.

Delsemme, A.H., 1976a. *The production rate of dust by comets*, Interplanetary Dust and Zodiacal Light, eds. Elsässer, H. & Fechtig, H., IAU Coll. No. 31, 314–318. (Lecture Notes in Physics, **48**.) Springer-Verlag, Berlin, New York.

Delsemme, A.H., 1976b. *Can comets be the only source of interplanetary dust?* Interplanetary Dust and Zodiacal Light, eds. Elsässer, H. & Fechtig, H., IAU Coll. No. 31, 481–484. (Lecture Notes in Physics, **48**.) Springer-Verlag, Berlin, New York.

Delsemme, A.H., 1977. *The origin of comets*, Comets Asteroids Meteorites: Interrelations, Evolution and Origins, ed. Delsemme, A.H., IAU Coll. No. 39, 453–467. University of Toledo, Toledo, Ohio.

Delsemme, A.H., 1982. *Chemical composition of cometary nuclei*, Comets, ed. Wilkening, L., IAU Coll. No. 61, 85–130. University of Arizona Press, Tucson.

Delsemme, A.H., 1985. *Empirical data from Oort's cloud*, Dynamics of Comets: Their Origin and Evolution, eds. Carusi, A. & Valsecchi, G.B., IAU Coll. No. 83, 71–85. (Astrophys. Space Sci. Lib. **115**.) Reidel, Dordrecht, The Netherlands.

Delsemme, A.H. 1986. *Cometary evidence for a solar companion?* The Galaxy and the Solar System, eds. Smoluchowski, R., Bahcall, J.N. & Matthews, M.S., 173–203. University of Arizona Press, Tucson.

Delsemme, A.H., 1989. *Whence come comets?* Sky & Telescope, **77**, No. 3 (March), 260–264.

Delsemme, A.H. & Patmiou, M., 1986. *Galactic tides affect the Oort cloud: an observational confirmation*, 20th ESLAB Symposium on the Exploration of Halley's Comet, eds. Battrick, B., Rolfe, E.J. & Reinhard, R., ESA SP-250, Vol. II, 409–412. ESA Publications, ESTEC, Noordwijk, The Netherlands.

Delsemme, A.H. & Rud, D.A., 1973. *Albedos and cross-sections for the nuclei of comets 1969 IX, 1970 II and 1971 I*, Astron. Astrophys., **28**, 1–6.

Dennison, B. & Mansfield, V.N., 1976. *Glaciations and dense interstellar clouds*, Nature, **261**, 32–34.

De Pater, I., Palmer, P. & Snyder, L., 1989. *Radio interferometric imaging of comets*, preprint. Presented at IAU Coll. No. 116 *Comets in the Post-Halley Era*, Bamberg (April 1989); eds. Newburn, R., Neugebauer, M. & Rahe, J., publisher Kluwer.

Dermott, S.F. & Gold, T., 1978. *On the origin of the Oort Cloud*, Astron. J., **83**, 449–450.

Dermott, S.F., Nicholson, P.D., Kim, Y., Wolven, B. & Tedesco, E.F., 1988. *The impact of IRAS on asteroidal science*, Comets to Cosmology, ed. Lawrence, A., 3–18. (Proceedings of Third IRAS Conference; Lecture Notes in Physics, **297**.) Springer-Verlag, Berlin.

de Santillano, G. & von Dechend, H., 1970. *Hamlet's Mill*. Macmillan & Co. Ltd., London.

De Sitter, W., 1917. *On Einstein's theory of gravitation, and its astronomical consequences*, Mon. Not. R. Astron. Soc., **78**, 3–28.

De Young, J.A. & Hilton, J.L., 1987. *Star of Bethlehem*, Sky & Telescope, **73**, No. 4 (April), 357–358.

d'Hendecourt, L.B., Allamandola, L.J., Baas, F. & Greenberg, J.M., 1982. *Interstellar grain explosions: molecule cycling between gas and dust*, Astron. Astrophys., **109**, L12–L14.

Dicke, R.H., 1962. *Mach's principle and equivalence*, Evidence For Gravitational Theories, ed. Moller, C., 1–49. (Proc. Internat. Sch. Phys. 'Enrico Fermi', Course XX.) Academic Press, New York.

Dicks, D.R., 1970. *Early Greek Astronomy to Aristotle*. Thames & Hudson, London.

Dimitrov, D.L., 1981. *On a simple model of chemical evolution and abundance of carbon, nitrogen and oxygen in interstellar matter*, Bull. Astron. Inst. Czechosl., **32**, 359–365.

Doake, C.S.M., 1978. *Climatic change and geomagnetic field reversals: a statistical correlation*, Earth Planet. Sci. Lett., **38**, 313–318.

Dodd, R.T., 1986. *Thunderstones and Shooting Stars. The Meaning of Meteorites*. Harvard University Press, Cambridge, Massachusetts.

Donn, B., 1973. *Comets, interstellar clouds and star clusters*, Bull. Amer. Astron. Soc., **5**, 342.

Donn, B., 1976. *Comets, interstellar clouds and star clusters*, The Study of Comets: Part 2, eds. Donn, B., Mumma, M., Jackson, W., A'Hearn, M. & Harrington, R., IAU Coll. No. 25, 663–670. NASA SP-393, Washington D.C.

Donn, B., 1977. *A comparison of the composition of new and evolved comets*, Comets Asteroids Meteorites: Interrelations, Evolution and Origins, ed. Delsemme, A.H., IAU Coll. No. 39, 15–23. University of Toledo, Toledo, Ohio.

Donn, B. & Sears, G.W., 1963. *Planets and comets: role of crystal growth in their formation*, Science, **140**, 1208–1211.

Donnison, J.R., 1986. *The distribution of cometary magnitudes*, Astron. Astrophys., **167**, 359–363.

Dorman, F.H., 1968. *Some Australian oxygen isotope temperatures and a theory for a 30-million year world-temperature cycle*, Journ. Geol., **76**, 297–313.

Dorman, J., Evans, S., Nakamura, Y. & Latham, G., 1978. *On the time-varying properties of the lunar seismic meteoroid population*, Proc. Lunar Planetary Sci. Conf., **9**, 3615–3626.

Drach, S.M., 1841. *Thoughts on shooting stars and comets, suggested by the perusal of Mr. Galloway's paper on the subject, read before the Society on January 8, 1841*, Mon. Not. R. Astron. Soc., **5**, 125–127.

Draine, B.T. & Salpeter, E.E., 1979. *On the physics of dust grains in hot gas*, Astrophys. J., **231**, 77–94.

Drake, M.J., Boynton, W.V. & Blanchard, D.P., 1987. *The case for planetary sample return missions: 1. Origin of the solar system*, Eos, **68**, (No. 8), pp.105, 111–113.

Drake, S. & O'Malley, C.D., 1960. *The Controversy of the Comets of 1618*. University of Pennsylvania Press, Philadelphia.

Drapatz, S., Larson, H.P. & Davis, D.S., 1987. *Search for methane in comet P/Halley*, Astron. Astrophys., **187**, 497–501.

Drobyshevski, E.M., 1974a. *On the origin of close binaries*, Astron. Astrophys., **36**, 409–413.

Drobyshevski, E.M., 1974b. *Was Jupiter the protosun's core?* Nature, **250**, 35–36.

Drobyshevski, E.M., 1978. *The origin of the solar system: implications for transneptunian planets and the nature of the long-period comets*, Moon & Planets, **18**, 145–194.

Drobyshevski, E.M., 1980. *Electrolysis in space and the fate of Phaethon*, Moon & Planets, **23**, 339–344.

Drobyshevski, E.M., 1981. *The history of Titan, of Saturn's rings and magnetic field, and the nature of short-period comets*, Moon & Planets, **24**, 13–45.

Drobyshevski, E.M., 1986. *The structure of Phaethon and detonation of its icy envelope*, Earth, Moon, Planets, **34**, 213–222.

Drobyshevski, E.M., 1987. *Burning as the prime cause of the Halley comet activity*, Fiz.-Tekh. Inst. Akad. Nauk. SSSR Preprint, No. 1132.

Drobyshevski, E.M., 1989. *Combustion as the cause of comet P/Halley's activity*, Earth, Moon, Planets, **43**, 87–99.

Drummond, J.D., 1982. *Theoretical meteor radiants of Apollo, Amor and Aten asteroids*, Icarus, **49**, 143–153.

Duley, W.W., 1984. *Evidence against biological grains in the interstellar medium*, Q. Jl. R. Astron. Soc., **25**, 109–113.

Duncan, M., Quinn, T. & Tremaine, S.D., 1987. *The formation and extent of the solar system comet cloud*, Astron. J., **94**, 1330–1338.

Duncan, M., Quinn, T. & Tremaine, S.D., 1988. *The origin of short-period comets*, Astrophys. J. Lett., **328**, L69–L73.

Duncan, M., Quinn, T. & Tremaine, S.D., 1989. *The long-term evolution of orbits in the solar system: a mapping approach*, CITA preprint.

Duncombe, R.L. & Seidelmann, P.K., 1980. *A history of the determination of Pluto's mass*, Icarus, **44**, 12–18.

Durrani, S.A. & Kahn, H.A., 1971. *Ivory coast microtektites: fission track age and geomagnetic reversals*, Nature, **232**, 320–323.

Eberhardt, P., Dolder, U., Schulte, W., Krankowsky, D., Lämmerzahl, P., Hoffman, J.H., Hodges, R.R., Bertheller, J.J. & Illiano, J.M., 1986. *The D/H ratio in Comet Halley*, 20th ESLAB Symposium on the Exploration of Halley's Comet, eds. Battrick, B., Rolfe, E.J. & Reinhard, R., ESA SP-250, Vol. I, 539–541. ESA Publications, ESTEC, Noordwijk, The Netherlands.

Eddington, A.S., 1913. *Some problems of astronomy III. The distribution of cometary orbits*, Observatory, **36**, 142–146.

Eddington, A.S., 1914. *Stellar Movements and the Structure of the Universe*. Macmillan & Co., London.

Edgeworth, K.E., 1949. *The origin and evolution of the solar system*, Mon. Not. R. Astron. Soc., **109**, 600–609.

Eggen, O.J., 1963. *Luminosities, colors and motions of the brightest A-type stars*, Astron. J., **68**, 697–714.

Eggen, O.J., 1965. *Moving groups of stars*, Galactic Structure, eds. Blaauw, A. & Schmidt, M., 111–129. (Stars and Stellar Systems, Volume V.) University of Chicago Press.

Eggen, O.J., 1987. *Stellar superclusters and groups*, The Galaxy, eds. Gilmore, G. & Carswell, R., 211–227. (NATO ASI Series, **C 207**.) Reidel, Dordrecht, The Netherlands.

Eisler, R., 1946. *The Royal Art of Astrology.* Herbert Joseph Ltd., London.

Ellis, G.F.R., 1988. *Innovation, resistance and change: the transition to the expanding universe,* Sissa-ISAS Preprint No. 89.

Elmegreen, D.M. & Elmegreen, B.G., 1984. *Blue and near-infrared surface photometry of spiral structure in 34 nonbarred grand design and flocculent galaxies,* Astrophys. J. Suppl. Ser., **54,** 127–149.

Elmegreen, B.G., 1981. *Grain formation behind shocks and the origin of isotopically anomalous meteoritic inclusions,* Astrophys. J., **251,** 820–833.

Elmegreen, B.G., 1987. *Formation and evolution of the largest cloud complexes in spiral galaxies,* Physical Processes in Interstellar Clouds, eds. Morfill, G.E. & Scholer, M., 1–12. (NATO ASI series **C 210.**) Reidel, Dordrecht, The Netherlands.

Elsässer, H., Birkle, K., Eiroa, C. & Lenzen, R., 1982. *On the Infrared Sources 1 and 2 in NGC 7538,* Astron. Astrophys., **108,** 274–278.

Emerich, C., Lamarre, J.M., Moroz, V.I., Combes, M., Sanko, N.F., Nikolsky, Yu.V., Rocard, F., Gispert, R., Coron, N., Bibring, J.P., Encrenaz, T. & Crovisier, J., 1986. *Temperature and size of the nucleus of Halley's comet deduced from I.K.S. infrared Vega 1 measurements,* 20th ESLAB Symposium on the Exploration of Halley's Comet, eds. Battrick, B., Rolfe, E.J. & Reinhard, R., ESA SP-250, Vol. II, 381–384. ESA Publications, ESTEC, Noordwijk, The Netherlands.

Emiliani, C., 1980. *Death and renovation at the end of the Mesozoic,* Eos, **61,** (No. 26), pp.505–506.

Emiliani, C., Kraus, E.B. & Shoemaker, E.M., 1981. *Sudden death at the end of the Mesozoic,* Earth Planet. Sci. Lett., **55,** 317–334.

Encrenaz, T., 1984. *Primordial matter in the outer solar system: a study of its chemical composition from remote spectroscopic analysis,* Space Sci. Rev., **38,** 35–87.

Encrenaz, T., 1985. *Isotopic ratios in comets,* Isotopic Ratios in the Solar System, 173–180. Cepadues-Editions, Toulouse, France.

Encrenaz, T., Puget, J.L., Bibring, J.P., Combes, M., Crovisier, J., Emerich, C., d'Hendecourt, L. & Rocard, F., 1987. *On the interpretation of the 3 μm emission feature in the spectrum of Comet Halley: abundances in Comet Halley and in interstellar matter,* Symposium on the Diversity and Similarity of Comets, eds. Rolfe, E.J. & Battrick, B., ESA SP-278, 369–376. ESA Publications, ESTEC, Noordwijk, The Netherlands.

Encrenaz, T., d'Hendecourt, L. & Puget, J.L., 1988. *The interpretation of the 3.2–3.5 μm spectrum of comet P/Halley: abundances in the comet and in interstellar matter,* Astron. Astrophys., **207,** 162–173.

Engel, S., Lewis, J.S. & Lunine, J.I., 1989. *Solar nebula origin for volatiles in Comet Halley,* preprint. Presented at IAU Coll. No. 116 Comets in the Post-Halley Era, Bamberg (April 1989), submitted to *Icarus.*

Erman, A., 1839a. *Ueber die Sternschnuppen der Augustperiode aus Beobachtungen derselben im Jahre 1839,* Astron. Nachr., **17,** (No. 385) 3–16.

Erman, A., 1839b. *Ueber einige Thatsachen, welche wahrscheinlich machen, dafs die Asteröiden der Augustperiode sich im Februar, und die der Novemberperiode im Mai eines Jahres zwischen der Sonne und der Erde auf dem Radiusvector der letzteren befinden,* Astron. Nachr., **17,** (No. 390) 81–94.

Esat, T.M., Brownlee, D.E., Papanastassiou, D.A. & Wasserburg, G.J., 1979. *Magnesium isotopic composition of interplanetary dust particles,* Science, **206,** 190–197.

Esat, T.M. & Taylor, S.R., 1987. *Mg isotopic composition of some interplanetary dust particles,* Lunar and Planet. Sci. Conf. **XVIII,** 269–270.

Etter, R.B. & Schneider, S.L., 1985. *Halley's Comet, Memories of 1910,* Abbeville Press, New York.

Everhart, E., 1967. *Intrinsic distributions of cometary perihelia and magnitudes,* Astron. J., **72,** 1002–1011.

Everhart, E., 1968. *Change in total energy of comets passing through the solar system*, Astron. J., **73**, 1039–1052.

Everhart, E., 1969. *Close encounters of comets and planets*, Astron. J., **74**, 735–750.

Everhart, E., 1972. *The origin of short-period comets*, Astrophys. Lett., **10**, 131–135.

Everhart, E., 1973. *Examination of several ideas of comet origins*, Astron. J., **78**, 329–337.

Everhart, E., 1974. *Origin and evolution of comets*, Asteroids, Comets, Meteoric Matter, eds. Cristescu, C., Klepczynski, W.J. & Milet, B., IAU Coll. No. 22, 223–225. Editura Academiei Republicii Socialiste România.

Everhart, E., 1976. *The evolution of comet orbits*, The Study of Comets: Part 1, eds. Donn, B., Mumma, M., Jackson, W., A'Hearn, M. & Harrington, R., IAU Coll. No. 25, 445–461. NASA SP-393, Washington D.C.

Everhart, E., 1977. *Evolution of comet orbits as perturbed by Uranus and Neptune*, Comets Asteroids Meteorites: Interrelations, Evolution and Origins, ed. Delsemme, A.H., IAU Coll. No. 39, 99–104. University of Toledo, Toledo, Ohio.

Everhart, E., 1979. *The shortage of long-period comets in elliptical orbits*, Dynamics of the Solar System, ed. Duncombe, R.L., IAU Symp. No. 81, 273–275. Reidel, Dordrecht, The Netherlands.

Everhart, E., 1982. *Evolution of long- and short-period orbits*, Comets, ed. Wilkening, L., IAU Coll. No. 61, 659–664. University of Arizona Press, Tucson.

Fabian, A.C., Arnaud, K.A. & Thomas, P.A., 1987. *Cooling flows and the formation of dark matter*, Dark Matter in the Universe, eds. Kormendy, J. & Knapp, G.R., IAU Symp. No. 117, 201–213. Reidel, Dordrecht, The Netherlands.

Fabry, L., 1893. *Études sur la probabilité des comètes hyperboliques et l'origine des comètes*. Thesis, Marseille. (Also see Bull. Astron., **12**, 43–48, 1895.)

Fairbanks, A., 1898. *The First Philosophers of Greece*. Kegan Paul, Trench, Trübner & Co. Ltd., London.

Farrington, B., 1944. *Greek Science*. Penguin, London.

Farrington, B., 1947. *Head and Hand in Ancient Greece*. Watts & Co., London.

Fay, T.D. & Wisniewski, W., 1978. *The light curve of the nucleus of Comet d'Arrest*, Icarus, **34**, 1–9.

Fayet, G., 1906. *Recherches concernant les excentricités des comètes*. Thèse, Paris.

Fayet, G., 1911. *Critérium de Tisserand pour les comètes a courte période. Proximités d'orbites*, Bull. Astron., **28**, 145–171.

Fechtig, H., 1982. *Cometary dust in the solar system*, Comets, ed. Wilkening, L., IAU Coll. No. 61, 370–382. University of Arizona Press, Tucson.

Feldman, P.D., 1989. *Ultraviolet spectroscopy of comets*, preprint. Presented at IAU Coll. No. 116 Comets in the Post-Halley Era, Bamberg (April 1989); eds. Newburn, R., Neugebauer, M. & Rahe, J., publisher Kluwer.

Fellgett, P., 1977. *Origin and nature of comets*, Observatory, **97**, 23–25.

Fellgett, P., 1985. *Comets and scientific method*, Earth, Moon, Planets, **33**, 223–227.

Ferguson, J., 1841. *Astronomy: Explained upon Sir Isaac Newton's Principles, with Notes and Supplementary Chapters by David Brewster*. 3rd Edition, Volume 2. Edinburgh.

Fernández, J.A., 1978. *Mass removed by the outer planets in the early Solar System*, Icarus, **34**, 173–181.

Fernández, J.A., 1980a. *On the existence of a comet belt beyond Neptune*, Mon. Not. R. Astron. Soc., **192**, 481–491.

Fernández, J.A., 1980b. *Evolution of comet orbits under the perturbing influence of the giant planets and nearby stars*, Icarus, **42**, 406–421.

Fernández, J.A., 1981. *New and evolved comets in the solar system*, Astron. Astrophys., **96**, 26–35.

Fernández, J.A., 1982a. *Dynamical aspects of the origin of comets*, Astron. J., **87**, 1318–1332.

524 References

Fernández, J.A., 1982b. *A dynamical study of possible birthplaces of comets*, Sun and Planetary System, eds. Fricke, W. & Teleki, G., 371–374. (Astrophys. Space Sci. Lib., **96.**) Reidel, Dordrecht, The Netherlands.

Fernández, J.A., 1985a. *The formation and dynamical survival of the Oort Cloud*, Dynamics of Comets: Their Origin and Evolution, eds. Carusi, A. & Valsecchi, G.B., IAU Coll. No. 83, 45–70. (Astrophys. Space Sci. Lib. **115.**) Reidel, Dordrecht, The Netherlands.

Fernández, J.A., 1985b. *Dynamical capture and physical decay of short-period comets*, Icarus, **64**, 308–319.

Fernández, J.A. & Ip, W.-H., 1983a. *On the time evolution of the planetary influx in the region of the terrestrial planets*, Icarus, **54**, 377–387.

Fernández, J.A. & Ip, W.-H., 1983b. *Dynamical origin of the short-period comets*, Asteroids Comets Meteors, eds. Lagerkvist, C.-I. & Rickman, H., 387–390. Uppsala Observatory, Uppsala, Sweden.

Fernández, J.A. & Ip, W.-H., 1987. *Time-dependent injection of Oort-cloud comets into Earth-crossing orbits*, Icarus, **71**, 46–56.

Fernández, J.A. & Jockers, K., 1983. *Nature and origin of comets*, Rep. Prog. Phys., **46**, 665–772.

Fessenkov, V.G., 1922. *Sur les perturbations séculaires dans le mouvement des comeètes non périodiques par des étoiles voisines*, Transactions Гn. Росс. Astrophys. Obs., **1**, 189–195.

Fessenkov, V.G., 1955. *Sikhoté-Aline meteorite*, Meteors, ed. Kaiser, T.R., 179–183. (Spec. Suppl. (Vol. 2) to J. Atmos. Terr. Phys.) Pergamon Press, London.

Festou, M.C., Drossart, P., Lecacheux, J., Encrenez, T., Puel, F. & Kohl-Moreira, J.L., 1987. *Periodicities in the light curve of P/Halley and the rotation of its nucleus*, Astron. Astrophys., **187**, 575–580.

Festou, M.C., Lecacheux, J., Kohl, J.L., Encrenez, T., Baudrand, J., Combes, M., Despiau, R., Laques, P., Lefèvre, O., Lemonnier, J.P., Lelièvre, G., Mathez, G., Pierre, M. & Vidal, J.L., 1986. *Photometry and activity of the nucleus of P/Halley at heliocentric distances larger than 4.6 AU, pre-perihelion*, Astron. Astrophys., **169**, 336–344.

Fischer, A.G. & Arthur, M.A., 1977. *Secular variations in the pelagic realm*, Soc. Econ. Paleont. Mineral. Spec. Publ., **25**, 19–50.

Fisher, W.J., 1931. *On a great meteor shower of the year 524 A.D., and its probable connection with the comet of Biela and with that of the year 1162*, Popular Astron., **39**, 573–583. (Translation of Klinkerfues 1873.)

Flannery, B.P. & Krook, M., 1978. *The sedimentation of grains in interstellar clouds*, Astrophys. J., **223**, 447–457.

Flynn, G.J., 1989. *Atmospheric entry heating: a criterion to distinguish between asteroidal and cometary sources of interplanetary dust*, Icarus, **77**, 287–310.

Fogg, M.J., 1989. *Unbound planets*, Earth, Moon, Planets, **43**, 123–130.

Forbes, G., 1880a. *On comets*, Proc. R. Soc. Edinb., **10**, 426–430.

Forbes, G., 1880b. *Additional note on an ultra-Neptunian planet*, Proc. R. Soc. Edinb., **11**, 89–91.

Forbes, G., 1909. *The comet of 1556; its possible breaking up by an unknown planet into the three parts seen in 1843, 1880 and 1882*, Mon. Not. R. Astron. Soc., **69**, 152–162.

Fox, K. Williams, I.P. & Hughes, D.W., 1984. *The 'Geminid' asteroid (1983 TB) and its orbital evolution*, Mon. Not. R. Astron. Soc., **208**, 11P–15P.

Fox, R.L., 1986. *Pagans and Christians*. Oxford University Press.

Frankfort, H., 1948. *Kingship and the Gods*. University of Chicago Press.

Frankfort, H., Frankfort, H.A., Wilson, J.A., Jacobsen, T. & Irwin, W.A., 1946. *The Intellectual Adventure of Ancient Man*. University of Chicago Press.

Fraundorf, P., 1981 *Interplanetary dust in the transmission electron microscope: diverse materials from the early solar system*, Geochim. Cosmochim. Acta, **45**, 915–943.

Fraundorf, P., Brownlee, D.E. & Walker, R.M., 1982. *Laboratory studies of interplanetary dust*, Comets, ed. Wilkening, L., IAU Coll. No. 61, 383–409. University of Arizona Press, Tucson.

Frerking, M.A., Wilson, R.W., Linke, R.A. & Wannier, P.G., 1980. *Isotopic abundance ratios in interstellar carbon monosulfide*, Astrophys. J., **240**, 65–73.

Fricke, K.J., 1973. *Dynamical phases of supermassive stars*, Astrophys. J., **183**, 941–958.

Fricke, K.J., 1974. *Dynamical phases of rotating supermassive stars*, Astrophys. J., **189**, 535–542.

Froeschlé, Cl. & Rickman, H., 1980. *New Monte Carlo simulations of the orbital evolution of short-period comets and comparison with observations*, Astron. Astrophys., **82**, 183–194.

Froeschlé, Cl. & Rickman, H., 1988. *Monte Carlo modelling of cometary dynamics*, Celest. Mech., **43**, 265–284.

Ganapathy, R., 1980. *A major meteorite impact on the earth 65 million years ago: evidence from the Cretaceous-Tertiary boundary clay*, Science, **209**, 921–923.

Ganapathy, R., 1982. *Evidence for a major meteorite impact on the earth 34 million years ago: implications for Eocene extinctions*, Science, **216**, 885–886.

Ganapathy, R., 1983. *The Tunguska explosion of 1908: discovery of meteoritic debris near the explosion site and at the South Pole*, Science, **220**, 1158–1161.

Gatley, I., Jones, T.J., Hyland, A.R., Wade, R., Geballe, T.R. & Krisciunas, K., 1986. *The spatial distribution and velocity field of the molecular hydrogen line emission from the centre of the Galaxy*, Mon. Not. R. Astron. Soc., **222**, 299–306.

Gauss, C.F., 1815. Göttingische gelehrte Anzeigen, 11 March 1815. See Carle Friedrich Gauss Werke, **6**, 581–583. Göttingen 1874.

Geiss, J., 1987. *Composition measurements and the history of cometary matter*, Astron. Astrophys., **187**, 859–866.

Geiss, J., 1988. *Composition in Halley's comet: clues to origin and history of cometary matter*, Cosmic Chemistry, ed. Klare, G., 1–27. (Reviews in Modern Astronomy **1**.) Springer-Verlag, Berlin.

Geiss, J. & Reeves, H., 1981. *Deuterium in the solar system*, Astron. Astrophys., **93**, 189–199.

Gething, P.J.D., 1951. *Accretion and the origin of comets*, Mon. Not. R. Astron. Soc., **111**, 468–477.

Gilden, D.L., 1984. *Thermal instability in molecular clouds*, Astrophys. J., **283**, 679–686.

Glass, B. & Heezen, B.C., 1967. *Tektites and geomagnetic reversals*, Nature, **214**, 372.

Goldreich, P. & Lynden-Bell, D., 1965a. *I. Gravitational instability of uniformly rotating disks*, Mon. Not. R. Astron. Soc., **130**, 97–124.

Goldreich, P. & Lynden-Bell, D., 1965b. *II. Spiral arms as sheared gravitational instabilities*, Mon. Not. R. Astron. Soc., **130**, 125–158.

Goldreich, P. & Ward, W.R., 1973. *The formation of planetesimals*, Astrophys. J., **183**, 1051–1061.

Goldstein, R.M., Jurgens, R.F. & Sekanina, Z., 1984. *A radar study of Comet IRAS-Araki-Alcock 1983d*, Astron. J., **89**, 1745–1754.

Goodwin, W.W., 1871. *Plutarch's Morals*. Five volumes. De Placitis Philosophorum translated by John Dowel, **3**, 104–193.

Gordon, M.A. & Burton, W.B., 1979. *Statistical modelling of CO emission in the Galaxy*, The Large-scale Characteristics of the Galaxy, ed. Burton, W.B., IAU Symp. No. 84, 271–276. Reidel, Dordrecht, The Netherlands.

Goswami, J.N. & Lal, D., 1978. *Temporal changes in the flux of meteorites in the recent past*, Moon & Planets, **18**, 371–382.

Gould, B.A., 1874. *On the number and distribution of the bright fixed stars*, Amer. Journ. Sci. Arts (3rd ser.) **8**, 325–334.

Grant, R., 1852. *History of Physical Astronomy from the earliest ages to the middle of the nineteenth century.* Bohn, London. Reprinted: Johnson Reprint Co., Sources of Science No. 38, 1966.

Green, S.F., McDonnell, J.A.M., Perry, C.H., Nappo, S. & Zarnecki, J.C., 1987. *P/Halley dust coma: grains or rocks?* Symposium on the Diversity and Similarity of Comets, eds. Rolfe, E.J. & Battrick, B., ESA SP-278, 379–384. ESA Publications, ESTEC, Noordwijk, The Netherlands.

Greenberg, J.M., 1974. *The interstellar depletion mystery, or where have all those atoms gone?* Astrophys. J. Lett., **189**, L81–L85.

Greenberg, J.M., 1982. *What are comets made of?* A model based on interstellar dust, Comets, ed. Wilkening, L., IAU Coll. No. 61, 131–163. University of Arizona Press, Tucson.

Greenberg, J.M., 1983. *Interstellar dust, comets, comet dust and carbonaceous meteorites*, Asteroids Comets Meteors, eds. Lagerkvist, C.-I. & Rickman, H., 259–268. Uppsala Observatory, Uppsala, Sweden.

Greenberg, J.M., 1984. *A fine mist of very small comet particles*, Adv. Space Res., **4**, 211–212.

Greenberg, J.M., 1986a. *Predicting that comet Halley is dark*, Nature, **321**, 385.

Greenberg, J.M., 1986b. *Fluffy comets*, Asteroids Comets Meteors II, eds, Lagerkvist, C.-I., Lindblad, B.A., Lundstedt, H. & Rickman, H., 221–223. Uppsala University, Uppsala, Sweden.

Greenberg, J.M., 1986c. *Evidence for the pristine nature of Comet Halley*, The Comet Nucleus Sample Return Mission, ed. Melita, O., ESA SP-249, 47–55. ESA Publications, ESTEC, Noordwijk, The Netherlands.

Greenberg, J.M., 1988. *The interstellar dust model of comets: post Halley*, Dust in the Universe, eds. Bailey, M.E. & Williams, D.A., 121–143. Cambridge University Press.

Greenberg, J.M. & Grim, R., 1986. *The origin and evolution of comet nuclei*, 20th ESLAB Symposium on the Exploration of Halley's Comet, eds. Battrick, B., Rolfe, E.J. & Reinhard, R., ESA SP-250, Vol. II, 255–263. ESA Publications, ESTEC, Noordwijk, The Netherlands.

Greenberg, J.M., Grim, R.J.A., & van IJzendoorn, L.J., 1986. *Interstellar S_2 in comets*, Asteroids Comets Meteors II, eds, Lagerkvist, C.-I., Lindblad, B.A., Lundstedt, H. & Rickman, H., 225–227. Uppsala University, Uppsala, Sweden.

Greenberg, R., 1985. *The origin of comets among the accreting outer planets*, Dynamics of Comets: Their Origin and Evolution, eds. Carusi, A. & Valsecchi, G.B., IAU Coll. No. 83, 3–10. (Astrophys. Space Sci. Lib. **115**.) Reidel, Dordrecht, The Netherlands.

Greenberg, R., Hartmann, W.K., Chapman, C.R. & Wacker, J.F., 1978. *The accretion of planets from planetesimals*, Protostars & Planets, ed. Gehrels, T., IAU Coll. No. 52, 599–622. University of Arizona Press, Tucson, Arizona, USA.

Greenberg, R., Weidenschilling, S.J., Chapman, C.R. & Davis, D.R., 1984. *From icy planetesimals to outer planets and comets*, Icarus, **59**, 87–113.

Gribbin, J., 1975. *Halley lecturer produces new theory of comet origins*, Nature, **255**, 196.

Grieve, R.A.F., 1984. *The impact cratering rate in recent time*, Proc. 14th Lunar Planet. Sci. Conf., Part 2; J. Geophys. Res., **89**, B403–B408.

Grieve, R.A.F., 1989. *Hypervelocity impact cratering: a catastrophic terrestrial geologic process*, Catastrophes and Evolution: Astronomical Foundation, ed. Clube, S.V.M., in press. Cambridge University Press.

Grieve, R.A.F. & Dence, M.R., 1979. *The terrestrial cratering record. II. The crater production rate*, Icarus, **38**, 230–242.

Grim, R.J.A. & Greenberg, J.M., 1987. *Photoprocessing of H$_2$S in interstellar grain mantles as an explanation for S$_2$ in comets*, Astron. Astrophys., **181**, 155–168.

Grove, J.M., 1988. *The Little Ice Age*. Methuen & Co., London.

Grün, E., Zook, H.A., Fechtig, H. & Giese, R.H., 1986. *Collisional balance of the meteoritic complex*, Icarus, **62**, 244–272.

Guillemin, A., 1865. *Le Ciel*. (2nd edition), Paris.

Guillemin, A., 1877. *The World of Comets*. Translated and edited by James Glaisher. Sampson Low, Marston, Searle and Rivington, London.

Gustafson, B.Å.S., Misconi, N.Y. & Rusk, E.T., 1987. *Interplanetary dust dynamics. III. Dust released from P/Encke: distribution with respect to the zodiacal cloud*, Icarus, **72**, 582–592.

Guthrie, W.K.C., 1962. *A History of Greek Philosophy. Vol. 1. The earlier presocratics and the pythagoreans*. Cambridge University Press.

Guthrie, W.K.C., 1965. *A History of Greek Philosophy. Vol. 2. The presocratic tradition from Parmenides to Democritus*. Cambridge University Press.

Hahn, G. & Rickman, H., 1985. *Asteroids in cometary orbits*, Icarus, **61**, 417–442.

Hallam, A., 1973. *A Revolution in the Earth Sciences, from Continental Drift to Plate Tectonics*. Clarendon Press, Oxford.

Hallam, A., 1979. *The end of the Cretaceous*, Nature, **281**, 430–431.

Hallam, A., 1984a. *The causes of mass extinctions*, Nature, **308**, 686–687.

Hallam, A., 1984b. *Pre-quarternary sea-level changes*, Annu. Rev. Earth Planet. Sci., **12**, 205–243.

Hallam, A., 1987. *End-Cretaceous mass extinction event: argument for terrestrial causation*, Science, **238**, 1237–1242.

Halley, E., 1714. *An account of several extraordinary meteors or lights in the sky*, Philos. Trans. R. Soc. London, **29**, 159–164.

Halliday, I., 1987. *Detection of a meteorite "stream": Observations of a second fall from the orbit of the Innisfree meteorite*, Icarus, **69**, 550–556. *Corrigendum 72*, 239.

Halm, J., 1914. *Further considerations relating to the systematic motions of the stars*, Mon. Not. R. Astron. Soc., **71**, 610–639.

Hamid, S.E., Marsden, B.G. & Whipple, F.L., 1968. *Influence of a comet belt beyond Neptune on the motions of periodic comets*, Astron. J., **73**, 727–729.

Harper, D.A., Lowenstein, R.F. & Davidson, J.A., 1984. *On the nature of the material surrounding Vega*, Astrophys. J., **285**, 808–812.

Harrington, R.S., 1985. *Implications of the observed distributions of very long period comet orbits*, Icarus, **61**, 60–62.

Harrington, R.S. & Christy, J.W., 1981. *The satellite of Pluto. III*, Astron. J., **86**, 442–443.

Hartmann, L. & Kenyon, S.J., 1985. *On the nature of FU Orionis objects*, Astrophys. J., **299**, 462–478.

Hartmann, W.K., Tholen, D.J. & Cruikshank, D.P., 1987. *The relationship of active comets, "extinct" comets and dark asteroids*, Icarus, **69**, 33–50.

Hasegawa, I., 1976. *Distribution of the aphelia of long-period comets*, Publ. Astron. Soc. Japan, **28**, 259–276.

Havnes, O., 1972. *Evolution of short-period cometary orbits due to close approaches to Jupiter*, The Motion, Evolution of Orbits, and Origin of Comets, eds. Chebotarev, G.A., Kazimirchak-Polonskaya, E.I. & Marsden, B.G., IAU Symp. No. 45, 364–369. Reidel, Dordrecht, The Netherlands.

Hawkins, G.S., 1964. *Meteors, Comets and Meteorites*. McGraw-Hill, New York.

Hawkins, I. & Jura, M., 1987. *The $^{12}C/^{13}C$ isotope ratio of the interstellar medium in the neighborhood of the sun*, Astrophys. J., **317**, 926–950.

Hawkins, M.R.S. & Bessel, M.S., 1988. *The luminosity function for low mass stars*, Mon. Not. R. Astron. Soc., **234**, 177–191.

Hayashi, C., Nakazawa, K. & Nakagawa, Y., 1985. *Formation of the solar system*, Protostars & Planets II, eds. Black, D.C. & Matthews, M.S., 1100–1153. University of Arizona Press, Tucson.

Heath, T., 1913. *Aristarchos of Samos: The Ancient Copernicus*. Clarendon Press, Oxford.

Heggie, D.C., 1981. *Megalithic Science: Ancient Mathematics and Astronomy in Northwest Europe*. Thames & Hudson, London.

Heisler, J. & Tremaine, S.D., 1986. *The influence of the galactic tidal field on the Oort comet cloud*, Icarus, **65**, 13–26.

Heisler, J. & Tremaine, S.D., 1989. *How dating uncertainties affect the detection of periodicity in extinctions and craters*, Icarus, **77**, 213–219.

Heisler, J., Tremaine, S.D. & Alcock, C., 1987. *The frequency and intensity of comet showers from the Oort cloud*, Icarus, **70**, 269–288.

Hellman, C.D., 1944. *The Comet of 1577: Its Place in the History of Astronomy*. Columbia University Press, New York.

Herbig, G.H., 1977. *Eruptive phenomena in early stellar evolution*, Astrophys. J., **217**, 693–715.

Herbig, G.H., 1983. *The origin and early history of the sun and planetary system in the context of stellar evolution*, Highlights in Astronomy, ed. West, R., **6**, 15–28. Reidel, Dordrecht, The Netherlands.

Herschel, J.F.W., 1858. *Outlines of Astronomy*. (Fifth edition.) Longman, Brown, Green, Longmans & Roberts, London.

Herschel, W., 1783. *On the proper motion of the Sun and Solar System; with an account of several changes that have happened among the fixed stars since the time of Mr. Flamstead*, Philos. Trans. R. Soc. London, **73**, 247–283.

Herschel, W., 1802. *Observations on the two lately discovered celestial Bodies*, Philos. Trans. R. Soc. London, **92**, 213–232.

Herschel, W., 1805. *Experiments for ascertaining how far telescopes will enable us to determine very small angles, and to distinguish the real from the spurious diameters of celestial and terrestrial objects: with an application of the results of the experiments to a series of observations on the nature and magnitude of Mr. Harding's lately discovered star*, Philos. Trans. R. Soc. London, **95**, 31–64.

Hevelius, J., 1668. *Cometographia*. Gedani.

Hill, G., Hilditch, R.W. & Barnes, J.V., 1979. *Studies of A and F stars in the region of the North Galactic Pole — IV. A determination of the local mass density*, Mon. Not. R. Astron. Soc., **186**, 813–829.

Hill, J., 1754. *Urania*. London.

Hills, J.G., 1973. *On the process of accretion in the formation of the planets and comets*, Icarus, **18**, 505–522.

Hills, J.G., 1981. *Comet showers and the steady-state infall of comets from the Oort Cloud*, Astron. J., **86**, 1730–1740.

Hills, J.G., 1982. *The formation of comets by radiation pressure in the outer protosun*, Astron. J., **87**, 906–910.

Hills, J.G., 1984. *Dynamical constraints on the mass and perihelion distance of Nemesis and the stability of its orbit*, Nature, **311**, 636–638.

Hills, J.G. & Sandford II, M.T., 1983a. *The formation of comets by radiation pressure in the outer protosun. II. Dependence on the radiation-grain coupling*, Astron. J., **88**, 1519–1521.

Hills, J.G. & Sandford II, M.T., 1983b. *The formation of comets by radiation pressure in the outer protosun. III. Dependence on the anisotropy of the radiation field*, Astron. J., **88**, 1522–1530.

Hind, J.R., 1850. Astron. Nachr., **31**, (No. 724) 62–63.

Hind, J.R., 1851. *Discovery of Irene*, Mon. Not. R. Astron. Soc., **11**, 149–155.

Hind, J.R., 1862. *Note on a dark, circular Spot upon the Sun's Disk, with rapid motion, as observed by W. Lummis, Esq., of Manchester, 1862, March 20*, Mon. Not. R. Astron. Soc., **22**, 232.

Hind, J.R., 1884. *The comet of 1729.* (Anonymous article in *Our Astronomical Column*, with orbit attributed to Hind.) Nature, **30**, 519.

Hirst, W.P., 1950. *The problem of the origin of comets*, Mon. Notes Astron. Soc. Southern Africa, **9**, 12–15.

Ho, Ping-Yü, 1962. *Ancient and mediaeval observations of comets and novae in Chinese sources*, Vistas Astron., **5**, 127–225.

Hoban, S., Samarasinha, N.H., A'Hearn, M.F. & Klinglesmith, D.A., 1988. *An investigation into periodicities in the morphology of CN jets in comet P/Halley*, Astron. Astrophys., **195**, 331–337.

Hoek, M., 1865. *On the comets 1860III., 1863I., and 1863VI*, Mon. Not. R. Astron. Soc., **25**, 243–251.

Hoek, M., 1866a. *On the comets of 1677 and 1683; 1860III., 1863I., and 1863VI.* Mon. Not. R. Astron. Soc., **26**, 1–12.

Hoek, M., 1866b *Additions to the investigations on cometary systems*, Mon. Not. R. Astron. Soc., **26**, 204–208.

Hoek, M., 1868. *On the comets of 1857III and V., and 1867III.* Mon. Not. R. Astron. Soc., **28**, 129–131.

Hoffman, A., 1985. *Patterns of family extinction depend on definition and geological timescale*, Nature, **315**, 659–662.

Hoffman, A., 1986. *Reply to Sepkoski & Raup 1986b*, Nature, **321**, 535.

Hoffman, A., 1988. *Muller's period piece*, Review of 'Nemesis the Death Star', by R.A. Muller (Weidenfeld & Nicolson, New York). Nature, **336**, 321.

Holland, P., 1603. *The Philosophie Commonlie called the The Morals, written by the learned philosopher Plutarch of Chaerona*. See Book III, Ch.2, p.827. Arnold Hatfield, London.

Holmes, A., 1927. *The Age of the Earth — an introduction to geological ideas*. Benn, London.

Hooke, R., 1678. *Lectures and Collections. Cometa. Microscopium.* J. Martyn, London.

Horanyi, M., Gombosi, T.I., Cravens, T.E., Korosmezey, A., Kecskemety, K., Nagy, A.F. & Szegő, K., 1984. *The friable sponge model of a cometary nucleus*, Astrophys. J., **278**, 449–455.

Horedt, G.P., 1979. *Cosmogony of the solar system*, Moon & Planets, **21**, 63–121.

Houzeau, J.C. & Lancaster, A., 1882. *Bibliographie Générale de l'Astronomie*. Volume 2, 1090–1099. Xavier Havermans, Bruxelles.

Howard, E.C., 1802. *Experiments and observations on certain stony and metalline substances, which at different times are said to have fallen on the earth; also on various kinds of native iron*, Philos. Trans. R. Soc. London, **92**, 168–212.

Hoyle, F., 1980. *Comets — a matter of life and death*, Vistas Astron., **24**, 123–139. (The text of the Milne Lecture, delivered at Oxford, 16 Jan. 1978).

Hoyle, F., 1982. *The Universe: past and present reflections*, Annu. Rev. Astron. Astrophys., **20**, 1–35.

Hoyle, F., 1984. *Comets*, Observatory, **104**, 132–133.

Hoyle, F., 1987. *The relation of a bilogical puzzle to the origin of ice-ages and to other phenomena*, Earth, Moon, Planets, **37**, 1–15.

Hoyle, F. & Fowler, W.A., 1963. *On the nature of strong radio sources*, Mon. Not. R. Astron. Soc., **125**, 169–176.

Hoyle, F. & Lyttleton, R.A., 1939. *The effect of interstellar matter on climatic variation*, Proc. Camb. Philos. Soc., **35**, 405–415.

Hoyle, F. & Lyttleton, R.A., 1942. *On the nature of red giant stars*, Mon. Not. R. Astron. Soc., **102**, 218–225.

Hoyle, F. & Narlikar, J.V., 1966. *On the formation of elliptical galaxies*, Proc. R. Soc. London, Ser. A, **290**, 177–185.

Hoyle, F. & Wickramasinghe, N.C., 1978. *Comets, ice ages, and ecological catastrophes*, Astrophys. Space Sci., **53**, 523–526.

Hoyle, F. & Wickramasinghe, N.C., 1981. *Comets — a vehicle for panspermia*, Comets and the Origin of Life, ed. Ponnamperuma, C., 227–239. Reidel, Dordrecht, Holland.

Hoyle, F. & Wickramasinghe, N.C., 1985. *Living Comets*. University College Cardiff Press.

Hsü, K.J., 1980. *Terrestrial catastrophe caused by cometary impact at the end of the Cretaceous*, Nature, **285**, 201–203.

Hughes, D.W., 1979. *The Star of Bethlehem: An Astronomer's Confirmation*. Pocket Books, New York.

Hughes, D.W., 1982a. *The history of meteors and meteor showers*, Vistas Astron., **26**, 325–345.

Hughes, D.W., 1982b. *Comets*, Contemp. Phys., **23**, 257–283.

Hughes, D.W., 1983. *Temporal variations of the absolute magnitude of Halley's comet*, Mon. Not. R. Astron. Soc., **204**, 1291–1295.

Hughes, D.W., 1985. *The size, mass, mass loss and age of Halley's comet*, Mon. Not. R. Astron. Soc., **213**, 103–109.

Hughes, D.W., 1986. *Meteoroids: the best clues to the structure of the cometary nucleus?* The Comet Nucleus Sample Return Mission, ed. Melita, O., ESA SP-249, 173–179. ESA Publications, ESTEC, Noordwijk, The Netherlands.

Hughes, D.W., 1987a. *On the distribution of cometary magnitudes*, Mon. Not. R. Astron. Soc., **226**, 309–316.

Hughes, D.W., 1987b. *Cometary magnitude distributions: the tabulated data*, Symposium on the Diversity and Similarity of Comets, eds. Rolfe, E.J. & Battrick, B., ESA SP-278, 43–48. ESA Publications, ESTEC, Noordwijk, The Netherlands.

Hughes, D.W., 1987c. *Cometary magnitude distribution and the fading of comets*, Nature, **325**, 231–232.

Hughes, D.W. & Daniels, P.A., 1980. *The magnitude distribution of comets*, Mon. Not. R. Astron. Soc., **191**, 511–520.

Hughes, D.W. & Daniels, P.A., 1982. *Temporal variations in the cometary mass distribution*, Mon. Not. R. Astron. Soc., **198**, 573–582.

Humphries, C.M., 1982. *Photodesorptive jet thrusting — a mechanism for efficient formation of kilometre-sized bodies in molecular clouds?* Proc. Workshop on Interstellar Comets, eds. Clube, S.V.M. & McInnes, B., Occ. Rep. Roy. Obs. Edinb., No. 9, 33–36.

Hurnik, H., 1959. *The distribution of the directions of perihelia and of the orbital poles of non-periodic comets*, Acta Astron., **9**, 208–221.

Hut, P., 1984. *How stable is an astronomical clock that can trigger mass extinctions on Earth?* Nature, **311**, 638–641.

Hut, P., 1986. *Evolution of the solar system in the presence of a solar companion star*, The Galaxy and the Solar System, eds. Smoluchowski, R., Bahcall, J.N. & Matthews, M.S., 313–337. University of Arizona Press, Tucson.

Hut, P., Alvarez, W., Elder, W.P., Hansen, T., Kauffman, E.G., Keller, G., Shoemaker, E.M. & Weissman, P.R., 1987. *Comet showers as a cause of mass extinctions*, Nature, **329**, 118–126.

Hut, P. & Tremaine, S.D., 1985. *Have interstellar clouds disrupted the Oort comet cloud?* Astron. J., **90**, 1548–1557.

Huxley, F., 1980. *The Way of the Sacred*. W.H. Allen & Co., London.

Icke, V., 1982. *Transitions between epicyclic stellar orbits induced by massive molecular clouds*, Astrophys. J., **254**, 517–537.

Ip, W.-H., 1977. *On the early scattering processes of the outer planets,* Comets Asteroids Meteorites: Interrelations, Evolution and Origins, ed. Delsemme, A.H., IAU Coll. No. 39, 485–490. University of Toledo, Toledo, Ohio.

Ip, W.-H. & Fernández, J.A., 1988. *Exchange of condensed matter among the outer and terrestrial proto-planets and the effect on surface impact and atmospheric accretion,* Icarus, **74,** 47–61.

Ipatov, S.I., 1987. *Accumulation and migration of the bodies from the zones of giant planets,* Earth, Moon, Planets, **39,** 101–128.

Izakov, M.N., 1988. *Region of formation of the nucleus of Comet Halley and certain processes in the preplanetary nebula,* Cosmic Research, **26,** 81–87.

Jackson, A.A. & Killen, R.M., 1988. *Infrared brightness of a comet belt beyond Neptune,* Earth, Moon, Planets, **42,** 41–47.

Jacobsen, T., 1946. *Mesopotamia,* The Intellectual Adventure of Ancient Man: an Essay on Speculative Thought in the Ancient Near East, by Frankfort, H., Frankfort, H.A., Wilson, J.A., Jacobsen, T. & Irwin, W.A., 125–219. University of Chicago Press, Chicago.

Jaki, S.L., 1972. *The Milky Way: An Elusive Road for Science.* Science History Publications, Neale Watson Academic Publications Inc., New York.

James, E.O., 1962. *The Ancient Gods.* Weidenfeld & Nicolson, London.

Jantzen, K., 1912. *Statistik der Kometenbahnelemente.* München. (Cited by Hurnik 1959.)

Jeans, J.H., 1917. *The motion of tidally-distorted masses, with special reference to theories of cosmogony,* Memoirs R. Astron. Soc., **62,** 1–48.

Jeans, J.H., 1919. *Problems of Cosmogony and Stellar Dynamics.* Cambridge University Press.

Jeans, J.H., 1928. *Astronomy and Cosmogony.* Cambridge University Press.

Jeans, J.H., 1947. *The Growth of Physical Science.* Cambridge University Press.

Jeffreys, H., 1916. *On certain possible distributions of meteoric bodies in the solar system,* Mon. Not. R. Astron. Soc., **77,** 84–112.

Jeffreys, H., 1918. *On the early history of the solar system,* Mon. Not. R. Astron. Soc., **78,** 424–441.

Jeffreys, H., 1929. *Collision and the origin of rotation in the solar system,* Mon. Not. R. Astron. Soc., **89,** 636–641.

Jenkins, E.B., 1987. *Element abundances in the interstellar atomic material,* Interstellar Processes, eds. Hollenbach, D.J. & Thronson, H.A., 533–560. Reidel, Dordrecht, The Netherlands.

Jervis, J.L., 1985. *Cometary Theory in Fifteenth-Century Europe.* Reidel, Dordrecht, Holland.

Jessberger, E.K., Christoforidis, A. & Kissel, J., 1988. *Aspects of the major element composition of Halley's dust,* Nature, **332,** 691–695.

Jessberger, E.K., Kissel, J., Fechtig, H. & Krueger, F.R., 1986. *On the average chemical composition of cometary dust,* The Comet Nucleus Sample Return Mission, ed. Melita, O., ESA SP-249, 27–30. ESA Publications, ESTEC, Noordwijk, The Netherlands.

Jewitt, D.C. & Luu, J.X., 1989. *A CCD portrait of Comet P/Tempel 2,* Astron. J., **97,** 1766–1790.

Jewitt, D.C. & Meech, K.J., 1987. *CCD photometry of Comet P/Encke,* Astron. J., **93,** 1542–1548.

Jewitt, D.C. & Meech, K.J., 1988. *Optical properties of cometary nuclei and a preliminary comparison with asteroids,* Astrophys. J., **328,** 974–986.

Johnson, F.R., 1968. *Astronomical thought in Renaissance England.* Octagon Books Inc., New York.

Jones, C.W., 1975. *Bede's De Natura Rerum Liber,* Corpus Christianorum, Series Latina **123A,** 174–234.

Jones, H.D., 1988. *Halley and comet impacts*, Journ. Br. Astron. Assoc., **98**, 339.

Joss, P.C., 1973a. *On the origin of short-period comets*, Astron. Astrophys., **25**, 271–273.

Joss, P.C., 1973b. *Orientation-dependent effects in Oort's theory of comet origin II. Anisotropies in the distribution of long-period comet orbits*, Icarus, **19**, 147–153.

Kadas, S., 1987. *Mount Athos*. Ekdotike Athenon S.A., Athens.

Kant, I., 1755. *Universal Natural History and Theory of the Heavens; or an essay on the constitution and mechanical origin of the whole universe treated according to Newton's principles*. (See Ley, 1968).

Kamoun, P.G., Campbell, D.B., Ostro, S.J., Pettengill, G.H. & Shapiro, I.I., 1982. *Comet Encke: radar detection of its nucleus*, Science, **216**, 293–295.

Kapkov, V.B., 1984. *An occultation by Pallas*, Sov. Astron. Lett., **10**, 26–27. Translated from Pis'ma Astron. Zh., **10**, 67–70, 1984.

Katasseff, I.A., 1955. *Meteoritika*, **13**, 76–86. (Cited by Dauvillier 1964, p.91.)

Kawara, K., Gregory, B., Yamamoto, T. & Shibai, H., 1988. *Infrared spectroscopic observation of methane in comet P/Halley*, Astron. Astrophys., **207**, 174–181.

Kazimirchak-Polonskaya, E.I., 1972. *The major planets as powerful transformers of cometary orbits*, The Motion, Evolution of Orbits, and Origin of Comets, eds. Chebotarev, G.A., Kazimirchak-Polonskaya, E.I. & Marsden, B.G., IAU Symp. No. 45, 373–397. Reidel, Dordrecht, The Netherlands.

Kazimirchak-Polonskaya, E.I., 1976. *Review of investigations performed in the U.S.S.R. on close approaches of comets to Jupiter and the evolution of cometary orbits*, The Study of Comets: Part 1, eds. Donn, B., Mumma, M., Jackson, W., A'Hearn, M. & Harrington, R., IAU Coll. No. 25, 490–536. NASA SP-393, Washington D.C.

Kazimirchak-Polonskaya, E.I., 1985. *Review of studies on capture of comets by Neptune and its role in the dynamic evolution of cometary orbits*, Dynamics of Comets: Their Origin and Evolution, eds. Carusi, A. & Valsecchi, G.B., IAU Coll. No. 83, 243–258. (Astrophys. Space Sci. Lib. **115**.) Reidel, Dordrecht, The Netherlands.

Keller, H.U. & Thomas, N., 1989. *Topography and morphology of Comet Halley's nucleus*, preprint. Presented at IAU Coll. No. 116 *Comets in the Post-Halley Era*, Bamberg (April 1989), submitted to *Icarus*.

Kendall, D.G., 1961. *Some problems in the theory of comets. I*, Proc. 4th Berkeley Symp. on Mathematical Statistics and Probability, **3**, 99–120, ed. Neyman, J. University of California Press.

Kerr, F.J., 1962. *Galactic velocity models and the interpretation of 21-cm surveys*, Mon. Not. R. Astron. Soc., **123**, 327–345.

Kerr, F.J. & Lynden-Bell, D., 1986. *Review of galactic constants*, Mon. Not. R. Astron. Soc., **221**, 1023–1038.

Kerr, R.H., 1961. *Perturbations of cometary orbits*, Proc. 4th Berkeley Symp. on Mathematical Statistics and Probability, **3**, 149–164, ed. Neyman, J. University of California Press.

Keynes, J.M., 1947. *Newton, the man*, The Royal Society Newton Tercentenary Celebrations (15–19 July 1946), pp.27–34. Cambridge University Press.

King, H.C., 1957. *The Background of Astronomy*. Watts & Co., London.

Kirkwood, D., 1861. Danville Quarterly Review, December 1861.

Kirkwood, D., 1872. *On the disintegration of comets*, Nature, **6**, 148–149.

Kissel, J. & Krueger, F.R., 1987. *The organic component in dust from comet Halley as measured by the PUMA mass spectrometer on board Vega 1*, Nature, **326**, 755–760.

Klinger, J., 1981. *Some consequences of a phase transition of water ice on the heat balance of comet nuclei*, Icarus, **47**, 320–324.

Klinger, J., 1983. *Modelling of cometary nuclei*, Asteroids Comets Meteors, eds. Lagerkvist, C.-I. & Rickman, H., 205–213. Uppsala Observatory, Uppsala, Sweden.

Klinkerfues, W., 1873. *On a great meteor shower of the year 524 A.D., and its probable connection with the comet of Biela and with that of the year 1162,* Göttinger Nachrichten (April 30, 1873), 275–296. (See translation by Fisher 1931.)

Koestler, A., 1968. *The Sleepwalkers.* Pelican Books, London.

Kohler, P., 1975. *Un objet mysterieux photographié devant Jupiter,* Ciel et Espace, No. 150, 11–12.

Kominz, M.A. & Pisias, N.G., 1979. *Pleistocene climate: deterministic or stochastic?* Science, **204,** 171–173.

Kopal, Z., 1969. *The Moon,* p.362. Reidel, Dordrecht, The Netherlands.

Kopal, Z., 1971. *The eclipsing system of Epsilon Aurigae and its possible relevance to the formation of a planetary system,* Astrophys. Space Sci., **10,** 332–339.

Kopal, Z., 1980. *Ice ages on the earth and their astronomical implications,* Moon & Planets, **23,** 253–258.

Kowal, C.T., 1979. *Chiron,* Asteroids, ed. Gehrels, T., 436–439. University of Arizona Press, Tucson.

Krankowsky, D., Lämmerzahl, P., Herrwerth, I., Woweries, J., Eberhardt, P., Dolder, U., Herrmann, U., Schulte, W., Berthelier, J.J., Illiano, J.M., Hodges, R.R. & Hoffman, J.H., 1986. *In situ gas and ion measurements at comet Halley,* Nature, **321,** 326–329.

Krat, V.A., 1952. *Voprosy Kosmogonii,* **1,** 34–91. (cf. Drobyshevski 1978, pp.169, 174.)

Kresák, Ĺ., 1977a. *An alternative interpretation of the Oort cloud of comets?* Comets Asteroids Meteorites: Interrelations, Evolution and Origins, ed. Delsemme, A.H., IAU Coll. No. 39, 93–97. University of Toledo, Toledo, Ohio.

Kresák, Ĺ., 1977b. *Asteroid versus comet discrimination from orbital data,* Comets Asteroids Meteorites: Interrelations, Evolution and Origins, ed. Delsemme, A.H., IAU Coll. No. 39, 313–321. University of Toledo, Toledo, Ohio.

Kresák, Ĺ., 1978a. *The Tunguska object: a fragment of Comet Encke?* Bull. Astron. Inst. Czechosl., **29,** 129–134.

Kresák, Ĺ., 1978b. *The comet and asteroid population of the earth's environment,* Bull. Astron. Inst. Czechosl., **29,** 114–125.

Kresák, Ĺ., 1980. *Sources of interplanetary dust,* Solid Particles in the Solar System, eds. Halliday, I. & McIntosh, B.A., IAU Symp. No. 90, 211–222. Reidel, Dordrecht, The Netherlands.

Kresák, Ĺ., 1981a. *Evolutionary aspects of the splits of cometary nuclei,* Bull. Astron. Inst. Czechosl., **32,** 19–40.

Kresák, Ĺ., 1981b. *The lifetimes and disappearance of periodic comets,* Bull. Astron. Inst. Czechosl., **32,** 321–339.

Kresák, Ĺ., 1984. *The lifetimes and disappearance of long-period comets,* Bull. Astron. Inst. Czechosl., **35,** 129–150.

Kresák, Ĺ. & Pittich, E.M., 1978. *The intrinsic number density of active long-period comets in the inner solar system,* Bull. Astron. Inst. Czechosl., **29,** 299–309.

Krinov, E.L., 1960. *Principles of Meteoritics.* Pergamon, Oxford.

Krinov, E.L., 1963. *The Tunguska and Sikhote-Alin meteorites,* The Moon, Meteorites and Comets, eds. Middlehurst, B.M. & Kuiper, G.P., 208–234. (The Solar System, **IV.**) University of Chicago Press.

Krishna Swamy, K.S. & Wallis, M.K., 1986. *Sulphur compounds in comets,* New Insights in Astrophysics: 8 Years of Astronomy with IUE, ed. Rolfe, E.J., ESA SP-263, 133–136. ESA Publications, ESTEC, Noordwijk, The Netherlands.

Krishna Swamy, K.S. & Wallis, M.K., 1987. *Sulphur compounds in cometary IUE spectra,* Mon. Not. R. Astron. Soc., **228,** 305–312.

Krueger, F.R. & Kissel, J., 1987. *The chemical composition of the dust of Comet P/Halley as measured by "PUMA" on board Vega-1,* Naturwissenschaften, **74,** 312–316.

Kugler, F.X., 1907+. *Sternkunde und Sterndienst in Babel.* Vol., 1+. Münster.

Kuhn, T.S., 1962. *The Structure of Scientific Revolutions.* International Encyclopaedia of Unified Science, Volume 2 Number 2. University of Chicago Press.

Kuijken, K. & Gilmore, G., 1989a. *The mass distribution in the Galactic disk. II. Determination of the surface mass density of the Galactic disk near the sun,* Mon. Not. R. Astron. Soc., in press.

Kuijken, K. & Gilmore, G., 1989b. *The mass distribution in the Galactic disk. III. The local volume density,* Mon. Not. R. Astron. Soc., in press.

Kuiper, G.P., 1949. *The law of planetary and satellite distances,* Astrophys. J., **109**, 308–313.

Kuiper, G.P., 1950. *The diameter of Pluto,* Publ. Astron. Soc. Pac., **62**, 133–137.

Kuiper, G.P., 1951a. *On the origin of the Solar System,* Astrophysics, ed. Hynek, J.A., 357–424. McGraw-Hill, New York.

Kuiper, G.P., 1951b. *On the origin of the Solar System,* Proc. Natl. Acad. Sci. (USA), **37**, 1–14.

Kulkarni, S.R. & Heiles, C., 1987. *The atomic component,* Interstellar Processes, eds. Hollenbach, D.J. & Thronson Jr., H.A., 87–122. (Astrophys. Space Sci. Lib., **134**.) Reidel, Dordrecht, The Netherlands.

Kuzmin, G.G., 1956. *Model of the steady galaxy allowing of the triaxial distribution of velocities,* Astron. Zh. **33**, 27–45.

Kyte, F.T. & Wasson, J.T., 1986. *Accretion rate of extraterrestrial matter: iridium deposited 33 to 67 million years ago,* Science, **232**, 1225–1229.

Kyte, F.T., Zhou, Z. & Wasson, J.T., 1980. *Siderophile-enriched sediments from the Cretaceous-Tertiary boundary,* Nature, **288**, 651–656.

Labs, D. & Neckel, H., 1968. *The radiation of the solar photosphere from 2000 Å to 100 μ,* Zeitschrift für Astrophysik, **69**, 1–73.

Lacey, C.G., 1984. *The influence of massive gas clouds on stellar velocity dispersions in galactic discs,* Mon. Not. R. Astron. Soc., **208**, 687–707.

Lacy, J.M., Baas, F., Allamandola, L.J., Persson, S.E., McGregor, P.J., Lonsdale, C.J., Geballe, T.R., Van de Bult, C.E.P.M., 1984. *4.6 micron absorption features due to solid phase CO and cyano group molecules toward compact infrared sources,* Astrophys. J., **276**, 533–543.

Lada, C.J., 1985. *Cold outflows, energetic winds, and enigmatic jets around young stellar objects,* Annu. Rev. Astron. Astrophys., **23**, 267–317.

Lagrange, J.L., 1814. *Sur l'origine des comètes,* Additions à la Connaissance des Temps, 211–223.

Lagrange-Henri, A.M., Vidal-Madjar, A. & Ferlet, R., 1988. *The β Pictoris circumstellar disk VI. Evidence for material falling on to the central star,* Astron. Astrophys., **190**, 275–282.

Lalande, J., 1792. *Astronomie.* Volume 3, p.819. (3rd edition.) Desaint, Paris.

Lambert, D.L. & Danks, A.C., 1983. *High-resolution spectra of C_2 Swan bands from Comet West 1976 VI,* Astrophys. J., **268**, 428–446.

Laplace, P.S., 1805. *Théorie des Comètes,* Méchanique Céleste, **4**, 193.

Laplace, P.S., 1816. *Sur les Comètes,* Additions à la Connaissance des Temps, 213–220.

Lardner, D., 1853. *On the classification of comets and the distribution of their orbits in space,* Mon. Not. R. Astron. Soc., **13**, 188–192.

Larmor, J., 1935a. *The origin of the comets,* Observatory, **58**, 52–55.

Larmor, J., 1935b. *The origin of the comets and meteorites,* Observatory, **58**, 153–155.

Larmor, J., 1935c. *The origin of the comets,* Observatory, **58**, 316–321.

Larson, H.P., Weaver, W.A., Mumma, M.J. & Drapatz, S., 1989. *Airborne IR observations of Comet Wilson and comparisons with Comet Halley,* preprint. Presented at IAU Coll. No. 116 *Comets in the Post-Halley Era,* Bamberg (April 1989), submitted to *Icarus.*

Larson, S.M. & Johnson, J.R., 1983. *Comet IRAS-Araki-Alcock (1983d),* IAU Circ. No. 3811.

Larson, S.M. & Minton, R.B., 1972. *Photographic observations of Comet Bennett 1970 II*, Comets: Scientific Data and Missions, eds. Kuiper, G.P. & Roemer, E., 183–208. Lunar and Planetary Laboratory, University of Arizona, Tucson, Arizona.

Laskar, J., 1989. *A numerical experiment on the chaotic behaviour of the Solar System*, Nature, **338**, 237–238.

Latham, R.E., 1951. *On the Nature of the Universe.* Translation of Leucretius: De Rerum Natura. Penguin, London.

Lebofsky, L.A., Tholen, D.J., Rieke, G.H. & Lebofsky, M.J., 1984. *2060 Chiron: visual and thermal infrared observations*, Icarus, **60**, 532–537.

Lee, H.D.P., 1952. *Meteorologica.* (Aristotle, in 23 volumes; Vol. VII.)

Leggett, J.K., McKerrow, W.S., Cocks, L.R.M. & Rickard, R.B., 1981. *Periodicity in the Lower Paleozoic marine realm.* Journ. Geol. Soc., **138**, 167–176.

Le Poole, R.S. & Katgert, P., 1968. *The major-axis distribution of long-period comets*, Observatory, **88**, 164–166.

Leuschner, A.O., 1927. *The Pons-Winnecke comet*, Publ. Astron. Soc. Pac., **39**, 275–294.

Le Verrier, J., 1860. *Passage d'une planète sur le disque du Soleil, observé à Orgères (Eure-et-Loir), par M. Lescarbault; Lettre à M. Le Verrier*, Comptes Rendus, **50**, 40–45.

Levin, B.J. & Simonenko, A.N., 1981. *On the implausibility of a cometary origin for most Apollo-Amor asteroids*, Icarus, **47**, 487–491.

Lewis, J.S. & Prinn, R.G., 1980. *Kinetic inhibition of CO and N_2 reduction in the solar nebula*, Astrophys. J., **238**, 357–364.

Ley, W., 1968. *Kant's Cosmogony.* Translated by W. Hastie; revised and edited by W. Ley. Greenwood Publishing Co., New York.

Lin, D.N.C. & Papaloizou, J., 1985. *On the dynamical evolution of the solar system*, Protostars & Planets II, eds. Black, D.C. & Matthews, M.S., 981–1072. University of Arizona Press, Tucson.

Lindsay, J.F. & Srnka, L.J., 1975. *Galactic dust lanes and lunar soil*, Nature, **257**, 776–778.

Link, F., 1958. *Kometen, Sonnentatigkeit und Klimeschwankungen*, Die Sterne, **34**, 129–140.

Lissauer, J.J., 1984. *Ballistic transport in Saturn's rings: an analytic theory*, Icarus, **57**, 63–71.

Lloyd, G.E.R., 1979. *Magic, Reason and Experience. Studies in the Origin and Development of Greek Science.* Cambridge University Press.

Lockyer, J.N., 1875. *Astronomy.* (2nd edition.) Macmillan & Co., London.

Lockyer, J.N., 1890. *The Meteoritic Hypothesis.* Macmillan & Co., London & New York.

Lopatnikov, A., Marochnik, L., Mukhin, L., Sagdeev, R., Usikov, D. & Zaslavsky, G., 1989. *Evolution of the Oort cloud mass and angular momentum: numerical simulation*, preprint. Presented at IAU Coll. No. 116 Comets in the Post-Halley Era, Bamberg (April 1989), submitted to Icarus.

Lowrie, W. & Kent, D.V., 1983. *Geomagnetic reversal frequency since the Late Cretaceous*, Earth Planet. Sci. Lett., **62**, 305–313.

Lüst, Rh., 1984. *The distribution of the aphelion directions of long-period comets*, Astron. Astrophys., **141**, 94–100.

Lüst, Rh., 1985. *Some remarks about the aphelion distribution of long period comets on the sky*, Dynamics of Comets: Their Origin and Evolution, eds. Carusi, A. & Valsecchi, G.B., IAU Coll. No. 83, 105–111. (Astrophys. Space Sci. Lib. **115.**) Reidel, Dordrecht, The Netherlands.

Lutz, T.M., 1985. *The magnetic reversal record is not periodic*, Nature, **317**, 404–407.

Lutz, T.M. & Watson, G.S., 1988. *Effects of long-term variation on the frequency spectrum of the geomagnetic reversal record*, Nature, **334**, 240–242.

Luu, J.X. & Jewitt, D.C., 1989. *New aphelion photometry and spectra of Comet P/Encke*, preprint. Presented at IAU Coll. No. 116 *Comets in the Post-Halley Era*, Bamberg (April 1989), submitted to *Icarus*.

Lynden-Bell, D., 1969. *Galactic nuclei as collapsed old quasars*, Nature, **223**, 690–694.

Lynden-Bell, D. & Pringle, J.E., 1974. *The evolution of viscous discs and the origin of the nebular variables*, Mon. Not. R. Astron. Soc., **168**, 603–637.

Lyttleton, R.A., 1948. *On the origin of comets*, Mon. Not. R. Astron. Soc., **108**, 465–475.

Lyttleton, R.A., 1950. *A link with the present*, Observatory, **70**, 25–29.

Lyttleton, R.A., 1952a. *Note on the origin of comets*, Astrophys. J., **115**, 333–334.

Lyttleton, R.A., 1952b. *The origin of comets*, Observatory, **72**, 33–35.

Lyttleton, R.A., 1953a. *The Comets and Their Origin*. Cambridge University Press.

Lyttleton, R.A., 1953b. *Discussion*, La Physique des Comètes, 386–387. Proc. 4th Int. Coll. Astrophys., Liège.

Lyttleton, R.A., 1963a. *The comets*, The Universe of Space and Time, ed. Butler, S.L. & Messel, H., 33–44. Pergamon Press, Oxford.

Lyttleton, R.A., 1963b. *Introduction to 'The Nature of Comets'.* (See Richter, 1963).

Lyttleton, R.A., 1964. *Review of 'Moon, Meteorites and Comets'.* (See Whipple 1963). Nature, **202**, 526–527.

Lyttleton, R.A., 1968a. *Mysteries of the Solar System*. Clarendon Press, Oxford.

Lyttleton, R.A., 1968b. *On the distribution of major-axes of long-period comets*, Mon. Not. R. Astron. Soc., **139**, 225–230.

Lyttleton, R.A., 1968c. Observatory, **88**, 9–11.

Lyttleton, R.A., 1970. *Comets*, Observatory, **90**, 178–186.

Lyttleton, R.A., 1972. *Does a continuous solid nucleus exist in comets?* Astrophys. Space Sci., **15**, 175–184.

Lyttleton, R.A., 1974. *The non-existence of the Oort cometary shell*, Astrophys. Space Sci., **31**, 385–401.

Lyttleton, R.A., 1975. *The development of a comet as it pursues its orbit*, Astrophys. Space Sci., **34**, 491–510.

Lyttleton, R.A., 1977. *What is a cometary nucleus?* Q. Jl. R. Astron. Soc., **18**, 213–233.

Lyttleton, R.A., 1985. *Journey to the centre of uncertainty*, Spec. Sci. Tech., **8**, 329–346.

Lyttleton, R.A. & Hammersley, J.M., 1964. *The loss of long-period comets from the solar system*, Mon. Not. R. Astron. Soc., **127**, 257–272.

Macintyre, R.M., 1971. *Apparent periodicity of carbonatite emplacement in Canada*, Nature Phys. Sci., **230**, 79–81.

MacKie, E.W., 1977. *The Megalithic Builders*. Phaidon Press.

Maddox, J., 1984. *Extinctions by catastrophe?* Nature, **308**, 685.

Marochnik, L.S. & Mukhin, L.M., 1987. *Is there an unseen mass in the solar system?* Acad. Sci. Space Res. Inst. USSR, Preprint No. 1319.

Marochnik, L.S. & Mukhin, L.M., 1988. *The Halley missions: does the solar system contain copious unseen mass?* Sov. Astron. Lett., **14**, 241–242. Translated from Pis'ma Astron. Zh., **14**, 564–568, 1988.

Marochnik, L.S., Mukhin, L.M. & Sagdeev, R.Z., 1988. *Estimates of mass and angular momentum in the Oort cloud*, Science, **242**, 547–550.

Marsden, B.G., 1967. *The sungrazing comet group*, Astron. J., **72**, 1170–1183.

Marsden, B.G., 1970. *On the relationship between comets and minor planets*, Astron. J., **75**, 206–217.

Marsden, B.G., 1977. *Orbital data on the existence of Oort's cloud of comets*, Comets Asteroids Meteorites: Interrelations, Evolution and Origins, ed. Delsemme, A.H., IAU Coll. No. 39, 79–86. University of Toledo, Toledo, Ohio.

Marsden, B.G., 1982. *Catalogue of Cometary Orbits*. (4th edition.) Smithsonian Astrophys. Obs., Cambridge Mass. (Also see Belyaev et al. 1986.)

Marsden, B.G., 1988. *Comet Levy (1988e), Comet Shoemaker-Holt (1988g)*, Minor Planet Circ. No. 13452.

Matese, J.J. & Whitman, P.G., 1989. *The galactic disk tidal field and the non-random distribution of observed Oort cloud comets*, Icarus, submitted.

Matese, J.J. & Whitmire, D.P., 1986a. *Planet X as the source of the periodic and steady-state flux of short-period comets*, The Galaxy and the Solar System, eds. Smoluchowski, R., Bahcall, J.N. & Matthews, M.S., 297–309. University of Arizona Press, Tucson.

Matese, J.J. & Whitmire, D.P., 1986b. *Planet X and the origins of the shower and steady state flux of short-period comets*, Icarus, **65**, 37–50.

Maurette, M., Hammer, C., Brownlee, D.E., Reeh, N. & Thomsen, H.H., 1986. *Placers of cosmic dust in the blue ice lakes of Greenland*, Science, **233**, 869–872.

Mazaud, A., Laj, C., de Sèze, L. & Verosub, K.B., 1983. *15 Myr periodicity in the frequency of geomagnetic reversals since 100 Myr*, Nature, **304**, 328–330.

McCrea, W.H., 1953. *Notes on the Lyttleton theory of comets*, La Physique des Comètes, 337–350. Proc. 4th Int. Coll. Astrophys., Liège.

McCrea, W.H., 1960. *The origin of the solar system*, Proc. R. Soc. London, Ser. A, **256**, 245–266.

McCrea, W.H., 1961. *Star formation with special reference to stellar clusters*, Proc. R. Soc. London, Ser. A, **260**, 152–159.

McCrea, W.H., 1975a. *Questions concerning interstellar matter in the Magellanic Clouds*, Mon. Notes Astron. Soc. Southern Africa, **34**, 45–49.

McCrea, W.H., 1975b. *Solar system as space probe*, Observatory, **95**, 239–255.

McCrea, W.H., 1975c. *Ice ages and the Galaxy*, Nature, **255**, 607–609.

McCrea, W.H., 1978. *The formation of the Solar System: a protoplanet theory*, The Origin of the Solar System, ed. Dermott, S.F., 75–110. Wiley, New York.

McCrea, W.H., 1981. *Long time-scale fluctuations in the evolution of the Earth*, Proc. R. Soc. London, Ser. A, **375**, 1–41.

McDonnell, J.A.M., 1988. *Solar system dust as a guide to interstellar matter*, Dust in the Universe, eds. Bailey, M.E. & Williams, D.A., 169–181. Cambridge University Press.

McDonnell, J.A.M., Alexander, W.M., Burton, W.M., Bussoletti, E., Clark, D.H., Grard, R.J.L., Grün, E., Hanner, M.S., Hughes, D.W., Igenbergs, E., Kuczera, H., Lindblad, B.A., Mandeville, J.-C., Minafra, A., Schwehm, G.H., Sekanina, Z., Wallis, M.K., Zarnecki, J.C., Chakaveh, S.C., Evans, G.C., Evans, S.T., Firth, J.G., Littler, A.N., Massonne, L., Olearczyk, R.E., Pankiewicz, G.S., Stevenson, T.J. & Turner, R.F., 1986. *Dust density and mass distribution near comet Halley*, Nature, **321**, 338–341.

McDonnell, J.A.M., Green, S.F., Nappo, S., Pankiewicz, G.S., Perry, C.H. & Zarnecki, J.C., 1989. *Dust mass distributions: the perspective from Giotto's measurements at P/Halley*, preprint. Presented at IAU Coll. No. 116 Comets in the Post-Halley Era, Bamberg (April 1989), submitted to *Icarus*.

McDonnell, J.A.M., Zarnecki, J.C., Olearczyk, R.E., Chakaveh, S.C., Pankiewicz, G.S.A. & Evans, S.T., 1987. *Giotto observations of Comet Halley dust*, Philos. Trans. R. Soc. London, Ser. A, **323**, 381–395.

McFadden, L.A., Gaffey, M.J. & McCord, T.B., 1984. *Mineralogical-petrological characterization of near-Earth asteroids*, Icarus, **59**, 25–40.

McFadden, P.L., 1984. *15-Myr periodicity in the frequency of geomagnetic reversals since 100 Myr*, Nature, **311**, 396.

McIntosh, B.A., 1989. *Comet P/Machholz (1986 VIII) and the Quadrantid meteor stream*, preprint. Presented at IAU Coll. No. 116 Comets in the Post-Halley Era, Bamberg (April 1989), submitted to *Icarus*.

McKeegan, K.D., Walker, R.M. & Zinner, E., 1985. *Ion microprobe isotopic measurements of individual interplanetary dust particles*, Geochim. Cosmochim. Acta, **49**, 1971–1987.

McKinnon, W.B. & Mueller, S., 1988. *Pluto's structure and composition suggest origin in the solar, not a planetary, nebula*, Nature, **335**, 240–243.

McLaren, D.J., 1970. *Time, life, and boundaries*, Journ. Paleontol., **44**, 801–815.

Meech, K.J., 1989. *Physical aging in comets*, preprint. Presented at IAU Coll. No. 116 *Comets in the Post-Halley Era*, Bamberg (April 1989); eds. Newburn, R., Neugebauer, M. & Rahe, J., publisher Kluwer.

Meech, K.J. & Belton, J.S., 1989. *(2060) Chiron*, IAU Circ. No. 4770.

Meech, K.J. & Jewitt, D., 1987. *Comet Bowell at record heliocentric distance*, Nature, **328**, 506–509.

Mendis, D.A., 1973. *The comet – meteor stream complex*, Astrophys. Space Sci., **20**, 165–176.

Mendis, D.A., 1988. *A postencounter view of comets*, Annu. Rev. Astron. Astrophys., **26**, 11–49.

Mendis, D.A. & Alfvén, H., 1976. *On the origin of comets*, The Study of Comets: Part 2, eds. Donn, B., Mumma, M., Jackson, W., A'Hearn, M. & Harrington, R., IAU Coll. No. 25, 638–659. NASA SP-393, Washington D.C.

Mendis, D.A. & Brin, G.D., 1977. *The monochromatic brightness variations of comets — II. The core-mantle model*, Moon & Planets, **17**, 359–372.

Mendis, D.A., Houpis, L.F. & Marconi, M.L., 1985. *The physics of comets*, Fundam. Cosmic Phys., **10**, 1–380.

Mendis, D.A. & Marconi, M.L., 1986. *A note on the total mass of comets in the solar system*, Earth, Moon, Planets, **36**, 187–191.

Menteşe, H.H., 1982. *Dependence on reddening of interstellar column densities in the direction of O stars*, Astrophys. Space Sci., **82**, 173–187.

Merton, G., 1951. *Comets and their origin*, Journ. Br. Astron. Assoc., **62**, 6–23.

Mewaldt, R.A., Spalding, J.D., Stone, E.C. & Vogt, R.E., 1980. *The isotopic composition of Galactic cosmic-ray iron nuclei*, Astrophys. J. Lett., **236**, L121–L125.

Mihalas, D. & Routly, P.M., 1968. *Galactic Astronomy*. W.H. Freeman & Co., San Francisco.

Mignard, F. & Remy, F., 1985. *Dynamical evolution of the Oort cloud II. A theoretical approach*, Icarus, **63**, 20–30.

Milankovitsch, M., 1920. *Théorie Mathematique des Phénomènes Thermiques Produit par la Radiation Solaire*. Gauthier-Villars, Paris.

Milne, E.A., 1948. *Kinematic Relativity*. Clarendon Press, Oxford.

Millis, R.L., A'Hearn, M.F. & Campins, H., 1988. *An investigation of the nucleus and coma of Comet P/Arend-Rigaux*, Astrophys. J., **324**, 1194–1209.

Millis, R.L. & Schleicher, D.G., 1986. *Rotational period of comet Halley*, Nature, **324**, 646–649.

Millman, P.M., 1972. *Cometary meteoroids*, From Plasma to Planet, ed. Elvius, A., Nobel Symp. No. 21, 157–168. Wiley Interscience, New York.

Millman, P.M., 1977. *The chemical composition of cometary meteoroids*, Comets Asteroids Meteorites: Interrelations, Evolution and Origins, ed. Delsemme, A.H., IAU Coll. No. 39, 127–132. University of Toledo, Toledo, Ohio.

Ming, T. & Anders, E., 1988. *Interstellar silicon carbide: how much older than the solar system?* Astrophys. J. Lett., **335**, L31–L34.

Ming, T., Anders, E., Hoppe, P. & Zinner, E., 1989. *Meteoritic silicon carbide and its stellar sources; implications for galactic chemical evolution*, Nature, **339**, 351–354.

Minnaert, M., 1954. *The Nature of Light and Colour in the Open Air*. See p.201. Dover Publications, New York.

Mitchell, G.F., Prasad, S.S. & Huntress Jr., W.T., 1981. *Chemical model calculations of C_2, C_3, CH, CN, OH, and NH_2 abundances in cometary comae*, Astrophys. J., **244**, 1087–1093.

Miyamoto, M. & Nagai, R., 1975. *Three-dimensional models for the distribution of mass in galaxies*, Publ. Astron. Soc. Japan, **27**, 533–543.

Möhlmann, D., Danz, M. & Börner, H., 1987. *Properties of the nucleus of P/Halley,* Symposium on the Diversity and Similarity of Comets, eds. Rolfe, E.J. & Battrick, B., ESA SP-278, 487–492. ESA Publications, ESTEC, Noordwijk, The Netherlands.

Mohn, H., 1860. See Carrington 1863.

Morfill, G., Röser, S., Tscharnuter, W. & Völk, H., 1978. *The dynamics of dust in a collapsing protostellar cloud and its possible rôle in planet formation.* Moon & Planets, **19**, 211–220.

Morfill, G. & Völk, H.J., 1984. *Transport of dust and vapor and chemical fractionation in the early protosolar cloud,* Astrophys. J., **287**, 371–395.

Morris, D.E. & Muller, R.A., 1986. *Tidal gravitational forces: the infall of "new" comets and comet showers,* Icarus, **65**, 1–12.

Morris, J., 1980. *Nennius: British History and the Welsh Annals.* Phillimore & Co. Ltd., London.

Morrison, D., 1982. *The satellites of Jupiter and Saturn,* Annu. Rev. Astron. Astrophys., **20**, 469–495.

Morrison, D. & Lebofsky, L.A., 1979. *Radiometry of asteroids,* Asteroids, ed. Gehrels, T., 184–205. University of Arizona Press, Tucson.

Morrison, D. & Zinner, E., 1977. *Distribution and flux of meteoroids,* Philos. Trans. R. Soc. London, Ser. A, **285**, 379–384.

Moulton, F.R., 1900. *An attempt to test the nebular hypothesis by an appeal to the laws of dynamics,* Astrophys. J., **11**, 103–130.

Moulton, F.R., 1905. *On the evolution of the solar system,* Astrophys. J., **22**, 165–181.

Mukai, T., 1985. *Small grains from comets,* Astron. Astrophys., **153**, 213–217.

Muller, R.E. & Morris, D.E., 1986. *Geomagnetic reversals from impacts on the earth,* Geophys. Res. Lett., **13**, 1177–1180.

Mumma, M.J., Blass, W.E., Weaver, H.A. & Larson, H.P., 1989. *Measurements of the ortho-para ratio and nuclear spin temperature of water vapor in comets Halley and Wilson (1986I) and implications for their origin and evolution,* preprint. Presented at IAU Coll. No. 116 Comets in the Post-Halley Era, Bamberg (April 1989), submitted to Icarus.

Mumma, M.J., Weaver, H.A. & Larson, H.P., 1987. *The ortho-para ratio of water vapor in comet P/Halley,* Astron. Astrophys., **187**, 419–424.

Mumma, M.J., Weaver, H.A., Larson, H.P., Davis, D.S. & Williams, M., 1986. *Detection of water vapor in Halley's comet,* Science, **232**, 1523–1528.

Murray, J., 1876. *On the distribution of volcanic debris over the floor of the ocean, — its character, source, and some of the products of its disintegration and decomposition,* Proc. R. Soc. Edinb., **9**, 247–261.

Murray, J. & Renard, A., 1884. *On the microscopic characters of volcanic ashes and cosmic dust, and their distribution in the deep sea deposits,* Proc. R. Soc. Edinb., **12**, 474–495.

Murrell, M.T., Davis Jr., P.A., Nishizumi, K. & Millard Jr., H.T., 1980. *Deep-sea spherules from Pacific clay: mass distribution and influx rate,* Geochim. Cosmochim. Acta, **44**, 2067–2074.

Myres, J.N.L., 1986. *The English Settlements.* Clarendon Press, Oxford.

Nakagawa, Y., Hayashi, C. & Nakazawa, K., 1983. *Accumulation of planetesimals in the solar nebula,* Icarus, **54**, 361–376.

Nakagawa, Y., Nakazawa, K. & Hayashi, C., 1981. *Growth and sedimentation of dust grains in the primordial solar nebula,* Icarus, **45**, 517–528.

Nakagawa, Y., Sekiya, M. & Hayashi, C., 1986. *Settling and growth of dust particles in a laminar phase of a low-mass solar nebula,* Icarus, **67**, 375–390.

Nakamura, T., 1981. *Orbital evolution of long-period comets I. Trivariate Monte Carlo simulation,* Icarus, **45**, 529–544.

Nakamura, T., 1983. *Steady-state number of the extinct comets in high-inclination orbits,* Dynamical Trapping and Evolution in the Solar System, eds. Markellos,

V.V. & Kozai, Y., IAU Coll. No. 74, 97–104. (Astrophys. Space Sci. Lib., **106.**) Reidel, Dordrecht, The Netherlands.

Nakano, T., 1987. *Formation of planets around stars of various masses — I. Formulation and a star of one solar mass*, Mon. Not. R. Astron. Soc., **224,** 107–130.

Nakano, T., 1988. *Formation of planets around stars of various masses — II. Stars of two and three solar masses and the origin and evolution of circumstellar dust clouds*, Mon. Not. R. Astron. Soc., **230,** 551–571.

Napier, W.M., 1982. *An interstellar origin for comets*, Sun and Planetary System, eds. Fricke, W. & Teleki, G., 375–378. (Proc. Sixth European Regional Meeting in Astronomy; Astrophys. Space Sci., **96.**) Reidel, Dordrecht, The Netherlands.

Napier, W.M., 1983. *The orbital evolution of short-period comets*, Asteroids Comets Meteors, eds. Lagerkvist, C.-I. & Rickman, H., 391–395. Uppsala Observatory, Uppsala, Sweden.

Napier, W.M., 1985. *Dynamical interactions of the solar system with massive nebulae*, Dynamics of Comets: Their Origin and Evolution, eds. Carusi, A. & Valsecchi, G.B., IAU Coll. No. 83, 31–41. (Astrophys. Space Sci. Lib. **115.**) Reidel, Dordrecht, The Netherlands.

Napier, W.M., 1987. *The origin and evolution of the Oort cloud*, Interplanetary Matter, eds. Ceplecha, Z. & Pecina, P., 13–19. (Proc. Tenth European Regional Meeting in Astronomy, Vol. 2, Prague).

Napier, W.M. & Clube, S.V.M., 1979. *A theory of terrestrial catastrophism*, Nature, **282,** 455–459.

Napier, W.M. & Dodd, R.J., 1973. *The missing planet*, Nature, **242,** 250–251.

Napier, W.M. & Dodd, R.J., 1974. *On the origin of asteroids*, Mon. Not. R. Astron. Soc., **166,** 469–489.

Napier, W.M. & Humphries, C.M., 1986. *Interstellar planetesimals — II. Radiative instability in dense molecular clouds*, Mon. Not. R. Astron. Soc., **221,** 105–117.

Napier, W.M. & Staniucha, M., 1982. *Interstellar planetesimals — I. Dissipation of a primordial cloud of comets by tidal encounters with nebulae*, Mon. Not. R. Astron. Soc., **198,** 723–735.

Nash, D.B., Carr, M.H., Gradie, J., Hunten, D.M. & Yoder, C.F., 1986. *Io*, Satellites, eds. Burns, J.A. & Matthews, M.S., 629–688. University of Arizona Press, Tucson.

Natanson, S.G., 1923. *On the origin of comets*, Publ. Astron. Obs. Univ. Petrograd, **4,** 18–24. (In Russian.)

Needham, J., 1959. *Science and Civilisation in China, Volume 3: Mathematics and the Sciences of the Heavens*, with the collaboration of Wang Ling. Cambridge University Press.

Negi, J.G. & Tiwari, R.K., 1983. *Matching long-term periodicities of geomagnetic reversals and galactic motions of the Solar System*, Geophys. Res. Lett., **10,** 713–716.

Neugebauer, O., 1945. *The history of ancient astronomy: problems and methods*, Journal of Near Eastern Studies, **4,** 1–38. See also Neugebauer 1946, 1983.

Neugebauer, O., 1946. *The history of ancient astronomy: Problems and methods*, Publ. Astron. Soc. Pac., **58,** 17–43; 104–142.

Neugebauer, O., 1948. *Mathematical methods in ancient astronomy*, Bull. Amer. Math. Soc., **54,** 1013–1041.

Neugebauer, O., 1967. *Problems and methods in Babylonian mathematical astronomy. Henry Norris Russell Lecture 1967*, Astron. J., **72,** 964–972.

Neugebauer, O., 1983. *Astronomy and History: Selected Essays.* Springer-Verlag, New York.

Newcomb, S., 1910. *Comets.* Encyclopaedia Britannica (11th edition), **6,** 759–763.

Newsom, H.E. & Taylor, S.R., 1989. *Geochemical implications of the formation of the Moon by a single giant impact*, Nature, **338,** 29–34.

Newton, H.A., 1878. *On the origin of comets*, Amer. Journ. Sci. Arts (3rd ser.) **16,** 165–179.

Newton, H.A., 1893. *On the capture of comets by planets, especially their capture by Jupiter*, Mem. Natl. Acad. Sci. Washington, **6**, 7–23.

Newton, H.A., 1891. *Capture of comets by planets*, Astron. J., **11**, 73–75.

Newton, H.A., 1897. *The worship of meteorites*, Amer. Journ. Sci. (4th ser.) **153**, 1–14.

Newton, R.R., 1972. *Medieval Chronicles and the Rotation of the Earth.* Johns Hopkins University Press, Baltimore.

Nezhinski, E.M., 1972. *On the stability of the Oort Cloud*, The Motion, Evolution of Orbits, and Origin of Comets, eds. Chebotarev, G.A., Kazimirchak-Polonskaya, E.I. & Marsden, B.G., IAU Symp. No. 45, 335–340. Reidel, Dordrecht, The Netherlands.

Nielsen, N.C., Hein, C., Reynolds, F.E., Miller, A.L., Karff, S.E., Cochran, A.C. & McLean, P., 1983. *Religions of the World.* St. Martins Press, New York.

Nininger, H.H., 1952. *Out of the Sky: An Introduction to Meteoritics.* University of Denver Press.

Noerdlinger, P.D., 1977. *An examination of an interstellar hypothesis for the source of comets*, Icarus, **30**, 566–573.

Nölke, F., 1908. *Das Problem der Entwicklung unseres Planetensystems.* Springer, Berlin. (See pp.192–194).

Nölke, F., 1909. *Neue Erklärung des Ursprungs der Kometen*, Abh. d. Nat. Ver. Bremen, **20**, 29.

Nölke, F., 1936. *Der Ursprung der Kometen, Meteore und der Zodiakalichtmaterie*, Sterne, **16**, 155.

Norman, C.A. & Paresce, F., 1989. *Circumstellar material around nearby stars: clues to the formation of planetary systems*, The Formation and Evolution of Planetary Systems, eds. Weaver, H.A. & Danly, L., in press. Cambridge University Press.

North, J.D., 1965. *The Measure of the Universe.* Clarendon Press, Oxford.

Oates, J., 1979. *Babylon.* (Ancient People and Places, **94**.) Thames & Hudson Ltd., London.

Oberst, J. & Nakamura, Y., 1989. *Temporal and spatial distribution of meteoroid impacts detected by the lunar seismic network — a summary report.* Paper presented at Asteroids Comets Meteors III, Uppsala 1989.

O'Dell, C.R., 1973. *A new model for cometary nuclei*, Icarus, **19**, 137–146.

O'Dell, C.R., 1986. *A possible comet and asteroid link in the formation of comets*, Icarus, **67**, 71–79.

Officer, C.B., Hallam, A., Drake, C.L. & Devine, J.D., 1987. *Late Cretaceous and paroxysmal Cretaceous/Tertiary extinctions*, Nature, **326**, 143–149.

Oikawa, S. & Everhart, E., 1979. *Past and future orbit of 1977UB, object Chiron*, Astron. J., **84**, 134–139.

Oja, H., 1975. *Perihelion distribution of near-parabolic comets*, Astron. Astrophys., **43**, 317–319.

O'Keefe, J.D. & Ahrens, T.J., 1989. *Impact production of CO_2 by the Cretaceous/Tertiary extinction bolide and the resultant heating of the Earth*, Nature, **338**, 247–249.

Olano, C.A., 1982. *On a model of local gas related to Gould's Belt*, Astron. Astrophys., **112**, 195–208.

Olbers, H.W.M., 1802. *Fortgesetzte Nachrichten über den neuen Haupt-Planeten unseres Sonnen-Systems, Pallas Olbersiana*, Monatliche Correspondenz zur Beförderung der Erd-und Himmels-Kunde, **6**, 71–96. See p.88; edited by Frhr. von Zach.

Olivier, C.P., 1925. *Meteors.* Williams & Wilkins Co., Baltimore.

Olivier, C.P., 1930. *Comets.* Ballière, Tindall & Cox, London.

Olmsted, D., 1834a. *Observations on the meteors of November 13th, 1833*, Amer. Journ. Sci. Arts (Silliman's Journal), **25**, 363–411.

Olmsted, D., 1834b. *Observations on the meteors of November 13th, 1833*, Amer. Journ. Sci. Arts (Silliman's Journal), **26**, 132–174.

Olsson-Steel, D.I., 1986. *The origin of the sporadic meteoroid component*, Mon. Not. R. Astron. Soc., **219**, 47–73.

Olsson-Steel, D.I., 1988a. *The Taurid complex and the giant comet hypothesis*, Observatory, **108**, 183–185.

Olsson-Steel, D.I., 1988b. *Identification of meteoroid streams from Apollo asteroids in the Adelaide radar orbit surveys*, Icarus, **75**, 64–96.

Olsson-Steel, D.I., 1988c. *Results of close encounters between Pluto and Neptune*, Astron. Astrophys., **195**, 327–330.

Oort, J.H., 1927a. *Observational evidence confirming Lindblad's hypothesis of a rotation of the galactic system*, Bull. Astron. Inst. Neth., **3**, 275–282.

Oort, J.H., 1927b. *Investigations concerning the rotational motion of the Galactic system, together with new determinations of secular parallaxes, precession and motion of the equinox*, Bull. Astron. Inst. Neth., **4**, 79–89. See also Nature, **120**, 491.

Oort, J.H., 1950. *The structure of the cloud of comets surrounding the solar system and a hypothesis concerning its origin*, Bull. Astron. Inst. Neth., **11**, 91–110.

Oort, J.H. & Schmidt, M., 1951. *Differences between new and old comets*, Bull. Astron. Inst. Neth., **11**, 259–269.

Öpik, E.J., 1932. *Note on stellar perturbations of nearly parabolic orbits*, Proc. Amer. Acad. Arts Sci., **67**, 169–183.

Öpik, E.J., 1955a. *The masses and structure of meteors*, Meteors, ed. Kaiser, T.R., 33–35. (Spec. Suppl. (Vol. 2) to J. Atmos. Terr. Phys.) Pergamon Press, London.

Öpik, E.J., 1955b. *Meteors and the upper atmosphere*, Ir. Astron. J., **3**, 165–181.

Öpik, E.J., 1958. *On the catastrophic effects of collisions with celestial bodies*, Ir. Astron. J., **5**, 34–36.

Öpik, E.J., 1963. *The stray bodies in the solar system. Part I. Survival of cometary nuclei and the asteroids*, Adv. Astron. Astrophys., **2**, 219–262.

Öpik, E.J., 1965. *Climatic change in cosmic perspective*, Icarus, **4**, 289–307.

Öpik, E.J., 1966a. *The dynamical aspects of the origin of comets*, Mem. Soc. Roy. des Sciences de Liège (Ser. 5), **12**, 523–574.

Öpik, E.J., 1966b. *Sun-grazing comets and tidal disruption*, Ir. Astron. J., **7**, 141–161.

Öpik, E.J., 1970. *Comets and the formation of planets*, Moon, **1**, 487–493.

Öpik, E.J., 1972. *Comet families and transneptunian planets*, Ir. Astron. J., **10**, 35–92.

Öpik, E.J., 1973. *Comets and the formation of planets*, Astrophys. Space Sci., **21**, 307–398.

Öpik, E.J., 1975. *Comets and planets: their interrelated origin*, Ir. Astron. J., **12**, 1–48.

Öpik, E.J., 1978. *The missing planet*, Moon & Planets, **18**, 327–337.

Oppenheim, A.L., 1964. *Ancient Mesopotamia*. University of Chicago Press.

Oppenheim, S., 1922. *Zur Kometenstatistik im Zusammenhange mit der Verteilung der Sterne*, Astron. Nachr., **216**, 47–48.

Oppenheim, S., 1924. *Zur Statistik der Kometen und Planeten im Zusammenhang mit der Verteilung der Sterne*, Probleme der Astronomie, Festschrift für Hugo von Seeliger, 131–143. Springer-Verlag, Berlin.

Orlov, S.V., 1939. *Evolution and origin of comets*, Astron. Zh., **16**, 3–27.

O'Sullivan, T., Jordan, T.J. & Bailey, M.E., 1985. *Rare Transit?* Sky & Telescope (September 1985), 196–197.

Ostro, S.J., 1987. *Physical properties of asteroids from radar observations*, The Evolution of Small Bodies in the Solar System, eds. Fulchignoni, M. & Kresák, Ľ., 131–146. (Proc. Internat. Sch. Phys. "Enrico Fermi", Course XCVIII.) North-Holland Publishing, Amsterdam, The Netherlands.

Ovenden, M.W., 1961. *The origin of the constellations*, Journ. Br. Astron. Assoc., **71**, 91–96.

Ovenden, M.W., 1966. *The origin of the constellations*, Philos. J., **3**, 1–18. (Trans. R. Soc. Glasgow.) Oliver and Boyd, Edinburgh.

Ovenden, M.W., 1972. *Bode's law and the missing planet*, Nature, **239**, 508–509.

Ovenden, M.W., 1973. *Planetary distances and the missing planet*, Recent Advances in Dynamical Astronomy, eds. Tapley, B.D. & Szebehely, V., 319–332. (Astrophys. Space Sci. Lib., **39**.) Reidel, Dordrecht, The Netherlands.

Ovenden, M.W., 1975. *Bode's law — truth or consequences?* Vistas Astron., **18**, 473–496.

Ovenden, M.W. & Byl, J., 1978. *Comets and the missing planet*, Dynamics of Planets and Satellites and Theories of Their Motion, ed. Szebehely, V.G., IAU Coll. No. 41, 101–107. (Astrophys. Space Sci. Lib. **72**.) Reidel, Dordrecht, The Netherlands.

Owen, T., Lutz, B.L. & de Bergh, C., 1986. *Deuterium in the outer solar system: evidence for two distinct reservoirs*, Nature, **320**, 244–246.

Ozernoy, L.M. & Usov, V.V., 1971. *Structure and evolution of supermassive rotating magnetic polytropes*, Astrophys. Space Sci., **13**, 3–35.

Ozernoy, L.M. & Usov, V.V., 1973. *Supermassive oblique rotator: electrodynamics, evolution, observational tests*, Astrophys. Space Sci., **25**, 149–194.

Ozernoy, L.M. & Usov, V.V., 1977. *Regular optical variability of quasars and nuclei of galaxies as a clue to the nature of their activity*, Astron. Astrophys., **56**, 163–172.

Padevět, V., 1987. *End heights of fireballs and planetary origin of comets*, Bull. Astron. Inst. Czechosl., **38**, 156–163.

Pal, P.C. & Creer, K.M., 1986. *Geomagnetic reversal spurts and episodes of extraterrestrial catastrophism*, Nature, **320**, 148–150.

Palla, F., 1988. *Primordial star formation*, Galactic and Extragalactic Star Formation, NATO Adv. Study Inst., in press.

Paneth, F.A., 1949. *The frequency of meteorite falls*, Proc. Roy. Inst., **34**, 375–381.

Paneth, F.A., 1956. *The frequency of meteorite falls throughout the ages*, Vistas Astron., **2**, 1681–1687.

Pannekoek, A., 1961. *A History of Astronomy*. George Allen & Unwin Ltd., London.

Paresce, F. & Burrows, C., 1987. *Broad-band imaging of the Beta Pictoris circumstellar disk*, Astrophys. J. Lett., **319**, L23–L25.

Parkin, D.W. & Tilles, D., 1968. *Influx measurements of extraterrestrial material*, Science, **159**, 936–946.

Patashnick, H., Rupprecht, G. & Schuerman, D., 1974. *Energy source for comet outbursts?* Nature, **250**, 313–314.

Patterson, C. & Smith, A.B., 1987. *Is the periodicity of extinctions a taxonomic artefact?* Nature, **330**, 248–251.

Pearson, L. & Sandbach, F.H., 1965. *Plutarch's Moralia*. Volume 11 of 15. (See prefatory note.) Harvard University Press, Cambridge, Mass.

Pearson, R., 1978. *Climate and Evolution*. (See Chapter 2.) Academic Press, London.

Peirce, B., 1849. Proc. Amer. Acad. Arts & Sci., **2**, 147–148.

Peirce, B., 1859. *Tail of Donati's Comet*, Proc. Amer. Acad. Arts & Sci., **4**, 202–206.

Pemberton, H., 1728. *A View of Sir Isaac Newton's Philosophy*. Dublin.

Penzias, A.A., 1980. *Measurements of isotopic abundances in interstellar clouds*, Interstellar Molecules, ed. Andrew, B.H., IAU Symp. No. 87, 397–404. Reidel, Dordrecht, The Netherlands.

Perlmutter, S. & Muller, R.A., 1988. *Evidence for comet storms in meteorite ages*, Icarus, **74**, 369–373.

Phillips, A.P., Gondhalekar, P.M. & Pettini, M., 1982. *A study of element depletions in interstellar gas*, Mon. Not. R. Astron. Soc., **200**, 687–703.

Pickering, W.H., 1909. *A search for a planet beyond Neptune*, Ann. Harvard Obs., **61**, (Part II) 109–162.

Pickering, W.H., 1911. *A statistical investigation of cometary orbits*, Ann. Harvard Obs., **61**, (Part III) 163–373.

Pickering, W.H., 1919. *The transneptunian planet*, Ann. Harvard Obs., **82**, 49–59.

Pickering, W.H., 1928. *The next planet beyond Neptune*, Popular Astron., **36**, 143–165, 218–222.

Pillinger, C.T., 1987. *Stable isotope measurements of meteorites and cosmic dust grains*, Philos. Trans. R. Soc. London, Ser. A, **323**, 313–322.

Pineault, S., 1987. *Accretion of gas and comets onto a nearby degenerate star*, Icarus, **70**, 52–60.

Piotrowski, S.L., 1965. *Mass accretion, and variations in shape and dimensions of comets' orbits*, Acta Astron., **15**, 281–284.

Piotrowski, S.L. & Sitarski, G., 1976. *Mass accretion and variation of elements of comets' orbits*, Acta Astron., **26**, 77–81.

Plutarch. *De Placitis Philosophorum*. Part of the *Moralia*. See Goodwin 1871, **3**, 104–193.

Podolak, M. & Cameron, A.G.W., 1974. *Models of the giant planets*, Icarus, **22**, 123–148.

Podolak, M. & Reynolds, R.T., 1985. *What have we learned from modelling giant planet interiors?* Protostars & Planets II, eds. Black, D.C. & Matthews, M.S., 847–872. University of Arizona Press, Tucson.

Porubčan, V. & Štohl, J., 1989. *Is P/Encke the only parent body of the Taurid complex?* preprint. Presented at IAU Coll. No. 116 *Comets in the Post-Halley Era*, Bamberg (April 1989), submitted to *Icarus.*

Porter, J.G., 1952. *Comets and Meteor Streams*. Chapman & Hall Ltd., London.

Prevost, P., 1783. *Mémoire sur le mouvement progressif du centre de gravité de tout le système solaire*, Mém. de l'Acad. Roy. de Berlin for year 1781, 481–421.

Pringle, J., 1759. *Some remarks upon the several accounts of the fiery meteor (which appeared on Sunday the 26th of November 1758), and upon other such bodies*, Philos. Trans. R. Soc. London, **51**, 259–274.

Pringle, J.E., 1989. *The Egg Nebula: a protostellar disc remnant around an evolved star?* Mon. Not. R. Astron. Soc., **238**, 37P–40P.

Proctor, M., 1926. *The Romance of Comets*. Harper, New York & London 1926.

Proctor, M. & Crommelin, A.C.D., 1937. *Comets*. Technical Press, London.

Proctor, R.A., 1873. *The Expanse of Heaven*. Henry S. King & Co., London.

Proctor, R.A., 1884. *The capture theory of comets*, Knowledge, **6**, 126–128.

Quetelet, A., 1837. Ann. de l'Obs. Bruxelles, p.272. (Cited by Clerke 1908, p.329.)

Radzievskii, V.V., 1987. *The origin and dynamics of the cometary system*, Kinematika Fiz. Nebesn. Tel., **3**, 66–77. (In Russian.)

Radzievskii, V.V. & Tomanov, V.P., 1977. *On the capture of comets by the Laplace scheme*, Sov. Astron., **21**, 218–223. Translated from Astron. Zh., **54**, 388–397.

Rampino, M.R., 1987. *Impact cratering and flood basalt volcanism*, Nature, **327**, 468.

Rampino, M.R., 1989. *Dinosaurs, comets and volcanoes*, New Scientist, 18th February 1989.

Rampino, M.R., Self, S. & Stothers, R.B., 1988. *Volcanic winters*, Annu. Rev. Earth Planet. Sci., **16**, 73–99.

Rampino, M.R. & Stothers, R.B., 1984a. *Terrestrial mass extinctions, cometary impacts and the Sun's motion perpendicular to the galactic plane*, Nature, **308**, 709–712.

Rampino, M.R. & Stothers, R.B., 1984b. *Geological rhythms and cometary impacts*, Science, **226**, 1427–1431.

Rampino, M.R. & Stothers, R.B., 1986a. *Geologic periodicities and the Galaxy*, The Galaxy and the Solar System, eds. Smoluchowski, R., Bahcall, J.N. & Matthews, M.S., 241–259. University of Arizona Press, Tucson.

Rampino, M.R. & Stothers, R.B., 1986b. *Periodic flood-basalt eruptions, mass extinctions and comet impacts*, Eos, **67**, (No. 44), 1247.

Rampino, M.R. & Stothers, R.B., 1988. *Flood basalt volcanism during the past 250 million years*, Science, **241**, 663–668.

Rauffner, J.A., 1971. *The curved and the straight: cometary theory from Kepler to Hevelius*, J. Hist. Astron., **2**, 178–194.

Raup, D.M., 1985a. *Magnetic reversals and mass extinctions*, Nature, **314**, 341–343.

Raup, D.M., 1985b. *Rise and fall of periodicity*, Nature, **317**, 384–385.

Raup, D.M. & Sepkoski Jr., J.J., 1984. *Periodicity of extinctions in the geologic past*, Proc. Natl. Acad. Sci. (USA), **81**, 801–805.

Raup, D.M. & Sepkoski Jr., J.J., 1986. *Periodic extinction of families and genera*, Science, **231**, 833–836.

Rees, M.J., 1978a. *Quasars*, Observatory, **98**, 210–223.

Rees, M.J., 1978b. *Accretion and the quasar phenomenon*, Physica Scripta, **17**, 193–200.

Reeves, H., 1974. *Comets, solar wind and the D/H ratio*, Nature, **248**, 398.

Reichenbach, Baron von, 1858. *Die Meteoriten und die Kometen nach ihren gegenseitigeu Beziehungen*, Poggendorff's Annallen der Physik und Chem., **105**, 438–460.

Reinhard, R., 1986. *The Giotto encounter with comet Halley*, Nature, **321**, 313–318.

Reitmeijer, F.J.M. & MacKinnon, I.D.R., 1987. *Cometary evolution: clues from chondritic interplanetary dust particles*, Symposium on the Diversity and Similarity of Comets, eds. Rolfe, E.J. & Battrick, B., ESA SP-278, 363–367. ESA Publications, ESTEC, Noordwijk, The Netherlands.

Remy, F., 1984. *Diffusion de Comètes du Nuage de Oort vers le Système Solaire*. Thesis, L'Observatoire de Paris.

Remy, F. & Mignard, F., 1985. *Dynamical evolution of the Oort cloud I. A Monte Carlo simulation*, Icarus, **63**, 1–19.

Richter, N.B., 1963. *The Nature of Comets*. Methuen & Co., London.

Rickard, T.A., 1941. *The use of meteoric iron*, J. R. Anthrop. Inst., **71**, 55–66.

Rickman, H., 1976. *Stellar perturbations of orbits of long-period comets and their significance for cometary capture*, Bull. Astron. Inst. Czechosl., **27**, 92–105.

Rickman, H., 1985. *Interrelations between comets and asteroids*, Dynamics of Comets: Their Origin and Evolution, eds. Carusi, A. & Valsecchi, G.B., IAU Coll. No. 83, 149–172. (Astrophys. Space Sci. Lib. **115**.) Reidel, Dordrecht, The Netherlands.

Rickman, H., 1986. *Masses and densities of comets Halley and Kopff*, The Comet Nucleus Sample Return Mission, ed. Melita, O., ESA SP-249, 195–205. ESA Publications, ESTEC, Noordwijk, The Netherlands.

Rickman, H. & Froeschlé, C., 1980. *A Monte Carlo estimate of the fraction of comets developing into sizeable asteroidal bodies*, Moon & Planets, **22**, 125–128.

Rickman, H., Kamél, L., Festou, M.C. & Froeschlé, C., 1987. *Estimates of the masses, volumes and densities of short-period comet nuclei*, Symposium on the Diversity and Similarity of Comets, eds. Rolfe, E.J. & Battrick, B., ESA SP-278, 471–481. ESA Publications, ESTEC, Noordwijk, The Netherlands.

Rickman, H. & Vaghi, S., 1976. *A Monte Carlo simulation of the orbital evolution of comets in the inner planetary region*, Astron. Astrophys., **51**, 327–342.

Riley-Smith, J.S.C., 1986. *The First Crusade and the Idea of Crusading*. The Athlone Press, London.

Rittenhouse, D., 1783. *Observations on the account of a meteor*. (Exchange of letters between J. Page and D. Rittenhouse, read 2nd May 1783.) Trans. Amer. Phil. Soc., **2**, 173–176, 1786.

Roemer, E., 1966. *The dimensions of cometary nuclei*, Mem. Soc. Roy. des Sciences de Liège (Ser. 5), **12**, 23–28.

Roller, M., 1870. Astron. Nachr., **75**, (No. 1797) 331.

Ross, W.D., 1968. *The Works of Aristotle. Vol. III.* Clarendon Press, Oxford.

Rouan, D. & Léger, A., 1984. *Large grains in Orion are indicated by IR polarization and flux data*, Astron. Astrophys., **132**, L1–L4.

Rougoor, G.W. & Oort, J.H., 1960. *Distribution and motion of interstellar hydrogen in the galactic system with particular reference to the region within 3 kiloparsecs of the center*, Proc. Natl. Acad. Sci. (USA), **46**, 1–13.

Rowan-Robinson, M., 1986. *Cosmological results from IRAS*, Light on Dark Matter, ed. Israel, F.P., 499–506. (Proceedings of the First IRAS Conference; Astrophys. Space Sci. Lib., **124**.) Reidel, Dordrecht, The Netherlands.

Roy, A.E., 1984. *The origin of the constellations*, Vistas Astron., **27**, 171–197.

Russell, C.T., Aroian, R., Arghavani, M. & Nock, K., 1984. *Interplanetary magnetic field enhancements and their association with the asteroid 2201 Oljato*, Science, **226**, 43–45.

Russell, D.A., 1979. *The enigma of the extinction of the dinosaurs*, Annu. Rev. Earth Planet. Sci., **7**, 163–182.

Russell, H.N., 1916. *On the albedo of the planets and their satellites*, Astrophys. J., **43**, 173–196.

Russell, H.N., 1920. *On the origin of periodic comets*, Astron. J., **33**, 49–61.

Russell, H.N., 1925. *The problem of stellar evolution*, Nature, **116**, 209–212.

Russell, H.N., 1935. *The Solar System and its Origin*. Macmillan Company, New York.

Russell, H.N., Dugan, R.S. & Stewart, J.Q., 1926. *Astronomy: A Revision of Young's Manual of Astronomy. Vol. I. The Solar System.* Ginn & Co., Boston.

Saarinen, S. & Gilmore, G., 1989. *The distribution of wide binaries on the sky*, Mon. Not. R. Astron. Soc., **237**, 311–331; microfiche 237/1.

Sachs, A., 1974. *Babylonian observational astronomy*, Philos. Trans. R. Soc. London, Ser. A, **276**, 43–50. (The Place of Astronomy in the Ancient World, ed. Hodson, F.R., 43–50. Oxford University Press, London.)

Safronov, V.S., 1960. *On the gravitational instability in flattened systems with axial symmetry and non-uniform rotation*, Annales d'Astrophys., **23**, 979–982.

Safronov, V.S., 1967. *The protoplanetary cloud and its evolution*, Sov. Astron., **10**, 650–658. Translated from Astron. Zh., **43**, 817–828.

Safronov, V.S., 1969. *Evolution of the protoplanetary cloud and formation of the Earth and the planets.* Translated by Israel program for scientific translations, Jerusalem 1972.

Safronov, V.S., 1972. *Ejection of bodies from the solar system in the course of the accumulation of the giant planets and the formation of the cometary cloud*, The Motion, Evolution of Orbits, and Origin of Comets, eds. Chebotarev, G.A., Kazimirchak-Polonskaya, E.I. & Marsden, B.G., IAU Symp. No. 45, 329–334. Reidel, Dordrecht, The Netherlands.

Safronov, V.S., 1977. *Oort's cometary cloud in the light of modern cosmogony*, Comets Asteroids Meteorites: Interrelations, Evolution and Origins, ed. Delsemme, A.H., IAU Coll. No. 39, 483–484. University of Toledo, Toledo, Ohio.

Safronov, V.S. & Ruzmaikina, T.V., 1978. *On angular momentum transfer and accumulation of solid bodies in the solar nebula*, Protostars & Planets, ed. Gehrels, T., IAU Coll. No. 52, 545–564. University of Arizona Press, Tucson, Arizona, USA.

Safronov, V.S. & Ruzmaikina, T.V., 1985. *Formation of the solar nebula and the planets*, Protostars & Planets II, eds. Black, D.C. & Matthews, M.S., 959–980. University of Arizona Press, Tucson.

Sagdeev, R.Z., Blamont, J., Galeev, A.A., Moroz, V.I., Shapiro, V.D., Shevchenko, V.I. & Szegő, K., 1986. *Vega spacecraft encounters with comet Halley*, Nature, **321**, 259–262.

Sagdeev, R.Z., Elyasberg, P.E. & Moroz, V.I., 1988. *Is the nucleus of comet Halley a low density body?* Nature, **331**, 240–242.

Sagdeev, R.Z., Szegő, K., Smith, B.A., Larson, S., Merenyi, E., Kondor, A. & Toth, I., 1989. *The rotation of P/Halley*, Astron. J., **97**, 546–551.

Samarasinha, N.H., A'Hearn, M.F., Hoban, S. & Klinglesmith, D.A., 1986. *CN jets of comet Halley — rotational properties*, 20th ESLAB Symposium on the Exploration of Halley's Comet, eds. Battrick, B., Rolfe, E.J. & Reinhard, R., ESA SP-250, Vol. I, 487–491. ESA Publications, ESTEC, Noordwijk, The Netherlands.

Sanders, D.B., Solomon, P.M. & Scoville, N.Z., 1984. *Giant molecular clouds in the Galaxy. I. The axisymmetric distribution of H_2*, Astrophys. J., **276**, 182–203.

Sanders, D.B., Scoville, N.Z. & Solomon, P.M., 1985. *Giant molecular clouds in the Galaxy. II. Characteristics of discrete features*, Astrophys. J., **289**, 373–387.

Sanders, R.H., 1981. *Recurrent Seyfert activity in spiral galaxy nuclei*, Nature, **294**, 427–429.

Sanders, R.H. & Wrixon, G.T., 1972. *An expanding and rotating ring of gas 2.4 kpc from the Galactic Center*, Astron. Astrophys., **18**, 92–96.

Sandford, S.A., 1987. *The collection and analysis of extraterrestrial dust particles*, Fundam. Cosmic Phys., **12**, 1–73.

Sargent, A.I. & Beckwith, S., 1987. *Kinematics of the circumstellar gas of HL Tauri and R Monocerotis*, Astrophys. J., **323**, 294–305.

Savage, B.D., 1987. *Hot interstellar gas in the galactic disk and halo*, Interstellar Processes, eds. Hollenbach, D.J. & Thronson Jr., H.A., 123–141. (Astrophys. Space Sci. Lib., **134**.) Reidel, Dordrecht, The Netherlands.

Sayce, A.H., 1874. *The astronomy and astrology of the Babylonians, with translations of the tablets relating to these subjects*. Trans. Soc. Bibl. Archaeology, **3** (Part I), 145–339. Longmans, Green, Reader & Dyer, London.

Scalo, J.M. & Smoluchowski, R., 1984. *Galactic gravitational shock and the extinction of species*, Bull. Amer. Astron. Soc., **16**, 493–494.

Schaeberle, J.M., 1893. *Preliminary note on a mechanical theory of comets*, Astron. J., **13**, 151–153.

Schafer, E.H., 1977. *Pacing the Void: T'ang Approaches to the Stars*. University of California Press.

Schaffer, S., 1980. *"The Great Laboratories of the Universe": William Herschel on matter theory and planetary life*, J. Hist. Astron., **11**, 81–111.

Schiaparelli, G.V., 1866. See Mon. Not. R. Astron. Soc., **27**, 133–134.

Schiaparelli, G.V., 1867. *Sur la relation qui existe entre les comètes et les étoiles filantes*, Astron. Nachr., **68**, (No. 1629) 331–332.

Schiaparelli, G.V., 1890. *Sur la probabilité des orbites hyperboliques*, Bull. Astron., **7**, 285–286.

Schmitt, B., Grim, R.J.A. & Greenberg, J.M., 1988. *Volatile molecules in interstellar grain mantles: diffusion and infrared band strength*, Dust in the Universe, eds. Bailey, M.E. & Williams, D.A., 291–296. Cambridge University Press.

Schütte, C.H., 1949. *Two new families of comets*, Popular Astron., **57**, 176–182.

Schwartz, R.D., 1983. *Herbig-Haro objects*, Annu. Rev. Astron. Astrophys., **21**, 209–237.

Schwartz, R.D. & James, P.B., 1984. *Periodic mass extinctions and the Sun's oscillation about the galactic plane*, Nature, **308**, 712–713.

Scoville, N.Z., Min Su Yun, Clemens, D.P., Sanders, D.B. & Waller, W.H., 1987. *Molecular clouds and cloud cores in the inner Galaxy*, Astrophys. J. Suppl. Ser., **63**, 821–915.

Seab, C.G., 1987. *Grain destruction, formation and evolution*, Interstellar Processes, eds. Hollenbach, D.J. & Thronson Jr., H.A., 491–512. (Astrophys. Space Sci. Lib., **134**.) Reidel, Dordrecht, The Netherlands.

Seab, C.G., 1988. *Grain destruction and growth*, Dust in the Universe, eds. Bailey, M.E. & Williams, D.A., 303–326. Cambridge University Press.

See, T.J.J., 1909. *On the cause of the remarkable circularity of the orbits of the planets and satellites and on the origin of the solar system*, Astron. Nachr., **180**, (No. 4308) 185–194.

Seeliger, H., 1890. *Sur la probabilité de l'existence d'orbites hyperboliques*, Bull. Astron., **7**, 219–221.

Seidelmann, P.K., Kaplan, G.H., Pulkkiner, K.F., Santoro, E.J. & Van Flandern, T.C., 1980. *Ephemeris of Pluto*, Icarus, **44**, 19–28.

Sekanina, Z., 1968. *On the perturbations of comets by near-by stars. I. Sphere of action of the Solar System*, Bull. Astron. Inst. Czechosl., **19**, 223–229.

Sekanina, Z., 1972. *A model for the nucleus of Encke's comet*, The Motion, Evolution of Orbits, and Origin of Comets, eds. Chebotarev, G.A., Kazimirchak-Polonskaya, E.I. & Marsden, B.G., IAU Symp. No. 45, 301–307. Reidel, Dordrecht, The Netherlands.

Sekanina, Z., 1976. *A probability of encounters with interstellar comets and the likelihood of their existence*, Icarus, **27**, 123–133.

Sekanina, Z., 1983. *The Tunguska event: no cometary signature in evidence*, Astron. J., **88**, 1382–1414. Corrigendum: **89**, 185.

Sekanina, Z., 1985. *Precession model for the nucleus of periodic comet Giacobini-Zinner*, Astron. J., **90**, 827–845.

Sekanina, Z., 1986. *Nucleus studies of comet Halley*, Adv. Space Res., **5**, 307–316.

Sekanina, Z., 1987. *Rotation vector of Halley's comet*, JPL Preprint 106. Comet Halley 1986: Worldwide Investigations, Results and Interpretations, eds. Mason, J. & Moore, P., in press. Ellis Horwood Publ. Co.

Sekanina, Z., 1988. *Nucleus of Comet IRAS-Iraki-Alcock (1983 VII)*, Astron. J., **95**, 1876–1894.

Sekanina, Z. & Larson, S.M., 1986a. *Dust jets in comet Halley observed by Giotto and from the ground*, Nature, **321**, 357–361.

Sekanina, Z. & Larson, S.M., 1986b. *Coma morphology and dust-emission pattern of periodic comet Halley. IV. Spin vector refinement and map of discrete dust sources for 1910*, Astron. J., **92**, 462–482.

Sekanina, Z. & Yeomans, D.K., 1984. *Close encounters and collisions of comets with the earth*, Astron. J., **89**, 154–161.

Sekiya, M., 1983. *Gravitational instabilities in a dust-gas layer and formation of planetesimals in the solar nebula*, Prog. Theor. Phys., **69**, 1116–1130.

Seneca, L.A., 65. *Quaestiones Naturales, Book VII.* (See Clarke & Geikie, 1910).

Sepkoski, J.J. & Raup, D.M., 1986a. *Periodicity in marine extinction events*, Dynamics of Extinction, ed. Elliot, D.K., 3–36. Wiley Interscience, New York.

Sepkoski, J.J. & Raup, D.M., 1986b. *Was there a 26-Myr periodicity of extinctions?* Nature, **321**, 533.

Serafin, R.A., 1988. *Admissible orbits in the Oort cloud and velocities on such orbits*, Celest. Mech., **41**, 79–98.

Seyfert, C.K. & Sirkin, L.A., 1979. *Earth History and Plate Tectonics.* Harper Row, New York.

Shackleton, N.J., 1989. *Climate and extinctions in the deep-sea sediment record*, Evolution and Extinction, Discussion Meeting of R. Soc. Lond. (9/10 November 1988), in press.

Shapley, H., 1921. *Note on a possible factor in changes of geological climate*, Journ. Geol., **29**, 502–504.

Sharma, S.D. & Khanna, M., 1988. *Analysis of perihelia of new comets*, Mon. Not. R. Astron. Soc., **235**, 1467–1471.

Shoemaker, E.M., 1977. *Astronomically observable crater-forming projectiles*, Impact and Explosion Cratering, eds. Roddy, D.J., Peppin, R.O. & Merrill, R.B., 617–628. Pergamon Press, New York.

Shoemaker, E.M., 1983. *Asteroid and comet bombardment of the earth*, Annu. Rev. Earth Planet. Sci., **11**, 461–494.

Shoemaker, E.M., Williams, J.G., Helin, E.F. & Wolfe, R.F., 1979. *Earth-crossing asteroids: orbital classes, collision rates with Earth, and origin*, Asteroids, ed. Gehrels, T., 253–282. University of Arizona Press, Tucson.

Shoemaker, E.M. & Wolfe, R.F., 1982. *Cratering time scales for the Galilean satellites*, Satellites of Jupiter, ed. Morrison, D., 277–339. University of Arizona Press, Tucson.

Shoemaker, E.M. & Wolfe, R.F., 1984a. *Evolution of the Uranus-Neptune planetesimal swarm*, Lunar Planet Sci. Conf., **XV**, 780–781.

Shoemaker, E.M. & Wolfe, R.F., 1984b. *Crater ages, comet showers, and the putative "death star"*, Meteoritics, **19**, 313.

Shoemaker, E.M. & Wolfe, R.F., 1986. *Mass extinctions, crater ages and comet showers*, The Galaxy and the Solar System, eds. Smoluchowski, R., Bahcall, J.N. & Matthews, M.S., 338–386. University of Arizona Press, Tucson.

Shteins, K.A. & Sture, S.Ya., 1962. *The diffusion of comets. IV*, Sov. Astron., **6**, 398–404. Translated from Astron. Zh., **39**, 506–515.

Shul'man, L.M., 1972. *The evolution of cometary nuclei*, The Motion, Evolution of Orbits, and Origin of Comets, eds. Chebotarev, G.A., Kazimirchak-Polonskaya, E.I. & Marsden, B.G., IAU Symp. No. 45, 271–276. Reidel, Dordrecht, The Netherlands.

Silver, L.T. & Schultz, P.H., 1982. *Geological Implications of Impacts of Large Asteroids and Comets on the Earth*, Geol. Soc. Amer. Spec. Pap. **190**.

Simonenko, A.N. & Levin, B.J., 1983. *Interrelations among asteroids, comets and meteoroids*, Highlights in Astronomy, ed. West, R., **6**, 391–398. Reidel, Dordrecht, The Netherlands.

Sinding, E., 1948. *On the systematic changes of the eccentricities of nearly parabolic orbits*, Publ. Copenhagen Obs., No. 146, 1–8.

Singer, C., 1943. *A Short History of Science to the Nineteenth Century.* See p.184. Clarendon Press, Oxford.

Smart, W.M., 1938. *Stellar Dynamics.* Cambridge University Press.

Smit, J. & Hertogen, J., 1980. *An extraterrestrial event at the Cretaceous-Tertiary boundary*, Nature, **285**, 198–200.

Smith, B.A., Larson, S.M., Szegö, K. & Sagdeev, R.Z., 1987. *Rejection of a proposed 7.4-day rotation period of the comet Halley nucleus*, Nature, **326**, 573–574.

Smith, B.A. & Terrile, R.J., 1984. *A circumstellar disk around β Pictoris*, Science, **226**, 1421–1424.

Smith, D., 1981. *Laboratory studies of isotope exchange in ion-neutral reactions: interstellar implications*, Philos. Trans. R. Soc. London, Ser. A, **303**, 535–542.

Smith, W.H., Schempp, W.V. & Baines, K.H., 1989. *The D/H ratio for Jupiter*, Astrophys. J., **336**, 967–970.

Smoluchowski, R., 1981. *Amorphous ice and the behavior of cometary nuclei*, Astrophys. J. Lett., **244**, L31–L34.

Smoluchowski, R., Bahcall, J.N. & Matthews, M.S., 1986. *The Galaxy and The Solar System.* University of Arizona Press, Tucson.

Smoluchowski, R. & Torbett, M.V., 1984. *The boundary of the solar system*, Nature, **311**, 38–39.

Šolc, M., Vanýsek, V. & Kissel, J., 1987a. *Isotopic composition of Halley dust*, Symposium on the Diversity and Similarity of Comets, eds. Rolfe, E.J. & Battrick, B., ESA SP-278, 359–362. ESA Publications, ESTEC, Noordwijk, The Netherlands.

Šolc, M., Jessburger, E.K., Hsiung, P. & Kissel, J., 1987b. *Halley dust composition*, Interplanetary Matter, eds. Ceplecha, Z. & Pecina, P., Publ. Astron. Inst. Czech. Acad. Sci. No. 67, 47–50. (Proc. Tenth European Regional Meeting of the IAU, Prague.)

Solomon, P.M., Rivolo, A.R., Barrett, J. & Yahil, A., 1987. *Mass, luminosity, and line width relations of galactic molecular clouds*, Astrophys. J., **319**, 730–741.

Spitzer, L., 1939. *The dissipation of planetary filaments*, Astrophys. J., **90**, 675–688.

Spitzer, L., 1941. *The dynamics of the interstellar medium II. Radiation pressure*, Astrophys. J., **94**, 232–244.

Spitzer, L. & Schwarzschild, M., 1951. *The possible influence of interstellar clouds on stellar velocities*, Astrophys. J., **114**, 385–397.

Spitzer, L. & Schwarzschild, M., 1953. *The possible influence of interstellar clouds on stellar velocities. II*, Astrophys. J., **118**, 106–112.

St. Cyr, O.C., 1988a. *Comet 1988m (SMM 4)*, IAU Circ. No. 4660.

St. Cyr, O.C., 1988b. *Comet 1988n (SMM 5)*, IAU Circ. No. 4668.

Stagg, C.R. & Bailey, M.E., 1989. *Stochastic capture of short-period comets*, Mon. Not. R. Astron. Soc., in press.

Staniucha, M.S. & Banaszkiewicz, M., 1988. *Passage of the sun through an interstellar nebula and the Oort cloud comets*, The Few Body Problem, ed. Valtonen, M.J., IAU Coll. No. 96, 201–205. (Astrophys. Space Sci. Lib., **140.**) Kluwer, Dordrecht, The Netherlands.

Stark, A.A. & Blitz, L., 1978. *On the masses of giant molecular cloud complexes*, Astrophys. J. Lett., **225**, L15–L19.

Stecchini, L.C., 1984. *The Newton affair*, Kronos **9**, (2), 34; **9**, (3), 52; **10**, (1), 62.

Steiner, J. & Grillmair, E., 1973. *Possible galactic causes for periodic and episodic glaciations*, Geol. Soc. Amer. Bull., **84**, 1003–1081.

Stewart, G.C., 1988. *A violent birth for Mercury*, Nature, **335**, 496–497.

Stigler, S.M. & Wagner, M.J., 1987. *A substantial bias in nonparametric tests for periodicity in geophysical data*, Science, **238**, 940–945.

Stimson, D., 1917. *The Gradual Acceptance of the Copernican Theory of the Universe.* New York.

Štohl, J., 1983. *On the distribution of sporadic meteor orbits*, Asteroids Comets Meteors, eds. Lagerkvist, C.-I. & Rickman, H., 419–424. Uppsala Observatory, Uppsala, Sweden.

Štohl, J., 1986. *On meteor contribution by short-period comets*, 20th ESLAB Symposium on the Exploration of Halley's Comet, eds. Battrick, B., Rolfe, E.J. & Reinhard, R., ESA SP-250, Vol. II, 225–228. ESA Publications, ESTEC, Noordwijk, The Netherlands.

Stothers, R.B., 1984. *Mass extinctions and missing matter*, Nature, **311**, 17.

Stothers, R.B., 1985. *Terrestrial record of the Solar System's oscillation about the galactic plane*, Nature, **317**, 338–341.

Stothers, R.B., 1986. *Periodicity of the Earth's magnetic reversals*, Nature, **322**, 444–446.

Stothers, R.B., 1988. *Structure of Oort's comet cloud inferred from terrestrial impact craters*, Observatory, **108**, 1–9.

Stothers, R.B., 1989. *Structure and dating errors in the geologic time scale and periodicity in mass extinctions*, Geophys. Res. Lett., **16**, 119–122.

Strom, K.M., Strom, S.E., Edwards, S., Cabrit, S. & Skrutskie, M.F., 1989. *Circumstellar material associated with solar-type pre-main-sequence stars: a possible constraint on the timescale for planet building*, Astron. J., **97**, 1451–1470.

Strömgren, E., 1914. *Ueber den Ursprung der Kometen*, Publ. Obs. Copenhagen No. 19, 189–250.

Struve, O., 1960. *Planets with rings*, Sky and Telescope, **20**, 20–23.

Sussman, G.J. & Wisdom, J., 1988. *Numerical evidence that the motion of Pluto is chaotic*, Science, **241**, 433–437.

Sykes, M.V., 1988. *IRAS observations of extended zodiacal structures*, Astrophys. J. Lett., **334**, L55–L58.

Sykes, M.V., Lebofsky, L.A., Hunten, D.M. & Low, F.J., 1986. *The discovery of dust trails in the orbits of periodic comets*, Science, **232**, 1115–1117.

Tarafdar, S.P., Prasad, S.S. & Huntress Jr., W.T., 1983. *Dependence of interstellar depletion on hydrogen column density: possibilities and implications*, Astrophys. J., **267**, 156–162.

Taylor, T., 1816. *The Six Books of Proclus on the Theology of Plato.* (2 Volumes.) London.

Taylor, T., 1820. *Commentaries of Proclus on the Timaeus of Plato.* (2 Volumes.) London.

Taylor, T., 1825. *Lost Writings of Proclus.* London.

Telesco, C.M., Becklin, E.E., Wolstencroft, R.D. & Decher, R., 1988. *Resolution of the circumstellar disk of β Pictoris at 10 and $20\,\mu m$*, Nature, **335**, 51–53.

Terentjeva, A.K., 1989. *Do fireball showers exist?* Preprint, presented at Asteroids Comets Meteors III, Uppsala 1989.

Ter Haar, D. & Cameron, A.G.W., 1963. *Historical review of theories of the origin of the solar system*, Origin of the Solar System, eds. Jastrow, R. & Cameron, A.G.W., 1–37. Academic Press, New York.

Thaddeus, P., 1986. *Molecular clouds and periodic events in the geologic past*, The Galaxy and the Solar System, eds. Smoluchowski, R., Bahcall, J.N. & Matthews, M.S., 61–68. University of Arizona Press, Tucson.

Thaddeus, P. & Chanan, G.A., 1985. *Cometary impacts, molecular clouds, and the motion of the Sun perpendicular to the galactic plane*, Nature, **314**, 73–75.

Thaddeus, P. & Dame, T.M., 1984. *The number and distribution of molecular clouds in the inner Galaxy*, Proc. Workshop on Star Formation, ed. Wolstencroft, R.D., Occ. Rep. Roy. Obs. Edinb., No. 13, 15–26.

Tholen, D.J., 1988. *(2060) Chiron*, IAU Circ. No. 4554.

Tholen, D.J., Cruikshank, D.P., Hartmann, W.K., Lark, N., Hammel, H.B. & Piscitelli, J.R., 1986. *A comparison of the continuum colors of P/Halley, other comets and asteroids*, 20th ESLAB Symposium on the Exploration of Halley's Comet, eds. Battrick, B., Rolfe, E.J. & Reinhard, R., ESA SP-250, Vol. III, 503–507. ESA Publications, ESTEC, Noordwijk, The Netherlands.

Thom, A., 1967. *Megalithic Sites in Britain*. Oxford University Press, London.

Thom, A., 1971. *Megalithic Lunar Observatories*. Oxford University Press, London.

Thomas, K., 1971. *Religion and the Decline of Magic*. Weidenfeld & Nicolson, London.

Thomas, N. & Keller, H.U., 1989. *The colour of comet P/Halley's nucleus and dust*, Astron. Astrophys., **213**, 487–494.

Thompson, R.C., 1900. *The Reports of the Magicians and Astrologers of Nineveh and Babylon*. Luzac & Co., London.

Thorndike, L., 1950. *Latin Treatises on Comets Between 1238 and 1368* AD. University of Chicago Press.

Thraen, A., 1894. *Untersuchung über die vormalige Bahn des Kometen 1886 II*, Astron. Nachr., **136**, (No. 3249) 133–138.

Tian-shan, Zhuang, 1977. *Ancient Chinese records of meteor showers*, Chinese Astron. Astrophys., **1**, 197–220. (Translated from Acta Astron. Sinica, **14**, 37–58, 1966.)

Tinsley, B.M. & Cameron, A.G.W., 1974. *Possible influence of comets on the chemical evolution of the Galaxy*, Astrophys. Space Sci., **31**, 31–35.

Tisserand, F., 1889. *Sur la théorie de la capture des comètes périodiques*, Bull. Astron., **6**, 241–257, 289–292.

Todd, D.P., 1880. *Preliminary account of a speculative and practical search for a trans-neptunian planet*, Amer. Journ. Sci. (3rd series), **20**, (No. 117) 225–234.

Tokunaga, A.T. & Hanner, M.S., 1985. *Does Comet P/Arend-Rigaux have a large, dark nucleus?* Astrophys. J. Lett., **296**, L13–L16.

Tomanov, V.P., 1973. *New statistical regularities in the system of long-period comets*, Astron. Vestn., **7**, 83–87, in Russian.

Tomanov, V.P., 1976. *The solar apex relative to the protocometary cloud*, Sov. Astron., **20**, 366–370. Translated from Astron. Zh., **53**, 647–654.

Tomeoka, K. & Buseck, P.R., 1986. *A carbonate-rich, hydrated, interplanetary dust particle: possible residue from protostellar clouds*, Science, **231**, 1544–1546.

Tomkin, J. & Lambert, D.L., 1976. *Isotopic abundances of magnesium in Arcturus*, Astrophys. J., **208**, 436–442.

Tomkin, J. & Lambert, D.L., 1980. *Isotopic abundances of magnesium in five G and K dwarfs*, Astrophys. J., **235**, 925–928.

Toomre, A., 1964. *On the gravitational instability of a disk of stars*, Astrophys. J., **139**, 1217–1238.

Torbett, M.V., 1986a. *Dynamical influence of galactic tides and molecular clouds on the Oort cloud of comets*, The Galaxy and the Solar System, eds. Smoluchowski, R., Bahcall, J.N. & Matthews, M.S., 147–172. University of Arizona Press, Tucson.

Torbett, M.V., 1986b. *Injection of Oort cloud comets to the inner solar system by galactic tidal fields,* Mon. Not. R. Astron. Soc., **223**, 885–895.

Torbett, M.V., 1989. *Chaotic motion in a comet disk beyond Neptune: the delivery of short-period comets,* preprint.

Torbett, M.V. & Smoluchowski, R., 1984. *Orbital stability of the unseen solar companion linked to periodic extinction events,* Nature, **311**, 641–642.

Tosi, M., 1988. *Models of galactic chemical evolution: the problem of uniqueness,* Astron. Astrophys., **197**, 33–46.

Toulmin, S., 1985. *The Return to Cosmology.* University of California Press, Berkeley & Los Angeles.

Tremaine, S.D., 1986. *Is there evidence for a solar companion star?* The Galaxy and the Solar System, eds. Smoluchowski, R., Bahcall, J.N. & Matthews, M.S., 409–416. University of Arizona Press, Tucson.

Trulsen, J., 1971. *Collisional focussing of particles in space causing jet-streams,* Physical Studies of Minor Planets, ed. Gehrels, T., 327–335. NASA SP-267, Washington D.C.

Tuman, V.S., 1986. *Astronomical dating of Kudurru SB 22 of the Louvre Museum,* Nineveh, **9**, 1, 11.

Tyror, J.G., 1957. *The distribution of the directions of the perihelia of long-period comets,* Mon. Not. R. Astron. Soc., **117**, 370–379.

Urasin, L.A., 1987. *Spiral model of the Galaxy from observations of interstellar extinction,* Sov. Astron. Lett., **13**, 356–358. Translated from Pis'ma Astron. Zh., **13**, 850–854, 1987.

Urey, H.C., 1952. *The Planets: Their Origin and Development.* Oxford University Press.

Urey, H.C., 1972. *Evidence for objects of lunar mass in the early solar system,* The Moon, **4**, 383–389.

Urey, H.C., 1973 *Cometary collisions and geological periods,* Nature, **242**, 32–33.

Vallée, J.P., 1989. *The search for knowledge: science versus religion?* J. R. Astron. Soc. Canada, **83**, 8–25.

Valtonen, M.J., 1983. *On the capture of comets into the solar system,* Observatory, **103**, 1–4.

Valtonen, M.J. & Innanen, K.A., 1982. *The capture of interstellar comets,* Astrophys. J., **255**, 307–315.

Van den Bergh, S., 1982. *Giant molecular clouds and the Solar System comets,* J. R. Astron. Soc. Canada, **76**, 303–308.

Van der Waerden, B.L., 1974. *Science Awakening II. The Birth of Astronomy.* Noordhoff International Publishing, Leyden; Oxford University Press, New York.

Van Flandern, T.C., 1975. *The asteroidal planet as the origin of comets,* Bull. Amer. Astron. Soc., **7**, 467.

Van Flandern, T.C., 1976. *A former major planet of the solar system,* Bull. Amer. Astron. Soc., **8**, 433.

Van Flandern, T.C., 1977. *A former major planet of the solar system,* Comets Asteroids Meteorites: Interrelations, Evolution and Origins, ed. Delsemme, A.H., IAU Coll. No. 39, 15–23. University of Toledo, Toledo, Ohio.

Van Flandern, T.C., 1978a. *The asteroidal planet as the origin of comets,* Dynamics of Planets and Satellites and Theories of Their Motion, ed. Szebehely, V.G., IAU Coll. No. 41, 89–99. (Astrophys. Space Sci. Lib. **72**.) Reidel, Dordrecht, The Netherlands.

Van Flandern, T.C., 1978b. *A former asteroidal planet as the origin of comets,* Icarus, **36**, 51–74.

Van Steenberg, M.E. & Shull, J.M., 1988. *Galactic interstellar abundance surveys with IUE. III. Silicon, manganese, iron, sulfur, and zinc,* Astrophys. J., **330**, 942–963.

Van Woerkom, A.J.J., 1948. *On the origin of comets,* Bull. Astron. Inst. Neth., **10**, 445–472.

Vanýsek, V., 1977. *Carbon isotope ratio in comets and interstellar matter*, Comets Asteroids Meteorites: Interrelations, Evolution and Origins, ed. Delsemme, A.H., IAU Coll. No. 39, 499–503. University of Toledo, Toledo, Ohio.

Vanýsek, V., 1983. *Deuterium in comets*, Asteroids Comets Meteors, eds. Lagerkvist, C.-I. & Rickman, H., 379–381. Uppsala Observatory, Uppsala, Sweden.

Vanýsek, V., 1984. *Prediction of deuterium abundance in comets*, Bull. Astron. Inst. Czechosl., **35**, 361–364.

Vanýsek, V., 1987a. *A note on comets and the chemical evolution of the Galaxy*, Symposium on the Diversity and Similarity of Comets, eds. Rolfe, E.J. & Battrick, B., ESA SP-278, 745–746. ESA Publications, ESTEC, Noordwijk, The Netherlands.

Vanýsek, V., 1987b. *Isotopic abundances in comets*, Astrochemistry, eds. Vardya, M.S. & Tarafdar, S.P., IAU Symp. No. 120, 461–467. Reidel, Dordrecht, The Netherlands.

Vasilevskis, S. & Klemola, A.R., 1971. *On determination of correction to precession from stellar proper motions*, Astron. J., **76**, 508–512.

Verniani, F., 1969. *Structure and fragmentation of meteoroids*, Space Sci. Rev., **10**, 230–261.

Virolleaud, Ch., 1905–12. *L'Astrologie Chaldéene*. 14 Vols., Q. Par Weltier, Paris.

Von Hoerner, S. & Saslaw, W.C., 1976. *The evolution of massive collapsing gas clouds*, Astrophys. J., **206**, 917–933.

Von Littrow, J.J. & Encke, J.F., 1835. *Ueber den Halleyschen Cometen*, The Quarterly Review, **55**, 195–233.

Vorontsov-Velyaminov, B., 1946. *Structure and mass of cometary nuclei*, Astrophys. J., **104**, 226–233.

Vsekhsvyatski, S.K., 1930. *On the disintegration of short-period comets: some remarks on the question of their origin*, Mon. Not. R. Astron. Soc., **90**, 706–721.

Vsekhsvyatski, S.K., 1935. *On the origin of comets*, Observatory, **58**, 271–272.

Vsekhsvyatski, S.K., 1962. *Comets, small bodies, and problems of the solar system*, Publ. Astron. Soc. Pac., **76**, 106–115.

Vsekhsvyatski, S.K., 1964. *Physical Characteristics of Comets*, NASA TT F-80, p.124. Israel Program for Scientific Translations, Jerusalem.

Vsekhsvyatski, S.K., 1966. *Comet cosmogony of Lagrange and the problem of the solar system*, Mem. Soc. Roy. des Sci. de Liège (Ser. 5) **12**, 495–515.

Vsekhsvyatski, S.K., 1972. *The origin and evolution of the comets and other small bodies in the solar system*, The Motion, Evolution of Orbits, and Origin of Comets, eds. Chebotarev, G.A., Kazimirchak-Polonskaya, E.I. & Marsden, B.G., IAU Symp. No. 45, 413–418. Reidel, Dordrecht, The Netherlands.

Vsekhsvyatski, S.K., 1977. *Comets and the cosmogony of the solar system*, Comets Asteroids Meteorites: Interrelations, Evolution and Origins, ed. Delsemme, A.H., IAU Coll. No. 39, 469–474. University of Toledo, Toledo, Ohio.

Walker, C.K., Lada, C.J., Young, E.T., Maloney, P.R. & Wilking, B.A., 1986. *Spectroscopic evidence for infall around an extraordinary IRAS source in Ophiuchus*, Astrophys. J. Lett., **309**, L47–L51.

Walker, C.K., Lada, C.J., Young, E.T., & Margulis, M., 1989. *An unusual outflow around IRAS 16293 – 2422*, Astrophys. J., in press.

Walker, J., 1980. *Light from the Sky*, Readings from Scientific American, W.H. Freeman & Co., San Francisco.

Walker, P.M.B., 1988. *Chambers Science and Technology Dictionary*. W.R. Chambers Ltd. and Cambridge University Press.

Wallis, M.K., 1978. *Cometary polemic and refutation*, Observatory, **98**, 174.

Wallis, M.K., 1984. *Rotation of cometary nuclei*, Philos. Trans. R. Soc. London, Ser. A, **A313**, 165–170.

Wallis, M.K. & Krishna Swamy, K.S., 1986. *Some molecular abundances in Halley's UV spectra*, 20th ESLAB Symposium on the Exploration of Halley's Comet, eds. Battrick, B., Rolfe, E.J. & Reinhard, R., ESA SP-250, Vol. III, 7–10. ESA Publications, ESTEC, Noordwijk, The Netherlands.

Wallis, M.K., Wickramasinghe, N.C., Hoyle, F. & Rabilizirov, R., 1989. *Biologic versus abiotic models of cometary grains*, Mon. Not. R. Astron. Soc., **238**, 1165–1170.

Wasserman, I., 1988. *Theoretical models for wide binary evolution*, Astrophys. Space Sci., **142**, 267–276.

Watson, F.G., 1948. *Between the Planets*. J.A. Churchill Ltd., London. (See pp.85–86).

Wayman, P.A. & Mullan, D.J., 1986. *Ernst Julius Öpik*, Q. Jl. R. Astron. Soc., **27**, 508–512.

Weber, P. & Greenberg, J.M., 1985. *Can spores survive in interstellar space?* Nature, **316**, 403–407.

Weertman, J., 1976. *Milankovitch solar radiation variations and ice age ice sheet sizes*, Nature, **261**, 17–20.

Wegmann, R., Schmidt, H.U., Heubner, W.F. & Boice, D.C., 1987. *Cometary MHD and chemistry*, Astron. Astrophys., **187**, 339–350.

Weidenschilling, S.J., 1977a. *The distribution of mass in the planetary system and solar nebula*, Astrophys. Space Sci., **51**, 153–158.

Weidenschilling, S.J., 1977b. *Aerodynamics of solid bodies in the solar nebula*, Mon. Not. R. Astron. Soc., **180**, 57–70.

Weidenschilling, S.J., 1980. *Dust to planetesimals: settling and coagulation in the solar nebula*, Icarus, **44**, 172–189.

Weidenschilling, S.J., 1987. *Accumulation of solid bodies in the solar nebula*, Gerlands Beitr. Geophysik, Leipzik, **96**, 21–33.

Weidenschilling, S.J., 1988. *Formation processes and time scales for meteoric parent bodies*, Meteorites and the Early Solar System, eds. Kerridge, J.F. & Matthews, M.S., 348–371. University of Arizona Press, Tucson.

Weidenschilling, S.J., Donn, B. & Meakin, P., 1989. *The physics of planetesimal formation*, Formation and Evolution of Planetary Systems, eds. Weaver, H., Paresce, F. & Danly, L., 117–136. Cambridge University Press.

Weinberg, M.D., Shapiro, S.L. & Wasserman, I., 1986. *The dynamical fate of wide binaries in the solar neighborhood: encounters with stars and molecular clouds*, Icarus, **65**, 27–36.

Weinberg, M.D., Shapiro, S.L. & Wasserman, I., 1987. *The dynamical fate of wide binaries in the solar neighborhood*, Astrophys. J., **312**, 367–389.

Weintraub, D.A., Sandell, G. & Duncan, W.D., 1989. *Submillimeter measurements of T Tauri and FU Orionis stars*, Astrophys. J. Lett., **340**, L69–L72.

Weissman, P.R., 1977. *Initial energy and perihelion distributions of Oort-cloud comets*, Comets Asteroids Meteorites: Interrelations, Evolution and Origins, ed. Delsemme, A.H., IAU Coll. No. 39, 87–91. University of Toledo, Toledo, Ohio.

Weissman, P.R., 1978. *Physical and Dynamical Evolution of Long-Period Comets*. Thesis, University of California, Los Angeles.

Weissman, P.R., 1979. *Physical and dynamical evolution of long-period comets*, Dynamics of the Solar System, ed. Duncombe, R.L., IAU Symp. No. 81, 277–282. Reidel, Dordrecht, The Netherlands.

Weissman, P.R., 1980a. *Stellar perturbations of the cometary cloud*, Nature, **288**, 242–243.

Weissman, P.R., 1980b. *Physical loss of long-period comets*, Astron. Astrophys., **85**, 191–196.

Weissman, P.R., 1982. *Dynamical history of the Oort cloud*, Comets, ed. Wilkening, L., IAU Coll. No. 61, 637–658. University of Arizona Press, Tucson.

Weissman, P.R., 1983a. *Cometary impacts with the sun: physical and dynamical considerations*, Icarus, **55**, 448–454.

Weissman, P.R., 1983b. *The mass of the Oort cloud*, Astron. Astrophys., **118**, 90–94.

Weissman, P.R., 1984. *The Vega particulate shell: comets or asteroids?* Science, **224**, 987–989.

Weissman, P.R., 1985a. *The origin of comets: implications for planetary formation,* Protostars & Planets II, eds. Black, D.C. & Matthews, M.S., 895–919. University of Arizona Press, Tucson.

Weissman, P.R., 1985b. *Cometary dynamics,* Sp. Sci. Rev., **41**, 299–349.

Weissman, P.R., 1985c. *Dynamical evolution of the Oort cloud,* Dynamics of Comets: Their Origin and Evolution, eds. Carusi, A. & Valsecchi, G.B., IAU Coll. No. 83, 87–96. (Astrophys. Space Sci. Lib. **115**.) Reidel, Dordrecht, The Netherlands.

Weissman, P.R., 1985d. *Terrestrial impactors at geological boundary events: comets or asteroids?* Nature, **314**, 517–518.

Weissman, P.R., 1986a. *The Oort cloud and the Galaxy: dynamical interactions,* The Galaxy and the Solar System, eds. Smoluchowski, R., Bahcall, J.N. & Matthews, M.S., 204–237. University of Arizona Press, Tucson.

Weissman, P.R., 1986b. *The mass of the Oort cloud: a post-Halley reassessment,* Bull. Amer. Astron. Soc., **18**, 799.

Weissman, P.R., 1986c. *Are primordial comet nuclei primordial rubble piles?* Nature, **320**, 242–244.

Weissman, P.R., 1988. *The impact history of the solar system: implications for the origin of atmospheres,* Origin and Evolution of Planetary and Satellite Atmospheres, in press. University of Arizona Press.

Weissman, P.R., 1989. *The cometary impactor flux at the earth,* preprint. Submitted to Proc. Conf. on Global Catastrophes in Earth History, Snowbird, Utah, October 1988.

Weissman, P.R., A'Hearn, M.F., McFadden, L.A. & Rickman, H., 1989. *Evolution of comets into asteroids,* Asteroids II, eds. Binzel, R., Gehrels, T. & Matthews, M.S., in press. University of Arizona Press, Tucson.

Weissman, P.R. & Keiffer, H.H., 1981. *Thermal modelling of cometary nuclei,* Icarus, **47**, 302–311.

West, M.L., 1971. *Early Greek Philosophy and the Orient.* Clarendon Press, Oxford.

Westfall, R.S., 1980. *Never at Rest: A Biography of Isaac Newton.* Cambridge University Press.

Wetherill, G.W., 1975. *Late heavy bombardment of the moon and terrestrial planets,* Proc. Sixth Lunar Science Conf., **2**, 1539–1561.

Wetherill, G.W., 1978. *Accumulation of the terrestrial planets,* Protostars & Planets, ed. Gehrels, T., IAU Coll. No. 52, 568–598. University of Arizona Press, Tucson, Arizona, USA.

Wetherill, G.W., 1980. *Formation of the terrestrial planets,* Annu. Rev. Astron. Astrophys., **18**, 77–113.

Wetherill, G.W., 1985. *Asteroidal source of ordinary chondrites.* Meteoritics, **20**, 1–22.

Wetherill, G.W., 1988. *Where do the Apollo objects come from?* Icarus, **76**, 1–18.

Whalley, P., 1987. *Insects and Cretaceous mass extinction,* Nature, **327**, 562.

Whipple, F.J.W., 1930. *The Great Siberian Meteor and the waves, seismic and aerial, which it produced,* Q. J. Roy. Meteorol. Soc., **56**, 287–304.

Whipple, F.L., 1940. *Photographic meteor studies. III. The Taurid shower,* Proc. Amer. Philos. Soc., **83**, 711–745.

Whipple, F.L., 1946. *Concentrations of the interstellar medium,* Astrophys. J., **104**, 1–11.

Whipple, F.L., 1948. *The dust cloud hypothesis,* Scientific American **178**, (No. 5) 34–45.

Whipple, F.L., 1949. *Comets, meteors and the interplanetary complex,* Astron. J., **54**, 179–180.

Whipple, F.L., 1950a. *On tests of the icy conglomerate model for comets,* Astron. J., **55**, 83.

Whipple, F.L., 1950b. *A comet model. I. The acceleration of Comet Encke*, Astrophys. J., **111**, 375–394.

Whipple, F.L., 1951. *A comet model. II. Physical relations for comets and meteors*, Astrophys. J., **113**, 464–474.

Whipple, F.L., 1953. *On the icy conglomerate model for comets*, La Physique des Comètes, 283–288. Proc. 4th Int. Coll. Astrophys., Liège.

Whipple, F.L., 1957. *A comment on the origin of short-period comets: On Oort's theory of the cometary cloud*, Trans. IAU, **9**, 249. Cambridge University Press.

Whipple, F.L., 1962. *On the distribution of semimajor axes among comet orbits*, Astron. J., **67**, 1–9.

Whipple, F.L., 1963. *On the structure of the comet nucleus*, The Moon, Meteorites and Comets, eds. Middlehurst, B.M. & Kuiper, G.P., 639–664. (The Solar System, **IV.**) University of Chicago Press.

Whipple, F.L., 1964a. *The evidence for a comet belt beyond Neptune*, Proc. Natl. Acad. Sci. (USA), **51**, 711–718.

Whipple, F.L., 1964b. *The history of the solar system*, Proc. Natl. Acad. Sci. (USA), **52**, 565–594.

Whipple, F.L., 1967. *On maintaining the meteoritic complex*, The Zodiacal Light and the Interplanetary Medium, ed. Weinberg, J., NASA SP-150, 409–426.

Whipple, F.L., 1968. *Origins of meteoritic material*, Physics and Dynamics of Meteors, eds. Kresák, Ľ. & Millman, P.M., IAU Symp. No. 33, 481–485. Reidel, Dordrecht, The Netherlands.

Whipple, F.L., 1972a. *The origin of comets*, The Motion, Evolution of Orbits, and Origin of Comets, eds. Chebotarev, G.A., Kazimirchak-Polonskaya, E.I. & Marsden, B.G., IAU Symp. No. 45, 401–408. Reidel, Dordrecht, The Netherlands.

Whipple, F.L., 1972b. *Discussion*, The Motion, Evolution of Orbits, and Origin of Comets, eds. Chebotarev, G.A., Kazimirchak-Polonskaya, E.I. & Marsden, B.G., IAU Symp. No. 45, 485. Reidel, Dordrecht, The Netherlands.

Whipple, F.L., 1972c. *Discussion*, From Plasma to Planet, ed. Elvius, A., Nobel Symp. No. 21, 266–272. Wiley Interscience, New York.

Whipple, F.L., 1972d. *The Collected Works of Fred L. Whipple. Vol. I. Meteors and Comets and the Interplanetary Complex.* Smithsonian Astrophysical Observatory, Cambridge, Massachusetts. (2 Volumes.)

Whipple, F.L., 1973. *Note on the number and origin of Apollo asteroids*, Moon, **8**, 340–345.

Whipple, F.L., 1975. *Do comets play a rôle in galactic chemistry and γ-ray bursts?* Astron. J., **80**, 525–531.

Whipple, F.L., 1976. *Background of modern comet theory*, Nature, **263**, 15–19.

Whipple, F.L., 1977. *The reality of comet groups and pairs*, Icarus, **30**, 736–746.

Whipple, F.L., 1978a. *Cometary brightness variation and nucleus structure*, Moon & Planets, **18**, 343–359.

Whipple, F.L., 1978b. *On the nature and origin of comets and their contribution to planets*, Moon & Planets, **19**, 305–315.

Whipple, F.L., 1982. *The rotation of comet nuclei*, Comets, ed. Wilkening, L., IAU Coll. No. 61, 227–250. University of Arizona Press, Tucson.

Whipple, F.L., 1983. *1983 TB and the Geminid meteors*, IAU Circ., No. 3881.

Whipple, F.L., 1985. *The Mystery of Comets.* Cambridge University Press.

Whipple, F.L. & Hamid, S.E., 1952. *On the origin of the Taurid meteor streams*, Helwan Obs. Bull. No. 41, 1–30. Royal Observatory, Helwan. Fouad I University Press, Cairo. (Also see Whipple 1972d, 224–252.)

Whipple, F.L. & Lecar, M., 1976. *Comet formation induced by the solar wind*, The Study of Comets: Part 2, eds. Donn, B., Mumma, M., Jackson, W., A'Hearn, M. & Harrington, R., IAU Coll. No. 25, 660. NASA SP-393, Washington D.C.

Whitmire, D.P. & Jackson, A.A., 1984. *Are periodic mass extinctions driven by a distant solar companion?* Nature, **308**, 713–715.

Whitmire, D.P. & Matese, J.J., 1985. *Periodic comet showers and Planet X*, Nature, **313**, 36–38.

Whittet, D.C.B., 1984. *Abundance constraints on grain composition*, Observatory, **104**, 131–132.

Whittet, D.C.B., 1988. *The observed properties of interstellar dust in the infrared*, Dust in the Universe, eds. Bailey, M.E. & Williams, D.A., 25–53. Cambridge University Press.

Whyte, M.A., 1977. *Turning points in Phanerozoic history*, Nature, **267**, 679–682.

Wickramasinghe, N.C., 1967. *Interstellar Grains.* (International Astrophysics Series, Vol. 9.) Chapman & Hall Ltd., London.

Wickramasinghe, N.C. & Hoyle, F., 1989. *Modelling the 5–30 μm spectrum of Comet Halley*, Earth, Moon, Planets, **43**, 145–153.

Wickramasinghe, N.C., Wallis, M.K., Al-Mufti, S. & Hoyle, F., 1988. *The organic nature of cometary grains*, Earth, Moon, Planets, **40**, 101–108.

Wielen, R., 1977. *The diffusion of stellar orbits derived from the observed age-dependence of the velocity dispersion*, Astron. Astrophys., **60**, 263–275.

Wilde, H., 1910. *On the origin of cometary bodies and Saturn's rings*, Mem. Proc. Manch. Lit. Philos. Soc., **55**, 1–20.

Wilhelm, K., 1987. *Rotation and precession of comet Halley*, Nature, **327**, 27–30.

Wilkening, L.L., 1982. *Comets*, ed. Wilkening, L.L., IAU Coll. No. 61. University of Arizona Press, Tucson, Arizona, USA.

Williams, G.E., 1975. *Possible relation between periodic glaciation and the flexure of the Galaxy*, Earth Planet. Sci. Lett., **26**, 361–369.

Williams, T.I., 1969. *A Biographical Dictionary of Scientists.* Adam and Charles Black, London.

Wilson, H.C., 1909. *The comet families of Saturn, Uranus and Neptune*, Popular Astron., **17**, 629–633.

Winterbottom, M., 1978. *Gildas: The Ruin of Britain and Other Works.* Phillimore & Co. Ltd., London.

Wisdom, J., 1983. *Chaotic behaviour near the 3/1 commensurability as a source of Earth crossing asteroids and meteorites*, Meteoritics, **18**, 422–423.

Wisdom, J., 1985a. *A perturbative treatment of motions near the 3/1 commensurability*, Icarus, **63**, 272–289.

Wisdom, J., 1985b. *Meteorites may follow a chaotic route to Earth*, Nature, **315**, 731–733.

Witkowski, J.M., 1958. *On the directions of perihelia of cometary orbits*, Observatory, **78**, 85–86.

Witkowski, J.M., 1968. *On cometary statistics*, Observatory, **88**, 27–28.

Witkowski, J.M., 1972. *On the problem of the origin of comets*, The Motion, Evolution of Orbits, and Origin of Comets, eds. Chebotarev, G.A., Kazimirchak-Polonskaya, E.I. & Marsden, B.G., IAU Symp. No. 45, 419–425. Reidel, Dordrecht, The Netherlands.

Wolbach, W.S., Gilmour, I., Anders, E., Orth, C.J. & Brooks, R.R., 1988. *Global fire at the Cretaceous-Tertiary boundary*, Nature, **334**, 665–669; *Corrigendum:* **335**, 744.

Wolfendale, A.W. & Wilkinson, D.A., 1989. *Periodic mass extinctions: some astronomical difficulties*, Catastrophes and Evolution: Astronomical Foundation, ed. Clube, S.V.M., in press. Cambridge University Press.

Wood, J.A., et al., 1986. *Interstellar material in the solar system*, Interrelationships Among Circumstellar, Interstellar, and Interplanetary Dust, eds. Nuth III, J.A. & Stencel, R.E., NASA CP-2403, WG-33–WG-78. Washington D.C.

Woolfson, M.M., 1978a. *Star formation and interactions between stars*, The Origin of the Solar System, ed. Dermott, S.F., 163–178. Wiley, New York.

Woolfson, M.M., 1978b. *The capture theory and the origin of the solar system*, The Origin of the Solar System, ed. Dermott, S.F., 179–198. Wiley, New York.

Woolfson, M.M., 1978c. *The evolution of the solar system*, The Origin of the Solar System, ed. Dermott, S.F., 199–217. Wiley, New York.

Woolley, R.v.d.R., 1957. *Motions of stars of type A perpendicular to the galactic plane*, Mon. Not. R. Astron. Soc., **117**, 198–211.

Woolley, R.v.d.R., 1965. *Motions of the nearby stars*, Galactic Structure, eds. Blaauw, A. & Schmidt, M., 85–110. University of Chicago Press.

Woosley, S.E. & Weaver, T.A., 1986. *Theoretical models for Type I and Type II supernovae*, Nucleosynthesis and its implications on Nuclear and Particle Physics, eds. Audouze, J. & Mathieu, N., 145–166. (NATO ASI Series **C 163.**) Reidel, Dordrecht, The Netherlands.

Wyatt, S.P. & Faintich, M.B., 1971. *The effect of interstellar clouds on the comet cloud*, Bull. Amer. Astron. Soc., **3**, 368.

Wyckoff, S., Wagner, R.M., Wehinger, P.A., Schleicher, D.G. & Festou, M.C., 1985. *Onset of sublimation in comet P/Halley*, Nature, **316**, 241–242.

Wyckoff, S., Tegler, S., Wehinger, P.A., Spinrad, H. & Belton, M.J.S., 1988. *Abundances in Comet Halley at the time of the spacecraft encounters*, Astrophys. J., **325**, 927–938.

Wyckoff, S., Lindholm, E., Wehinger, A., Peterson, B.A., Zucconi, J.-M. & Festou, M.C., 1989. *The $^{12}C/^{13}C$ abundance ratio in Comet Halley*, Astrophys. J., **339**, 488–500.

Xi Ze-zong, 1984. *The cometary atlas in the Silk Book of the Han tomb at Mawangdui*, Chinese Astron. Astrophys., **8**, 1–7. (Translated from Kejishi Wenjie No. 1, 39–43, 1978.)

Yabushita, S., 1972a. *Planetary perturbation of orbits of long-period comets with large perihelion distances*, Astron. Astrophys., **16**, 471–477.

Yabushita, S., 1972b. *Stellar perturbations of orbits of long-period comets*, Astron. Astrophys., **16**, 395–403.

Yabushita, S., 1979. *A statistical study of the evolution of the orbits of the long-period comets*, Mon. Not. R. Astron. Soc., **187**, 445–462.

Yabushita, S., 1983a. *Distribution of cometary binding energies based on the assumption of steady state*, Mon. Not. R. Astron. Soc., **204**, 1185–1191.

Yabushita, S., 1983b. *On the formation of cometary nuclei in dense globules*, Astrophys. Space Sci., **89**, 159–161.

Yabushita, S., 1983c. *Processes of dynamical evolution of cometary orbits*, Q. Jl. R. Astron. Soc., **24**, 430–442.

Yabushita, S., 1985. *Statistical test of the distribution of perihelion points and its implication for cometary origin*, Dynamics of Comets: Their Origin and Evolution, eds. Carusi, A. & Valsecchi, G.B., IAU Coll. No. 83, 11–17. (Astrophys. Space Sci. Lib. **115.**) Reidel, Dordrecht, The Netherlands.

Yabushita, S., 1988. *The rate of supply and removal of new comets by the galactic tidal force*, Mon. Not. R. Astron. Soc., **231**, 723–733.

Yabushita, S., 1989a. *Galactic tidal perturbations of long-period comets and the distribution of inclinations*, Earth, Moon, Planets, **44**, 29–37.

Yabushita, S., 1989b. *On the discrepancy between supply and loss of observable long-period comets*, Mon. Not. R. Astron. Soc., in press.

Yabushita, S. & Allen, A.J., 1985. *On the effect of interstellar matter on terrestrial climate*, Observatory, **105**, 198–200.

Yabushita, S. & Allen, A.J., 1989. *On the effect of accreted interstellar matter on the terrestrial environment*, Mon. Not. R. Astron. Soc., **238**, 1465–1478.

Yabushita, S. & Hasegawa, I., 1978. *A note on the possible origin of comets in an interstellar gas cloud*, Mon. Not. R. Astron. Soc., **185**, 549–553.

Yabushita, S., Hasegawa, I. & Kobayashi, K., 1982. *The stellar perturbations of orbital elements of long-period comets*, Mon. Not. R. Astron. Soc., **200**, 661–671.

Yamamoto, T., 1985a. *Formation history and environment of cometary nuclei*, Ices in the Solar System, eds. Klinger, J., Benest, D., Dollfus, A. & Smoluchowski, R., 205–219. (NATO ASI series **C 156.**) Reidel, Dordrecht, The Netherlands.

Yamamoto, T., 1985b. *Formation environment of cometary nuclei in the primordial solar nebula*, Astron. Astrophys., **142**, 31–36.

Yamamoto, T. & Kozasa, T., 1987. *The cometary nucleus as an aggregate of planetesimals*, Icarus, **75**, 540–551.

Yamamoto, T., Nakagawa, N. & Fukui, Y., 1983. *The chemical composition and thermal history of the ice of a cometary nucleus*, Astron. Astrophys., **122**, 171–176.

Yeomans, D.K., 1986. *Physical interpretations from the motions of comets Halley and Giacobini-Zinner*, 20th ESLAB Symposium on the Exploration of Halley's Comet, eds. Battrick, B., Rolfe, E.J. & Reinhard, R., ESA SP-250, Vol. II, 419–425. ESA Publications, ESTEC, Noordwijk, The Netherlands.

Yeomans, D.K. & Kiang, T., 1981. *The-long term motion of Halley's comet*, Mon. Not. R. Astron. Soc., **197**, 633–646.

Young, C.A., 1898. *General Astronomy.* See p.455. Ginn & Co., Boston.

Zheng, J.-Q. & Valtonen, M.J., 1989. *Interstellar origin of comets*, preprint. Presented at IAU Coll. No. 116 *Comets in the Post-Halley Era*, Bamberg (April 1989), submitted to *Icarus.*

Zimmer, G.F., 1916. *The use of meteoric iron by primitive man*, J. Iron & Steel Inst., **94**, 306–349.

Zinner, E., 1988. *Interstellar cloud material in meteorites*, Meteorites and the Early Solar System, eds. Kerridge, J.F. & Matthews, M.S., 956–983. University of Arizona Press, Tucson.

Zinner, E., McKeegan, K.D. & Walker, R.M., 1983. *Laboratory measurements of D/H in interplanetary dust*, Nature, **305**, 119–121.

Zinner, E., Ming, T. & Anders, E., 1987. *Large isotopic anomalies of Si, C, N and noble gases in interstellar silicon carbide from the Murray meteorite*, Nature, **330**, 730–732.

Ziołkowski, K., 1989. *Comet 1967 II Rudnicki and the Taurid complex of small interplanetary bodies*, preprint. Presented at IAU Coll. No. 116 *Comets in the Post-Halley Era*, Bamberg (April 1989), submitted to *Icarus.*

Zwicky, F., 1955. *Some novel features of the Whirlpool Nebula as revealed by composite analytical photography*, Publ. Astron. Soc. Pac., **67**, 232–236.

Principal abbreviations

Acta Astron., Acta Astronomica.
Adv. Astron. Astrophys., Advances in Astronomy and Astrophysics.
Amer. Journ. Sci. Arts, American Journal of Science and Arts.
Amer. Journ. Sci., American Journal of Science.
Ann. Harvard Obs., Annals of the Harvard College Observatory.
Ann. N.Y. Acad. Sci., Annales of the New York Academy of Sciences.
Annu. Rev. Astron. Astrophys., Annual Review of Astronomy and Astrophysics.
Astron. Astrophys., Astronomy and Astrophysics.
Astron. Inst. Slovak Acad. Sci., Astronomical Institute of the Slovak Academy of
    Sciences.
Astron. J., Astronomical Journal.
Astron. Nachr., Astronomische Nachrichten.
Astron. Vestn., Astronomicheskij Vestnik.
Astron. Zh., Astronomicheskij Zhurnal.
Astrophys. J., Astrophysical Journal.
Astrophys. J. Lett., Astrophysical Journal Letters.
Astrophys. J. Suppl. Ser., Astrophysical Journal Supplement Series.
Astrophys. Space Sci., Astrophysics and Space Science.
Bull. Amer. Astron. Soc., Bulletin of the American Astronomical Society.
Bull. Astron., Bulletin Astronomique.
Bull. Astron. Inst. Czechosl., Bulletin of the Astronomical Institute of Czechoslovakia.
Bull. Astron. Inst. Neth., Bulletin of the Astronomical Institutes of the Netherlands.
Celest. Mech., Celestial Mechanics.
Contemp. Phys., Contemporary Physics.
Eos, Eos, Transactions of the American Geophysical Union.
Earth Planet. Sci. Lett., Earth and Planetary Science Letters.
Geochim. Cosmochim. Acta, Geochimica et Cosmochimica Acta.
Geol. Soc. Amer. Bull., Geological Society of America Bulletin.
Geol. Soc. Amer. Spec. Pap., Geological Society of America Special Paper.
Geophys. Res. Lett., Geophysical Research Letters.
IAU Circ., International Astronomical Union Circular.
IAU Coll., International Astronomical Union Colloquium.
IAU Symp., International Astronomical Union Symposium.
Ir. Astron. J., Irish Astronomical Journal.
Journ. Br. Astron. Assoc., Journal of the British Astronomical Association.
J. Geophys. Res., Journal of Geophysical Research.
J. Hist. Astron., Journal of the History of Astronomy.
Journ. Geol., Journal of Geology.
Journ. Geol. Soc., Journal of the Geological Society.
Journ. Paleontol., Journal of Paleontology.
J. R. Astron. Soc. Canada, Journal of the Royal Astronomical Society of Canada.
Mem. Proc. Manch. Lit. Philos. Soc., Memoirs and Proceedings of the Manchester
    Literary and Philosophical Society.
Mon. Notes Astron. Soc. Southern Africa, Monthly Notes of the Astronomical Society
    of Southern Africa.
Mon. Not. R. Astron. Soc., Monthly Notices of the Royal Astronomical Society.
Q. Jl. R. Astron. Soc., Quarterly Journal of the Royal Astronomical Society.
Philos. Trans. R. Soc. London, Philosophical Transactions of the Royal Society of
    London.
Popular Astron., Popular Astronomy.
Proc. Amer. Acad. Arts Sci., Proceedings of the American Academy of Arts and
    Science

Proc. Amer. Philos. Soc., Proceedings of the American Philosophical Society.

Proc. Lunar Planetary Sci. Conf., Proceedings of the Lunar and Planetary Science Conference.

Proc. Natl. Acad. Sci. (USA), Proceedings of the National Academy of Science of the United States of America.

Proc. R. Soc. Edinb., Proceedings of the Royal Society of Edinburgh.

Proc. R. Soc. London, Proceedings of the Royal Society of London.

Publ. Astron. Soc. Japan, Publications of the Astronomical Society of Japan.

Publ. Astron. Soc. Pac., Publications of the Astronomical Society of the Pacific.

Q. J. Roy. Meteorol. Soc., Quarterly Journal of the Royal Meteorological Society.

Rep. Prog. Phys., Reports on Progress in Physics.

Sov. Astron., Soviet Astronomical Journal. (A translation of Astr. Zh.)

Sp. Sci. Rev., Space Science Reviews.

Trans. IAU, Transactions of the International Astronomical Union.

Name index

Subject index